SPECIAL INDIAN EDITION

# CRYPTOGRAPHY
# AND
# NETWORK SECURITY

## Second Edition

# About the Authors

**Behrouz A Forouzan** was born in 1944 and retired as a Professor from the Department of Computer Information Systems, DeAnza College, California, USA. He graduated from the University of California, Irvine. Forouzan has written many textbooks about computer science, networking, programming and databases and presently resides in Los Angeles, USA.

**Debdeep Mukhopadhyay** is presently working as an Assistant Professor in the Computer Science and Engineering department of Indian Institute of Technology, Kharagpur. Prior to this, he worked as an Assistant Professor in the Department of Computer Science and Engineering, IIT Madras. Debdeep obtained his BTech degree from the Department of Electrical Engineering, IIT Kharagpur. Subsequently, he obtained his MS degree and PhD from the Department of Computer Science and Engineering, IIT Kharagpur. He has been the author of several international conference and journal papers in Cryptography and Security. Debdeep has been the recipient of the *Indian Semiconductor Association (ISA) TechnoInventor Award* for best PhD Thesis in 2008, and has been selected for the *Indian National Science Academy Young Scientist Award 2010*.

# CRYPTOGRAPHY

# AND

# NETWORK SECURITY

## Second Edition

**Behrouz A Forouzan**

*Retired Professor*
*Department of Computer Science and Engineering*
*DeAnza College, California, USA*

**Debdeep Mukhopadhyay**

*Assistant Professor*
*Department of Computer Science and Engineering*
*Indian Institute of Technology, Kharagpur*

## McGraw Hill Education (India) Private Limited

### NEW DELHI

*McGraw Hill Education Offices*

**New Delhi**  New York  St Louis  San Francisco  Auckland  Bogotá  Caracas
Kuala Lumpur  Lisbon  London  Madrid  Mexico City  Milan  Montreal
San Juan  Santiago  Singapore  Sydney  Tokyo  Toronto

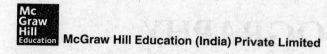

**McGraw Hill Education (India) Private Limited**

**Cryptography and Network Security, 2e**

Adapted in India by arrangement with The McGraw-Hill Companies, Inc., New York

**Sales territories: India, Pakistan, Nepal, Bangladesh, Sri Lanka and Bhutan**

Copyright © 2010, 2008 by The McGraw-Hill Companies, Inc.

Tenth reprint 2013
**RQZCRRAORBYRX**

All rights reserved no part of this publication may be reproduced or distributed in any form or by any means, electronic, mechanical, photocopying, recording, or otherwise or stored in a database or retrieval system without the prior written Permission of The McGraw-Hill Companies, Inc., including, but not limited to, in any network or other electronic storage or transmission, or broadcast for distance learning.

ISBN (13 digit): 978-0-07-070208-0
ISBN (10 digit): 0-07-070208-X

Vice President and Managing Director: *Ajay Shukla*
Head—Higher Education (Publishing and Marketing): *Vibha Mahajan*
Publishing Manager—SEM & Tech. Ed.: *Shalini Jha*
Asst Sponsoring Editor: *Surabhi Shukla*
Development Editor: *Surbhi Suman*
Executive—Editorial Services: *Sohini Mukherjee*
Jr Production Manager: *Anjali Razdan*

General Manager—Production: *Rajender P Ghansela*

Published by McGraw Hill Education (India) Private Limited,
P-24, Green Park Extension, New Delhi 110 016 and typeset at Text-o-Graphics, B1/56 Arawali Apartment, Sector 34, Noida 201 301 and printed at Magic International Pvt. Ltd., Greater Noida 201 306

Cover Printer: Magic International Pvt. Ltd.

# Dedicated to

*My beloved daughter and son-in-law*
*Satara and Shane*

—**Behrouz A Forouzan**


*Budding cryptographers and security professionals*

—**Debdeep Mukhopadhyay**

# Contents

# Preface to the Adapted Edition

## Overview of the Book

Security is ubiquitous. With the advent of e-commerce and electronic transactions, the need for development of secured systems has grown tremendously. Cryptography is the study of building ciphers to ensure the confidentiality and integrity of information. Along with it is the activity of analyzing the strength of a cipher by subjecting it to several forms of attack. This field of cryptology, known as cryptanalysis, ensures that the ciphers are strong enough to defend against all known forms of attack. Formally, cryptology is cryptography and cryptanalysis taken together, but often is referred to as cryptography, simply because of its popularity through ages. Starting from prehistoric ages, cryptography has evolved a lot. Modern cryptography, although has ideas from ancient ciphers, has fascinating improvements which rely on heuristics and precise mathematical arguments. However, strong cryptographic algorithms are just one aspect, and in spite of its development may not be useful for an end-to-end security if not deployed properly. Here comes the importance of network security. This part of the subject, in turn, deals with issues of design and usage of protocols for security which, in turn, uses the cryptographic algorithms developed by the cryptographers. As a matter of fact, for an end to end security one has to take care of the network, the operating system and even the policies used for security.

The present book details this important subject and attempts to explain the underlying principles to a non-specialist reader. However, the book targets a reader who studies the subject with an interest to understand the details of the subject and get to the 'whys' behind the topics, rather than be satisfied with the 'whats' only. The challenge of the book was to explain the intricate details to a reader who has just taken up the subject. In my opinion, the biggest difference a new reader finds when he reads, for example, a DES (Data Encryption System) algorithm from when he reads, say, a sorting algorithm, is that while he is convinced that the latter really terminates after doing what is intended, the former can be done in many other ways. So, a mere description of an encryption algorithm creates a kind of eerie feeling in the reader and often a disinterest. As a matter of fact, the essential beauty of the subject lies in the underlying science, the 'whys' rather than the 'whats'. However, these reasons are often based on involved mathematics. The present book steps in at this point and attempts to provide a fresher in this subject not only information but also the often not-so-apparent reasons. The book builds the necessary mathematical background and tries to explain the techniques and methodologies using several illustrations and examples. At the same time, whenever necessary, the mathematical rigor and preciseness has been maintained.

## Intended Audience

This book has been prepared considering the syllabus for the course in various colleges, universities and institutes in India. The objective of the book is to bridge the gap between textbooks which are very introductory and others which are very advanced. Hence, it will completely suit the requirements of the undergraduate, graduate and postgraduate courses in Computer Science, Information Technology and Computer Applications.

## Highlights of the Adapted Edition

Some of the important highlights of this edition are as follows—

1. New chapter on System Security covering the concepts of Buffer Overflow, Malicious Programs, Firewalls, Intrusion Detection Systems.
2. Inclusion of important topics such as index of coincidence, types of conventional algorithms (Multiple DES, IDEA, CAST, Blowfish) MD4 Hash Function, Hacking, Secure Electronic Transaction (SET), etc.
3. Discussion of modern techniques like Advanced Encryption Techniques, Random Oracle Model, Zero-knowledge and Biometrics
4. Extensive explanation of classical cryptography along with a detailed coverage on the cryptanalytic techniques
5. Elaborate discussion on symmetric ciphers, explaining the techniques for their construction and justifications
6. In-depth treatment of block ciphers influenced by the DES, mathematical backgrounds for asymmetric ciphers, cryptographic hash functions and their security criteria and algorithms for several number theoretic problems, like primality test, etc.
7. Stream Ciphers and the Berlekamp-Massey Algorithm treated in depth to show how single LFSRs can be reconstructed from their key streams
8. Elucidification of Message Authentication Codes (MACs) to pin-point the security assumptions and their reliance on internal hash functions
9. Lucid explanation for Advanced Encryption Standard, Elliptic Curve Cryptosystems, etc.
10. Pseudocodes illustrating the algorithm implementation
11. Several worked-out examples describing the underlying principles of linear and differential cryptanalysis (more details of these topics may be found in the appendix)
12. Pedagogical features including—
    – over 250 Solved Examples
    – over 400 Exercise Problems
    – over 200 Review Questions

## Chapter Organization

The book is organized as follows:

**Chapter 1** introduces the subject and describes the various security goals and types of existing attacks in the literature. It also briefly explains the various techniques and types of ciphers known to achieve the above said goals.

**Chapter 2** provides an introduction to the important mathematical principles necessary to design and analyze ciphers. It discusses in detail the concepts of modular arithmetic, a central concept to understand the working of ciphers. The chapter further provides some discussions on matrix algebra and solutions for linear congruences, which are also important tools to define and analyze cryptographic algorithms.

**Chapter 3** describes the classical symmetric key ciphers. It explains concepts like substitution and transposition, which existed in traditional cryptographic algorithms and are being used in the design of modern block and stream ciphers. It also covers cryptanalytic methods for such ciphers and explains them with simple examples. Finally, the chapter also defines two important categories of ciphers, commonly referred to as block and stream ciphers.

**Chapter 4** elucidates some mathematical concepts, such as Algebraic structures and Galois Field Arithmetic, which are useful to understand the working and analysis of modern ciphers. Numerous examples and illustrations are provided to explain the underlying concepts.

**Chapter 5** presents a detailed overview on the construction of modern block and stream ciphers. It describes the principles of block ciphers and D-Boxes and S-Boxes, which are important components of block ciphers. The chapter also gives an overview on LFSRs and explains the Berlekamp-Massey algorithm.

**Chapter 6** concentrates on the Data Encryption Standard (DES) and presents a detailed study on the design and analysis of DES. It presents discussions on the security and analysis of DES and the effect of multiple DES applications on the security achieved. It provides discussion on various other block ciphers that were later designed under the influence of DES.

**Chapter 7** explains the structure of AES and explains its various rounds. The concepts of Galois Fields, described in Chapter 4, are used to explain the working of the internal rounds of AES. The chapter also describes the key expansion algorithm of AES and presents an overview on existing analysis of AES.

**Chapter 8** presents the application and usage of modern block and stream ciphers to encrypt information.

**Chapter 9** covers the important mathematical tools required to understand asymmetric key cryptography. It discusses several important concepts like prime numbers, factorization and Chinese Remainder Theorem. It also introduces the topic of quadratic congruence and performing exponentiation and logarithm in finite fields.

**Chapter 10** deals with various asymmetric key algorithms like RSA, Rabin, ElGamal and Elliptic Curve Cryptography. The concepts are explained through several examples and illustrations.

**Chapter 11** presents concepts of message integrity and describes the Random Oracle assumption, which is used to model hash functions and analyze their properties. The chapter further explains message authentication, necessary to ensure the integrity of information.

**Chapter 12** details cryptographic hash functions and presents descriptions of standard hash functions, like belonging to the MD Hash family, Whirlpool and SHA.

**Chapter 13** describes the topic of digital signatures, and presents techniques, attacks and applications of digital signatures.

**Chapter 14** offers coverage on password based authentication, challenge-response methods for authentication and preliminaries of zero-knowledge in authentication. The chapter also discusses about the method of biometrics commonly used for authentication in various applications.

**Chapter 15** explains key management techniques for symmetric key encryption. The chapter presents a discussion on Kerberos, and symmetric key agreement. It discusses public key distribution, and hijacking or meet-in-the-middle attacks used against networks.

**Chapter 16** discusses the security at the application layer, describing PGP and S-MIME.

**Chapter 17** describes security at the transport layer, detailing Secured Socket Layer and Transport Layer Security.

**Chapter 18** illustrates the security at the network layer, describing topics on Security protocols and policies for network layer security. It concludes with descriptions of Internet Security Association and Key Management Protocol.

**Chapter 19** provides a description on system security, detailing the concepts of Buffer overflows, Malicious Softwares, Intrusion Detection System, and Firewalls.

Finally, there are 12 appendices provided to briefly present some important facts or theory needed to understand portions of the text. Each chapter contains an exhaustive list of **Key Terms**, **Practice Set (Review Questions** and **Exercises)** to help the student get hands-on practice in grasping the concepts. A **Summary** provides a quick recap of the topics discussed in the chapter.

## Web Supplements

The web supplements can be accessed at *http://www.mhhe.com/forouzan/cns2* which contain chapterwise PowerPoint Slides, Solution Manual, Image Library for **Instructors**. For **Students**, the website hosts a sample chapter, solutions to odd-numbered problems given in the book, reference material for extra reading and a list of 10 projects.

## Acknowledgements

The book would not have been completed without the help and support of many individuals. To begin with, I am indebted to my colleagues, Abhijit Das, Dipanwita Roy Chowdhury, Indranil Sengupta from Indian Institute of Technology, Kharagpur; N Narayanaswamy and V Kamakoti from Indian Institute of Technology, Madras and Sanjay Burman from Center for Artificial Intelligence and Robotics (DRDO), Bangalore for their consistent support and encouragement. I would also like to recognise the sincere endeavors of my students Bodhisattwa Majumder, Chester Rebeiro, Dhiman Saha, Dibyendu Mallik, D Sankara Reddy, Mainak Mondal, Sandip Karmakar, Santosh Ghosh, Somnath Ghosh, Subidh Ali and Sujoy Sinha Roy.

I take this opportunity to acknowledge the contributions of the following reviewers whose valuable comments and suggestions helped me in giving shape to this edition.

**Shekhar Verma**
Indian Institute of Information Technology, (IIIT), Allahabad, Uttar Pradesh

**Pramod Kumar Singh**
Indian Institute of Information Technology and Management, (IIITM), Gwalior, Madhya Pradesh

**SK Basu**
Banaras Hindu University (BHU), Varanasi, Uttar Pradesh

**Bhupendra Gupta**
Indian Institute of Information Technology, Design and Manufacturing (IIIT-DM),
Jabalpur, Madhya Pradesh

**Manik Lal Das**
Dhirubhai Ambani Institute of Information and Communication Technology (DA-IICT),
Gandhinagar, Gujarat

**Garimella Rama Murthy**
International Institute of Information Technology, Hyderabad, Andhra Pradesh

**V Vijay Kumar**
Godavari Institute of Engineering and Technology, Rajahmundry, Andhra Pradesh

I appreciate wholeheartedly the efforts of the staff of Tata McGraw-Hill in helping me at different stages of the project. The entire team deserves a special note of thanks for making the project possible, especially Surabhi Shukla, Surbhi Suman and Anjali Razdan for their constant support and reminders of deadlines, which helped me to bring out the book in reasonable time. I also thank Sohini Mukherjee for her help in preparing the preliminary section for the book.

I would like to express my deep sense of gratitude to my parents, Niharendu and Dipa Mukhopadhyay, for their teachings, constant blessings and sacrifices which have made me see this day. I am very grateful to my brother Rajdeep for being a wonderful friend and being a constant source of encouragement. Last but not the least, I am also thankful to my wife, Ayantika, for her support and patience as I have been dispensing off my professional duties sometimes oblivious of my other responsibilities.

**Author**

## Feedback

Constructive suggestions and criticism always go a long way in enhancing any endeavor. We request all readers to email us their valuable comments/views/feedback for the betterment of the book at *tmh.csefeedback@gmail.com*, mentioning the title and author name in the subject line. Please report any piracy-related issue spotted by you as well!

# Preface to the First Edition

The Internet, as a worldwide communication network, has changed our daily life in many ways. A new paradigm of commerce allows individuals to shop online. The World Wide Web (WWW) allows people to share information. The E-mail technology connect people in far-flung corners of the world. This inevitable evolution has also created dependency on the Internet.

The Internet, as an open forum, has created some security problems. Confidentiality, integrity, and authentication are needed. People need to be sure that their Internet communication is kept confidential. When they shop online, they need to be sure that the vendors are authentic. When they send their transactions request to their banks, they want to be certain that the integrity of the message is preserved.

Network security is a set of protocols that allow us to use the Internet comfortably—without worrying about security attacks. The most common tool for providing network security is cryptography, an old technique that has been revived and adapted to network security. This book first introduces the reader to the principles of cryptography and then applies those principles to describe network security protocols.

## Features of the Book

Several features of this text are designed to make it particularly easy for readers to understand cryptography and network security.

**Structure**  This text uses an incremental approach to teaching cryptography and network security. It assumes no particular mathematical knowledge, such as number theory or abstract algebra. However, because cryptography and network security cannot be discussed without some background in these areas of mathematics, these topics are discussed in Chapters 2, 4, and 9. Readers who are familiar with these areas of mathematics can ignore these chapters. Chapters 1 through 15 discuss cryptography. Chapters 16 through 18 discuss network security.

**Visual Approach**  This text presents highly technical subject matters without complex formulas by using a balance of text and figures. More than 400 figures accompanying the text provide a visual and intuitive opportunity for understanding the materials. Figures are particularly important in explaining difficult cryptographic concepts and complex network security protocols.

**Algorithms**  Algorithms play an important role in teaching cryptography. To make the presentation independent from any computer language, the algorithms have been given in pseudocode that can be easily programmed in a modern language. At the website for this text, the corresponding programs are available for download.

**Highlighted Points**   Important concepts are emphasized in highlighted boxes for quick reference and immediate attention.

**Examples**   Each chapter presents a large number of examples that apply concepts discussed in the chapter. Some examples merely show the immediate use of concepts and formulae; some show the actual input/output relationships of ciphers; others give extra information to better understand some difficult ideas.

**Recommended Reading**   At the end of each chapter, the reader will find a list of books for further reading.

**Key Terms**   Key terms appear in bold in the chapter text, and a list of key terms appear at the end of each chapter. All key terms are also defined in the glossary at the end of the book.

**Summary**   Each chapter ends with a summary of the material covered in that chapter. The summary provides a brief overview of all the important points in the chapter.

**Practice Set**   At the end of each chapter, the students will find a practice set designed to reinforce and apply salient concepts. The practice set consists of two parts: review questions and exercises. The review questions are intended to test the reader's first-level understanding of the material presented in the chapter. The exercises require deeper understanding of the material.

**Appendices**   The appendices provide quick reference material or a review of materials needed to understand the concepts discussed in the book. Some discussions of mathematical topics are also presented in the appendices to avoid distracting those readers who are already familiar with these materials.

**Proofs**   Mathematical facts are mentioned in the chapters without proofs to emphasize the results of applying the facts. For those interested reader the proofs are given in Appendix Q.

**Glossary and Acronyms**   At the end of the text, the reader will find an extensive glossary and a list of acronyms.

## Contents
After the introductory Chapter 1, the book is divided into four parts:

## Part One: Symmetric-Key Encipherment
Part One introduces the symmetric-key cryptography, both traditional and modern. The chapters in this part emphasize the use of symmetric-key cryptography in providing secrecy. Part One includes Chapters 2 through 8.

## Part Two: Asymmetric-Key Encipherment
Part Two discusses asymmetric-key cryptography. The chapters in this part show how asymmetric-key cryptography can provide security. Part Two includes Chapters 9 and 10.

## *Part Three: Integrity, Authentication, and Key Management*

Part Three shows how cryptographic hashing functions can provide other security services, such as message integrity and authentication. The chapters in this part also show how asymmetric-key and symmetric-key cryptography can complement each other. Part Three includes Chapters 11 through 15.

## *Part Four: Network Security*

Part Four shows how the cryptography discussed in Part One through Three can be used to create network security protocols at three levels of the Internet networking model. Part Four includes Chapters 16 to 18.

## How to Use this Book

This book is written for both an academic and a professional audience. Interested professionals can use it for self-guidance study. As a textbook, it can be used for a one-semester or one-quarter course. The following are some guidelines.

❑ Parts one to three are strongly recommended.

❑ Part four is recommended if the course needs to move beyond cryptography and enter the domain of network security. A course in networking is a prerequisite for Part four.

## Online Learning Center

The McGraw-Hill Online Learning Center contains much additional material related to *Cryptography and Network Security*. Readers can access the site at *http://www.mhhe.com/forouzan/cns*. Professors and students can access lecture materials, such as PowerPoint slides. The solutions to odd-numbered problems are provided to students, and professors can use a password to access the complete set of solutions. Additionally, McGraw-Hill makes it easy to create a website for the course with an exclusive McGraw-Hill product called PageOut. It requires no prior knowledge of HTML, no long hours, and no design skills on your part. Instead, PageOut offers a series of templates. Simply fill them with your course information and click on one of 16 designs. The process takes under an hour and leaves you with a professionally designed website. Although PageOut offers "instant" development, the finished website provides powerful features. An interactive course syllabus allows you to post content to coincide with your lectures, so when students visit your PageOut website, your syllabus will direct them to components of Forouzan's Online Learning Center, or specific material of your own.

## Acknowledgments

It is obvious that the development of a book of this scope needs the support of many people.

**Peer Review**  The most important contribution to the development of a book such as this comes from peer reviews. I cannot express my gratitude in words to the many reviewers who spent numerous hours reading the manuscript and providing me with helpful comments and ideas. I would especially like to acknowledge the contributions of the following reviewers:

Kaufman, Robert, *University of Texas, San Antonio*
Kesidis, George, *Penn State*
Stephens, Brooke, *U. of Maryland, Baltimore County*
Koc, Cetin, *Oregon State University*

Uminowicz, Bill, *Westwood College*
Wang, Xunhua, *James Madison University*
Kak, Subhash, *Louisiana State U.*
Dunigan, Tom, *U. of Tennessee, Knoxville*

**McGraw-Hill Staff**  Special thanks go to the staff of McGraw-Hill. Alan Apt, publisher, proved how a proficient publisher can make the impossible possible. Melinda Bilecki, the development editor, gave me help whenever I needed it. Sheila Frank, project manager, guided me through the production process with enormous enthusiasm. I also thank David Hash in design, Kara Kudronowicz in production, and Wendy Nelson, the copy editor.

**Behrouz A Forouzan**

# 1

# Introduction

## Objectives

This chapter has several objectives:
- ☞ To define three security goals
- ☞ To define security attacks that threaten security goals
- ☞ To define security services and how they are related to the three security goals
- ☞ To define security mechanisms to provide security services
- ☞ To introduce two techniques, cryptography and steganography, to implement security mechanisms.

We are living in the information age. We need to keep information about every aspect of our lives. In other words, information is an asset that has a value like any other asset. As an asset, information needs to be secured from attacks.

To be secured, information needs to be hidden from unauthorized access (*confidentiality*), protected from unauthorized change (*integrity*), and available to an authorized entity when it is needed (*availability*).

Until a few decades ago, the information collected by an organization was stored on physical files. The confidentiality of the files was achieved by restricting the access to a few authorized and trusted people in the organization. In the same way, only a few authorized people were allowed to change the contents of the files. Availability was achieved by designating at least one person who would have access to the files at all times.

With the advent of computers, information storage became electronic. Instead of being stored on physical media, it was stored in computers. The three security requirements, however, did not change. The files stored in computers require confidentiality, integrity, and availability. The implementation of these requirements, however, is different and more challenging.

During the last two decades, computer networks created a revolution in the use of information. Information is now distributed. Authorized people can send and retrieve information from a distance using computer networks. Although the three above-mentioned requirements—confidentiality, integrity, and availability—have not changed, they now have some new dimensions. Not only should information be confidential when it is stored in a computer; there should also be a way to maintain its confidentiality when it is transmitted from one computer to another.

In this chapter, we first discuss the three major goals of information security. We then see how attacks can threaten these three goals. We then discuss the security services in relation to these security goals. Finally we define mechanisms to provide security services and introduce techniques that can be used to implement these mechanisms.

## 1.1 SECURITY GOALS

Let us first discuss three **security goals: confidentiality, integrity,** and **availability** (Figure 1.1).

**Fig. 1.1** *Taxonomy of security goals*

***Confidentiality*** **Confidentiality** is probably the most common aspect of information security. We need to protect our confidential information. An organization needs to guard against those malicious actions that endanger the confidentiality of its information. In the military, concealment of sensitive information is the major concern. In industry, hiding some information from competitors is crucial to the operation of the organization. In banking, customers' accounts need to be kept secret.

As we will see later in this chapter, confidentiality not only applies to the storage of the information, it also applies to the transmission of information. When we send a piece of information to be stored in a remote computer or when we retrieve a piece of information from a remote computer, we need to conceal it during transmission.

***Integrity*** Information needs to be changed constantly. In a bank, when a customer deposits or withdraws money, the balance of her account needs to be changed. **Integrity** means that changes need to be done only by authorized entities and through authorized mechanisms. Integrity violation is not necessarily the result of a malicious act; an interruption in the system, such as a power surge, may also create unwanted changes in some information.

***Availability*** The third component of information security is **availability.** The information created and stored by an organization needs to be available to authorized entities. Information is useless if it is not available. Information needs to be constantly changed, which means it must be accessible to authorized entities. The unavailability of information is just as harmful for an organization as the lack of confidentiality or integrity. Imagine what would happen to a bank if the customers could not access their accounts for transactions.

## 1.2 CRYPTOGRAPHIC ATTACKS

Cryptographic attacks can be broadly categorized into two distinct types: 1. *Cryptanalytic* and 2. *Non-cryptanalytic.*

## 1.2.1 Cryptanalytic Attacks

These attacks are combinations of statistical and algebraic techniques aimed at ascertaining the secret key of a cipher. These methods inspect the mathematical properties of the cryptographic algorithms and aims at finding distinguishers of the output distribution of cryptographic algorithms from uniform distributions. Ideally, all cryptographic algorithms act upon the message distribution and converts it using the key to a ciphertext distribution which looks random (i, e., all the symbols in the ciphertext are equally likely). The objective of cryptanalysis is to find properties of the cipher which does not exist in a random function. That is what we mean by "distinguishers", and all attacks are fundamentally distinguishers. The attacker thus guesses the key and looks for the distinguishing property. If the property is detected, the guess is correct otherwise the next guess is tried. Efficient attacks will try to adopt a "divide and conquer" strategy to reduce the complexity of guessing the key from the brute force search complexity. An attack is said to be theoretically successful if the guessing complexity is lesser than the brute force search complexity, although it may be practically still infeasible. However, such an attack surely points out a flaw in the design, which may be exploited in future attacks. This idea is clarified in the context of Linear and Differential Cryptanalysis in Chapter 5.

## 1.2.2 Non-cryptanalytic Attacks

The other types of attacks are non-cryptanalytic attacks, which do not exploit the mathematical weakness of the cryptographic algorithm. However the three goals of security, namely confidentiality, integrity and availability can be very much threatened by this class of attacks.

Our three goals of security—confidentiality, integrity, and availability—can be threatened by security **attacks.** Although the literature uses different approaches to categorizing the attacks, we will first divide them into three groups related to the security goals. Later, we will divide them into two broad categories based on their effects on the system. Figure 1.2 shows the first taxonomy.

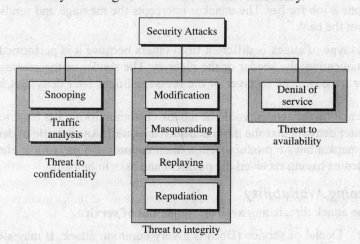

**Fig. 1.2** *Taxonomy of attacks with relation to security goals*

## *Attacks Threatening Confidentiality*

In general, two types of attacks threaten the confidentiality of information: **snooping** and **traffic analysis.**

*Snooping*   Snooping refers to unauthorized access to or interception of data. For example, a file transferred through the Internet may contain confidential information. An unauthorized entity may intercept the transmission and use the contents for her own benefit. To prevent snooping, the data can be made nonintelligible to the intercepter by using encipherment techniques discussed in this book.

*Traffic Analysis*   Although encipherment of data may make it nonintelligible for the intercepter, she can obtain some other type information by monitoring online traffic. For example, she can find the electronic address (such as the e-mail address) of the sender or the receiver. She can collect pairs of requests and responses to help her guess the nature of transaction.

## Attacks Threatening Integrity

The integrity of data can be threatened by several kinds of attacks: **modification, masquerading, replaying,** and **repudiation.**

*Modification*   After intercepting or accessing information, the attacker modifies the information to make it beneficial to herself. For example, a customer sends a message to a bank to do some transaction. The attacker intercepts the message and changes the type of transaction to benefit herself. Note that sometimes the attacker simply deletes or delays the message to harm the system or to benefit from it.

*Masquerading*   Masquerading, or spoofing, happens when the attacker impersonates somebody else. For example, an attacker might steal the bank card and PIN of a bank customer and pretend that she is that customer. Sometimes the attacker pretends instead to be the receiver entity. For example, a user tries to contact a bank, but another site pretends that it is the bank and obtains some information from the user.

*Replaying*   Replaying is another attack. The attacker obtains a copy of a message sent by a user and later tries to replay it. For example, a person sends a request to her bank to ask for payment to the attacker, who has done a job for her. The attacker intercepts the message and sends it again to receive another payment from the bank.

*Repudiation*   This type of attack is different from others because it is performed by one of the two parties in the communication: the sender or the receiver. The sender of the message might later deny that she has sent the message; the receiver of the message might later deny that he has received the message.

An example of denial by the sender would be a bank customer asking her bank to send some money to a third party but later denying that she has made such a request. An example of denial by the receiver could occur when a person buys a product from a manufacturer and pays for it electronically, but the manufacturer later denies having received the payment and asks to be paid.

## Attacks Threatening Availability

We mention only one attack threatening availability: **denial of service.**

*Denial of Service*   Denial of service (DoS) is a very common attack. It may slow down or totally interrupt the service of a system. The attacker can use several strategies to achieve this. She might send so many bogus requests to a server that the server crashes because of the heavy load. The attacker might intercept and delete a server's response to a client, making the client to believe that the server is not responding. The attacker may also intercept requests from the clients, causing the clients to send requests many times and overload the system.

## Passive Versus Active Attacks

Let us now categorize the attacks into two groups: passive and active. Table 1.1 shows the relationship between this and the previous categorization.

**Table 1.1** *Categorization of passive and active attacks*

| Attacks | Passive/Active | Threatening |
|---------|----------------|-------------|
| Snooping Traffic analysis | Passive | Confidentiality |
| Modification Masquerading Replaying Repudiation | Active | Integrity |
| Denial of service | Active | Availability |

**Passive Attacks**   In a **passive attack,** the attacker's goal is just to obtain information. This means that the attack does not modify data or harm the system. The system continues with its normal operation. However, the attack may harm the sender or the receiver of the message. Attacks that threaten confidentiality—snooping and traffic analysis—are passive attacks. The revealing of the information may harm the sender or receiver of the message, but the system is not affected. For this reason, it is difficult to detect this type of attack until the sender or receiver finds out about the leaking of confidential information. Passive attacks, however, can be prevented by encipherment of the data.

**Active Attacks**   An **active attack** may change the data or harm the system. Attacks that threaten the integrity and availability are active attacks. Active attacks are normally easier to detect than to prevent, because an attacker can launch them in a variety of ways.

## 1.3            SERVICES AND MECHANISM

The **International Telecommunication Union-Telecommunication Standardization Sector (ITU-T)** (see Appendix B) provides some security services and some mechanisms to implement those services. Security services and mechanisms are closely related because a mechanism or combination of mechanisms are used to provide a service. Also, a mechanism can be used in one or more services. We briefly discuss them here to give the general idea; we will discuss them in detail in later chapters devoted to specific services or mechanisms.

### 1.3.1   Security Services

ITU-T (X.800) has defined five services related to the security goals and attacks we defined in the previous sections. Figure 1.3 shows the taxonomy of those five common services.

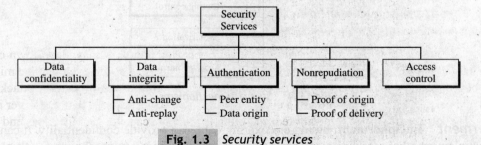

**Fig. 1.3**  *Security services*

It is easy to relate one or more of these services to one or more of the security goals. It is also easy to see that these services have been designed to prevent the security attacks that we have mentioned.

**Data Confidentiality**     **Data confidentiality** is designed to protect data from disclosure attack. The service as defined by X.800 is very broad and encompasses confidentiality of the whole message or part of a message and also protection against traffic analysis. That is, it is designed to prevent snooping and traffic analysis attack.

**Data Integrity**     **Data integrity** is designed to protect data from modification, insertion, deletion, and replaying by an adversary. It may protect the whole message or part of the message.

**Authentication**     This service provides the **authentication** of the party at the other end of the line. In -connection-oriented communication, it provides authentication of the sender or receiver during the connection establishment (peer entity authentication). In connectionless communication, it authenticates the source of the data (data origin authentication).

**Nonrepudiation**     **Nonrepudiation** service protects against repudiation by either the sender or the receiver of the data. In nonrepudiation with proof of the origin, the receiver of the data can later prove the identity of the sender if denied. In nonrepudiation with proof of delivery, the sender of data can later prove that data were delivered to the intended recipient.

**Access Control**     **Access control** provides protection against unauthorized access to data. The term *access* in this definition is very broad and can involve reading, writing, modifying, executing programs, and so on.

### 1.3.2   Security Mechanisms

ITU-T (X.800) also recommends some **security mechanisms** to provide the security services defined in the previous section. Figure 1.4 gives the taxonomy of these mechanisms.

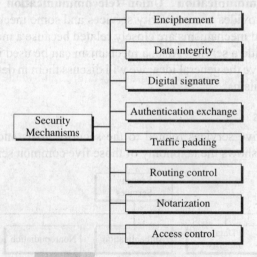

**Fig. 1.4**     *Security mechanisms*

**Encipherment**     **Encipherment,** hiding or covering data, can provide confidentiality. It can also be used to complement other mechanisms to provide other services. Today two techniques—cryptography and steganography—are used for enciphering. We will discuss these shortly.

*Data Integrity*    The **data integrity** mechanism appends to the data a short checkvalue that has been created by a specific process from the data itself. The receiver receives the data and the checkvalue. He creates a new checkvalue from the received data and compares the newly created checkvalue with the one received. If the two checkvalues are the same, the integrity of data has been preserved.

*Digital Signature*    A **digital signature** is a means by which the sender can electronically sign the data and the receiver can electronically verify the signature. The sender uses a process that involves showing that she owns a private key related to the public key that she has announced publicly. The receiver uses the sender's public key to prove that the message is indeed signed by the sender who claims to have sent the message.

*Authentication Exchange*    In **authentication exchange,** two entities exchange some messages to prove their identity to each other. For example, one entity can prove that she knows a secret that only she is supposed to know.

*Traffic Padding*    **Traffic padding** means inserting some bogus data into the data traffic to thwart the adversary's attempt to use the traffic analysis.

*Routing Control*    **Routing control** means selecting and continuously changing different available routes between the sender and the receiver to prevent the opponent from eavesdropping on a particular route.

*Notarization*    **Notarization** means selecting a third trusted party to control the communication between two entities. This can be done, for example, to prevent repudiation. The receiver can involve a trusted party to store the sender request in order to prevent the sender from later denying that she has made such a request.

*Access Control*    **Access control** uses methods to prove that a user has access right to the data or resources owned by a system. Examples of proofs are passwords and PINs.

## 1.3.3   Relation between Services and Mechanisms

Table 1.2 shows the relationship between the security services and the security mechanisms. The table shows that three mechanisms (encipherment, digital signature, and authentication exchange) can be used to provide authentication.

**Table 1.2**    *Relation between security services and security mechanisms*

| Security Service | Security Mechanism |
|---|---|
| Data confidentiality | Encipherment and routing control |
| Data integrity | Encipherment, digital signature, data integrity |
| Authentication | Encipherment, digital signature, authentication exchanges |
| Nonrepudiation | Digital signature, data integrity, and notarization |
| Access control | Access control mechanism |

The table also shows that encipherment mechanism may be involved in three services (data confidentiality, data integrity, and authentication)

## 1.4                                  TECHNIQUES

Mechanisms discussed in the previous sections are only theoretical recipes to implement security. The actual implementation of security goals needs some techniques. Two techniques are prevalent today: one is very general (cryptography) and one is specific (steganography).

### 1.4.1   Cryptography

Some security mechanisms listed in the previous section can be implemented using cryptography. **Cryptography,** a word with Greek origins, means "secret writing." However, we use the term to refer to the science and art of transforming messages to make them secure and immune to attacks. Although in the past *cryptography* referred only to the **encryption** and **decryption** of messages using secret keys, today it is defined as involving three distinct mechanisms: symmetric-key encipherment, asymmetric-key encipherment, and hashing. We will briefly discuss these three mechanisms here.

*Symmetric-Key Encipherment*   In **symmetric-key encipherment** (sometimes called secret-key encipherment or secret-key cryptography), an entity, say Alice, can send a message to another entity, say Bob, over an insecure channel with the assumption that an adversary, say Eve, cannot understand the contents of the message by simply eavesdropping over the channel. Alice encrypts the message using an encryption algorithm; Bob decrypts the message using a decryption algorithm. Symmetric-key encipherment uses a single **secret key** for both encryption and decryption. Encryption/decryption can be thought of as electronic locking. In symmetric-key enciphering, Alice puts the message in a box and locks the box using the shared secret key; Bob unlocks the box with the same key and takes out the message.

*Asymmetric-Key Encipherment*   In **asymmetric-key encipherment** (sometimes called public-key encipherment or public-key cryptography), we have the same situation as the symmetric-key encipherment, with a few exceptions. First, there are two keys instead of one: one **public key** and one **private key.** To send a secured message to Bob, Alice first encrypts the message using Bob's public key. To decrypt the message, Bob uses his own private key.

*Hashing*   In **hashing,** a fixed-length message digest is created out of a variable-length message. The digest is normally much smaller than the message. To be useful, both the message and the digest must be sent to Bob. Hashing is used to provide checkvalues, which were discussed earlier in relation to providing data integrity.

### 1.4.2   Steganography

Although this book is based on cryptography as a technique for implementing security mechanisms, another technique that was used for secret communication in the past is being revived at the present time: steganography. The word **steganography,** with origin in Greek, means "covered writing," in contrast with cryptography, which means "secret writing." Cryptography means concealing the contents of a message by enciphering; steganography means concealing the message itself by covering it with something else.

*Historical Use*   History is full of facts and myths about the use of steganography. In China, war messages were written on thin pieces of silk and rolled into a small ball and swallowed by the messenger. In Rome and Greece, messages were carved on pieces of wood, that were later dipped into wax to cover the writing. Invisible inks (such as onion juice or ammonia salts) were also used to write a secret message between the lines of the covering message or on the back of the paper; the secret message was exposed when the paper was heated or treated with another substance.

In recent times other methods have been devised. Some letters in an innocuous message might be overwritten in a pencil lead that is visible only when exposed to light at an angle. Null ciphers were used to hide a secret message inside an innocuous simple message. For example, the first or second letter of each word in the covering message might compose a secret message. Microdots were also used for this purpose. Secret messages were photographed and reduced to a size of a dot (period) and inserted into simple cover messages in place of regular periods at the end of sentences.

## Modern Use

Today, any form of data, such as text, image, audio, or video, can be digitized, and it is possible to insert secret binary information into the data during digitization process. Such hidden information is not necessarily used for secrecy; it can also be used to protect copyright, prevent tampering, or add extra information.

*Text Cover*   The cover of secret data can be text. There are several ways to insert binary data into an innocuous text. For example, we can use single space between words to represent the binary digit 0 and double space to represent binary digit 1. The following short message hides the 8-bit binary representation of the letter A in ASCII code (01000001).

This book  is mostly about cryptography, not  steganography.

    0  1 0    0    0     0  1

In the above message there are two spaces between the "book" and "is" and between the "not" and "steganography". Of course, sophisticated software can insert spaces that differ only slightly to hide the code from immediate recognition.

Another, more efficient method, is to use a dictionary of words organized according to their grammatical usages. We can have a dictionary containing 2 articles, 8 verbs, 32 nouns, and 4 prepositions. Then we agree to use cover text that always use sentences with the pattern *article-noun-verb-article-noun*. The secret binary data can be divided into 16-bit chunks. The first bit of binary data can be represented by an article (for example, 0 for *a* and 1 for *the*). The next five bits can be represented by a noun (subject of the sentence), the next four bits can be represented by a verb, the next bit by the second article, and the last five bits by another noun (object). For example, the secret data "Hi", which is 01001000 01001001 in ASCII, could be a sentence like the following:

A   friend   called   a   doctor.
0   10010   0001   0   01001

This is a very trivial example. The actual approach uses more sophisticated design and a variety of patterns.

*Image Cover*   Secret data can also be covered under a color image. Digitized images are made of pixels (picture elements), in which normally each pixel uses 24 bits (three bytes). Each byte represents one of the primary colors (red, green, or blue). We can therefore have $2^8$ different shades of each color. In a method called LSB (least significant bit), the least significant bit of each byte is set to zero. This may make the image a little bit lighter in some areas, but this is not normally noticed. Now we can hide a binary data in the image by keeping or changing the least significant bit. If our binary digit is 0, we keep the bit; if it is 1, we change the bit to 1. In this way, we can hide a character (eight ASCII bits) in three pixels. For example, the following three pixels can represent the letter M.

```
01010011   10111100   01010101
01011110   10111100   01100101
01111110   01001010   00010101
```

Of course, more sophisticated approaches are used these days.

*Other Covers*   Other covers are also possible. The secret message, for example, can be covered under audio (sound and music) and video. Both audio and video are compressed today; the secret data can be embedded during or before the compression. We leave the discussion of these techniques to more specialized books in steganography.

## 1.5   THE REST OF THE BOOK

The rest of this book is divided into four parts.

*Part One: Symmetric-Key Encipherment*   The chapters in Part One discuss encipherment, both classic and modern, using symmetric-key cryptography. These chapters show how the first goal of security can be implemented using this technique.

*Part Two: Asymmetric-Key Encipherment*   The chapters in Part Two discuss encipherment using asymmetric-key cryptography. These chapters also show how the first goal of the security can be implemented using this technique.

*Part Three: Integrity, Authentication, and Key Management*   The chapters in Part Three introduce the third application of cryptography—hashing— and show how it can be combined with the materials discussed in Part I and II for implementing the second goal of security.

*Part Four: Network Security*   The chapters in Part Four show how the methods learned in the first three parts of the book can be combined to create network security using the Internet model.

## 1.6   RECOMMENDED READING

For more details about subjects discussed in this chapter, the following books and websites are good places to start. The items enclosed in brackets refer to the reference list at the end of the book.

### Books
Several books discuss security goals, attacks, and mechanisms. We recommend [Bis05] and [Sta06].

### WebSites
The following websites give more information about topics discussed in this chapter.
    http://www.faqs.org/rfcs/rfc2828.html
    fag.grm.hia.no/IKT7000/litteratur/paper/x800.pdf

## Key Terms

| | |
|---|---|
| access control | masquerading |
| active attack | modification |
| asymmetric-key encipherment | nonrepudiation |
| authentication | notarization |
| authentication exchange | passive attack |
| availability | private key |
| confidentiality | public key |
| cryptography | replaying |
| data confidentiality | repudiation |
| data integrity | routing control |
| decryption | secret key |
| denial of service | security attacks |
| digital signature | security goals |
| encipherment | security mechanisms |
| encryption | snooping |
| hashing | steganography |
| integrity | symmetric-key encipherment |
| International Telecommunication Union- | traffic analysis |
| Telecommunication Standardization Sector (ITU-T) | traffic padding |

## Summary

★ Three general goals have been defined for security: confidentiality, integrity, and availability.

★ Two types of attacks threaten the confidentiality of information: snooping and traffic analysis. Four types of attacks can threaten the integrity of information: modification, masquerading, replaying, and repudiation. Denial-of-service attacks threaten the availability of information.

★ Some organizations involved in data communication and networking, such as ITU-T or the Internet, have defined several security services that are related to the security goals and security attacks. This chapter discussed five common security services: data confidentiality, data integrity, authentication, nonrepudiation, and access control.

★ ITU-T also recommends some mechanisms to provide security. We discussed eight of these mechanisms: encipherment, data integrity, digital signature, authentication exchange, traffic padding, routing control, notarization, and access control.

★ There are two techniques—cryptography and steganography—that can implement some or all of the mechanisms. Cryptography or "secret writing" involves scrambling a message or creating a digest of the message. Steganography or "covered writing" means concealing the message by covering it with something else.

## *Practice Set*

### Review Questions

**1.1** Define the three security goals.

**1.2** Distinguish between passive and active security attacks. Name some passive attacks. Name some active attacks.

**1.3** List and define five security services discussed in this chapter.

**1.4** Define eight security mechanisms discussed in this chapter.

**1.5** Distinguish between cryptography and steganography.

### Exercises

**1.6** Which security service(s) are guaranteed when using each of the following methods to send mail at the post office?

    a.   Regular mail
    b.   Regular mail with delivery confirmation
    c.   Regular mail with delivery and recipient signature
    d.   Certified mail
    e.   Insured mail
    f.   Registered mail

**1.7** Define the type of security attack in each of the following cases:

    a.   A student breaks into a professor's office to obtain a copy of the next day's test.
    b.   A student gives a check for $10 to buy a used book. Later she finds that the check was cashed for $100.
    c.   A student sends hundreds of e-mails per day to another student using a phony return e-mail address.

**1.8** Which security mechanism(s) are provided in each of the following cases?

    a.   A school demands student identification and a password to let students log into the school server.
    b.   A school server disconnects a student if she is logged into the system for more than two hours.
    c.   A professor refuses to send students their grades by e-mail unless they provide student identification they were preassigned by the professor.
    d.   A bank requires the customer's signature for a withdrawal.

**1.9** Which technique (cryptography or steganography) is used in each of the following cases for confidentiality?

    a.   A student writes the answers to a test on a small piece of paper, rolls up the paper, and inserts it in a ball-point pen, and passes the pen to another student.
    b.   To send a message, a spy replaces each character in the message with a symbol that was agreed upon in advance as the character's replacement.
    c.   A company uses special ink on its checks to prevent forgeries.
    d.   A graduate student uses watermarks to protect her thesis, which is posted on her website.

**1.10** What type of security mechanism(s) are provided when a person signs a form he has filled out to apply for a credit card?

# PART

# I

# Symmetric-Key Encipherment

In Chapter 1, we saw that cryptography provides three techniques: symmetric-key ciphers, asymmetric-key ciphers, and hashing. Part One is devoted to symmetric-key ciphers. Chapters 2 and 4 review the mathematical background necessary for understanding the rest of the chapters in this part. Chapter 3 explores the traditional ciphers used in the past. Chapters 5, 6, and 7 explain modern block ciphers that are used today. Chapter 8 shows how modern block and stream ciphers can be used to encipher long messages.

## Chapter 2: Mathematics of Cryptography

Chapter 2 reviews some mathematical concepts needed to understand the next few chapters. It discusses integer and modular arithmetic, matrices, and congruence relations.

## Chapter 3: Traditional Symmetric-Key Ciphers

Chapter 3 introduces traditional symmetric-key ciphers. Although these ciphers are not used today, they are the foundation of modern symmetric-key ciphers. This chapter emphasizes the two categories of traditional ciphers: substitution ciphers and transposition ciphers. It also introduces the concepts of stream ciphers and block ciphers.

## Chapter 4: Mathematics of Symmetric-Key Cryptography

Chapter 4 is another review of mathematics needed to understand the contents of the subsequent chapters. It reviews some algebraic structures, such as groups, rings, and finite fields, which are used in modern block ciphers.

## Chapter 5: Introduction to Modern Symmetric-Key Ciphers

Chapter 5 is an introduction to modern symmetric-key ciphers. Understanding the individual elements used in modern symmetric-key ciphers paves the way to a better understanding and analysis of modern ciphers. This chapter introduces components of block ciphers such as P-boxes and S-boxes. It also distinguishes between two classes of product ciphers: Feistel and non-Feistel ciphers.

## Chapter 6: Data Encryption Standard (DES)

Chapter 6 uses the elements defined in Chapter 5 to discuss and analyze one of the common symmetric-key ciphers used today, the Data Encryption Standard (DES). The emphasis is on how DES uses 16 rounds of Feistel ciphers.

## Chapter 7: Advanced Encryption Standard (AES)

Chapter 7 shows how some algebraic structures discussed in Chapter 4 and some elements discussed in Chapter 5 can create a very strong cipher, the Advanced Encryption Standard (AES). The emphasis is on how the algebraic structures discussed in Chapter 4 achieve the AES security goals.

## Chapter 8: Encipherment Using Modern Symmetric-Key Ciphers

Chapter 8 shows how modern block and stream ciphers can actually be used to encipher long messages. It explains five modes of operation designed to be used with modern block ciphers. It also introduces two stream ciphers used for real-time processing of data.

# 2

# Mathematics of Cryptography
## Modular Arithmetic, Congruence, and Matrices

## Objectives

This chapter is intended to prepare the reader for the next few chapters in cryptography. The chapter has several objectives:

☞ To review integer arithmetic, concentrating on divisibility and finding the greatest common divisor using the Euclidean algorithm

☞ To understand how the extended Euclidean algorithm can be used to solve linear Diophantine equations, to solve linear congruent equations, and to find the multiplicative inverses

☞ To emphasize the importance of modular arithmetic and the modulo operator, because they are extensively used in cryptography

☞ To emphasize and review matrices and operations on residue matrices that are extensively used in cryptography

☞ To solve a set of congruent equations using residue matrices

C ryptography is based on some specific areas of mathematics, including number theory, linear algebra, and algebraic structures. In this chapter, we discuss only the topics in the above areas that are needed to understand the contents of the next few chapters. Readers who are familiar with these topics can skip this chapter entirely or partially. Similar chapters are provided throughout the book when needed. Proofs of theorems and algorithms have been omitted, and only their applications are shown. The interested reader can find proofs of the theorems and algorithms in Appendix Q.

**Proofs of theorems and algorithms discussed in this chapter can be found in Appendix Q.**

## 2.1                           INTEGER ARITHMETIC

In **integer arithmetic,** we use a set and a few operations. You are familiar with this set and the corresponding operations, but they are reviewed here to create a background for modular arithmetic.

***Set of Integers*** The **set of integers,** denoted by **Z,** contains all integral numbers (with no fraction) from negative infinity to positive infinity (Fig. 2.1).

$$\mathbf{Z} = \{ \ldots, -2, -1, 0, 1, 2, \ldots \}$$

**Fig. 2.1** *The set of integers*

***Binary Operations*** In cryptography, we are interested in three binary operations applied to the set of integers. A **binary operation** takes two inputs and creates one output. Three common binary operations defined for integers are *addition, subtraction,* and *multiplication.* Each of these operations takes two inputs (*a* and *b*) and creates one output (*c*) as shown in Fig. 2.2. The two inputs come from the set of integers; the output goes into the set of integers.

Note that *division* does not fit in this category because, as we will see shortly, it produces two outputs instead of one.

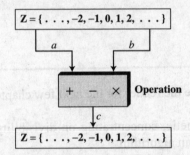

**Fig. 2.2** *Three binary operations for the set of integers*

---

**Example 2.1** The following shows the results of the three binary operations on two integers. Because each input can be either positive or negative, we can have four cases for each operation.

| | | | | |
|---|---|---|---|---|
| Add: | $5 + 9 = 14$ | $(-5) + 9 = 4$ | $5 + (-9) = -4$ | $(-5) + (-9) = -14$ |
| Subtract: | $5 - 9 = -4$ | $(-5) - 9 = -14$ | $5 - (-9) = 14$ | $(-5) - (-9) = +4$ |
| Multiply: | $5 \times 9 = 45$ | $(-5) \times 9 = -45$ | $5 \times (-9) = -45$ | $(-5) \times (-9) = 45$ |

---

### 2.1.1 Integer Division

In integer arithmetic, if we divide *a* by *n*, we can get *q* and *r*. The relationship between these four integers can be shown as

$$a = q \times n + r$$

In this relation, *a* is called the *dividend; q,* the *quotient; n,* the *divisor;* and *r,* the *remainder.* Note that this is not an operation, because the result of dividing *a* by *n* is two integers, *q* and *r*. We can call it *division relation.*

**Example 2.2** Assume that $a = 255$ and $n = 11$. We can find $q = 23$ and $r = 2$ using the division algorithm we have learned in arithmetic as shown in Fig. 2.3.

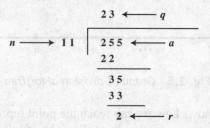

**Fig. 2.3** *Example 2.2, finding the quotient and the remainder*

Most computer languages can find the quotient and the remainder using language-specific operators. For example, in the C language, the operator / can find the quotient and the operator % can find the remainder.

***Two Restrictions*** For our purpose, we impose two restrictions. First, we require that the divisor be a positive integer ($n > 0$). Second, we require that the remainder be a nonnegative integer ($r \geq 0$). Figure 2.4 shows this relationship with the two above-mentioned restrictions.

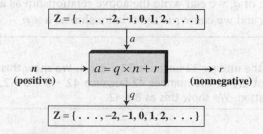

**Fig. 2.4** *Division algorithm for integers*

**Example 2.3** When we use a computer or a calculator, $r$ and $q$ are negative when $a$ is negative. How can we apply the restriction that $r$ needs to be positive? The solution is simple, we decrement the value of $q$ by 1 and we add the value of $n$ to $r$ to make it positive.
$$-255 = (-23 \times 11) + (-2) \leftrightarrow -255 = (-24 \times 11) + 9$$
We have decremented -23 to become -24 and added 11 to -2 to make it 9. The above relation is still valid.

***The Graph of the Relation*** We can show the above relation with the two restrictions on $n$ and $r$ using two graphs in Fig. 2.5. The first one shows the case when $a$ is positive; the second when $a$ is negative.

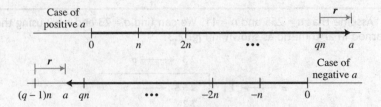

**Fig. 2.5** *Graph of division algorithm*

Starting from zero, the graph shows how we can reach the point representing the integer $a$ on the line. In case of a positive $a$, we need to move $q \times n$ units to the right and then move extra $r$ units in the same direction. In case of a negative $a$, we need to move $(q - 1) \times n$ units to the left ($q$ is negative in this case) and then move $r$ units in the opposite direction. In both cases the value of $r$ is positive.

### 2.1.2  Divisibility

Let us briefly discuss **divisibility,** a topic we often encounter in cryptography. If $a$ is not zero and we let $r = 0$ in the division relation, we get

$$a = q \times n$$

We then say that $n$ divides $a$ (or $n$ is a divisor of $a$). We can also say that $a$ is divisible by $n$. When we are not interested in the value of $q$, we can write the above relationship as $\mathbf{a} \mid \boldsymbol{n}$. If the remainder is not zero, then $n$ does not divide $a$ and we can write the relationship as $\mathbf{a} \times \boldsymbol{n}$.

---

**Example 2.4**

    a.    The integer 4 divides the integer 32 because **32** = 8 × 4. We show this as 4 | 32.
    b.    The number 8 does not divide the number 42 because **42** = 5 × **8** + 2. There is a remainder, the number 2, in the equation. We show this as 8 + 42.

---

**Example 2.5**

    a.    We have 13 | 78, 7 | 98, –6 | 24, 4 | 44, and 11 | (–33).
    b.    We have 13 + 27, 7 + 50, –6 + 23, 4 + 41, and 11 B (–32).

---

***Properties***  Following are several properties of divisibility. The interested reader can check Appendix Q for proofs.

    **Property 1:** if $a \mid 1$, then $a = \pm 1$.
    **Property 2:** if $a \mid b$ and $b \mid a$, then $a = \pm b$.
    **Property 3:** if $a \mid b$ and $b \mid c$, then $a \mid c$.
    **Property 4:** if $a \mid b$ and $a \mid c$, then $a \mid (m \times b + n \times c)$, where $m$ and $n$ are arbitrary integers.

---

**Example 2.6**

    a.    Since 3 | 15 and 15 | 45, according to the third property, 3 | 45.
    b.    Since 3 | 15 and 3 | 9, according to the fourth property, 3 | (15 × 2 + 9 × 4), which means 3 | 66.

---

***All Divisors*** A positive integer can have more than one divisor. For example, the integer 32 has six divisors: 1, 2, 4, 8, 16, and 32. We can mention two interesting facts about divisors of positive integers:

**Fact 1:** The integer 1 has only one divisor, itself.

**Fact 2:** Any positive integer has at least two divisors, 1 and itself (but it can have more).

***Greatest Common Divisor*** One integer often needed in cryptography is the **greatest common divisor** of two positive integers. Two positive integers may have many common divisors, but only one greatest common divisor. For example, the common divisors of 12 and 140 are 1, 2, and 4. However, the greatest common divisor is 4. See Fig. 2.6.

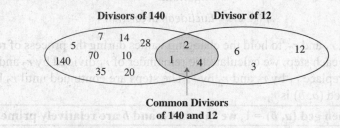

**Fig. 2.6** *Common divisors of two integers*

---

**The greatest common divisor of two positive integers is the largest integer that can divide both integers.**

---

***Euclidean Algorithm*** Finding the greatest common divisor (gcd) of two positive integers by listing all common divisors is not practical when the two integers are large. Fortunately, more than 2000 years ago a mathematician named Euclid developed an algorithm that can find the greatest common divisor of two positive integers. The **Euclidean algorithm** is based on the following two facts (see Appendix Q for the proof):

---

**Fact 1:** gcd $(a, 0) = a$

**Fact 2:** gcd $(a, b) =$ gcd $(b, r)$, where $r$ is the remainder of dividing $a$ by $b$

---

The first fact tells us that if the second integer is 0, the greatest common divisor is the first one. The second fact allows us to change the value of $a$, $b$ until $b$ becomes 0. For example, to calculate the gcd (36, 10), we can use the second fact several times and the first fact once, as shown below.

gcd $(36, 10) =$ gcd $(10, 6) =$ gcd $(6, 4) =$ gcd $(4, 2) =$ gcd $(2, 0) = 2$

In other words, gcd (36, 10) = 2, gcd (10, 6) = 2, and so on. This means that instead of calculating gcd (36, 10), we can find gcd (2, 0). Figure 2.7 shows how we use the above two facts to calculate gcd $(a, b)$.

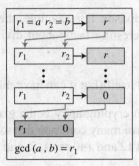

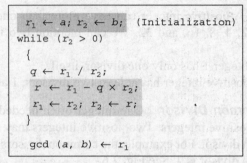

a. Process        b. Algorithm

**Fig. 2.7** *Euclidean algorithm*

We use two variables, $r_1$ and $r_2$, to hold the changing values during the process of reduction. They are initialized to $a$ and $b$. In each step, we calculate the remainder of $r_1$ divided by $r_2$ and store the result in the variable $r$. We then replace $r_1$ by $r_2$ and $r_2$ by $r$. The steps are continued until $r_2$ becomes 0. At this moment, we stop. The gcd $(a, b)$ is $r_1$.

---

**When gcd $(a, b) = 1$, we say that $a$ and $b$ are relatively prime.**

---

**Example 2.7**    Find the greatest common divisor of 2740 and 1760.

**Solution**    We apply the above procedure using a table. We initialize $r_1$ to 2740 and $r_2$ to 1760. We have also shown the value of $q$ in each step. We have gcd $(2740, 1760) = 20$.

| $q$ | $r_1$ | $r_2$ | $r$ |
|---|---|---|---|
| 1 | 2740 | 1760 | 980 |
| 1 | 1760 | 980 | 780 |
| 1 | 980 | 780 | 200 |
| 3 | 780 | 200 | 180 |
| 1 | 200 | 180 | 20 |
| 9 | 180 | 20 | 0 |
| | **20** | 0 | |

**Example 2.8**    Find the greatest common divisor of 25 and 60.

**Solution**    We chose this particular example to show that it does not matter if the first number is smaller than the second number. We immediately get our correct ordering. We have gcd $(25, 65) = 5$.

| $q$ | $r_1$ | $r_2$ | $r$ |
|---|---|---|---|
| 0 | 25 | 60 | 25 |
| 2 | 60 | 25 | 10 |
| 2 | 25 | 10 | 5 |
| 2 | 10 | 5 | 0 |
| | **5** | 0 | |

***The Extended Euclidean Algorithm***   Given two integers $a$ and $b$, we often need to find other two integers, $s$ and $t$, such that

$$s \times a + t \times b = \gcd(a, b)$$

The **extended Euclidean algorithm** can calculate the gcd $(a, b)$ and at the same time calculate the value of $s$ and $t$. The algorithm and the process is shown in Fig. 2.8.

As shown in Fig. 2.8, the extended Euclidean algorithm uses the same number of steps as the Euclidean algorithm. However, in each step, we use three sets of calculations and exchanges instead of one. The algorithm uses three sets of variables, $r$'s, $s$'s, and $t$'s. In each step, $r_1$, $r_2$, and $r$ have the same values in the Euclidean algorithm. The variables $r_1$ and $r_2$ are initialized to the values of $a$ and $b$, respectively. The variables $s_1$ and $s_2$ are initialized to 1 and 0, respectively. The variables $t_1$ and $t_2$ are initialized to 0 and 1, respectively. The calculations of $r$, $s$, and $t$ are similar, with one warning. Although $r$ is the remainder of dividing $r_1$ by $r_2$, there is no such relationship between the other two sets. There is only one quotient, $q$, which is calculated as $r_1 / r_2$ and used for the other two calculations.

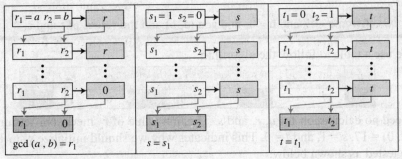

a. Process

```
r₁ ← a;  r₂ ← b;
s₁ ← 1;  s₂ ← 0;        (Initialization)
t₁ ← 0;  t₂ ← 1;
while (r₂ > 0)
{
  q ← r₁ / r₂;

    r ← r₁ - q × r₂;
    r₁ ← r₂;  r₂ ← r;     (Updating r's)

    s ← s₁ - q × s₂;
    s₁ ← s₂;  s₂ ← s;     (Updating s's)

    t ← t₁ - q × t₂;
    t₁ ← t₂;  t₂ ← t;     (Updating t's)

}
  gcd (a , b) ← r₁;  s ← s₁;  t ← t₁;
```

b. Algorithm

**Fig. 2.8**  *Extended Euclidean algorithm*

**Example 2.9** Given $a = 161$ and $b = 28$, find gcd $(a, b)$ and the values of $s$ and $t$.

**Solution**

$$r = r_1 - q \times r_2 \quad s = s_1 - q \times s_2 \quad t = t_1 - q \times t_2$$

We use a table to follow the algorithm.

| $q$ | $r_1$ | $r_2$ | $r$ | $s_1$ | $s_2$ | $s$ | $t_1$ | $t_2$ | $t$ |
|---|---|---|---|---|---|---|---|---|---|
| 5 | 161 | 28 | 21 | 1 | 0 | 1 | 0 | 1 | −5 |
| 1 | 28 | 21 | 7 | 0 | 1 | −1 | 1 | −5 | 6 |
| 3 | 21 | 7 | 0 | 1 | −1 | 4 | −5 | 6 | −23 |
| | 7 | 0 | | −1 | 4 | | 6 | −23 | |

We get gcd $(161, 28) = 7$, $s = -1$ and $t = 6$. The answers can be tested because we have

$$(-1) \times 161 + 6 \times 28 = 7$$

**Example 2.10** Given $a = 17$ and $b = 0$, find gcd $(a, b)$ and the values of $s$ and $t$.

**Solution** We use a table to follow the algorithm.

| $q$ | $r_1$ | $r_2$ | $r$ | $s_1$ | $s_2$ | $s$ | $t_1$ | $t_2$ | $t$ |
|---|---|---|---|---|---|---|---|---|---|
| | 17 | 0 | | 1 | 0 | | 0 | 1 | |

Note that we need no calculation for $q$, $r$, and $s$. The first value of $r_2$ meets our termination condition. We get gcd $(17, 0) = 17$, $s = 1$, and $t = 0$. This indicates why we should initialize $s_1$ to 1 and $t_1$ to 0. The answers can be tested as shown below:

$$(1 \times 17) + (0 \times 0) = 17$$

**Example 2.11** Given $a = 0$ and $b = 45$, find gcd $(a, b)$ and the values of $s$ and $t$.

**Solution** We use a table to follow the algorithm.

| $q$ | $r_1$ | $r_2$ | $r$ | $s_1$ | $s_2$ | $s$ | $t_1$ | $t_2$ | $t$ |
|---|---|---|---|---|---|---|---|---|---|
| 0 | 0 | 45 | 0 | 1 | 0 | 1 | 0 | 1 | 0 |
| | 45 | 0 | | 0 | 1 | | 1 | 0 | |

We get gcd $(0, 45) = 45$, $s = 0$, and $t = 1$. This indicates why we should initialize $s_2$ to 0 and $t_2$ to 1. The answer can be tested as shown below:

$$(0 \times 0) + (1 \times 45) = 45$$

### 2.1.3 Linear Diophantine Equations

Although we will see a very important application of the extended Euclidean algorithm in the next section, one immediate application is to find the solutions to the **linear Diophantine equations** of two variables, an equation of type $ax + by = c$. We need to find integer values for $x$ and $y$ that satisfy the equation. This type of equation has either no solution or an infinite number of solutions. Let $d = $ gcd $(a, b)$. If $d + c$, then the equation has no solution. If $d \mid c$, then we have an infinite number of solutions. One of them is called the particular; the rest, general.

---

**A linear Diophantine equation of two variables is $ax + by = c$.**

---

## Particular Solution

If $d \mid c$, a particular solution to the above equation can be found using the following steps:

1. Reduce the equation to $a_1 x + b_1 y = c_1$ by dividing both sides of the equation by $d$. This is possible because $d$ divides $a$, $b$, and $c$ by the assumption.
2. Solve for $s$ and $t$ in the relation $a_1 s + b_1 t = 1$ using the extended Euclidean algorithm.
3. The particular solution can be found:

---

**Particular solution: $x_0 = (c/d)s$ and $y_0 = (c/d)t$**

---

## General Solutions

After finding the particular solution, the general solutions can be found:

---

**General solutions: $x = x_0 + k\,(b/d)$ and $y = y_0 - k\,(a/d)$ where $k$ is an integer**

---

**Example 2.12** Find the particular and general solutions to the equation $21x + 14y = 35$.

**Solution** We have $d = \gcd(21, 14) = 7$. Since $7 \mid 35$, the equation has an infinite number of solutions. We can divide both sides by 7 to find the equation $3x + 2y = 5$. Using the extended Euclidean algorithm, we find $s$ and $t$ such as $3s + 2t = 1$. We have $s = 1$ and $t = -1$. The solutions are

Particular: $x_0 = 5 \times 1 = 5$ and $y_0 = 5 \times (-1) = -5$ since $35/7 = 5$

General: $x = 5 + k \times 2$ and $y = -5 - k \times 3$ where $k$ is an integer

Therefore, the solutions are $(5, -5)$, $(7, -8)$, $(9, -11)$, . . . We can easily test that each of these solutions satisfies the original equation.

---

**Example 2.13** A very interesting application in real life is when we want to find different combinations of objects having different values. For example, imagine we want to cash a $100 check and get some $20 and some $5 bills. We have many choices, which we can find by solving the corresponding Diophantine equation $20x + 5y = 100$. Since $d = \gcd(20, 5) = 5$ and $5 \mid 100$, the equation has an infinite number of solutions, but only a few of them are acceptable in this case (only answers in which both $x$ and $y$ are nonnegative integers). We divide both sides by 5 to get $4x + y = 20$. We then solve the equation $4s + t = 1$. We can find $s = 0$ and $t = 1$ using the extended Euclidean algorithm. The particular solutions are $x_0 = 0 \times 20 = 0$ and $y_0 = 1 \times 20 = 20$. The general solutions with $x$ and $y$ nonnegative are $(0, 20)$, $(1, 16)$, $(2, 12)$, $(3, 8)$, $(4, 4)$, $(5, 0)$. The rest of the solutions are not acceptable because $y$ becomes negative. The teller at the bank needs to ask which of the above combinations we want. The first has no $20 bills; the last has no $5 bills.

---

## 2.2        MODULAR ARITHMETIC

---

The division relationship ($a = q \times n + r$) discussed in the previous section has two inputs ($a$ and $n$) and two outputs ($q$ and $r$). In **modular arithmetic,** we are interested in only one of the outputs, the remainder $r$. We don't care about the quotient $q$. In other words, we want to know what is the value of $r$ when we divide $a$ by $n$. This implies that we can change the above relation into a binary operator with two inputs $a$ and $n$ and one output $r$.

## 2.2.1 Modulo Operator

The above-mentioned binary operator is called the **modulo operator** and is shown as *mod*. The second input (*n*) is called the **modulus.** The output *r* is called the **residue.** Figure 2.9 shows the division relation compared with the modulo operator.

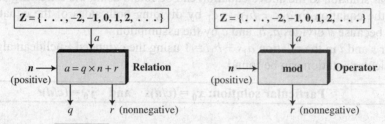

**Fig. 2.9** *Division relation and modulo operator*

As Fig. 2.9 shows, the modulo operator (**mod**) takes an integer (*a*) from the set **Z** and a positive modulus (*n*). The operator creates a nonnegative residue (*r*). We can say

$a$ **mod** $n = r$

> **Example 2.14**   Find the result of the following operations:
> a.   27 mod 5
> b.   36 mod 12
> c.   −18 mod 14
> d.   −7 mod 10

**Solution**   We are looking for the residue *r*. We can divide the *a* by *n* and find *q* and *r*. We can then disregard *q* and keep *r*.
   a.   Dividing 27 by 5 results in $r = 2$. This means that 27 mod 5 = 2.
   b.   Dividing 36 by 12 results in $r = 0$. This means that 36 mod 12 = 0.
   c.   Dividing −18 by 14 results in $r = -4$. However, we need to add the modulus (14) to make it nonnegative. We have $r = -4 + 14 = 10$. This means that −18 mod 14 = 10.
   d.   Dividing −7 by 10 results in $r = -7$. After adding the modulus to −7, we have $r = 3$. This means that −7 mod 10 = 3.

## 2.2.2 Set of Residues: $Z_n$

The result of the modulo operation with modulus *n* is always an integer between 0 and $n - 1$. In other words, the result of *a* mod *n* is always a nonnegative integer less than *n*. We can say that the modulo operation creates a set, which in modular arithmetic is referred to as the **set of least residues modulo n**, or $Z_n$. However, we need to remember that although we have only one set of integers (**Z**), we have infinite instances of the set of residues ($Z_n$), one for each value of *n*. Figure 2.10 shows the set $Z_n$ and three instances, $Z_2$, $Z_6$, and $Z_{11}$.

$$Z_n = \{ 0, 1, 2, 3, \ldots , (n-1) \}$$

$$Z_2 = \{ 0, 1 \} \qquad Z_6 = \{ 0, 1, 2, 3, 4, 5 \} \qquad Z_{11} = \{ 0, 1, 2, 3, 4, 5, 6, 7, 8, 9, 10 \}$$

**Fig. 2.10** *Some $Z_n$ sets*

### 2.2.3 Congruence

In cryptography, we often used the concept of **congruence** instead of equality. Mapping from **Z** to $\mathbf{Z}_n$ is not one-to-one. Infinite members of **Z** can map to one member of $\mathbf{Z}_n$. For example, the result of 2 mod 10 = 2, 12 mod 10 = 2, 22 mod 2 = 2, and so on. In modular arithmetic, integers like 2, 12, and 22 are called congruent mod 10. To show that two integers are congruent, we use the **congruence operator** ($\equiv$). We add the phrase (mod $n$) to the right side of the congruence to define the value of modulus that makes the relationship valid. For example, we write:

| | | | |
|---|---|---|---|
| $2 \equiv 12 \pmod{10}$ | $13 \equiv 23 \pmod{10}$ | $34 \equiv 24 \pmod{10}$ | $-8 \equiv 12 \pmod{10}$ |
| $3 \equiv 8 \pmod 5$ | $8 \equiv 13 \pmod 5$ | $23 \equiv 33 \pmod 5$ | $-8 \equiv 2 \pmod 5$ |

Figure 2.11 shows the idea of congruence. We need to explain several points.

a.  The congruence operator looks like the equality operator, but there are differences. First, an equality operator maps a member of **Z** to itself; the congruence operator maps a member from **Z** to a member of $\mathbf{Z}_n$. Second, the equality operator is one-to-one; the congruence operator is many-to-one.

b.  The phrase (mod $n$) that we insert at the right-hand side of the congruence operator is just an indication of the destination set ($\mathbf{Z}_n$). We need to add this phrase to show what modulus is used in the mapping. The symbol *mod* used here does not have the same meaning as the binary operator. In other words, the symbol *mod* in 12 mod 10 is an operator; the phrase (mod 10) in $2 \equiv 12 \pmod{10}$ means that the destination set is $\mathbf{Z}_{10}$.

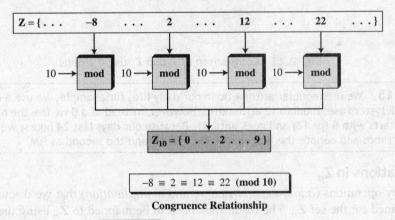

**Congruence Relationship**

**Fig. 2.11**   *Concept of congruence*

***Residue Classes***   A **residue class** [a] or $[a]_n$ is the set of integers congruent modulo $n$. In other words, it is the set of all integers such that $x = a \pmod n$. For example, if $n = 5$, we have five sets [0], [1], [2], [3], and [4] as shown below:

| |
|---|
| $[0] = \{\ldots, -15, -10, -5, 0, 5, 10, 15, \ldots\}$ |
| $[1] = \{\ldots, -14, -9, -4, 1, 6, 11, 16, \ldots\}$ |
| $[2] = \{\ldots, -13, -8, -3, 2, 7, 12, 17, \ldots\}$ |
| $[3] = \{\ldots, -12, -7, -5, 3, 8, 13, 18, \ldots\}$ |
| $[4] = \{\ldots, -11, -6, -1, 4, 9, 14, 19, \ldots\}$ |

The integers in the set [0] are all reduced to 0 when we apply the modulo 5 operation on them. The integers in the set [1] are all reduced to 1 when we apply the modulo 5 operation, and so on. In each set, there is one element called the least (nonnegative) residue. In the set [0], this element is 0; in the set [1], this element is 1; and so on. The set of all of these least residues is what we have shown as $\mathbf{Z_5} = \{0, 1, 2, 3, 4\}$. In other words, the set $\mathbf{Z_n}$ is the set of all **least residue** modulo $n$.

***Circular Notation*** The concept of congruence can be better understood with the use of a circle. Just as we use a line to show the distribution of integers in $\mathbf{Z}$, we can use a circle to show the distribution of integers in $\mathbf{Z_n}$. Figure 2.12 shows the comparison between the two. Integers 0 to $n - 1$ are spaced evenly around a circle. All congruent integers modulo $n$ occupy the same point on the circle. Positive and negative integers from $\mathbf{Z}$ are mapped to the circle in such a way that there is a symmetry between them.

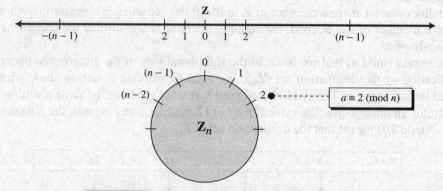

**Fig. 2.12** *Comparison of Z and $Z_n$ using graphs*

**Example 2.15** We use modular arithmetic in our daily life; for example, we use a clock to measure time. Our clock system uses modulo 12 arithmetic. However, instead of a 0 we use the number 12. So our clock system starts with 0 (or 12) and goes until 11. Because our days last 24 hours, we navigate around the circle two times and denote the first revolution as A.M. and the second as P.M.

### 2.2.4 Operations in $Z_n$

The three binary operations (*addition, subtraction,* and *multiplication*) that we discussed for the set $\mathbf{Z}$ can also be defined for the set $\mathbf{Z_n}$. The result may need to be mapped to $\mathbf{Z_n}$ using the mod operator as shown in Fig. 2.13.

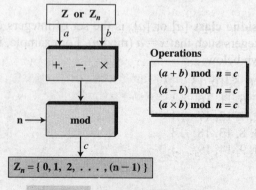

**Fig. 2.13** *Binary operations in $Z_n$*

Actually, two sets of operators are used here. The first set is one of the binary operators $(+, -, \times)$; the second is the mod operator. We need to use parentheses to emphasize the order of operations. As Fig. 2.13 shows, the inputs ($a$ and $b$) can be members of $\mathbf{Z}_n$ or $\mathbf{Z}$.

---

**Example 2.16**   Perform the following operations (the inputs come from $\mathbf{Z}_n$):
   a.   Add 7 to 14 in $\mathbf{Z}_{15}$.
   b.   Subtract 11 from 7 in $\mathbf{Z}_{13}$.
   c.   Multiply 11 by 7 in $\mathbf{Z}_{20}$.

---

*Solution*   The following shows the two steps involved in each case:

$(14 + 7) \bmod 15 \rightarrow (21) \bmod 15 = 6$
$(7 - 11) \bmod 13 \rightarrow (-4) \bmod 13 = 9$
$(7 \times 11) \bmod 20 \rightarrow (77) \bmod 20 = 17$

---

**Example 2.17**   Perform the following operations (the inputs come from either $\mathbf{Z}$ or $\mathbf{Z}_n$):
   a.   Add 17 to 27 in $\mathbf{Z}_{14}$.
   b.   Subtract 34 from 12 in $\mathbf{Z}_{13}$.
   c.   Multiply 123 by -10 in $\mathbf{Z}_{19}$.

---

*Solution*   The following shows the two steps involved in each case:

$(17 + 27) \bmod 14 \qquad \rightarrow (44) \bmod 14 = 2$
$(12 - 43) \bmod 13 \qquad \rightarrow (-31) \bmod 13 = 8$
$(123 \times (-10)) \bmod 19 \rightarrow (-1230) \bmod 19 = 5$

## Properties

We mentioned that the two inputs to the three binary operations in the modular arithmetic can come from $\mathbf{Z}$ or $\mathbf{Z}_n$. The following properties allow us to first map the two inputs to $\mathbf{Z}_n$ (if they are coming from $\mathbf{Z}$) before applying the three binary operations $(+, -, \times)$. Interested readers can find proofs for these properties in Appendix Q.

**First Property:**   $(a + b) \bmod n$   $= [(a \bmod n) + (b \bmod n)] \bmod n$
**Second Property:** $(a - b) \bmod n$   $= [(a \bmod n) - (b \bmod n)] \bmod n$
**Third Property:**   $(a \times b) \bmod n$   $= [(a \bmod n) \times (b \bmod n)] \bmod n$

Figure 2.14 shows the process before and after applying the above properties. Although the figure shows that the process is longer if we apply the above properties, we should remember that in cryptography we are dealing with very large integers. For example, if we multiply a very large integer by another very large integer, we may have an integer that is too large to be stored in the computer. Applying the above properties make the first two operands smaller before the multiplication operation is applied. In other words, the properties allow us to work with smaller numbers. This fact will manifest itself more clearly in discussion of the exponential operation in later chapters.

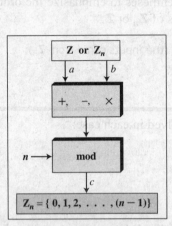 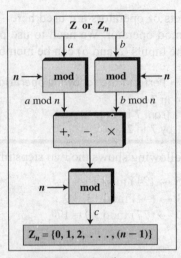

a. Original process  b. Applying properties

**Fig. 2.14** *Properties of mod operator*

---

**Example 2.18**  The following shows the application of the above properties:

1.  $(1,723,345 + 2,124,945) \bmod 11 = (8 + 9) \bmod 11 = 6$
2.  $(1,723,345 - 2,124,945) \bmod 16 = (8 - 9) \bmod 11 = 10$
3.  $(1,723,345 \times 2,124,945) \bmod 16 = (8 \times 9) \bmod 11 = 6$

---

**Example 2.19**  In arithmetic, we often need to find the remainder of powers of 10 when divided by an integer. For example, we need to find $10 \bmod 3$, $10^2 \bmod 3$, $10^3 \bmod 3$, and so on. We also need to find $10 \bmod 7$, $10^2 \bmod 7$, $10^3 \bmod 7$, and so. The third property of the mod operator mentioned above makes life much easier.

$10^n \bmod x = (10 \bmod x)^n$ Applying the third property $n$ times.

We have

$10 \bmod 3 = 1 \rightarrow 10^n \bmod 3 = (10 \bmod 3)^n = 1$
$10 \bmod 9 = 1 \rightarrow 10^n \bmod 9 = (10 \bmod 9)^n = 1$
$10 \bmod 7 = 3 \rightarrow 10^n \bmod 7 = (10 \bmod 7)^n = 3^n \bmod 7$

---

**Example 2.20**  We have been told in arithmetic that the remainder of an integer divided by 3 is the same as the remainder of the sum of its decimal digits. In other words, the remainder of dividing 6371 by 3 is the same as dividing 17 by 3 because $6 + 3 + 7 + 1 = 17$. We can prove this claim using the properties of the mod operator. We write an integer as the sum of its digits multiplied by the powers of 10.

$a = a_n \times 10^n + \cdots + a_1 \times 10^1 + a_0 \times 10^0$
For example: $6371 = 6 \times 10^3 + 3 \times 10^2 + 7 \times 10^1 + 1 \times 10^0$

Now we can apply the mod operator to both sides of the equality and use the result of the previous example that $10^n \bmod 3$ is 1.

$a \bmod 3 = (a_n \times 10^n + \cdots + a_1 \times 10^1 + a_0 \times 10^0) \bmod 3$
$= (a_n \times 10^n) \bmod 3 + \cdots + (a_1 \times 10^1) \bmod 3 + (a_0 \times 10^0) \bmod 3$
$= (a_n \bmod 3) \times (10^n \bmod 3) + \cdots + (a_1 \bmod 3) \times (10^1 \bmod 3) +$
$(a_0 \bmod 3) \times (10^0 \bmod 3)$
$= a_n \bmod 3 + \cdots + a_1 \bmod 3 + a_0 \bmod 3 = (a_n + \cdots + a_1 + a_0) \bmod 3$

## 2.2.5 Inverses

When we are working in modular arithmetic, we often need to find the inverse of a number relative to an operation. We are normally looking for an **additive inverse** (relative to an addition operation) or a **multiplicative inverse** (relative to a multiplication operation).

### Additive Inverse

In $Z_n$, two numbers $a$ and $b$ are additive inverses of each other if

$$a + b \equiv 0 \ (\text{mod } n)$$

In $Z_n$, the additive inverse of $a$ can be calculated as $b = n - a$. For example, the additive inverse of 4 in $Z_{10}$ is $10 - 4 = 6$.

> In modular arithmetic, each integer has an additive inverse. The sum of an integer and its additive inverse is congruent to 0 modulo $n$.

Note that in modular arithmetic, each number has an additive inverse and the inverse is unique; each number has one and only one additive inverse. However, the inverse of the number may be the number itself.

**Example 2.21**   Find all additive inverse pairs in $Z_{10}$.

*Solution*   The six pairs of additive inverses are (0, 0), (1, 9), (2, 8), (3, 7), (4, 6), and (5, 5). In this list, 0 is the additive inverse of itself; so is 5. Note that the additive inverses are reciprocal; if 4 is the additive inverse of 6, then 6 is also the additive inverse of 4.

### Multiplicative Inverse

In $Z_n$, two numbers $a$ and $b$ are the multiplicative inverse of each other if

$$a \times b \equiv 1 \ (\text{mod } n)$$

For example, if the modulus is 10, then the multiplicative inverse of 3 is 7. In other words, we have $(3 \times 7) \bmod 10 = 1$.

> In modular arithmetic, an integer may or may not have a multiplicative inverse. When it does, the product of the integer and its multiplicative inverse is congruent to 1 modulo $n$.

It can be proved that $a$ has a multiplicative inverse in $Z_n$ if and only if gcd $(n, a) = 1$. In this case, $a$ and $n$ are said to be **relatively prime**.

**Example 2.22**   Find the multiplicative inverse of 8 in $Z_{10}$.

*Solution*   There is no multiplicative inverse because gcd $(10, 8) = 2 \neq 1$. In other words, we cannot find any number between 0 and 9 such that when multiplied by 8, the result is congruent to 1.

**Example 2.23**   Find all multiplicative inverses in $Z_{10}$.

*Solution*   There are only three pairs: (1, 1), (3, 7) and (9, 9). The numbers 0, 2, 4, 5, 6, and 8 do not have a multiplicative inverse. We can see that

$$(1 \times 1) \bmod 10 = 1 \quad (3 \times 7) \bmod 10 = 1 \quad (9 \times 9) \bmod 10 = 1$$

**Example 2.24**   Find all multiplicative inverse pairs in $Z_{11}$.

**Solution**   We have seven pairs: $(1, 1), (2, 6), (3, 4), (5, 9), (7, 8), (9, 9),$ and $(10, 10)$. In moving from $Z_{10}$ to $Z_{11}$, the number of pairs doubles. The reason is that in $Z_{11}$, gcd $(11, a)$ is 1 (relatively prime) for all values of $a$ except 0. It means all integers 1 to 10 have multiplicative inverses.

---

**The integer $a$ in $Z_n$ has a multiplicative inverse if and only if gcd $(n, a) \equiv 1$ (mod $n$)**

---

The extended Euclidean algorithm we discussed earlier in the chapter can find the multiplicative inverse of $b$ in $Z_n$ when $n$ and $b$ are given and the inverse exists. To show this, let us replace the first integer $a$ with $n$ (the modulus). We can say that the algorithm can find $s$ and $t$ such $s \times n + b \times t = $ gcd $(n, b)$. However, if the multiplicative inverse of $b$ exists, gcd $(n, b)$ must be 1. So the relationship is

$$(s \times n) + (b \times t) = 1$$

Now we apply the modulo operator to both sides. In other words, we map each side to $Z_n$. We will have

$(s \times n + b \times t) \bmod n = 1 \bmod n$
$[(s \times n) \bmod n] + [(b \times t) \bmod n] = 1 \bmod n$
$0 + [(b \times t) \bmod n] = 1$
$(b \times t) \bmod n = 1$       → This means $t$ is the multiplicative inverse of $b$ in $Z_n$

Note that $[(s \times n) \bmod n]$ in the third line is 0 because if we divide $(s \times n)$ by $n$, the quotient is $s$ but the remainder is 0.

---

**The extended Euclidean algorithm finds the multiplicative inverses of $b$ in $Z_n$
when $n$ and $b$ are given and gcd $(n, b) = 1$.
The multiplicative inverse of $b$ is the value of $t$ after being mapped to $Z_n$.**

---

Figure 2.15 shows how we find the multiplicative inverse of a number using the extended Euclidean algorithm.

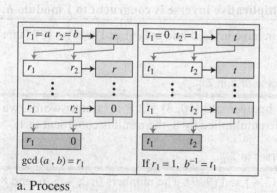

a. Process

b. Algorithm

**Fig. 2.15**   *Using the extended Euclidean algorithm to find the multiplicative inverse*

**Example 2.25**    Find the multiplicative inverse of 11 in $Z_{26}$.

*Solution*    We use a table similar to the one we used before with $r_1 = 26$ and $r_2 = 11$. We are interested only in the value of $t$.

| $q$ | $r_1$ | $r_2$ | $r$ | $t_1$ | $t_2$ | $t$ |
|---|---|---|---|---|---|---|
| 2 | 26 | 11 | 4 | 0 | 1 | −2 |
| 2 | 11 | 4 | 3 | 1 | −2 | 5 |
| 1 | 4 | 3 | 1 | −2 | 5 | −7 |
| 3 | 3 | 1 | 0 | 5 | −7 | 26 |
| | 1 | 0 | | −7 | 26 | |

The gcd (26, 11) is 1, which means that the multiplicative inverse of 11 exists. The extended Euclidean algorithm gives $t_1 = -7$. The multiplicative inverse is $(-7)$ mod 26 = 19. In other words, 11 and 19 are multiplicative inverse in $Z_{26}$. We can see that $(11 \times 19)$ mod 26 = 209 mod 26 = 1.

**Example 2.26**    Find the multiplicative inverse of 23 in $Z_{100}$.

*Solution*    We use a table similar to the one we used before with $r_1 = 100$ and $r_2 = 23$. We are interested only in the value of $t$.

| $q$ | $r_1$ | $r_2$ | $r$ | $t_1$ | $t_2$ | $t$ |
|---|---|---|---|---|---|---|
| 4 | 100 | 23 | 8 | 0 | 1 | −4 |
| 2 | 23 | 8 | 7 | 1 | −4 | 19 |
| 1 | 8 | 7 | 1 | −4 | 9 | −13 |
| 7 | 7 | 1 | 0 | 9 | −13 | 100 |
| | 1 | 0 | | −13 | 100 | |

The gcd (100, 23) is 1, which means the inverse of 23 exists. The extended Euclidean algorithm gives $t_1 = -13$. The inverse is $(-13)$ mod 100 = 87. In other words, 13 and 87 are multiplicative inverses in $Z_{100}$. We can see that $(23 \times 87)$ mod 100 = 2001 mod 100 = 1.

**Example 2.27**    Find the inverse of 12 in $Z_{26}$.

*Solution*    We use a table similar to the one we used before, with $r_1 = 26$ and $r_2 = 12$.

| $q$ | $r_1$ | $r_2$ | $r$ | $t_1$ | $t_2$ | $t$ |
|---|---|---|---|---|---|---|
| 2 | 26 | 12 | 2 | 0 | 1 | −2 |
| 6 | 12 | 2 | 0 | 1 | −2 | 13 |
| | 2 | 0 | | −2 | 13 | |

The gcd (26, 12) = 2 ≠ 1, which means there is no multiplicative inverse for 12 in $Z_{26}$.

### 2.2.6  Addition and Multiplication Tables

Figure 2.16 shows two tables for addition and multiplication. In the addition table, each integer has an additive inverse. The inverse pairs can be found when the result of addition is zero. We have (0, 0), (1, 9), (2, 8), (3, 7), (4, 6), and (5, 5). In the multiplication table we have only three multiplicative pairs

(1, 1), (3, 7) and (9, 9). The pairs can be found whenever the result of multiplication is 1. Both tables are symmetric with respect to the diagonal of elements that moves from the top left to the bottom right, revealing the commutative property for addition and multiplication ($a + b = b + a$ and $a \times b = b \times a$). The addition table also shows that each row or column is a permutation of another row or column. This is not true for the multiplication table.

|   | 0 | 1 | 2 | 3 | 4 | 5 | 6 | 7 | 8 | 9 |
|---|---|---|---|---|---|---|---|---|---|---|
| **0** | 0 | 1 | 2 | 3 | 4 | 5 | 6 | 7 | 8 | 9 |
| **1** | 1 | 2 | 3 | 4 | 5 | 6 | 7 | 8 | 9 | 0 |
| **2** | 2 | 3 | 4 | 5 | 6 | 7 | 8 | 9 | 0 | 1 |
| **3** | 3 | 4 | 5 | 6 | 7 | 8 | 9 | 0 | 1 | 2 |
| **4** | 4 | 5 | 6 | 7 | 8 | 9 | 0 | 1 | 2 | 3 |
| **5** | 5 | 6 | 7 | 8 | 9 | 0 | 1 | 2 | 3 | 4 |
| **6** | 6 | 7 | 8 | 9 | 0 | 1 | 2 | 3 | 4 | 5 |
| **7** | 7 | 8 | 9 | 0 | 1 | 2 | 3 | 4 | 5 | 6 |
| **8** | 8 | 9 | 0 | 1 | 2 | 3 | 4 | 5 | 6 | 7 |
| **9** | 9 | 0 | 1 | 2 | 3 | 4 | 5 | 6 | 7 | 8 |

Addition Table in $\mathbf{Z}_{10}$

|   | 0 | 1 | 2 | 3 | 4 | 5 | 6 | 7 | 8 | 9 |
|---|---|---|---|---|---|---|---|---|---|---|
| **0** | 0 | 0 | 0 | 0 | 0 | 0 | 0 | 0 | 0 | 0 |
| **1** | 0 | 1 | 2 | 3 | 4 | 5 | 6 | 7 | 8 | 9 |
| **2** | 0 | 2 | 4 | 6 | 8 | 0 | 2 | 4 | 6 | 8 |
| **3** | 0 | 3 | 6 | 9 | 2 | 5 | 8 | 1 | 4 | 7 |
| **4** | 0 | 4 | 8 | 2 | 6 | 0 | 4 | 8 | 2 | 6 |
| **5** | 0 | 5 | 0 | 5 | 0 | 5 | 0 | 5 | 0 | 5 |
| **6** | 0 | 6 | 2 | 8 | 4 | 0 | 6 | 2 | 8 | 4 |
| **7** | 0 | 7 | 4 | 1 | 8 | 5 | 2 | 9 | 6 | 3 |
| **8** | 0 | 8 | 6 | 4 | 2 | 0 | 8 | 6 | 4 | 2 |
| **9** | 0 | 9 | 8 | 7 | 6 | 5 | 4 | 3 | 2 | 1 |

Multiplication Table in $\mathbf{Z}_{10}$

**Fig. 2.16**   *Addition and multiplication tables for $Z_{10}$*

## Different Sets for Addition and Multiplication

In cryptography we often work with inverses. If the sender uses an integer (as the encryption key), the receiver uses the inverse of that integer (as the decryption key). If the operation (encryption/decryption algorithm) is addition, $\mathbf{Z}_n$ can be used as the set of possible keys because each integer in this set has an additive inverse. On the other hand, if the operation (encryption/decryption algorithm) is multiplication, $\mathbf{Z}_n$ cannot be the set of possible keys because only some members of this set have a multiplicative inverse. We need another set. The new set, which is a subset of $\mathbf{Z}_n$ includes only integers in $\mathbf{Z}_n$ that have a unique multiplicative inverse. This set is called $\mathbf{Z}_{n*}$. Figure 2.17 shows some instances of two sets. Note that $\mathbf{Z}_{n*}$ can be made from multiplication tables, such as the one shown in Fig. 2.16.

Each member of $\mathbf{Z}_n$ has an additive inverse, but only some members have a multiplicative inverse. Each member of $\mathbf{Z}_{n*}$ has a multiplicative inverse, but only some members have an additive inverse.

---

**We need to use $Z_n$ when additive inverses are needed; we need to use $Z_n^*$ when multiplicative inverses are needed.**

---

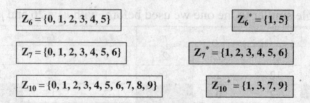

$Z_6 = \{0, 1, 2, 3, 4, 5\}$   $Z_6^* = \{1, 5\}$

$Z_7 = \{0, 1, 2, 3, 4, 5, 6\}$   $Z_7^* = \{1, 2, 3, 4, 5, 6\}$

$Z_{10} = \{0, 1, 2, 3, 4, 5, 6, 7, 8, 9\}$   $Z_{10}^* = \{1, 3, 7, 9\}$

**Fig. 2.17**   *Some $Z_n$ and $Z_{n*}$ sets*

### 2.2.7   Two More Sets

Cryptography often uses two more sets: $\mathbf{Z}_p$ and $\mathbf{Z}_{p*}$. The modulus in these two sets is a prime number. Prime numbers will be discussed in later chapters; suffice it to say that a prime number has only two divisors: integer 1 and itself.

The set $\mathbf{Z}_p$ is the same as $\mathbf{Z}_n$ except that $n$ is a prime. $\mathbf{Z}_p$ contains all integers from 0 to $p - 1$. Each member in $\mathbf{Z}_p$ has an additive inverse; each member except 0 has a multiplicative inverse.

The set $\mathbf{Z}_{p*}$ is the same as $\mathbf{Z}_{n*}$ except that $n$ is a prime. $\mathbf{Z}_{p*}$ contains all integers from 1 to $p - 1$. Each member in $\mathbf{Z}_{p*}$ has an additive and a multiplicative inverse. $\mathbf{Z}_{p*}$ is a very good candidate when we need a set that supports both additive and multiplicative inverse.

The following shows these two sets when $p = 13$.

$$Z_{13} = \{0, 1, 2, 3, 4, 5, 6, 7, 8, 9, 10, 11, 12\}$$
$$Z_{13}* = \{1, 2, 3, 4, 5, 6, 7, 8, 9, 10, 11, 12\}$$

## 2.3                                                MATRICES

In cryptography we need to handle matrices. Although this topic belongs to a special branch of algebra called linear algebra, the following brief review of matrices is necessary preparation for the study of cryptography. Readers who are familiar with this topic can skip part or all of this section. The section begins with some definitions and then shows how to use matrices in modular arithmetic.

### 2.3.1   Definitions

A **matrix** is a rectangular array of $l \times m$ elements, in which $l$ is the number of rows and $m$ is the number of columns. A matrix is normally denoted with a boldface uppercase letter such as **A**. The element $a_{ij}$ is located in the $i$th row and $j$th column. Although the elements can be a set of numbers, we discuss only matrices with elements in **Z**. Figure 2.18 shows a matrix.

$$\text{Matrix A:} \quad \begin{matrix} & m \text{ columns} \\ l \text{ rows} & \begin{bmatrix} a_{11} & a_{12} & \cdots & a_{1m} \\ a_{21} & a_{22} & \cdots & a_{2m} \\ \vdots & \vdots & & \vdots \\ a_{l1} & a_{l2} & \cdots & a_{lm} \end{bmatrix} \end{matrix}$$

**Fig. 2.18** *A matrix of size $l \times m$*

If a matrix has only one row ($l = 1$), it is called a **row matrix;** if it has only one column ($m = 1$), it is called a **column matrix.** In a **square matrix,** in which there is the same number of rows and columns ($l = m$), the elements $a_{11}, a_{22}, \ldots, a_{mm}$ make the **main diagonal.** An additive identity matrix, denoted as **0**, is a matrix with all rows and columns set to 0's. An **identity matrix,** denoted as **I**, is a square matrix with 1s on the main diagonal and 0s elsewhere. Figure 2.19 shows some examples of matrices with elements from **Z**.

$$\begin{bmatrix} 2 & 1 & 5 & 11 \end{bmatrix} \qquad \begin{bmatrix} 2 \\ 4 \\ 12 \end{bmatrix} \qquad \begin{bmatrix} 23 & 14 & 56 \\ 12 & 21 & 18 \\ 10 & 8 & 31 \end{bmatrix} \qquad \begin{bmatrix} 0 & 0 \\ 0 & 0 \\ 0 & 0 \end{bmatrix} \qquad \begin{bmatrix} 1 & 0 \\ 0 & 1 \end{bmatrix}$$

Row matrix       Column matrix       Square matrix       **0**       **I**

**Fig. 2.19** *Example of matrices*

## 2.3.2 Operations and Relations

In linear algebra, one relation (equality) and four operations (addition, subtraction, multiplication, and scalar multiplication) are defined for matrices.

*Equality*    Two matrices are equal if they have the same number of rows and columns and the corresponding elements are equal. In other words, $\mathbf{A} = \mathbf{B}$ if we have $a_{ij} = b_{ij}$ for all $i$'s and $j$'s.

*Addition and Subtraction*    Two matrices can be added if they have the same number of columns and rows. This addition is shown as $\mathbf{C} = \mathbf{A} + \mathbf{B}$. In this case, the resulting matrix $\mathbf{C}$ has also the same number of rows and columns as $\mathbf{A}$ or $\mathbf{B}$. Each element of $\mathbf{C}$ is the sum of the two corresponding elements of $\mathbf{A}$ and $\mathbf{B}$: $c_{ij} = a_{ij} + b_{ij}$. Subtraction is the same except that each element of $\mathbf{B}$ is subtracted from the corresponding element of $\mathbf{A}$: $d_{ij} = a_{ij} - b_{ij}$.

**Example 2.28**    Figure 2.20 shows an example of addition and subtraction.

$$\begin{bmatrix} 12 & 4 & 4 \\ 11 & 12 & 30 \end{bmatrix} = \begin{bmatrix} 5 & 2 & 1 \\ 3 & 2 & 10 \end{bmatrix} + \begin{bmatrix} 7 & 2 & 3 \\ 8 & 10 & 20 \end{bmatrix} \qquad \begin{bmatrix} -2 & 0 & -2 \\ -5 & -8 & 10 \end{bmatrix} = \begin{bmatrix} 5 & 2 & 1 \\ 3 & 2 & 10 \end{bmatrix} - \begin{bmatrix} 7 & 2 & 3 \\ 8 & 10 & 20 \end{bmatrix}$$

$$\mathbf{C} = \mathbf{A} + \mathbf{B} \qquad\qquad\qquad\qquad\qquad\qquad \mathbf{D} = \mathbf{A} - \mathbf{B}$$

**Fig. 2.20**    *Addition and subtraction of matrices*

*Multiplication*    We can multiply two matrices of different sizes if the number of columns of the first matrix is the same as the number of rows of the second matrix. If $\mathbf{A}$ is an $l \times m$ matrix and $\mathbf{B}$ is an $m \times p$ matrix, the product of the two is a matrix $\mathbf{C}$ of size $l \times p$. If each element of matrix $\mathbf{A}$ is called $a_{ij}$, each element of matrix $\mathbf{B}$ is called $b_{jk}$, then each element of matrix $\mathbf{C}$, $c_{ik}$, can be calculated as

$$c_{ik} = \Sigma\, a_{ij} \times b_{jk} = a_{i1} \times b_{1j} + a_{i2} \times b_{2j} + \cdots + a_{im} \times b_{mj}$$

**Example 2.29**    Figure 2.21 shows the product of a row matrix (1 × 3) by a column matrix (3 × 1). The result is a matrix of size 1 × 1.

$$\begin{bmatrix} 53 \end{bmatrix} = \begin{bmatrix} 5 & 2 & 1 \end{bmatrix} \times \begin{bmatrix} 7 \\ 8 \\ 2 \end{bmatrix}$$

In which:    $\boxed{53 = 5 \times 7 + 2 \times 8 + 1 \times 2}$

**Fig. 2.21**    *Multiplication of a row matrix by a column matrix*

**Example 2.30**    Figure 2.22 shows the product of a 2 × 3 matrix by a 3 × 4 matrix. The result is a 2 × 4 matrix.

$$\begin{bmatrix} 52 & 18 & 14 & 9 \\ 41 & 21 & 22 & 7 \end{bmatrix} = \begin{bmatrix} 5 & 2 & 1 \\ 3 & 2 & 4 \end{bmatrix} \times \begin{bmatrix} 7 & 3 & 2 & 1 \\ 8 & 0 & 0 & 2 \\ 1 & 3 & 4 & 0 \end{bmatrix}$$

**Fig. 2.22**    *Multiplication of a 2 × 3 matrix by a 3 × 4 matrix*

## Scalar Multiplication

We can also multiply a matrix by a number (called a **scalar**). If **A** is an $l \times m$ matrix and $x$ is a scalar, $\mathbf{C} = x\mathbf{A}$ is a matrix of size $l \times m$, in which $c_{ij} = x \times a_{ij}$.

$$\underset{\mathbf{B}}{\begin{bmatrix} 15 & 6 & 3 \\ 9 & 6 & 12 \end{bmatrix}} = 3 \times \underset{\mathbf{A}}{\begin{bmatrix} 5 & 2 & 1 \\ 3 & 2 & 4 \end{bmatrix}}$$

**Fig. 2.23** *Scalar multiplication*

**Example 2.31** Figure 2.23 shows an example of scalar multiplication.

## Determinant

The **determinant** of a square matrix **A** of size $m \times m$ denoted as det (**A**) is a scalar calculated recursively as shown below:

1. If $m = 1$, det (**A**) $= a_{11}$
2. If $m > 1$, det (**A**) $= \displaystyle\sum_{i=1\ldots m} (-1)^{i+j} \times a_{ij} \times \det(\mathbf{A}_{ij})$

Where $\mathbf{A}_{ij}$ is a matrix obtained from **A** by deleting the $i$th row and $j$th column.

---

**The determinant is defined only for a square matrix.**

---

**Example 2.32** Figure 2.24 shows how we can calculate the determinant of a $2 \times 2$ matrix based on the determinant of a $1 \times 1$ matrix using the above recursive definition. The example shows that when $m$ is 1 or 2, it is very easy to find the determinant of a matrix.

$$\det\begin{bmatrix} 5 & 2 \\ 3 & 4 \end{bmatrix} = (-1)^{1+1} \times 5 \times \det[4] + (-1)^{1+2} \times 2 \times \det[3] \longrightarrow 5 \times 4 - 2 \times 3 = 14$$

$$\text{or} \quad \det\begin{bmatrix} a_{11} & a_{12} \\ a_{21} & a_{22} \end{bmatrix} = a_{11} \times a_{22} - a_{12} \times a_{21}$$

**Fig. 2.24** *Calculating the determinant of a $2 \times 2$ matrix*

**Example 2.33** Figure 2.25 shows the calculation of the determinant of a $3 \times 3$ matrix.

$$\det\begin{bmatrix} 5 & 2 & 1 \\ 3 & 0 & -4 \\ 2 & 1 & 6 \end{bmatrix} = (-1)^{1+1} \times 5 \times \det\begin{bmatrix} 0 & -4 \\ 1 & 6 \end{bmatrix} + (-1)^{1+2} \times 2 \times \det\begin{bmatrix} 3 & -4 \\ 2 & 6 \end{bmatrix} + (-1)^{1+3} \times 1 \times \det\begin{bmatrix} 3 & 0 \\ 2 & 1 \end{bmatrix}$$

$$= (+1) \times 5 \times (+4) \quad + \quad (-1) \times 2 \times (24) \quad + \quad (+1) \times 1 \times (3) = -25$$

**Fig. 2.25** *Calculating the determinant of a $3 \times 3$ matrix*

### 2.3.3 Inverses

Matrices have both additive and multiplicative inverses.

***Additive Inverse*** The additive inverse of matrix **A** is another matrix **B** such that $\mathbf{A} + \mathbf{B} = \mathbf{0}$. In other words, we have $b_{ij} = -a_{ij}$ for all values of $i$ and $j$. Normally the additive inverse of **A** is defined by $-\mathbf{A}$.

***Multiplicative Inverse***   The multiplicative inverse is defined only for square matrices. The multiplicative inverse of a square matrix **A** is a square matrix **B** such that $\mathbf{A} \times \mathbf{B} = \mathbf{B} \times \mathbf{A} = \mathbf{I}$. Normally the multiplicative inverse of **A** is defined by $\mathbf{A}^{-1}$. The multiplicative inverse exists only if the $\det(\mathbf{A})$ has a multiplicative inverse in the corresponding set. Since no integer has a multiplicative inverse in **Z**, there is no multiplicative inverse of a matrix in **Z**. However, matrices with real elements have inverses only if $\det(\mathbf{A}) \neq 0$.

---

**Multiplicative inverses are only defined for square matrices.**

---

### 2.3.4   Residue Matrices

Cryptography uses residue matrices: matrices with all elements are in $\mathbf{Z}_n$. All operations on residue matrices are performed the same as for the integer matrices except that the operations are done in modular arithmetic. One interesting result is that a residue matrix has a multiplicative inverse if the determinant of the matrix has a multiplicative inverse in $\mathbf{Z}_n$. In other words, a residue matrix has a multiplicative inverse if $\gcd(\det(\mathbf{A}), n) = 1$.

---

**Example 2.34**   Figure 2.26 shows a residue matrix A in $\mathbf{Z}_{26}$ and its multiplicative inverse $\mathbf{A}^{-1}$. We have det(A) = 21 which has the multiplicative inverse 5 in $\mathbf{Z}_{26}$. Note that when we multiply the two matrices, the result is the multiplicative identity matrix in $\mathbf{Z}_{26}$.

$$\mathbf{A} = \begin{bmatrix} 3 & 5 & 7 & 2 \\ 1 & 4 & 7 & 2 \\ 6 & 3 & 9 & 17 \\ 13 & 5 & 4 & 16 \end{bmatrix} \qquad \mathbf{A}^{-1} = \begin{bmatrix} 15 & 21 & 0 & 15 \\ 23 & 9 & 0 & 22 \\ 15 & 16 & 18 & 3 \\ 24 & 7 & 15 & 3 \end{bmatrix}$$

$$\det(\mathbf{A}) = 21 \qquad\qquad \det(\mathbf{A}^{-1}) = 5$$

**Fig. 2.26**   *A residue matrix and its multiplicative inverse*

---

***Congruence***   Two matrices are congruent modulo *n*, written as $\mathbf{A} \equiv \mathbf{B}$ (mod *n*), if they have the same number of rows and columns and all corresponding elements are congruent modulo *n*. In other words, $\mathbf{A} \equiv \mathbf{B}$ (mod *n*) if $a_{ij} \equiv b_{ij}$ (mod *n*) for all *i*'s and *j*'s.

## 2.4                                    LINEAR CONGRUENCE

Cryptography often involves solving an equation or a set of equations of one or more variables with coefficient in $\mathbf{Z}_n$. This section shows how to solve equations when the power of each variable is 1 (linear equation).

### 2.4.1   Single-Variable Linear Equations

Let us see how we can solve equations involving a single variable —that is, equations of the form $ax \equiv b$ (mod *n*). An equation of this type might have no solution or a limited number of solutions. Assume that the gcd $(a, n) = d$. If $d + b$, there is no solution. If $d \mid b$, there are *d* solutions.

If $d \mid b$, we use the following strategy to find the solutions:

1.   Reduce the equation by dividing both sides of the equation (including the modulus) by *d*.
2.   Multiply both sides of the reduced equation by the multiplicative inverse of *a* to find the particular solution $x_0$.
3.   The general solutions are $x = x_0 + k(n/d)$ for $k = 0, 1, \ldots, (d-1)$.

**Example 2.35** Solve the equation $10x \equiv 2 \pmod{15}$.

**Solution** First we find the gcd (10 and 15) = 5. Since 5 does not divide 2, we have no solution.

**Example 2.36** Solve the equation $14x \equiv 12 \pmod{18}$.

**Solution** Note that gcd (14 and 18) = 2. Since 2 divides 12, we have exactly two solutions, but first we reduce the equation.

$$14x \equiv 12 \pmod{18} \rightarrow 7x \equiv 6 \pmod{9} \rightarrow x \equiv 6 \, (7^{-1}) \pmod{9}$$
$$x_0 = (6 \times 7^{-1}) \bmod 9 = (6 \times 4) \pmod 9 = 6$$
$$x_1 = x_0 + 1 \times (18/2) = 15$$

Both solutions, 6 and 15 satisfy the congruence relation, because $(14 \times 6) \bmod 18 = 12$ and also $(14 \times 15) \bmod 18 = 12$.

**Example 2.37** Solve the equation $3x + 4 \equiv 6 \pmod{13}$.

**Solution** First we change the equation to the form $ax \equiv b \pmod n$. We add $-4$ (the additive inverse of 4) to both sides, which give $3x \equiv 2 \pmod{13}$. Because gcd (3, 13) = 1, the equation has only one solution, which is $x_0 = (2 \times 3^{-1}) \bmod 13 = 18 \bmod 13 = 5$. We can see that the answer satisfies the original equation: $3 \times 5 + 4 \equiv 6 \pmod{13}$.

## 2.4.2 Set of Linear Equations

We can also solve a set of linear equations with the same modulus if the matrix formed from the coefficients of the variables is invertible. We make three matrices. The first is the square matrix made from the coefficients of variables. The second is a column matrix made from the variables. The third is a column matrix made from the values at the right-hand side of the congruence operator. We can interpret the set of equations as matrix multiplication. If both sides of congruence are multiplied by the multiplicative inverse of the first matrix, the result is the variable matrix at the right-hand side, which means the problem can be solved by a matrix multiplication as shown in Fig. 2.27.

$$
\begin{aligned}
a_{11}x_1 + a_{12}x_2 + \cdots + a_{1n}x_n &\equiv b_1 \\
a_{21}x_1 + a_{22}x_2 + \cdots + a_{2n}x_n &\equiv b_2 \\
&\vdots \\
a_{n1}x_1 + a_{n2}x_2 + \cdots + a_{nn}x_n &\equiv b_n
\end{aligned}
$$

a. Equations

$$
\begin{bmatrix}
a_{11} & a_{12} & \cdots & a_{1n} \\
a_{21} & a_{22} & \cdots & a_{2n} \\
\vdots & \vdots & & \vdots \\
a_{n1} & a_{n2} & \cdots & a_{nn}
\end{bmatrix}
\begin{bmatrix}
x_1 \\ x_2 \\ \vdots \\ x_n
\end{bmatrix}
\equiv
\begin{bmatrix}
b_1 \\ b_2 \\ \vdots \\ b_n
\end{bmatrix}
\qquad
\begin{bmatrix}
x_1 \\ x_2 \\ \vdots \\ x_n
\end{bmatrix}
\equiv
\begin{bmatrix}
a_{11} & a_{12} & \cdots & a_{1n} \\
a_{21} & a_{22} & \cdots & a_{2n} \\
\vdots & \vdots & & \vdots \\
a_{n1} & a_{n2} & \cdots & a_{nn}
\end{bmatrix}^{-1}
\begin{bmatrix}
b_1 \\ b_2 \\ \vdots \\ b_n
\end{bmatrix}
$$

b. Interpretation                                    c. Solution

**Fig. 2.27** *Set of linear equations*

**Example 2.38** Solve the set of following three equations:

$$3x + 5y + 7z \equiv 3 \text{ (mod 16)}$$
$$x + 4y + 13z \equiv 5 \text{ (mod 16)}$$
$$2x + 7y + 3z \equiv 4 \text{ (mod 16)}$$

**Solution** Here $x$, $y$, and $z$ play the roles of $x_1$, $x_2$, and $x_3$. The matrix formed by the set of equations is invertible. We find the multiplicative inverse of the matrix and multiply it by the column matrix formed from 3, 5, and 4. The result is $x \equiv 15$ (mod 16), $y \equiv 4$ (mod 16), and $z \equiv 14$ (mod 16). We can check the answer by inserting these values into the equations.

## 2.5           RECOMMENDED READING

For more details about subjects discussed in this chapter, we recommend the following books and sites. The items enclosed in brackets refer to the reference list at the end of the book.

### Books

Several books give an easy but thorough coverage of number theory including [Ros06], [Sch99], [Cou99], and [BW00]. Matrices are discussed in any book about linear algebra; [LEF04], [DF04], and [Dur05] are good texts to start with.

### WebSites

The following websites give more information about topics discussed in this chapter.

http://en.wikipedia.org/wiki/Euclidean_algorithm
http://en.wikipedia.org/wiki/Multiplicative_inverse
http://en.wikipedia.org/wiki/Additive_inverse

## *Key Terms*

| | |
|---|---|
| additive inverse | main diagonal |
| binary operation | matrix |
| column matrix | modular arithmetic |
| congruence | modulo operator (mod) |
| congruence operator | modulus |
| determinant | multiplicative inverse |
| divisibility | relatively prime |
| Euclidean algorithm | residue |
| extended Euclidean algorithm | residue class |
| greatest common divisor | row matrix |
| identity matrix | scalar |
| integer arithmetic | set of integers, **Z** |
| least residue | set of residues, $\mathbf{Z}_n$ |
| linear congruence | square matrix |
| linear Diophantine equation | |

# Summary

★ The set of integers, denoted by **Z**, contains all integral numbers from negative infinity to positive infinity. Three common binary operations defined for integers are addition, subtraction, and multiplication. Division does not fit in this category because it produces two outputs instead of one.

★ In integer arithmetic, if we divide $a$ by $n$, we can get $q$ and $r$. The relationship between these four integers can be shown as $a = q \times n + r$. We say a | b if $a = q \times n$. We mentioned four properties of divisibility in this chapter.

★ Two positive integers can have more than one common divisor. But we are normally interested in the greatest common divisor. The Euclidean algorithm gives an efficient and systematic way to calculation of the greatest common divisor of two integer.

★ The extended Euclidean algorithm can calculate gcd $(a, b)$ and at the same time calculate the value of $s$ and $t$ to satisfy the equation $as + bt = \text{gcd}\,(a, b)$.

★ A linear Diophantine equation of two variables is $ax + by = c$. It has a particular and general solution.

★ In modular arithmetic, we are interested only in remainders; we want to know the value of $r$ when we divide $a$ by $n$. We use a new operator called modulo operator (mod) so that $a$ mod $n = r$. Now $n$ is called the modulus; $r$ is called the residue.

★ The result of the modulo operation with modulus $n$ is always an integer between 0 and. We can say that the modulo operation creates a set, which in modular arithmetic is referred to as the set of least residues modulo $n$, or $\mathbf{Z}_n$.

★ Mapping from **Z** to $\mathbf{Z}_n$ is not one-to-one. Infinite members of **Z** can map to one member of $\mathbf{Z}_n$. In modular arithmetic, all integers in **Z** that map to one integer in $\mathbf{Z}_n$ are called congruent modulo $n$. To show that two integers are congruent, we use the congruence operator ($\equiv$).

★ A residue class $[a]$ is the set of integers congruent modulo $n$. It is the set of all integers such that $x = a$ (mod $n$).

★ The three binary operations (addition, subtraction, and multiplication) defined for the set **Z** can also be defined for the set $\mathbf{Z}_n$. The result may need to be mapped to $\mathbf{Z}_n$ using the mod operator.

★ Several properties were defined for the modulo operation in this chapter.

★ In $\mathbf{Z}_n$, two numbers $a$ and $b$ are additive inverses of each other if $a + b \equiv 0$ (mod $n$). They are the multiplicative inverse of each other if $a \times b \equiv 1$ (mod $n$). The integer $a$ has a multiplicative inverse in $\mathbf{Z}_n$ if and only if gcd $(n, a) = 1$ ($a$ and $n$ are relatively prime).

★ The extended Euclidean algorithm finds the multiplicative inverses of $b$ in $\mathbf{Z}_n$ when $n$ and $b$ are given and gcd $(n, b) = 1$. The multiplicative inverse of $b$ is the value of $t$ after being mapped to $\mathbf{Z}_n$.

★ A matrix is a rectangular array of $l \times m$ elements, in which $l$ is the number of rows and $m$ is the number of columns. We show a matrix with a boldface uppercase letter such as **A**. The element $a_{ij}$ is located in the $i$th row and $j$th column.

★ Two matrices are equal if they have the same number of rows and columns and the corresponding elements are equal.

★ Addition and subtraction are done only on matrices of equal sizes. We can multiply two matrices of different sizes if the number of columns of the first matrix is the same as the number of rows of the second matrix.

★ In residue matrices, all elements are in $\mathbf{Z}_n$. All operations on residue matrices are done in modular arithmetic. A residue matrix has an inverse if the determinant of the matrix has an inverse.

★ An equation of the form $ax \equiv b$ (mod $n$) may have no solution or a limited number of solutions. If gcd $(a, n)$ | $b$, there is a limited number of solutions.

★ A set of linear equations with the same modulus can be solved if the matrix formed from the coefficients of variables has an inverse.

# Practice Set

## Review Questions

**2.1** Distinguish between $\mathbf{Z}$ and $\mathbf{Z}_n$. Which set can have negative integers? How can we map an integer in $\mathbf{Z}$ to an integer in $\mathbf{Z}_n$?

**2.2** List four properties of divisibility discussed in this chapter. Give an integer with only one divisor. Give an integer with only two divisors. Give an integer with more than two divisors.

**2.3** Define the greatest common divisor of two integers. Which algorithm can effectively find the greatest common divisor?

**2.4** What is a linear Diophantine equation of two variables? How many solutions can such an equation have? How can the solution(s) be found?

**2.5** What is the modulo operator, and what is its application? List all properties we mentioned in this chapter for the modulo operation.

**2.6** Define congruence and compare with equality.

**2.7** Define a residue class and a least residue.

**2.8** What is the difference between the set $\mathbf{Z}_n$ and the set $\mathbf{Z}_{n*}$? In which set does each element have an additive inverse? In which set does each element have a multiplicative inverse? Which algorithm is used to find the multiplicative inverse of an integer in $\mathbf{Z}_n$?

**2.9** Define a matrix. What is a row matrix? What is a column matrix? What is a square matrix? What type of matrix has a determinant? What type of matrix can have an inverse?

**2.10** Define linear congruence. What algorithm can be used to solve an equation of type $ax \equiv b \pmod{n}$? How can we solve a set of linear equations?

## Exercises

**2.11** Which of the following relations are true and which are false?

5 | 26    3 | 123    27 + 127    15 + 21    23 | 96    8 | 5

**2.12** Using the Euclidean algorithm, find the greatest common divisor of the following pairs of integers.

    a.    88 and 220
    b.    300 and 42
    c.    24 and 320
    d.    401 and 700

**2.13** Solve the following.

    a.    Given gcd (a, b) = 24, find gcd (a, b, 16).
    b.    Given gcd (a, b, c) = 12, find gcd (a, b, c, 16)
    c.    Find gcd (200, 180, and 450).
    d.    Find gcd (200, 180, 450, 610).

**2.14** Assume that $n$ is a nonnegative integer.

    a.    Find gcd (2n + 1, n).
    b.    Using the result of part a, find gcd (201, 100), gcd (81, 40), and gcd (501, 250).

**2.15** Assume that $n$ is a nonnegative integer.

a. Find gcd $(3n + 1, 2n + 1)$.

b. Using the result of part a, find gcd $(301, 201)$ and gcd $(121, 81)$.

**2.16** Using the extended Euclidean algorithm, find the greatest common divisor of the following pairs and the value of $s$ and $t$.

a. 4 and 7

b. 291 and 42

c. 84 and 320

d. 400 and 60

**2.17** Find the results of the following operations.

a. 22 mod 7

b. 140 mod 10

c. −78 mod 13

d. 0 mod 15

**2.18** Perform the following operations using reduction first.

a. $(273 + 147)$ mod 10

b. $(4223 + 17323)$ mod 10

c. $(148 + 14432)$ mod 12

d. $(2467 + 461)$ mod 12

**2.19** Perform the following operations using reduction first.

a. $(125 \times 45)$ mod 10

b. $(424 \times 32)$ mod 10

c. $(144 \times 34)$ mod 12

d. $(221 \times 23)$ mod 22

**2.20** Use the properties of the mod operator to prove the following:

a. The remainder of any integer when divided by 10 is the rightmost digit.

b. The remainder of any integer when divided by 100 is the integer made of the two rightmost digits.

c. The remainder of any integer when divided by 1000 is the integer made of the three rightmost digits.

**2.21** We have been told in arithmetic that the remainder of an integer divided by 5 is the same as the remainder of division of the rightmost digit by 5. Use the properties of the mod operator to prove this claim.

**2.22** We have been told in arithmetic that the remainder of an integer divided by 2 is the same as the remainder of division of the rightmost digit by 2. Use the properties of the mod operator to prove this claim.

**2.23** We have been told in arithmetic that the remainder of an integer divided by 4 is the same as the remainder of division of the two rightmost digits by 4. Use the properties of the mod operator to prove this claim.

**2.24** We have been told in arithmetic that the remainder of an integer divided by 8 is the same as the remainder of division of the rightmost three digits by 8. Use the properties of the mod operator to prove this claim.

**2.25** We have been told in arithmetic that the remainder of an integer divided by 9 is the same as the remainder of division of the sum of its decimal digits by 9. In other words, the remainder of dividing 6371 by 9 is the same as dividing 17 by 9 because $6 + 3 + 7 + 1 = 17$. Use the properties of the mod operator to prove this claim.

**2.26** The following shows the remainders of powers of 10 when divided by 7. We can prove that the pattern will be repeated for higher powers.

$$10^0 \bmod 7 = 1 \quad 10^1 \bmod 7 = 3 \quad 10^2 \bmod 7 = 2$$
$$10^3 \bmod 7 = -1 \quad 10^4 \bmod 7 = -3 \quad 10^5 \bmod 7 = -2$$

Using the above information, find the remainder of an integer when divided by 7. Test your method with 631453672.

**2.27** The following shows the remainders of powers of 10 when divided by 11. We can prove that the pattern will be repeated for higher powers.

$$10^0 \bmod 11 = 1 \quad 10^1 \bmod 11 = -1 \quad 10^2 \bmod 11 = 1 \quad 10^3 \bmod 11 = -1$$

Using the above information, find the remainder of an integer when divided by 11. Test your method with 631453672.

**2.28** The following shows the remainders of powers of 10 when divided by 13. We can prove that the pattern will be repeated for higher powers.

$$10^0 \bmod 13 = 1 \quad 10^1 \bmod 13 = -3 \quad 10^2 \bmod 13 = -4$$
$$10^3 \bmod 13 = -1 \quad 10^4 \bmod 13 = 3 \quad 10^5 \bmod 13 = 4$$

Using the above information, find the remainder of an integer when divided by 13. Test your method with 631453672.

**2.29** Let us assign numeric values to the uppercase alphabet (A = 0, B = 1, ... Z = 25). We can now do modular arithmetic on the system using modulo 26.
  a. What is $(A + N) \bmod 26$ in this system?
  b. What is $(A + 6) \bmod 26$ in this system?
  c. What is $(Y - 5) \bmod 26$ in this system?
  d. What is $(C - 10) \bmod 26$ in this system?

**2.30** List all additive inverse pairs in modulus 20.

**2.31** List all multiplicative inverse pairs in modulus 20.

**2.32** Find the multiplicative inverse of each of the following integers in $Z_{180}$ using the extended Euclidean algorithm.
  a. 38
  b. 7
  c. 132
  d. 24

**2.33** Find the particular and the general solutions to the following linear Diophantine equations.
  a. $25x + 10y = 15$
  b. $19x + 13y = 20$
  c. $14x + 21y = 77$
  d. $40x + 16y = 88$

**2.34** Show that there are no solutions to the following linear Diophantine equations:
  a. $15x + 12y = 13$
  b. $18x + 30y = 20$
  c. $15x + 25y = 69$
  d. $40x + 30y = 98$

**2.35**   A post office sells only 39-cent and 15-cent stamps. Find the number of stamps a customer needs to buy to put \$2.70 postage on a package. Find a few solutions.

**2.36**   Find all solutions to each of the following linear equations:
  a.   $3x \equiv 4 \pmod 5$
  b.   $4x \equiv 4 \pmod 6$
  c.   $9x \equiv 12 \pmod 7$
  d.   $256x \equiv 442 \pmod{60}$

**2.37**   Find all solutions to each of the following linear equations:
  a.   $3x + 5 \equiv 4 \pmod 5$
  b.   $4x + 6 \equiv 4 \pmod 6$
  c.   $9x + 4 \equiv 12 \pmod 7$
  d.   $232x + 42 \equiv 248 \pmod{50}$

**2.38**   Find $(\mathbf{A} \times \mathbf{B})$ mod 16 using the matrices in Fig. 2.28.

$$\begin{bmatrix} 3 & 7 & 10 \end{bmatrix} \times \begin{bmatrix} 2 \\ 4 \\ 12 \end{bmatrix} \qquad \begin{bmatrix} 3 & 4 & 6 \\ 1 & 1 & 8 \\ 5 & 8 & 3 \end{bmatrix} \times \begin{bmatrix} 2 & 0 & 1 \\ 1 & 1 & 0 \\ 5 & 2 & 4 \end{bmatrix}$$
$$\ \ \mathbf{A} \qquad\qquad \mathbf{B} \qquad\qquad \mathbf{A} \qquad\qquad \mathbf{B}$$

**Fig. 2.28**   *Matrices for Exercise 38*

**2.39**   In Fig. 2.29, find the determinant and the multiplicative inverse of each residue matrix over $\mathbf{Z}_{10}$.

$$\begin{bmatrix} 3 & 0 \\ 1 & 1 \end{bmatrix} \qquad \begin{bmatrix} 4 & 2 \\ 1 & 1 \end{bmatrix} \qquad \begin{bmatrix} 3 & 4 & 6 \\ 1 & 1 & 8 \\ 5 & 8 & 3 \end{bmatrix}$$
$$\ \ \mathbf{A} \qquad\qquad \mathbf{B} \qquad\qquad\qquad \mathbf{C}$$

**Fig. 2.29**   *Matrices for Exercise 39*

**2.40**   Find all solutions to the following sets of linear equations:
  a.   $3x + 5y \equiv 4 \pmod 5$
        $2x + y \equiv 3 \pmod 5$
  b.   $3x + 2y \equiv 5 \pmod 7$
        $4x + 6y \equiv 4 \pmod 7$
  c.   $7x + 3y \equiv 3 \pmod 7$
        $4x + 2y \equiv 5 \pmod 7$
  d.   $2x + 3y \equiv 5 \pmod 8$
        $x + 6y \equiv 3 \pmod 8$

# 3

# Traditional Symmetric-Key Ciphers

## Objectives

This chapter presents a survey of traditional symmetric-key ciphers used in the past. By explaining the principles of such ciphers, it prepares the reader for the next few chapters, which discuss modern symmetric-key ciphers. This chapter has several objectives:

☞ To define the terms and the concepts of symmetric-key ciphers
☞ To emphasize the two categories of traditional ciphers: substitution ciphers and transposition ciphers
☞ To describe the categories of cryptanalysis used to break the symmetric ciphers
☞ To introduce the concepts of the stream ciphers and block ciphers
☞ To discuss some very dominant ciphers used in the past, such as the Enigma machine

The general idea behind symmetric-key ciphers will be introduced here using examples from cryptography. The terms and definitions presented are used in all later chapters on symmetric-key ciphers. We then discuss traditional symmetric-key ciphers. These ciphers are not used today, but we study them for several reasons. First, they are simpler than modern ciphers and easier to understand. Second, they show the basic foundation of cryptography and encipherment: This foundation can be used to better understand modern ciphers. Third, they provide the rationale for using modern ciphers, because the traditional ciphers can be easily attacked using a computer. Ciphers that were secure in earlier eras are no longer secure in this computer age.

## 3.1              INTRODUCTION

Figure 3.1 shows the general idea behind a symmetric-key cipher.

In Fig. 3.1, an entity, Alice, can send a message to another entity, Bob, over an insecure channel with the assumption that an adversary, Eve, cannot understand the contents of the message by simply eavesdropping over the channel.

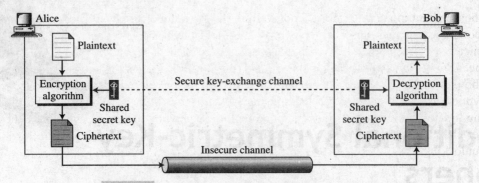

**Fig. 3.1** *General idea of symmetric-key cipher*

The original message from Alice to Bob is called **plaintext;** the message that is sent through the channel is called the **ciphertext.** To create the ciphertext from the plaintext, Alice uses an **encryption algorithm** and a **shared secret key.** To create the plaintext from ciphertext, Bob uses a **decryption algorithm** and the same secret key. We refer to encryption and decryption algorithms as **ciphers.** A **key** is a set of values (numbers) that the cipher, as an algorithm, operates on.

Note that the symmetric-key encipherment uses a single key (the key itself may be a set of values) for both encryption and decryption. In addition, the encryption and decryption algorithms are inverses of each other. If P is the plaintext, C is the ciphertext, and K is the key, the encryption algorithm $E_k(x)$ creates the ciphertext from the plaintext; the decryption algorithm $D_k(x)$ creates the plaintext from the ciphertext. We assume that $E_k(x)$ and $D_k(x)$ are inverses of each other: they cancel the effect of each other if they are applied one after the other on the same input. We have

$$\text{Encryption: } C = E_k(P) \qquad\qquad \text{Decryption: } P = D_k(C)$$

$$\text{In which, } D_k(E_k(x)) = E_k(D_k(x)) = x$$

We can prove that the plaintext created by Bob is the same as the one originated by Alice. We assume that Bob creates $P_1$; we prove that $P_1 = P$:

$$\textbf{Alice: } C = E_k(P) \qquad\qquad \textbf{Bob: } P_1 = D_k(C) = D_k(E_k(P)) = P$$

We need to emphasize that, according to Kerckhoff's principle (described later), it is better to make the encryption and decryption public but keep the shared key secret. This means that Alice and Bob need another channel, a secured one, to exchange the secret key. Alice and Bob can meet once and exchange the key personally. The secured channel here is the face-to-face exchange of the key. They can also trust a third party to give them the same key. They can create a temporary secret key using another kind of cipher—asymmetric-key ciphers—which will be described in later chapters. The concern will be dealt with in future chapters. In this chapter, we assume that there is an established secret key between Alice and Bob.

Using symmetric-key encipherment, Alice and Bob can use the same key for communication on the other direction, from Bob to Alice. This is why the method is called symmetric.

Another element in symmetric-key encipherment is the number of keys. Alice needs another secret key to communicate with another person, say David. If there are $m$ people in a group who need to communicate with each other, how many keys are needed? The answer is $(m \times (m - 1))/2$ because each person needs $m - 1$ keys to communicate with the rest of the group, but the key between A and B can be used in both directions. We will see in later chapters how this problem is being handled.

Encryption can be thought of as locking the message in a box; decryption can be thought of as unlocking the box. In symmetric-key encipherment, the same key locks and unlocks as shown in Fig. 3.2. Later chapters show that the asymmetric-key encipherment needs two keys, one for locking and one for unlocking.

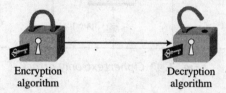

Encryption algorithm          Decryption algorithm

**Fig. 3.2** *Symmetric-key encipherment as locking and unlocking with the same key*

### 3.1.1 Kerckhoff's Principle

Although it may appear that a cipher would be more secure if we hide both the encryption/decryption algorithm and the secret key, this is not recommended. Based on **Kerckhoff's principle,** one should always assume that the adversary, Eve, knows the encryption/decryption algorithm. The resistance of the cipher to attack must be based only on the secrecy of the key. In other words, guessing the key should be so difficult that there is no need to hide the encryption/decryption algorithm. This principle manifests itself more clearly when we study modern ciphers. There are only a few algorithms for modern ciphers today. The **key domain** for each algorithm, however, is so large that it makes it difficult for the adversary to find the key.

### 3.1.2 Cryptanalysis

As cryptography is the science and art of creating secret codes, **cryptanalysis** is the science and art of breaking those codes. In addition to studying cryptography techniques, we also need to study cryptanalysis techniques. This is needed, not to break other people's codes, but to learn how vulnerable our cryptosystem is. The study of cryptanalysis helps us create better secret codes. There are four common types of cryptanalysis attacks, as shown in Fig. 3.3. We will study some of these attacks on particular ciphers in this and future chapters.

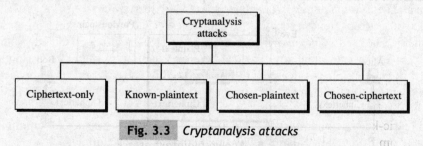

**Fig. 3.3** *Cryptanalysis attacks*

***Ciphertext-Only Attack*** In a **ciphertext-only attack,** Eve has access to only some ciphertext. She tries to find the corresponding key and the plaintext. The assumption is that Eve knows the algorithm and can intercept the ciphertext. The ciphertext-only attack is the most probable one because Eve needs only the ciphertext for this attack. To thwart the decryption of a message by an adversary, a cipher must be very resisting to this type of attack. Figure 3.4 shows the process.

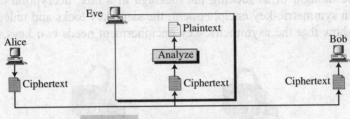

**Fig. 3.4** *Ciphertext-only attack*

Various methods can be used in ciphertext-only attack. We mention some common ones here.

***Brute-Force Attack*** In the **brute-force method** or **exhaustive-key-search method,** Eve tries to use all possible keys. We assume that Eve knows the algorithm and knows the key domain (the list of all possible keys). Using the intercepted cipher, Eve decrypts the ciphertext with every possible key until the plaintext makes sense. Using brute-force attack was a difficult task in the past; it is easier today using a computer. To prevent this type of attack, the number of possible keys must be very large.

***Statistical Attack*** The cryptanalyst can benefit from some inherent characteristics of the plaintext language to launch a **statistical attack.** For example, we know that the letter E is the most-frequently used letter in English text. The cryptanalyst finds the mostly-used character in the ciphertext and assumes that the corresponding plaintext character is E. After finding a few pairs, the analyst can find the key and use it to decrypt the message. To prevent this type of attack, the cipher should hide the characteristics of the language.

***Pattern Attack*** Some ciphers may hide the characteristics of the language, but may create some patterns in the ciphertext. A cryptanalyst may use a **pattern attack** to break the cipher. Therefore, it is important to use ciphers that make the ciphertext look as random as possible.

***Known-Plaintext Attack*** In a **known-plaintext attack,** Eve has access to some plaintext/ciphertext pairs in addition to the intercepted ciphertext that she wants to break, as shown in Fig. 3.5.

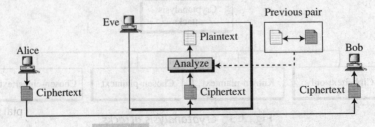

**Fig. 3.5** *Known-plaintext attack*

The plaintext/ciphertext pairs have been collected earlier. For example, Alice has sent a secret message to Bob, but she has later made the contents of the message public. Eve has kept both the ciphertext and the plaintext to use them to break the next secret message from Alice to Bob, assuming that Alice has not changed her key. Eve uses the relationship between the previous pair to analyze the current ciphertext. The same methods used in a ciphertext-only attack can be applied here. This attack is easier to implement because Eve has more information to use for analysis. However, it is less likely to happen because Alice may have changed her key or may have not disclosed the contents of any previous messages.

### Chosen-Plaintext Attack

The **chosen-plaintext attack** is similar to the known-plaintext attack, but the plaintext/ciphertext pairs have been chosen by the attacker herself. Figure 3.6 shows the process.

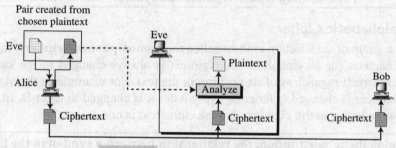

**Fig. 3.6** *Chosen-plaintext attack*

This can happen, for example, if Eve has access to Alice's computer. She can choose some plaintext and intercept the created ciphertext. Of course, she does not have the key because the key is normally embedded in the software used by the sender. This type of attack is much easier to implement, but it is much less likely to happen.

### Chosen-Ciphertext Attack

The **chosen-ciphertext attack** is similar to the chosen-plaintext attack, except that Eve chooses some ciphertext and decrypts it to form a ciphertext/plaintext pair. This can happen if Eve has access to Bob's computer. Figure 3.7 shows the process.

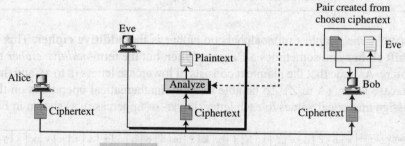

**Fig. 3.7** *Chosen-ciphertext attack*

### 3.1.3 Categories of Traditional Ciphers

We can divide traditional symmetric-key ciphers into two broad categories: substitution ciphers and transposition ciphers. In a substitution cipher, we replace one symbol in the ciphertext with another symbol; in a transposition cipher, we reorder the position of symbols in the plaintext.

## 3.2                         SUBSTITUTION CIPHERS

A **substitution cipher** replaces one symbol with another. If the symbols in the plaintext are alphabetic characters, we replace one character with another. For example, we can replace letter A with letter D, and letter T with letter Z. If the symbols are digits (0 to 9), we can replace 3 with 7, and 2 with 6. Substitution ciphers can be categorized as either monoalphabetic ciphers or polyalphabetic ciphers.

---

**A substitution cipher replaces one symbol with another.**

---

### 3.2.1 Monoalphabetic Ciphers

We first discuss a group of substitution ciphers called the **monoalphabetic ciphers.** In monoalphabetic substitution, a character (or a symbol) in the plaintext is always changed to the same character (or symbol) in the ciphertext regardless of its position in the text. For example, if the algorithm says that letter A in the plaintext is changed to letter D, every letter A is changed to letter D. In other words, the relationship between letters in the plaintext and the ciphertext is one-to-one.

---

**In monoalphabetic substitution, the relationship between a symbol in the plaintext to a symbol in the ciphertext is always one-to-one.**

---

**Example 3.1**   The following shows a plaintext and its corresponding ciphertext. We use lowercase characters to show the plaintext; we use uppercase characters to show the ciphertext. The cipher is probably monoalphabetic because both l's (els) are encrypted as O's.

**Plaintext:** hello          **Ciphertext:** KHOOR

---

**Example 3.2**   The following shows a plaintext and its corresponding ciphertext. The cipher is not monoalphabetic because each l (el) is encrypted by a different character. The first l (el) is encrypted as N; the second as Z.

**Plaintext:** hello          **Ciphertext:** ABNZF

---

*Additive Cipher*   The simplest monoalphabetic cipher is the **additive cipher.** This cipher is sometimes called a **shift cipher** and sometimes a **Caesar cipher,** but the term *additive cipher* better reveals its mathematical nature. Assume that the plaintext consists of lowercase letters (a to z), and that the ciphertext consists of uppercase letters (A to Z). To be able to apply mathematical operations on the plaintext and ciphertext, we assign numerical values to each letter (lower- or uppercase), as shown in Fig. 3.8.

| Plaintext → | a | b | c | d | e | f | g | h | i | j | k | l | m | n | o | p | q | r | s | t | u | v | w | x | y | z |
|---|---|---|---|---|---|---|---|---|---|---|---|---|---|---|---|---|---|---|---|---|---|---|---|---|---|---|
| Ciphertext → | A | B | C | D | E | F | G | H | I | J | K | L | M | N | O | P | Q | R | S | T | U | V | W | X | Y | Z |
| Value → | 00 | 01 | 02 | 03 | 04 | 05 | 06 | 07 | 08 | 09 | 10 | 11 | 12 | 13 | 14 | 15 | 16 | 17 | 18 | 19 | 20 | 21 | 22 | 23 | 24 | 25 |

**Fig. 3.8** *Representation of plaintext and ciphertext characters in $Z_{26}$*

In Fig. 3.8 each character (lowercase or uppercase) is assigned an integer in $Z_{26}$. The secret key between Alice and Bob is also an integer in $Z_{26}$. The encryption algorithm adds the key to the plaintext character; the decryption algorithm subtracts the key from the ciphertext character. All operations are done in $Z_{26}$. Figure 3.9 shows the process.

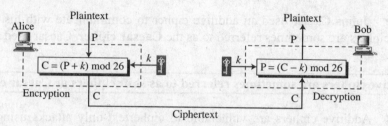

**Fig. 3.9** *Additive cipher*

We can easily prove that the encryption and decryption are inverse of each other because plaintext created by Bob ($P_1$) is the same as the one sent by Alice (P).

$$P_1 = (C - k) \bmod 26 = (P + k - k) \bmod e \ 26 = P$$

---

**When the cipher is additive, the plaintext, ciphertext, and key are integers in $Z_{26}$.**

---

**Example 3.3**  Use the additive cipher with key = 15 to encrypt the message "hello".

**Solution**  We apply the encryption algorithm to the plaintext, character by character:

| | | |
|---|---|---|
| Plaintext: h → 07 | Encryption: (07 + 15) mod 26 | Ciphertext: 22 → W |
| Plaintext: e → 04 | Encryption: (04 + 15) mod 26 | Ciphertext: 19 → T |
| Plaintext: l → 11 | Encryption: (11 + 15) mod 26 | Ciphertext: 00 → A |
| Plaintext: l → 11 | Encryption: (11 + 15) mod 26 | Ciphertext: 00 → A |
| Plaintext: o → 14 | Encryption: (14 + 15) mod 26 | Ciphertext: 03 → D |

The result is "WTAAD". Note that the cipher is monoalphabetic because two instances of the same plaintext character (l's) are encrypted as the same character (A).

**Example 3.4**  Use the additive cipher with key = 15 to decrypt the message "WTAAD".

**Solution**  We apply the decryption algorithm to the plaintext character by character:

| | | |
|---|---|---|
| Ciphertext: W → 22 | Decryption: (22 − 15) mod 26 | Plaintext: 07 → h |
| Ciphertext: T → 19 | Decryption: (19 − 15) mod 26 | Plaintext: 04 → e |
| Ciphertext: A → 00 | Decryption: (00 − 15) mod 26 | Plaintext: 11 → l |
| Ciphertext: A → 00 | Decryption: (00 − 15) mod 26 | Plaintext: 11 → l |
| Ciphertext: D → 03 | Decryption: (03 − 15) mod 26 | Plaintext: 14 → o |

The result is "hello". Note that the operation is in modulo 26 (see Chapter 2), which means that a negative result needs to be mapped to $Z_{26}$ (for example −15 becomes 11).

***Shift Cipher***  Historically, additive ciphers are called shift ciphers. The reason is that the encryption algorithm can be interpreted as "shift *key* characters down" and the encryption algorithm can be interpreted as "shift *key* character up". For example, if the key = 15, the encryption algorithm shifts 15 characters down (toward the end of the alphabet). The decryption algorithm shifts 15 characters up (toward the beginning of the alphabet). Of course, when we reach the end or the beginning of the alphabet, we wrap around (manifestation of modulo 26).

***Caesar Cipher***   Julius Caesar used an additive cipher to communicate with his officers. For this reason, additive ciphers are sometimes referred to as the **Caesar cipher.** Caesar used a key of 3 for his communications.

---

**Additive ciphers are sometimes referred to as shift ciphers or Caesar cipher.**

---

***Cryptanalysis***   Additive ciphers are vulnerable to ciphertext-only attacks using exhaustive key searches (brute-force attacks). The key domain of the additive cipher is very small; there are only 26 keys. However, one of the keys, zero, is useless (the ciphertext is the same as the plaintext). This leaves only 25 possible keys. Eve can easily launch a brute-force attack on the ciphertext.

**Example 3.5**   Eve has intercepted the ciphertext "UVACLYFZLJBYL". Show how she can use a brute-force attack to break the cipher.

***Solution***   Eve tries keys from 1 to 7. With a key of 7, the plaintext is "not very secure", which makes sense.

**Ciphertext:** UVACLYFZLJ BYL

$$K = 1 \rightarrow \textbf{Plaintext: } \text{tuzbkxeykiaxk}$$
$$K = 2 \rightarrow \textbf{Plaintext: } \text{styajwdxjhzwj}$$
$$K = 3 \rightarrow \textbf{Plaintext: } \text{rsxzivcwigyvi}$$
$$K = 4 \rightarrow \textbf{Plaintext: } \text{qrwyhubvhfxuh}$$
$$K = 5 \rightarrow \textbf{Plaintext: } \text{pqvxgtaugewtg}$$
$$K = 6 \rightarrow \textbf{Plaintext: } \text{opuwfsztfdvsf}$$
$$K = 7 \rightarrow \textbf{Plaintext: } \text{notverysecure}$$

Additive ciphers are also subject to statistical attacks. This is especially true if the adversary has a long ciphertext. The adversary can use the frequency of occurrence of characters for a particular language. Table 3.1 shows the frequency for an English text of 100 characters.

**Table 3.1**   *Frequency of occurrence of letters in an English text*

| Letter | Frequency | Letter | Frequency | Letter | Frequency | Letter | Frequency |
|--------|-----------|--------|-----------|--------|-----------|--------|-----------|
| E | 12.7 | H | 6.1 | W | 2.3 | K | 0.08 |
| T | 9.1 | R | 6.0 | F | 2.2 | J | 0.02 |
| A | 8.2 | D | 4.3 | G | 2.0 | Q | 0.01 |
| O | 7.5 | L | 4.0 | Y | 2.0 | X | 0.01 |
| I | 7.0 | C | 2.8 | P | 1.9 | Z | 0.01 |
| N | 6.7 | U | 2.8 | B | 1.5 | | |
| S | 6.3 | M | 2.4 | V | 1.0 | | |

However, sometimes it is difficult to analyze a ciphertext based only on information about the frequency of a single letter; we may need to know the occurrence of specific letter combinations. We need to know the frequency of two-letter or three-letter strings in the ciphertext and compare them with the frequency of two-letter or three-letter strings in the underlying language of the plaintext.

The most common two-letter groups (**digrams**) and three-letter groups (**trigrams**) for the English text are shown in Table 3.2.

**Table 3.2** *Grouping of digrams and trigrams based on their frequency in English*

| Digram | TH, HE, IN, ER, AN, RE, ED, ON, ES, ST, EN, AT, TO, NT, HA, ND, OU, EA, NG, AS, OR, TI, IS, ET, IT, AR, TE, SE, HI, OF |
|--------|---|
| Trigram | THE, ING, AND, HER, ERE, ENT, THA, NTH, WAS, ETH, FOR, DTH |

**Example 3.6** Eve has intercepted the following ciphertext. Using a statistical attack, find the plaintext.

XLILSYWIMWRSAJSVWEPIJSVJSYVQMPPMSRHSPPEVWMXMWASVX-LQSVILY-
VVCFIJSVIXLIWIPPIVVIGIMZIWQSVISJJIVW

**Solution** When Eve tabulates the frequency of letters in this ciphertext, she gets: I =14, V =13, S =12, and so on. The most common character is I with 14 occurrences. This shows that character I in the ciphertext probably corresponds to the character e in plaintext. This means key = 4. Eve deciphers the text to get

the house is now for sale for four million dollars it is worth more hurry before the seller
receives more offers

## Multiplicative Ciphers

In a **multiplicative cipher,** the encryption algorithm specifies multiplication of the plaintext by the key and the decryption algorithm specifies division of the ciphertext by the key as shown in Fig. 3.10. However, since operations are in $Z_{26}$, decryption here means multiplying by the multiplicative inverse of the key. Note that the key needs to belong to the set $Z_{26}^*$ to guarantee that the encryption and decryption are inverses of each other.

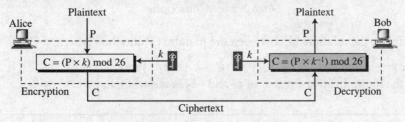

**Fig. 3.10** *Multiplicative cipher*

In a multiplicative cipher, the plaintext and ciphertext are integers in $Z_{26}$;
the key is an integer in $Z_{26}^*$.

**Example 3.7** What is the key domain for any multiplicative cipher?

***Solution*** The key needs to be in $Z_{26}$*. This set has only 12 members: 1, 3, 5, 7, 9, 11, 15, 17, 19, 21, 23, 25.

---

**Example 3.8**  We use a multiplicative cipher to encrypt the message "hello" with a key of 7. The ciphertext is "XCZZU".

| | | |
|---|---|---|
| Plaintext: h → 07 | Encryption: (07 × 07) mod 26 | ciphertext: 23 → X |
| Plaintext: e → 04 | Encryption: (04 × 07) mod 26 | ciphertext: 02 → C |
| Plaintext: l → 11 | Encryption: (11 × 07) mod 26 | ciphertext: 25 → Z |
| Plaintext: l → 11 | Encryption: (11 × 07) mod 26 | ciphertext: 25 → Z |
| Plaintext: o → 14 | Encryption: (14 × 07) mod 26 | ciphertext: 20 → U |

---

***Affine Cipher*** We can combine the additive and multiplicative ciphers to get what is called the **affine cipher**—a combination of both ciphers with a pair of keys. The first key is used with the multiplicative cipher; the second key is used with the additive cipher. Figure 3.11 shows that the affine cipher is actually two ciphers, applied one after another. We could have shown only one complex operation for the encryption or decryption such as $C = (P \times k_1 + k_2) \bmod 26$ and $P = ((C - k_2) \times k_1^{-1}) \bmod 26$. However, we have used a temporary result (T) and have indicated two separate operations to show that whenever we use a combination of ciphers we should be sure that each one has an inverse at the other side of the line and that they are used in reverse order in the encryption and decryption. If addition is the last operation in encryption, then subtraction should be the first in decryption.

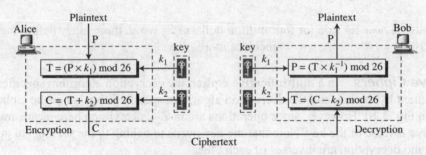

**Fig. 3.11** *Affine cipher*

In the affine cipher, the relationship between the plaintext P and the ciphertext C is

$$C = (P \times k_1 + k_2) \bmod 26 \qquad P = ((C - k_2) \times k_1^{-1}) \bmod 26$$

where $k_1^{-1}$ is the multiplicative inverse of $k_1$ and $-k_2$ is the additive inverse of $k_2$

---

**Example 3.9**  The affine cipher uses a pair of keys in which the first key is from $Z_{26}$* and the second is from $Z_{26}$. The size of the key domain is 26 × 12 = 312.

---

**Example 3.10**  Use an affine cipher to encrypt the message "hello" with the key pair (7, 2).

---

***Solution*** We use 7 for the multiplicative key and 2 for the additive key. We get "ZEBBW".

| | | |
|---|---|---|
| P: h → 07 | Encryption: $(07 \times 7 + 2) \bmod 26$ | C: $25 \to Z$ |
| P: e → 04 | Encryption: $(04 \times 7 + 2) \bmod 26$ | C: $04 \to E$ |
| P: l → 11 | Encryption: $(11 \times 7 + 2) \bmod 26$ | C: $01 \to B$ |
| P: l → 11 | Encryption: $(11 \times 7 + 2) \bmod 26$ | C: $01 \to B$ |
| P: o → 14 | Encryption: $(14 \times 7 + 2) \bmod 26$ | C: $22 \to W$ |

**Example 3.11**  Use the affine cipher to decrypt the message "ZEBBW" with the key pair (7, 2) in modulus 26.

**Solution**  Add the additive inverse of $-2 \equiv 24 \pmod{26}$ to the received ciphertext. Then multiply the result by the multiplicative inverse of $7^{-1} \equiv 15 \pmod{26}$ to find the plaintext characters. Because 2 has an additive inverse in $Z_{26}$ and 7 has a multiplicative inverse in $Z_{26}*$, the plaintext is exactly what we used in Example 3.10.

| | | |
|---|---|---|
| C: Z → 25 | Decryption: $((25 - 2) \times 7^{-1}) \bmod 26$ | P: 07 → h |
| C: E → 04 | Decryption: $((04 - 2) \times 7^{-1}) \bmod 26$ | P: 04 → e |
| C: B → 01 | Decryption: $((01 - 2) \times 7^{-1}) \bmod 26$ | P: 11 → l |
| C: B → 01 | Decryption: $((01 - 2) \times 7^{-1}) \bmod 26$ | P: 11 → l |
| C: W → 22 | Decryption: $((22 - 2) \times 7^{-1}) \bmod 26$ | P: 14 → o |

**Example 3.12**  The additive cipher is a special case of an affine cipher in which $k_1 = 1$. The multiplicative cipher is a special case of affine cipher in which $k_2 = 0$.

**Cryptanalysis of Affine Cipher**  Although the brute-force and statistical method of ciphertext-only attack can be used, let us try a chosen-plaintext attack. Assume that Eve intercepts the following ciphertext:

PWUFFOGWCHFDWIWEJOUUNJORSMDWRHVCMWJUPVCCG

Eve also very briefly obtains access to Alice's computer and has only enough time to type a two-letter plaintext: "et". She then tries to encrypt the short plaintext using two different algorithms, because she is not sure which one is the affine cipher.

| | | |
|---|---|---|
| Algorithm 1: | Plaintext: et | ciphertext: → WC |
| Algorithm 2: | Plaintext: et | ciphertext: → WF |

To find the key, Eve uses the following strategy:

a.  Eve knows that if the first algorithm is affine, she can construct the following two equations based on the first data set.

| | | |
|---|---|---|
| e→W | 04 → 22 | $(04 \times k_1 + k_2) \equiv 22 \pmod{26}$ |
| t→C | 19 → 02 | $(19 \times k_1 + k_2) \equiv 02 \pmod{26}$ |

As we learned in Chapter 2, these two congruence equations can be solved and the values of $k_1$ and $k_2$ can be found. However, this answer is not acceptable because $k_1 = 16$ cannot be the first part of the key. Its value, 16, does not have a multiplicative inverse in $Z_{26}*$.

$$\begin{bmatrix} k_1 \\ k_2 \end{bmatrix} = \begin{bmatrix} 4 & 1 \\ 19 & 1 \end{bmatrix}^{-1} \begin{bmatrix} 22 \\ 2 \end{bmatrix} = \begin{bmatrix} 19 & 7 \\ 3 & 24 \end{bmatrix} \begin{bmatrix} 22 \\ 2 \end{bmatrix} = \begin{bmatrix} 16 \\ 10 \end{bmatrix} \rightarrow k_1 = 16 \quad k_2 = 10$$

b.   Eve now tries the result of the second set of data.

| | | |
|---|---|---|
| e → W | 04 → 22 | $(04 \times k_1 + k_2) \equiv 22 \ (\text{mod } 26)$ |
| t → F | 19 → 05 | $(19 \times k_1 + k_2) \equiv 05 \ (\text{mod } 26)$ |

The square matrix and its inverse are the same. Now she has $k_1 = 11$ and $k_2 = 4$. This pair is acceptable because $k_1$ has a multiplicative inverse in $\mathbf{Z}_{26}*$. She tries the pair of keys (19, 22), which are the inverse of the pair (11, 4), to decipher the message. The plaintext is

> best time of the year is spring when flowers bloom

**Monoalphabetic Substitution Cipher**   Because additive, multiplicative, and affine ciphers have small key domains, they are very vulnerable to brute-force attack. After Alice and Bob agreed to a single key, that key is used to encrypt each letter in the plaintext or decrypt each letter in the ciphertext. In other words, the key is independent from the letters being transferred.

A better solution is to create a mapping between each plaintext character and the corresponding ciphertext character. Alice and Bob can agree on a table showing the mapping for each character. Figure 3.12 shows an example of such a mapping.

Plaintext → a b c d e f g h i j k l m n o p q r s t u v w x y z
Ciphertext → N O A T R B E C F U X D Q G Y L K H V I J M P Z S W

**Fig. 3.12**   *An example key for monoalphabetic substitution cipher*

---

**Example 3.13**   We can use the key in Fig. 3.12 to encrypt the message

> this message is easy to encrypt but hard to find the key

The ciphertext is

> ICFVQRVVNEFVRNVSIYRGAHSLIOJICNHTIYBFGTICRXRS

---

**Cryptanalysis**   The size of the key space for the monoalphabetic substitution cipher is 26! (almost $4 \times 10^{26}$). This makes a brute-force attack extremely difficult for Eve even if she is using a powerful computer. However, she can use statistical attack based on the frequency of characters. The cipher does not change the frequency of characters.

---

**The monoalphabetic ciphers do not change the frequency of characters in the ciphertext, which makes the ciphers vulnerable to statistical attack.**

---

### 3.2.2   Polyalphabetic Ciphers

In **polyalphabetic substitution,** each occurrence of a character may have a different substitute. The relationship between a character in the plaintext to a character in the ciphertext is one-to-many.

For example, "a" could be enciphered as "D" in the beginning of the text, but as "N" at the middle. Polyalphabetic ciphers have the advantage of hiding the letter frequency of the underlying language. Eve cannot use single-letter frequency statistic to break the ciphertext.

To create a polyalphabetic cipher, we need to make each ciphertext character dependent on both the corresponding plaintext character and the position of the plaintext character in the message. This implies that our key should be a stream of subkeys, in which each subkey depends somehow on the position of the plaintext character that uses that subkey for encipherment. In other words, we need to have a key stream $k = (k_1, k_2, k_3, \ldots)$ in which $k_i$ is used to encipher the $i$th character in the plaintext to create the $i$th character in the ciphertext.

***Autokey Cipher*** To see the position dependency of the key, let us discuss a simple polyalphabetic cipher called the **autokey cipher.** In this cipher, the key is a stream of subkeys, in which each subkey is used to encrypt the corresponding character in the plaintext. The first subkey is a predetermined value secretly agreed upon by Alice and Bob. The second subkey is the value of the first plaintext character (between 0 and 25). The third subkey is the value of the second plaintext. And so on.

$$P = P_1P_2P_3 \ldots \qquad C = C_1C_2C_3 \ldots \qquad k = (k_1, P_1, P_2, \ldots)$$

$$\text{Encryption: } C_i = (P_i + k_i) \bmod 26 \qquad\qquad \text{Decryption: } P_i = (C_i - k_i) \bmod 26$$

The name of the cipher, *autokey*, implies that the subkeys are automatically created from the plaintext cipher characters during the encryption process.

---

**Example 3.14** Assume that Alice and Bob agreed to use an autokey cipher with initial key value $k_1 = 12$. Now Alice wants to send Bob the message "Attack is today". Enciphering is done character by character. Each character in the plaintext is first replaced by its integer value as shown in Fig. 3.8. The first subkey is added to create the first ciphertext character. The rest of the key is created as the plaintext characters are read. Note that the cipher is polyalphabetic because the three occurrences of "a" in the plaintext are encrypted differently. The three occurrences of the "t" are enciphered differently.

| Plaintext:   | a  | t  | t  | a  | c  | k  | i  | s  | t  | o  | d  | a  | y  |
|--------------|----|----|----|----|----|----|----|----|----|----|----|----|----|
| P's Values:  | 00 | 19 | 19 | 00 | 02 | 10 | 08 | 18 | 19 | 14 | 03 | 00 | 24 |
| Key stream:  | 12 | 00 | 19 | 19 | 00 | 02 | 10 | 08 | 18 | 19 | 14 | 03 | 00 |
| C's Values:  | 12 | 19 | 12 | 19 | 02 | 12 | 18 | 00 | 11 | 7  | 17 | 03 | 24 |
| Ciphertext:  | M  | T  | M  | T  | C  | M  | S  | A  | L  | H  | R  | D  | Y  |

---

***Cryptanalysis*** The autokey cipher definitely hides the single-letter frequency statistics of the plaintext. However, it is still as vulnerable to the brute-force attack as the additive cipher. The first subkey can be only one of the 25 values (1 to 25). We need polyalphabetic ciphers that not only hide the characteristics of the language but also have large key domains.

***Playfair Cipher*** Another example of a polyalphabetic cipher is the **Playfair cipher** used by the British army during World War I. The secret key in this cipher is made of 25 alphabet letters arranged in a $5 \times 5$ matrix (letters I and J are considered the same when encrypting). Different arrangements of the letters in the matrix can create many different secret keys. One of the possible arrangements is shown in Fig. 3.13. We have dropped the letters in the matrix diagonally starting from the top right-hand corner.

$$
\text{Secret Key} =
\begin{array}{|c|c|c|c|c|}
\hline
L & G & D & B & A \\
\hline
Q & M & H & E & C \\
\hline
U & R & N & I/J & F \\
\hline
X & V & S & O & K \\
\hline
Z & Y & W & T & P \\
\hline
\end{array}
$$

**Fig. 3.13** *An example of a secret key in the Playfair cipher*

Before encryption, if the two letters in a pair are the same, a bogus letter is inserted to separate them. After inserting bogus letters, if the number of characters in the plaintext is odd, one extra bogus character is added at the end to make the number of characters even.

The cipher uses three rules for encryption:

a. If the two letters in a pair are located in the same row of the secret key, the corresponding encrypted character for each letter is the next letter to the right in the same row (with wrapping to the beginning of the row if the plaintext letter is the last character in the row).

b. If the two letters in a pair are located in the same column of the secret key, the corresponding encrypted character for each letter is the letter beneath it in the same column (with wrapping to the beginning of the column if the plaintext letter is the last character in the column).

c. If the two letters in a pair are not in the same row or column of the secret, the corresponding encrypted character for each letter is a letter that is in its own row but in the same column as the other letter.

The Playfair cipher meets our criteria for a polyalphabetic cipher. The key is a stream of subkeys in which the subkeys are created two at a time. In Playfair cipher, the key stream and the cipher stream are the same. This means that the above-mentioned rules can be thought of as the rules for creating the key stream. The encryption algorithm takes a pair of characters from the plaintext and creates a pair of subkeys by following the above-mentioned rules. We can say that the key stream depends on the position of the character in the plaintext. Position dependency has a different interpretation here: the subkey for each plaintext character depends on the next or previous neighbor. Looking at the Playfair cipher in this way, the ciphertext is actually the key stream.

$$P = P_1 P_2 P_3 \ldots \qquad C = C_1 C_2 C_3 \ldots \qquad k = [(k_1, k_2), (k_3, k_4), \ldots]$$

$$\text{Encryption: } C_i = k_i \qquad\qquad \text{Decryption: } P_i = k_i$$

**Example 3.15** Let us encrypt the plaintext "hello" using the key in Fig. 3.13. When we group the letters in two-character pairs, we get "he, ll, o". We need to insert an x between the two l's (els), giving "he, lx, lo". We have

$$\text{he} \rightarrow \text{EC} \qquad \text{lx} \rightarrow \text{QZ} \qquad \text{lo} \rightarrow \text{BX}$$

Plaintext: hello        Ciphertext: ECQZBX

We can see from this example that the cipher is actually a polyalphabetic cipher: the two occurrences of the letter "l" (el) are encrypted as "Q" and "B".

*Cryptanalysis of a Playfair Cipher*   Obviously a brute-force attack on a Playfair cipher is very difficult. The size of the key domain is 25! (factorial 25). In addition, the encipherment hides the single-letter frequency of the characters. However, the frequencies of diagrams are preserved (to some extent because of filler insertion), so a cryptanalyst can use a ciphertext-only attack based on the digram frequency test to find the key.

*Vigenere Cipher*   One interesting kind of polyalphabetic cipher was designed by Blaise de Vigenere, a sixteenth-century French mathematician. A **Vigenere cipher** uses a different strategy to create the key stream. The key stream is a repetition of an initial secret key stream of length $m$, where we have $1 \leq m \leq 26$. The cipher can be described as follows where $(k_1, k_2, ..., k_m)$ is the initial secret key agreed to by Alice and Bob.

$$P = P_1P_2P_3 \ldots \qquad C = C_1C_2C_3 \ldots \qquad K = [(k_1, k_2, ..., k_m), (k_1, k_2, ..., k_m), ...]$$

$$\text{Encryption: } C_i = P_i + k_i \qquad\qquad \text{Decryption: } P_i = C_i - k_i$$

One important difference between the Vigenere cipher and the other two poly-alphabetic ciphers we have looked at, is that the Vigenere key stream does not depend on the plaintext characters; it depends only on the position of the character in the plaintext. In other words, the key stream can be created without knowing what the plaintext is.

**Example 3.16**   Let us see how we can encrypt the message "She is listening" using the 6-character keyword "*PASCAL*". The initial key stream is (15, 0, 18, 2, 0, 11). The key stream is the repetition of this initial key stream (as many times as needed).

| Plaintext:   | s  | h  | e  | i  | s  | l  | i  | s  | t  | e | n  | i  | n  | g  |
|--------------|----|----|----|----|----|----|----|----|----|---|----|----|----|----|
| P's values:  | 18 | 07 | 04 | 08 | 18 | 11 | 08 | 18 | 19 | 04| 13 | 08 | 13 | 06 |
| Key stream:  | 15 | 00 | 18 | 02 | 00 | 11 | 15 | 00 | 18 | 02| 00 | 11 | 15 | 00 |
| C's values:  | 07 | 07 | 22 | 10 | 18 | 22 | 23 | 18 | 11 | 6 | 13 | 19 | 02 | 06 |
| Ciphertext:  | H  | H  | W  | K  | S  | W  | X  | S  | L  | G | N  | T  | C  | G  |

**Example 3.17**   Vigenere cipher can be seen as combinations of $m$ additive ciphers. Figure 3.14 shows how the plaintext of the previous example can be thought of as six different pieces, each encrypted separately. The figure helps us later understand the cryptanalysis of Vigenere ciphers. There are $m$ pieces of the plaintext, each encrypted with a different key, to make $m$ pieces of cipher text.

**Example 3.18**   Using Example 3.18, we can say that the additive cipher is a special case of Vigenere cipher in which $m = 1$.

*Vigenere Tableau*   Another way to look at Vigenere ciphers is through what is called a **Vigenere tableau** shown in Table 3.3.

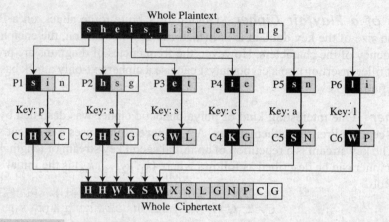

**Fig. 3.14** *A Vigenere cipher as a combination of m additive ciphers*

**Table 3.3** *A Vigenere tableau*

|   | a | b | c | d | e | f | g | h | i | j | k | l | m | n | o | p | q | r | s | t | v | v | w | x | y | z |
|---|---|---|---|---|---|---|---|---|---|---|---|---|---|---|---|---|---|---|---|---|---|---|---|---|---|---|
| **A** | A | B | C | D | E | F | G | H | I | J | K | L | M | N | O | P | Q | R | S | T | U | V | W | X | Y | Z |
| **B** | B | C | D | E | F | G | H | I | J | K | L | M | N | O | P | Q | R | S | T | U | V | W | X | Y | Z | A |
| **C** | C | D | E | F | G | H | I | J | K | L | M | N | O | P | Q | R | S | T | U | V | W | X | Y | Z | A | B |
| **D** | D | E | F | G | H | I | J | K | L | M | N | O | P | Q | R | S | T | U | V | W | X | Y | Z | A | B | C |
| **E** | E | F | G | H | I | J | K | L | M | N | O | P | Q | R | S | T | U | V | W | X | Y | Z | A | B | C | D |
| **F** | F | G | H | I | J | K | L | M | N | O | P | Q | R | S | T | U | V | W | X | Y | Z | A | B | C | D | E |
| **G** | G | H | I | J | K | L | M | N | O | P | Q | R | S | T | U | V | W | X | Y | Z | A | B | C | D | E | F |
| **H** | H | I | J | K | L | M | N | O | P | Q | R | S | T | U | V | W | X | Y | Z | A | B | C | D | E | F | G |
| **I** | I | J | K | L | M | N | O | P | Q | R | S | T | U | V | W | X | Y | Z | A | B | C | D | E | F | G | H |
| **J** | J | K | L | M | N | O | P | Q | R | S | T | U | V | W | X | Y | Z | A | B | C | D | E | F | G | H | I |
| **K** | K | L | M | N | O | P | Q | R | S | T | U | V | W | X | Y | Z | A | B | C | D | E | F | G | H | I | J |
| **L** | L | M | N | O | P | Q | R | S | T | U | V | W | X | Y | Z | A | B | C | D | E | F | G | H | I | J | K |
| **M** | M | N | O | P | Q | R | S | T | U | V | W | X | Y | Z | A | B | C | D | E | F | G | H | I | J | K | L |
| **N** | N | O | P | Q | R | S | T | U | V | W | X | Y | Z | A | B | C | D | E | F | G | H | I | J | K | L | M |
| **O** | O | P | Q | R | S | T | U | V | W | X | Y | Z | A | B | C | D | E | F | G | H | I | J | K | L | M | N |
| **P** | P | Q | R | S | T | U | V | W | X | Y | Z | A | B | C | D | E | F | G | H | I | J | K | L | M | N | O |
| **Q** | Q | R | S | T | U | V | W | X | Y | Z | A | B | C | D | E | F | G | H | I | J | K | L | M | N | O | P |
| **R** | R | S | T | U | V | W | X | Y | Z | A | B | C | D | E | F | G | H | I | J | K | L | M | N | O | P | Q |
| **S** | S | T | U | V | W | X | Y | Z | A | B | C | D | E | F | G | H | I | J | K | L | M | N | O | P | Q | R |
| **T** | T | U | V | W | X | Y | Z | A | B | C | D | E | F | G | H | I | J | K | L | M | N | O | P | Q | R | S |
| **U** | U | V | W | X | Y | Z | A | B | C | D | E | F | G | H | I | J | K | L | M | N | O | P | Q | R | S | T |
| **V** | V | W | X | Y | Z | A | B | C | D | E | F | G | H | I | J | K | L | M | N | O | P | Q | R | S | T | U |
| **W** | W | X | Y | Z | A | B | C | D | E | F | G | H | I | J | K | L | M | N | O | P | Q | R | S | T | U | V |
| **X** | X | Y | Z | A | B | C | D | E | F | G | H | I | J | K | L | M | N | O | P | Q | R | S | T | U | V | W |
| **Y** | Y | Z | A | B | C | D | E | F | G | H | I | J | K | L | M | N | O | P | Q | R | S | T | U | V | W | X |
| **Z** | Z | A | B | C | D | E | F | G | H | I | J | K | L | M | N | O | P | Q | R | S | T | U | V | W | X | Y |

The first row shows the plaintext character to be encrypted. The first column contains the characters to be used by the key. The rest of the tableau shows the ciphertext characters. To find the ciphertext for the plaintext "she is listening" using the word "*PASCAL*" as the key, we can find "s" in the first row, "*P*" in the first column, the cross section is the ciphertext character "H". We can find "h" in the first row and "*A*" in the second column, the cross section is the ciphertext character "H". We do the same until all ciphertext characters are found.

### Cryptanalysis of Vigenere Ciphers

Vigenere ciphers, like all polyalphabetic ciphers, do not preserve the frequency of characters. However, Eve still can use some techniques to decipher an intercepted ciphertext. The cryptanalysis here consists of two parts: finding the length of the key and finding the key itself.

1.  Several methods have been devised to find the length of the key. One method is discussed here. In the so-called **Kasiski test,** the cryptanalyst searches for repeated text segments, of at least three characters, in the ciphertext. Suppose that two of these segments are found and the distance between them is $d$. The cryptanalyst assumes that $d|m$ where $m$ is the key length. If more repeated segments can be found with distances $d_1, d_2, \ldots, d_n$, then

$$\gcd(d_1, d_2, \ldots, d_n) \mid m$$

This assumption is logical because if two characters are the same and are $k \times m$ ($k = 1, 2, \ldots$) characters apart in the plaintext, they are the same and $k \times m$ characters apart in the ciphertext. Cryptanalyst uses segments of at least three characters to avoid the cases where the characters in the key are not distinct. Example 3.19 may help us to understand the reason.

The **Index of Coincidence** (IC) method is often used to confirm the $m$ value determined by the **Kasiski test**. The Index of Coincidence is defined as follows:

**Definition** The Index of Coincidence of $x = x_1 x_2 \ldots x_n$, which is a string of length $n$ formed by the alphabets A, B, ..., Z, is defined as the probability that the random elements of $x$ are the same. Thus if the frequencies of A, B, ..., Z in $x$ are denoted by the $f_0, \ldots, f_{25}$,

$$I_c(x) = \frac{\sum \binom{f_i}{2}}{\binom{n}{2}} = \frac{\sum f_i(f_i - 1)}{n(n-1)} \approx \sum \left(\frac{f_i}{2}\right)^2 = \sum p_i^2$$

The Index of coincidence is an invariant for any shift cipher. This is because in a shift cipher, the individual probabilities will get permuted but the sum of the squares of the probabilities will remain constant, thus keeping the IC value invariant. For standard English language text, the value of IC is approximately 0.065. However, if all the letters are equally likely then the IC value is $26(1/26)^2 \approx 0.038$. Since these two values are quite far apart, the IC serves as an important tool to "distinguish" between English text and a random string of English alphabets. This fact is used in the following discussion.

Now, we shall discuss how the Index of Coincidence method can be used to check the $m$ value reported by the Kasiski test for a *Vignere cipher*.

Using the $m$ value of the Kasiski test, we arrange the given alphabetic string $y = y_1 \ldots y_n$ into $m$ substrings as follows:

$$Y_1 = y_1 y_{m+1} y_{2m+1} \cdots$$

$$Y_2 = y_2 y_{m+2} y_{2m+2} \cdots$$

$$\cdots$$

$$Y_m = y_m y_{2m} y_{3m} \cdots$$

If the value of $m$ reported by Kasiski test is correct, each substring $Y_i$, $1 \leq i \leq m$ is a shift cipher which has been shifted by a key $K_i$. Hence the expected value of $I_c(Y_i)$ is about 0.065. However, if the guess of $m$ is incorrect, each substring is a random string and thus the IC value is about 0.038. Thus we can confirm the value of m reported by the Kasiski test.

Next we investigate a method to actually determine the key $K = (k_1, \ldots, k_m)$.

For this we need the concept of *Mutual Index of Coincidence* (MI) between two alphabetic strings $x$ and $y$.

**Definition** Suppose $x = x_1 x_2 \ldots x_n$ and $y = y_1 y_2 \ldots y_n$, are two alphabetic strings. Then the Mutual Index of Coincidence between $x$ and $y$ is the probability that a random element of $x$ is equal to that of $y$. Thus if the probabilities of $A, B, \ldots$ are $f_0, f_1, \ldots, f_{25}$ and $f'_0, f'_1, \ldots, f'_{25}$ respectively in $x$ and $y$, then:

$$MI_c(x, y) = \frac{\sum_{i=0}^{25} f_i f'_i}{nn'}$$

Consider Table 3.4 containing the alphabets and their corresponding probability distributions.

| $A$ | $B$ | ... | $Z$ |
|-----|-----|-----|-----|
| p0 | p1 | ... | p25 |

Imagine that due to a key $K_i$ being used as a key in a shift cipher, the corresponding probability distribution is as shown in Table 3.5.

| $A + k_i$ | $B + k_i$ | ... | $Z + k_i$ |
|-----------|-----------|-----|-----------|
| P0 | p1 | ... | p25 |

Now what is the probability that in the cryptogram a character is A? If the letters A, ..., Z are numbered from 0, ..., 25 then a letter denoted by a number say $j$ in the unencrypted text thus becomes $j + k_i$. Thus when $j + k_i$ is A in the ciphertext, we may write numerically $j + k_i = 0$ (mod 26), or $j = -k_i$ (mod 26)

Hence the corresponding probability of A in the encrypted text is $p_j = p_{-ki}$. Note that the value in the suffix is modulo 26.

Thus if we consider two strings $x$ and $y$, which have been shifted by $k_i$ and $k_j$ respectively, the probability that both characters in $x$ and $y$ are A is $p_{-ki} p_{-kj}$. Likewise the probability that both the characters are B is $p_{1-ki} p_{1-kj}$ and so on.

$$MI_c(x, y) = \sum_{h=0}^{25} p_{h-k_i} p_{h-k_j} = \sum_{h=0}^{25} p_h p_{h+k_i-k_j}$$

1.  For two strings, $x$ and $y$ ciphered using keys $k_i$ and $k_j$ the value of $MI_c(x,y)$ depends on the difference $k_i - k_j$ (mod 26).

2. A relative shift of s yields the same value as 26-s. This is left as an exercise to the reader.

When $k_i - k_j = 0$, the value of $MI_c$ is maximum and is equal to 0.065. However for other values, the estimate is comparatively less and ranges from 0.032 to 0.045 on an average.

So in order to find the actual key, we divide the given string of encrypted characters into m rows as described before. Each row is a shift cipher, which has been shifted by a key say, $k_i$. Thus for each row we find the Mutual Index of Coincidence with respect to an unencrypted English text. We compute the MI values by varying the keys, $k_i$ from 0 to 25. The values for which the MI values become close to 0.065 will indicate the correct key, $k_i$. This process is repeated for the m rows to obtain the entire key.

**Example 3.19** Let us assume that the intercepted text is as follows:

LIOMWGFEGGDVWGHHCQUCRHRWAGWIOWQLKGZETKKMEVLWPCZVGTHVTSGXQOVGCSVETQLTJSUMV-
WVEUVLXEWSLGFZMVVWLGYHCUSWXQHKVGSHEEVFLCFDGVSUMPHKIRZDMPHHBVWVWJWIXGFWLTSH-
GJOUEEHHVUCFVGOWICQLTJSUXGLW

Kasiski test for repetition of three character segments yields the results as shown in Table 3.4.

**Table 3.4** *Kasiski test for Example 3.19*

| String | First Index | Second Index | Difference |
|--------|-------------|--------------|------------|
| QLT | 65 | 165 | 100 |
| LTJ | 66 | 166 | 100 |
| TJS | 67 | 167 | 100 |
| JSU | 68 | 168 | 100 |
| SUM | 69 | 117 | 48 |
| VWV | 72 | 132 | 60 |

The greatest common divisor is thus 4, thus suggesting that the key length is a multiple of 4. We try confirm this guess by the Index of Coincidence test.

We divide the ciphertext into 4 rows as shown below. We also mention the corresponding Index of Coincidence values. The high values of the IC confirms the key length reported in the Kasiski test.

1st string : LWGWCRAOKTEPGTQCTJVUEGVGUQGECVPRPVJGTJEUGCJG

IC = 0.067677

2nd string : IGGGQHGWGKVCTSOSQSWVWFVYSHSVFSHZHWWFSOHCOQSL

IC = 0.074747

3rd string: OFDHURWQZKLZHGVVLUVLSZWHWKHFDUKDHVIWHUHFWLUW

IC = 0.070707

4th string: MEVHCWILEMWVVXGETMEXLMLCXVELGMIMBWXLGEVVITX

IC = 0.076768

Then we perform the Mutual Index of Coiucidence to obtain the actual key value. Running the test, we obtain that the key value is CODE, and the corresponding plaintext is:

JULIUSCAESARUSEDACRYPTOSYSTEMINHISWARWHICHISNOWREFERR
EDTOASCAESARCIPHERITISASHIFTCIPHERWITHTHEKEYSETTOTHREEE
ACHCHARACTERINTHEPLAINTEXTISSHIFTERTHREECHARACTERSOCRE
ATEACIPHERTEXT

Note that the plaintext makes sense and hence we believe the decryption is correct. We format the obtained as follows:

---

**Julius Caesar used a cryptosystem in his wars, which is now referred to as Caesar cipher. It is anadditive cipher with the key set to three. Each character in the plaintext is shifted three characters to create ciphertext.**

---

*Hill Cipher*   Another interesting example of a polyalphabetic cipher is the **Hill cipher** invented by Lester S. Hill. Unlike the other polyalphabetic ciphers we have already discussed, the plaintext is divided into equal-size blocks. The blocks are encrypted one at a time in such a way that each character in the block contributes to the encryption of other characters in the block. For this reason, the Hill cipher belongs to a category of ciphers called *block ciphers*. The other ciphers we studied so far belong to the category called *stream ciphers*. The differences between block and stream ciphers are discussed at the end of this chapter.

In a Hill cipher, the key is a square matrix of size $m \times m$ in which $m$ is the size of the block. If we call the key matrix **K**, each element of the matrix is $k_{i,j}$ as shown in Fig. 3.15.

$$\mathbf{K} = \begin{bmatrix} k_{11} & k_{12} & \cdots & k_{1m} \\ k_{21} & k_{22} & \cdots & k_{2m} \\ \vdots & \vdots & & \vdots \\ k_{m1} & k_{m2} & \cdots & k_{mm} \end{bmatrix}$$

**Fig. 3.15**   *Key in the Hill cipher*

Let us show how one block of the ciphertext is encrypted. If we call the $m$ characters in the plaintext block $P_1, P_2, \ldots, P_m$, the corresponding characters in the ciphertext block are $C_1, C_2, \ldots, C_m$. Then we have

$$C_1 = P_1 k_{11} + P_2 k_{21} + \cdots + P_m k_{m1}$$
$$C_2 = P_1 k_{12} + P_2 k_{22} + \cdots + P_m k_{m2}$$
$$\cdots$$
$$C_m = P_1 k_{1m} + P_2 k_{2m} + \cdots + P_m k_{mm}$$

The equations show that each ciphertext character such as $C_1$ depends on all plaintext characters in the block ($P_1, P_2, \ldots, P_m$). However, we should be aware that not all square matrices have multiplicative inverses in $\mathbf{Z}_{26}$, so Alice and Bob should be careful in selecting the key. Bob will not be able to decrypt the ciphertext sent by Alice if the matrix does not have a multiplicative inverse.

---

**The key matrix in the Hill cipher needs to have a multiplicative inverse.**

---

**Example 3.20**  Using matrices allows Alice to encrypt the whole plaintext. In this case, the plaintext is an $l \times m$ matrix in which $l$ is the number of blocks. For example, the plaintext "code is ready" can make a $3 \times 4$ matrix when adding extra bogus character "z" to the last block and removing the spaces. The ciphertext is "OHKNIHGKLISS". Bob can decrypt the message using the inverse of the key matrix. Encryption and decryption are shown in Fig. 3.16.

$$
\begin{array}{c}\mathbf{C}\\ \begin{bmatrix} 14 & 07 & 10 & 13 \\ 08 & 07 & 06 & 11 \\ 11 & 08 & 18 & 18 \end{bmatrix}\end{array}
=
\begin{array}{c}\mathbf{P}\\ \begin{bmatrix} 02 & 14 & 03 & 04 \\ 08 & 18 & 17 & 04 \\ 00 & 03 & 24 & 25 \end{bmatrix}\end{array}
\begin{array}{c}\mathbf{K}\\ \begin{bmatrix} 09 & 07 & 11 & 13 \\ 04 & 07 & 05 & 06 \\ 02 & 21 & 14 & 09 \\ 03 & 23 & 21 & 08 \end{bmatrix}\end{array}
$$

a. Encryption

$$
\begin{array}{c}\mathbf{P}\\ \begin{bmatrix} 02 & 14 & 03 & 04 \\ 08 & 18 & 17 & 04 \\ 00 & 03 & 24 & 25 \end{bmatrix}\end{array}
=
\begin{array}{c}\mathbf{C}\\ \begin{bmatrix} 14 & 07 & 10 & 13 \\ 08 & 07 & 06 & 11 \\ 11 & 08 & 18 & 18 \end{bmatrix}\end{array}
\begin{array}{c}\mathbf{K}^{-1}\\ \begin{bmatrix} 02 & 15 & 22 & 03 \\ 15 & 00 & 19 & 03 \\ 09 & 09 & 03 & 11 \\ 17 & 00 & 04 & 07 \end{bmatrix}\end{array}
$$

b. Decryption

**Fig. 3.16**  *Example 3.20*

## Cryptanalysis of Hill Ciphers

Ciphertext-only cryptanalysis of Hill ciphers is difficult. First, a brute-force attack on a Hill cipher is extremely difficult because the key is an $m \times m$ matrix. Each entry in the matrix can have one of the 26 values. At first glance, this means that the size of the key domain is $26^{m \times m}$. However, not all of the matrices have multiplicative inverses. The key domain is smaller, but still huge.

Second, Hill ciphers do not preserve the statistics of the plaintext. Eve cannot run frequency analysis on single letters, digrams, or trigrams. A frequency analysis of words of size $m$ might work, but this is very rare that a plaintext has many strings of size $m$ that are the same.

Eve, however, can do a known-plaintext attack on the cipher if she knows the value of $m$ and knows the plaintext/ciphertext pairs for at least $m$ blocks. The blocks can belong to the same message or different messages but should be distinct. Eve can create two $m \times m$ matrices, **P** (plaintext) and **C** (ciphertext) in which the corresponding rows represent the corresponding known plaintext/ciphertext pairs. Because $\mathbf{C} = \mathbf{PK}$, Eve can use the relationship $\mathbf{K} = \mathbf{CP}^{-1}$ to find the key if **P** is invertible. If **P** is not invertible, then Eve needs to use a different set of $m$ plaintext/ciphertext pairs.

If Eve does not know the value of $m$, she can try different values provided that $m$ is not very large.

**Example 3.21**  Assume that Eve knows that $m = 3$. She has intercepted three plaintext/ciphertext pair blocks (not necessarily from the same message) as shown in Fig. 3.17.

$$\begin{bmatrix} 05 & 07 & 10 \end{bmatrix} \longleftrightarrow \begin{bmatrix} 03 & 06 & 00 \end{bmatrix}$$

$$\begin{bmatrix} 13 & 17 & 07 \end{bmatrix} \longleftrightarrow \begin{bmatrix} 14 & 16 & 09 \end{bmatrix}$$

$$\begin{bmatrix} 00 & 05 & 04 \end{bmatrix} \longleftrightarrow \begin{bmatrix} 03 & 17 & 11 \end{bmatrix}$$

$$\text{P} \qquad\qquad\qquad\qquad \text{C}$$

**Fig. 3.17**  *Example 3.22, forming the ciphertext cipher*

She makes matrices **P** and **C** from these pairs. Because P is invertible, she inverts the P matrix and multiplies it by C to get the K matrix as shown in Fig. 3.18.

$$\begin{bmatrix} 02 & 03 & 07 \\ 05 & 07 & 09 \\ 01 & 02 & 11 \end{bmatrix} = \begin{bmatrix} 21 & 14 & 01 \\ 00 & 08 & 25 \\ 13 & 03 & 08 \end{bmatrix} \begin{bmatrix} 03 & 06 & 00 \\ 14 & 16 & 09 \\ 03 & 17 & 11 \end{bmatrix}$$

$$\text{K} \qquad\qquad \text{P}^{-1} \qquad\qquad \text{C}$$

**Fig. 3.18**  *Example 3.22, finding the key*

Now she has the key and can break any ciphertext encrypted with that key.

***One-Time Pad***  One of the goals of cryptography is perfect secrecy. A study by Shannon has shown that perfect secrecy can be achieved if each plaintext symbol is encrypted with a key randomly chosen from a key domain. For example, an additive cipher can be easily broken because the same key is used to encrypt every character. However, even this simple cipher can become a perfect cipher if the key that is used to encrypt each character is chosen randomly from the key domain (00, 01, 02, ..., 25)—that is, if the first character is encrypted using the key 04, the second character is encrypted using the key 02, the third character is encrypted using the key 21; and so on. Ciphertext-only attack is impossible. Other types of attacks are also impossible if the sender changes the key each time she sends a message, using another random sequence of integers.

This idea is used in a cipher called **one-time pad,** invented by Vernam. In this cipher, the key has the same length as the plaintext and is chosen completely in random.

A one-time pad is a perfect cipher, but it is almost impossible to implement commercially. If the key must be newly generated each time, how can Alice tell Bob the new key each time she has a message to send? However, there are some occasions when a one-time pad can be used. For example, if the president of a country needs to send a completely secret message to the president of another country, she can send a trusted envoy with the random key before sending the message.

Some variations of the one-time pad cipher will be discussed in later chapters when modern use of cryptography is introduced.

***Rotor Cipher***  Although one-time pad ciphers are not practical, one step toward more secured encipherment is the **rotor cipher.** It uses the idea behind monoalphabetic substitution but changes the mapping between the plaintext and the ciphertext characters for each plaintext character. Figure 3.19 shows a simplified example of a rotor cipher.

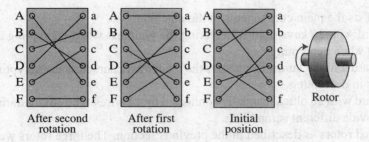

| After second rotation | After first rotation | Initial position | Rotor |
| --- | --- | --- | --- |

**Fig. 3.19** *A rotor cipher*

The rotor shown in Fig. 3.19 uses only 6 letters, but the actual rotors use 26 letters. The rotor is permanently wired, but the connection to encryption/decryption characters is provided by brushes. Note that the wiring is shown as though the rotor were transparent and one could see the inside.

The initial setting (position) of the rotor is the secret key between Alice and Bob. The first plaintext character is encrypted using the initial setting; the second character isencrypted after the first rotation (in Figure 3.19 at 1/6 turn, but the actual setting is 1/26 turn); and so on.

A three-letter word such as "bee" is encrypted as "BAA" if the rotor is stationary (the monoalphabetic substitution cipher), but it will encrypted as "BCA" if it is rotating (the rotor cipher). This shows that the rotor cipher is a polyalphabetic cipher because two occurrences of the same plaintext character are encrypted as different characters.

The rotor cipher is as resistant to a brute-force attack as the monoalphabetic substitution cipher because Eve still needs to find the first set of mappings among 26! possible ones. The rotor cipher is much more resistant to statistical attack than the monoalphabetic substitution cipher because it does not preserve letter frequency.

### *Enigma Machine*

The **Enigma machine** was originally invented by Sherbius, but was modified by the German army and extensively used during World War II. The machine was based on the principle of rotor ciphers. Figure 3.20 shows a simple schematic diagram of the machine.

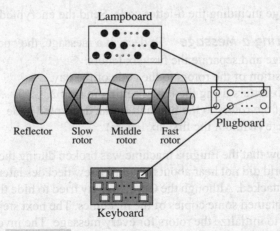

**Fig. 3.20** *A schematic of the Enigma machine*

The following lists the main components of the machine:

1. A keyboard with 26 keys used for entering the plaintext when encrypting and for entering the ciphertext when decrypting.
2. A lampboard with 26 lamps that shows the ciphertext characters in encrypting and the plaintext characters in decrypting.
3. A plugboard with 26 plugs manually connected by 13 wires. The configuration is changed every day to provide different scrambling.
4. Three wired rotors as described in the previous section. The three rotors were chosen daily out of five available rotors. The fast rotor rotates 1/26 of a turn for each character entered on the keyboard. The middle rotor makes 1/26 turn for each complete turn of the fast rotor. The slow rotor makes 1/26 turn for each complete turn of the middle rotor.
5. A reflector, which is stationary and prewired.

**Code Book**    To use the Enigma machine, a code book was published that gives several settings for each day, including:

a. The three rotors to be chosen, out of the five available ones.
b. The order in which the rotors are to be installed.
c. The setting for the plugboard.
d. A three-letter code of the day.

**Procedure for Encrypting a Message**    To encrypt a message, the operator followed these steps:

1. Set the starting position of the rotors to the code of the day. For example, if the code was "HUA", the rotors were initialized to "H", "U", and "A", respectively.
2. Choose a random three-letter code, such as "ACF". Encrypt the text "ACFACF" (repeated code) using the initial setting of rotors in step 1. For example, assume the encrypted code is "OPNABT".
3. Set the starting positions of the rotors to OPN (half of the encrypted code).
4. Append the encrypted six letters obtained from step 2 ("OPNABT") to the beginning of the message.
5. Encrypt the message including the 6-letter code. Send the encrypted message.

**Procedure for Decrypting a Message**    To decrypt a message, the operator followed these steps:

1. Receive the message and separate the first six letters.
2. Set the starting position of the rotors to the code of the day.
3. Decrypt the first six letters using the initial setting in step 2.
4. Set the positions of the rotors to the first half of the decrypted code.
5. Decrypt the message (without the first six letters).

**Cryptanalysis**    We know that the Enigma machine was broken during the war, although the German army and the rest of the world did not hear about this until a few decades later. The question is how such a complicated cipher was attacked. Although the German army tried to hide the internal wiring of the rotors, the Allies somehow obtained some copies of the machines. The next step was to find the setting for each day and the code sent to initialize the rotors for every message. The invention of the first computer helped the Allies to overcome these difficulties. The full picture of the machine and its cryptanalysis can be found at some of the Enigma Websites.

## 3.3                    TRANSPOSITION CIPHERS

A **transposition cipher** does not substitute one symbol for another, instead it changes the location of the symbols. A symbol in the first position of the plaintext may appear in the tenth position of the ciphertext. A symbol in the eighth position in the plaintext may appear in the first position of the ciphertext. In other words, a transposition cipher reorders (transposes) the symbols.

---

**A transposition cipher reorders symbols.**

---

### 3.3.1   Keyless Transposition Ciphers

Simple transposition ciphers, which were used in the past, are keyless. There are two methods for permutation of characters. In the first method, the text is written into a table column by column and then transmitted row by row. In the second method, the text is written into the table row by row and then transmitted column by column.

---

**Example 3.22**   A good example of a keyless cipher using the first method is the **rail fence cipher.** In this cipher, the plaintext is arranged in two lines as a zigzag pattern (which means column by column); the ciphertext is created reading the pattern row by row. For example, to send the message "Meet me at the park" to Bob, Alice writes

```
m     e     m     a     t     e     a     k
   e     t     e     t     h     p     r
```

She then creates the ciphertext "MEMATEAKETETHPR" by sending the first row followed by the second row. Bob receives the ciphertext and divides it in half (in this case the second half has one less character). The first half forms the first row; the second half, the second row. Bob reads the result in zigzag. Because there is no key and the number of rows is fixed (2), the cryptanalysis of the ciphertext would be very easy for Eve. All she needs to know is that the rail fence cipher is used.

---

**Example 3.23**   Alice and Bob can agree on the number of columns and use the second method. Alice writes the same plaintext, row by row, in a table of four columns.

```
m   e   e   t
m   e   a   t
t   h   e   p
a   r   k
```

She then creates the ciphertext "MMTAEEHREAEKTTP" by transmitting the characters column by column. Bob receives the ciphertext and follows the reverse process. He writes the received message, column by column, and reads it row by row as the plaintext. Eve can easily decipher the message if she knows the number of columns.

---

**Example 3.24**   The cipher in Example 3.23 is actually a transposition cipher. The following shows the permutation of each character in the plaintext into the ciphertext based on the positions.

```
01  02  03  04  05  06  07  08  09  10  11  12  13  14  15
 ↓   ↓   ↓   ↓   ↓   ↓   ↓   ↓   ↓   ↓   ↓   ↓   ↓   ↓   ↓
01  05  09  13  02  06  10  13  03  07  11  15  04  08  12
```

The second character in the plaintext has moved to the fifth position in the ciphertext; the third character has moved to the ninth position; and so on. Although the characters are permuted, there is a pattern in the permutation: (01, 05, 09, 13), (02, 06, 10, 13), (03, 07, 11, 15), and (08, 12). In each section, the difference between the two adjacent numbers is 4.

---

### 3.3.2  Keyed Transposition Ciphers

The keyless ciphers permute the characters by using writing plaintext in one way (row by row, for example) and reading it in another way (column by column, for example). The permutation is done on the whole plaintext to create the whole ciphertext. Another method is to divide the plaintext into groups of predetermined size, called blocks, and then use a key to permute the characters in each block separately.

---

**Example 3.25**  Alice needs to send the message "Enemy attacks tonight" to Bob. Alice and Bob have agreed to divide the text into groups of five characters and then permute the characters in each group. The following shows the grouping after adding a bogus character at the end to make the last group the same size as the others.

---

    e n e m y     a t t a c     k s t o n     i g h t z

The key used for encryption and decryption is a permutation key, which shows how the character are permuted. For this message, assume that Alice and Bob used the following key:

| 3 | 1 | 4 | 5 | 2 |
|---|---|---|---|---|
| 1 | 2 | 3 | 4 | 5 |

Encryption ↓            ↑ Decryption

The third character in the plaintext block becomes the first character in the ciphertext block; the first character in the plaintext block becomes the second character in the ciphertext block; and so on. The permutation yields

**E E M Y N     T A A C T     T K O N S     H I T Z G**

Alice sends the ciphertext "EEMYNTAACTTKONSHITZG" to Bob. Bob divides the ciphertext into 5-character groups and, using the key in the reverse order, finds the plaintext.

### 3.3.3  Combining Two Approaches

More recent transposition ciphers combine the two approaches to achieve better scrambling. Encryption or decryption is done in three steps. First, the text is written into a table row by row. Second, the permutation is done by reordering the columns. Third, the new table is read column by column. The first and third steps provide a keyless global reordering; the second step provides a blockwise keyed reordering. These types of ciphers are often referred to as keyed columnar transposition ciphers or just columnar transposition ciphers.

---

**Example 3.26**  Suppose Alice again enciphers the message in Example 3.25, this time using the combined approach. The encryption and decryption is shown in Fig. 3.21.

---

The first table is created by Alice writing the plaintext row by row. The columns are permuted using the same key as in the previous example. The ciphertext is created by reading the second table column by column. Bob does the same three steps in the reverse order. He writes the ciphertext column by column into the first table, permutes the columns, and then reads the second table row by row.

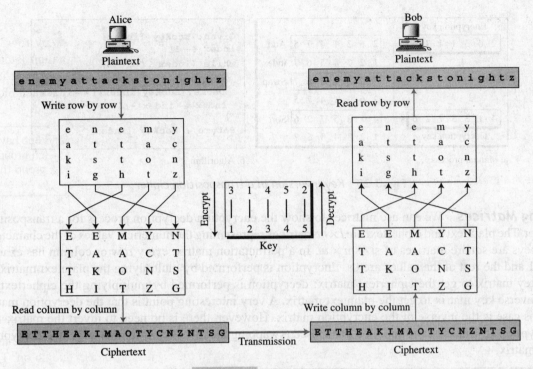

**Fig. 3.21** *Example 3.27*

***Keys*** In Example 3.27, a single key was used in two directions for the column exchange: downward for encryption, upward for decryption. It is customary to create two keys from this graphical representation: one for encryption and one for direction. The keys are stored in tables with one entry for each column. The entry shows the source column number; the destination column number is understood from the position of the entry. Figure 3.22 shows how the two tables can be made from the graphical representation of the key.

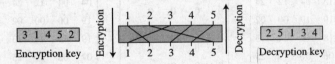

**Fig. 3.22** *Encryption/decryption keys in transpositional ciphers*

The encryption key is (3 1 4 5 2). The first entry shows that column 3 (contents) in the source becomes column 1 (position or index of the entry) in the destination. The decryption key is (2 5 1 3 4). The first entry shows that column 2 in the source becomes column 1 in the destination.

How can the decryption key be created if the encryption key is given, or vice versa? The process can be done manually in a few steps, as shown in Fig. 3.23. First add indices to the key table, then swap the contents and indices, finally sort the pairs according to the index.

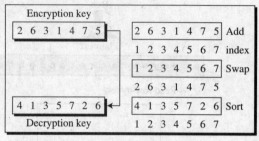

Given: EncKey [index]
index ← 1
while (index ≤ Column)
{
  DecKey[EncKey[index]] ← index
  index ← index + 1
}
Return : DecKey [index]

a. Manual process
b. Algorithm

**Fig. 3.23** *Key inversion in a transposition cipher*

***Using Matrices*** We can use matrices to show the encryption/decryption process for a transposition cipher. The plaintext and ciphertext are $l \times m$ matrices representing the numerical values of the characters; the keys are square matrices of size $m \times m$. In a permutation matrix, every row or column has exactly one 1 and the rest of the values are 0s. Encryption is performed by multiplying the plaintext matrix by the key matrix to get the ciphertext matrix; decryption is performed by multiplying the ciphertext by the inverse key matrix to get the plaintext matrix. A very interesting point is that the decryption matrix in this case is the inverse of the encryption matrix. However, there is no need to invert the matrix, the encryption key matrix can simply be transposed (swapping the rows and columns) to get the decryption key matrix.

> **Example 3.27** Figure 3.24 shows the encryption process. Multiplying the $4 \times 5$ plaintext matrix by the $5 \times 5$ encryption key gives the $4 \times 5$ ciphertext matrix. Matrix manipulation requires changing the characters in Example 3.27 to their numerical values (from 00 to 25). Note that the matrix multiplication provides only the column permutation of the transposition; reading and writing into the matrix should be provided by the rest of the algorithm.

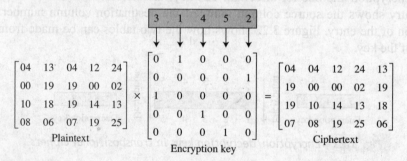

**Fig. 3.24** *Representation of the key as a matrix in the transposition cipher*

***Cryptanalysis of Transposition Ciphers*** Transposition ciphers are vulnerable to several kinds of ciphertext-only attacks.

***Statistical Attack*** A transposition cipher does not change the frequency of letters in the ciphertext; it only reorders the letters. So the first attack that can be applied is single-letter frequency analysis. This method can be useful if the length of the ciphertext is long enough. We have seen this attack before.

However, transposition ciphers do not preserve the frequency of digrams and trigrams. This means that Eve cannot use these tools. In fact, if a cipher does not preserve the frequency of digrams and trigrams, but does preserve the frequency of single letters, it is probable that the cipher is a transposition cipher.

**Brute-Force Attack** Eve can try all possible keys to decrypt the message. However, the number of keys can be huge ($1! + 2! + 3! + ... + L!$), where $L$ is the length of the ciphertext. A better approach is to guess the number of columns. Eve knows that the number of columns divides $L$. For example, if the length of the cipher is 20 characters, then $20 = 1 \times 2 \times 2 \times 5$. This means the number of columns can be a combination of these factors (1, 2, 4, 5, 10, 20). However, the first (only one column) is out of the question and the last (only one row) is unlikely.

---

**Example 3.28** Suppose that Eve has intercepted the ciphertext message "EEMYNTAACTTKON-SHITZG". The message length $L = 20$ means the number of columns can be 1, 2, 4, 5, 10, or 20. Eve ignores the first value because it means only one column and no permutation.

a. If the number of columns is 2, the only two permutations are (1, 2) and (2, 1). The first one means there would be no permutation. Eve tries the second one. Eve divides the ciphertext into two-character units: "EE MY NT AA CT TK ON SH IT ZG". She then tries to permute each of these getting "ee ym nt aa tc kt no hs ti gz", which does not make sense.

b. If the number of columns is 4, there are $4! = 24$ permutations. The first one (1 2 3 4) means there would be no permutation. Eve needs to try the rest. After trying all 23 possibilities, Eve finds no plaintext that makes sense.

c. If the number of columns is 5, there are $5! = 120$ permutations. The first one (1 2 3 4 5) means there would be no permutation. Eve needs to try the rest. The permutation (2 5 1 3 4) yields a plaintext "enemyattackstonightz" that makes sense after removing the bogus letter z and adding spaces.

---

**Pattern Attack** Another attack on the transposition cipher can be called pattern attack. The ciphertext created from a keyed transposition cipher has some repeated patterns. The following show where each character in the ciphertext in Example 3.28 comes from.

| **03** | **08** | **13** | **18** | *01* | *06* | *11* | *16* | **04** | **09** | **14** | **19** | *05* | *10* | *15* | *20* | **02** | **07** | **12** | **17** |
|---|---|---|---|---|---|---|---|---|---|---|---|---|---|---|---|---|---|---|---|

The 1st character in the ciphertext comes from the 3rd character in the plaintext. The 2nd character in the ciphertext comes from the 8th character in the plaintext. The 20th character in the ciphertext comes from the 17th character in the plaintext, and so on. There is a pattern in the above list. We have five groups: (3, 8, 13, 18), (1, 6, 11, 16), (4, 9, 14, 19), (5, 10, 15, 20), and (2, 7, 12, 17). In all groups, the difference between the two adjacent numbers is 5. This regularity can be used by the cryptanalyst to break the cipher. If Eve knows or can guess the number of columns (which is 5 in this case), she can organize the ciphertext in groups of four characters. Permuting the groups can provide the clue to finding the plaintext.

## Double Transposition Ciphers

**Double transposition ciphers** can make the job of the cryptanalyst difficult. An example of such a cipher would be the one that repeats twice the algorithm used for encryption and decryption in Example 3.26. A different key can be used in each step, but normally the same key is used.

**Example 3.29** Let us repeat Example 3.26 using double transposition. Figure 3.25 shows the process.

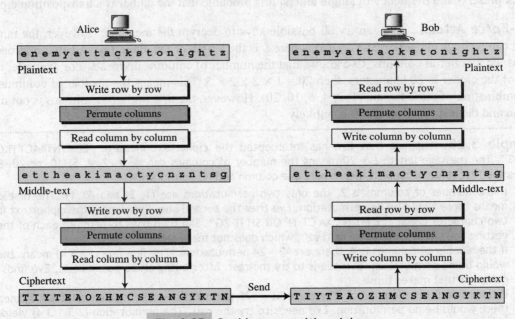

**Fig. 3.25** *Double transposition cipher*

Although, the cryptanalyst can still use the single-letter frequency attack on the ciphertext, a pattern attack is now much more difficult. The pattern analysis of the text shows

| 13 | 16 | 05 | 07 | 03 | 06 | 10 | 20 | 18 | 04 | 10 | 12 | 01 | 09 | 15 | 17 | 08 | 11 | 19 | 02 |
|----|----|----|----|----|----|----|----|----|----|----|----|----|----|----|----|----|----|----|----|

Comparing the above set with the result in Example 3.28, we see that there is no repetitive pattern. Double transposition removes the regularities we have seen before.

## 3.4 STREAM AND BLOCK CIPHERS

The literature divides the symmetric ciphers into two broad categories: stream ciphers and block ciphers. Although the definitions are normally applied to modern ciphers, this categorization also applies to traditional ciphers.

### 3.4.1 Stream Ciphers

In a **stream cipher,** encryption and decryption are done typically on one symbol (such as a character or a bit) at a time. We have a plaintext stream, a ciphertext stream, and a key stream. Call the plaintext stream P, the ciphertext stream C, and the key stream K.

$$P = P_1P_2P_3, \ldots \qquad C = C_1C_2C_3, \ldots \qquad K = (k_1, k_2, k_3, \ldots)$$
$$C_1 = E_{k1}(P_1) \quad C_2 = E_{k2}(P_2) \quad C_3 = E_{k3}(P_3) \ldots$$

Figure 3.26 shows the idea behind a stream cipher. Characters in the plaintext are fed into the encryption algorithm, one at a time; the ciphertext characters are also created one at a time. The key stream, can be created in many ways. It may be a stream of predetermined values; it may be created one value at a time using an algorithm. The values may depend on the plaintext or ciphertext characters. The values may also depend on the previous key values.

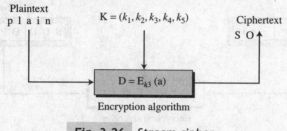

Plaintext
p l a i n

$K = (k_1, k_2, k_3, k_4, k_5)$

Ciphertext
S O

$D = E_{k3} (a)$

Encryption algorithm

**Fig. 3.26** *Stream cipher*

Figure 3.26 shows the moment where the third character in the plaintext stream is being encrypted using the third value in the key stream. The result creates the third character in the ciphertext stream.

**Example 3.30**  Additive ciphers can be categorized as stream ciphers in which the key stream is the repeated value of the key. In other words, the key stream is considered as a predetermined stream of keys or $K = (k, k, ..., k)$. In this cipher, however, each character in the ciphertext depends only on the corresponding character in the plaintext, because the key stream is generated independently.

**Example 3.31**  The monoalphabetic substitution ciphers discussed in this chapter are also stream ciphers. However, each value of the key stream in this case is the mapping of the current plaintext character to the corresponding ciphertext character in the mapping table.

**Example 3.32**  Vigenere ciphers are also stream ciphers according to the definition. In this case, the key stream is a repetition of $m$ values, where $m$ is the size of the keyword. In other words,

$$K = (k_1, k_2, ... k_m, k_1, k_2, ... k_m, ...)$$

**Example 3.33**  We can establish a criterion to divide stream ciphers based on their key streams. We can say that a stream cipher is a monoalphabetic cipher if the value of $k_i$ does not depend on the position of the plaintext character in the plaintext stream; otherwise, the cipher is polyalphabetic.

- ❑ Additive ciphers are definitely monoalphabetic because $k_i$ in the key stream is fixed; it does not depend on the position of the character in the plaintext.
- ❑ Monoalphabetic substitution ciphers are definitely *monoalphabetic* because $k_i$ does not depend on the position of the corresponding character in the plaintext stream; it depends only on the value of the plaintext character.
- ❑ Vigenere ciphers are polyalphabetic ciphers because $k_i$ definitely depends on the position of the plaintext character. However, the dependency is cyclic. The key is the same for two characters $m$ positions apart.

### 3.4.2  Block Ciphers

In a **block cipher,** a group of plaintext symbols of size $m$ ($m > 1$) are encrypted together creating a group of ciphertext of the same size. Based on the definition, in a block cipher, a single key is used to encrypt the whole block even if the key is made of multiple values. Figure 3.27 shows the concept of a block cipher.

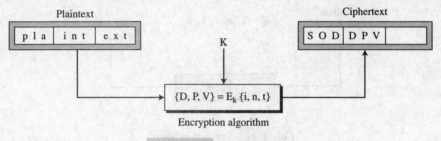

**Fig. 3.27** *Block cipher*

In a block cipher, a ciphertext block depends on the whole plaintext block.

**Example 3.34**  Playfair ciphers are block ciphers. The size of the block is $m = 2$. Two characters are encrypted together.

**Example 3.35**  Hill ciphers are block ciphers. A block of plaintext, of size 2 or more is encrypted together using a single key (a matrix). In these ciphers, the value of each character in the ciphertext depends on all the values of the characters in the plaintext. Although the key is made of $m \times m$ values, it is considered as a single key.

**Example 3.36**  From the definition of the block cipher, it is clear that every block cipher is a polyalphabetic cipher because each character in a ciphertext block depends on all characters in the plaintext block.

### 3.4.3  Combination

In practice, blocks of plaintext are encrypted individually, but they use a stream of keys to encrypt the whole message block by block. In other words, the cipher is a block cipher when looking at the individual blocks, but it is a stream cipher when looking at the whole message considering each block as a single unit. Each block uses a different key that may be generated before or during the encryption process. Examples of this will appear in later chapters.

### 3.5  RECOMMENDED READING

The following books and websites give more details about subjects discussed in this chapter. The items enclosed in brackets refer to the reference list at the end of the book.

### Books

Several books discuss classic symmetric-key ciphers. [Kah96] and [Sin99] give a thorough history of these ciphers. [Sti06], [Bar02], [TW06], [Cou99], [Sta06], [Sch01], [Mao03], and [Gar01] provide good accounts of the technical details.

## WebSites

The following websites give more information about topics discussed in this chapter.

http://www.cryptogram.org
http://www.cdt.org/crypto/
http://www.cacr.math.uwaterloo.ca/
http://www.acc.stevens.edu/crypto.php
http://www.crypto.com/
http://theory.lcs.mit.edu/~rivest/crypto-security.html
http://www.trincoll.edu/depts/cpsc/cryptography/substitution.html
http://hem.passagen.se/tan01/transpo.html
http://www.strangehorizons.com/2001/20011008/steganography.shtml

## *Key Terms*

| | |
|---|---|
| additive cipher | key domain |
| affine cipher | known-plaintext attack |
| autokey cipher | monoalphabetic cipher |
| block cipher | monoalphabetic substitution cipher |
| brute-force attack | multiplicative cipher |
| Caesar cipher | one-time pad |
| chosen-ciphertext attack | pattern attack |
| chosen-plaintext attack | plaintext |
| cipher | Playfair cipher |
| ciphertext | polyalphabetic cipher |
| ciphertext-only attack | polyalphabetic substitution cipher |
| cryptanalysis | rail fence cipher |
| decryption algorithm | rotor cipher |
| digram | shared secret key |
| double transposition cipher | shift cipher |
| encryption algorithm | statistical attack |
| Enigma machine | stream cipher |
| exhaustive-key-search method | substitution cipher |
| Hill cipher | transposition cipher |
| Kasiski test | trigram |
| Kerckhoff's principle | Vigenere cipher |
| key | Vigenere tableau |

## *Summary*

★ Symmetric-key encipherment uses a single key for both encryption and decryption. In addition, the encryption and decryption algorithms are inverse of each other.

★ The original message is called the plaintext; the message that is sent through the channel is called the ciphertext. To create the ciphertext from the plaintext, an encryption algorithm is used with the shared secret key. To create the plaintext from ciphertext, a decryption algorithm is used and the same secret key. We refer to encryption and decryption algorithms as ciphers.

★ Based on Kerckhoff's principle, one should always assume that the adversary knows the encryption/decryption algorithm. The resistance of the cipher to attack should be based only on the secrecy of the key.

★ Cryptanalysis is the science and art of breaking ciphers. There are four common types of cryptanalysis attacks: ciphertext-only, known-plaintext, chosen-plaintext, and chosen-ciphertext.

★ Traditional symmetric-key ciphers can be divided into two broad categories: substitution ciphers and transposition ciphers. A substitution cipher replaces one character with another character. A transposition cipher reorders the symbols.

★ Substitution ciphers can be divided into two broad categories: monoalphabetic ciphers and polyalphabetic ciphers. In monoalphabetic substitution, the relationship between a character in the plaintext and the characters in the ciphertext is one-to-one. In polyalphabetic substitution, the relationship between a character in the plaintext and the characters in the ciphertext is one-to-many.

★ Monoalphabetic ciphers include additive, multiplicative, affine, and monoalphabetic substitution ciphers.

★ Polyalphabetic ciphers include autokey, Playfair, Vigenere, Hill, one-time pad, rotor, and Enigma ciphers.

★ Transposition ciphers include keyless, keyed, and double transposition ciphers.

★ Symmetric ciphers can also be divided into two broad categories: stream ciphers and block ciphers. In a stream cipher, encryption and decryption are done one symbol at a time. In a block cipher, symbols in a block are encrypted together. In practice, blocks of plaintext are encrypted individually, but they use a stream of keys to encrypt the whole message block by block.

# *Practice Set*

## Review Questions

**3.1** Define a symmetric-key cipher.

**3.2** Distinguish between a substitution cipher and a transposition cipher.

**3.3** Distinguish between a monoalphabetic and a polyalphabetic cipher.

**3.4** Distinguish between a stream cipher and a block cipher.

**3.5** Are all stream ciphers monoalphabetic? Explain.

**3.6** Are all block ciphers polyalphabetic? Explain.

**3.7** List three monoalphabetic ciphers.

**3.8** List three polyalphabetic ciphers.

**3.9** List two transposition ciphers.

**3.10** List four kinds of cryptanalysis attacks.

## Exercises

**3.11** A small private club has only 100 members. Answer the following questions:
   a. How many secret keys are needed if all members of the club need to send secret messages to each other?
   b. How many secret keys are needed if everyone trusts the president of the club? If a member needs to send a message to another member, she first sends it to the president; the president then sends the message to the other member.
   c. How many secret keys are needed if the president decides that the two members who need to communicate should contact him first. The president then creates a temporary key to be used between the two. The temporary key is encrypted and sent to both members.

**3.12** Some archeologists found a new script written in an unknown language. The archeologists later found a small tablet at the same place that contains a sentence in the same language with the translation in Greek. Using the tablet, they were able to read the original script. What type of attack did the archeologists use?

**3.13** Alice can use only the additive cipher on her computer to send a message to a friend. She thinks that the message is more secure if she encrypts the message two times, each time with a different key. Is she right? Defend you answer.

**3.14** Alice has a long message to send. She is using the monoalphabetic substitution cipher. She thinks that if she compresses the message, it may protect the text from single-letter frequency attack by Eve. Does the compression help? Should she compress the message before the encryption or after the encryption? Defend your answer.

**3.15** Alice often needs to encipher plaintext made of both letters (a to z) and digits (0 to 9).
  a. If she uses an additive cipher, what is the key domain? What is the modulus?
  b. If she uses a multiplication cipher, what is the key domain? What is the modulus?
  c. If she uses an affine cipher, what is the key domain? What is the modules?

**3.16** Suppose that spaces, periods, and question marks are added to the plaintext to increase the key domain of simple ciphers.
  a. What is the key domain if an additive cipher is used?
  b. What is the key domain if a multiplicative cipher is used?
  c. What is the key domain if an affine cipher is used?

**3.17** Alice and Bob have decided to ignore Kerckhoff's principle and hide the type of the cipher they are using.
  a. How can Eve decide whether a substitution or a transposition cipher was used?
  b. If Eve knows that the cipher is a substitution cipher, how can she decide whether it was an additive, multiplicative, or affine cipher?
  c. If Eve knows that the cipher is a transposition, how can she find the size of the section ($m$)?

**3.18** In each of the following ciphers, what is the maximum number of characters that will be changed in the ciphertext if only a single character is changed in the plaintext?
  a. Additive
  b. Multiplicative
  c. Affine
  d. Vigenere
  e. Auto-key
  f. One-time pad
  g. Rotor
  h. Enigma

**3.19** In each of the following ciphers, what is the maximum number of characters that will be changed in the ciphertext if only one character is changed in plaintext?
  a. Single transposition
  b. Double transposition
  c. Playfair

**3.20** For each of the following ciphers, say whether it is a stream cipher or block cipher. Defend your answers.
  a. Playfair
  b. Auto-key
  c. One-time pad
  d. Rotor
  e. Enigma

**3.21** Encrypt the message "this is an exercise" using one of the following ciphers. Ignore the space between words. Decrypt the message to get the original plaintext.

    a.   Additive cipher with key = 20

    b.   Multiplicative cipher with key = 15

    c.   Affine cipher with key = (15, 20)

**3.22** Encrypt the message "the house is being sold tonight" using one of the following ciphers. Ignore the space between words. Decrypt the message to get the plaintext:

    a.   Vigenere cipher with key: "dollars"

    b.   Autokey cipher with key = 7

    c.   Playfair cipher with the key created in the text (see Figure 3.13)

**3.23** Use the Vigenere cipher with keyword "HEALTH" to encipher the message "Life is full of surprises".

**3.24** Use the Playfair cipher to encipher the message "The key is hidden under the door pad". The secret key can be made by filling the first and part of the second row with the word "GUIDANCE" and filling the rest of the matrix with the rest of the alphabet.

**3.25** Use a Hill cipher to encipher the message "We live in an insecure world". Use the following key:

$$K = \begin{bmatrix} 03 & 02 \\ 05 & 07 \end{bmatrix}$$

**3.26** John is reading a mystery book involving cryptography. In one part of the book, the author gives a ciphertext "CIW" and two paragraphs later the author tells the reader that this is a shift cipher and the plaintext is "yes". In the next chapter, the hero found a tablet in a cave with "XVIEWYWI" engraved on it. John immediately found the actual meaning of the ciphertext. What type of attack did John launch here? What is the plaintext?

**3.27** Eve secretly gets access to Alice's computer and using her cipher types "abcdefghij". The screen shows "CABDEHFGIJ". If Eve knows that Alice is using a keyed transposition cipher, answer the following questions:

    a.   What type of attack is Eve launching?

    b.   What is the size of the permutation key?

**3.28** Use a brute-force attack to decipher the following message enciphered by Alice using an additive cipher. Suppose that Alice always uses a key that is close to her birthday, which is on the 13th of the month:

NCJAEZRCLASJLYODEPRLYZRCLASJLCPEHZDTOPDZQLNZTY

**3.29** Use a brute-force attack to decipher the following message. Assume that you know it is an affine cipher and that the plaintext "ab" is enciphered to "GL".

XPALASXYFGFUKPXUSOGEUTKCDGFXANMGNVS

**3.30** Use a one-letter frequency attack to decipher the following message. Assume that you know it is enciphered using monoalphabetic substitution cipher.

ONHOVEJHWOBEVGWOCBWHNUGBLHGBGR

**3.31** Assume that punctuation marks (periods, question marks, and spaces) are added to the encryption alphabet of a Hill cipher, then a $2 \times 2$ key matrix in $Z_{29}$ can be used for encryption and decryption.

    a.   Find the total number of possible matrices.

    b.   It has been proved that the total number of invertible matrices is $(N^2 - 1)(N^2 - N)$, where N is the number of alphabet size. Find the key domain of a Hill cipher using this alphabet.

**3.32** Use a single-letter frequency attack to break the following ciphertext. You know that it has been created with an additive cipher

OTWEWNGWCBPQABIZVQAPMLJGZWTTQVOBQUMAPMIDGZCAB
EQVBMZLZIXMLAXZQVOQVLMMXAVWEIVLLIZSNZWAB
JQZLWNLMTQOPBVIUMLGWCBPAEQNBTGTMNBBPMVMAB
ITIAKWCTLVBBQUMQBEPQTMQBEIAQVUGBZCAB

**3.33** Use a Kasiski test and single-frequency attack to break the following ciphertext. You know that it has been created with a Vigenere cipher

MPYIGOBSRMIDBSYRDIKATXAILFDFKXTPPSNTTJIGTHDELT
TXAIREIHSVOBSMLUCFIOEPZIWACRFXICUVXVTOPXDLWPENDHPTSI
DDBXWWTZPHNSOCLOUMSNRCCVUUXZHHNWSVXAUHIK
LXTIMOICHTYPBHMHXGXHOLWPEWWWWDALOCTSQZELT

**3.34** The encryption key in a transposition cipher is (3, 2, 6, 1, 5, 4). Find the decryption key.

**3.35** Show the matrix representation of the transposition-cipher encryption key with the key (3, 2, 6, 1, 5, 4). Find the matrix representation of the decryption key.

**3.36** The plaintext "letusmeetnow" and the corresponding ciphertext "HBCDFNOPIKLB" are given. You know that the algorithm is a Hill cipher, but you don't know the size of the key. Find the key matrix.

**3.37** Hill ciphers and multiplicative ciphers are very similar. Hill ciphers are block ciphers using multiplication of matrices; multiplicative ciphers are stream ciphers using multiplication of scalars.
   a. Define a block cipher that is similar to an additive cipher using the addition of matrices.
   b. Define a block cipher that is similar to an affine cipher using the multiplication and addition of matrices.

**3.38** Let us define a new stream cipher. The cipher is affine, but the keys depend on the position of the character in the plaintext. If the plaintext character to be encrypted is in position $i$, we can find the keys as follow:
   a. The multiplicative key is the ($i \bmod 12$)th element in $\mathbf{Z}_{26}^{*}$.
   b. The additive key is the ($i \bmod 26$)th element in $\mathbf{Z}_{26}$.

   Encrypt the message "cryptography is fun" using this new cipher.

**3.39** Suppose that for a Hill cipher the plaintext is a multiplicative identity matrix ($\mathbf{I}$). Find the relationship between the key and ciphertext. Use the result of your finding to launch a chosen-plaintext attack on the Hill cipher.

**3.40** Atbash was a popular cipher among Biblical writers. In Atbash, "A" is encrypted as "Z", "B" is encrypted as "Y", and so on. Similarly, "Z" is encrypted as "A", "Y" is encrypted as "B", and so on. Suppose that the alphabet is divided into two halves and the letters in the first half are encrypted as the letters in the second and vice versa. Find the type of cipher and key. Encipher the message "an exercise" using the Atbash cipher.

**3.41** In a Polybius cipher, each letter is enciphered as two integers. The key is a $5 \times 5$ matrix of characters as in Playfair cipher. The plaintext is the character in the matrix, the ciphertext is the two integers (each between 1 and 5) representing row and column numbers. Encipher the message "An exercise" using the Polybius cipher with the following key:

|   | 1 | 2 | 3 | 4 | 5 |
|---|---|---|---|---|---|
| 1 | z | q | p | f | e |
| 2 | y | r | o | g | d |
| 3 | x | s | n | h | c |
| 4 | w | t | m | i / j | b |
| 5 | v | u | l | k | a |

# 4

# Mathematics of Symmetric-Key Cryptography

## *Algebraic Structures*

## Objectives

This chapter prepares the reader for the next few chapters, which will discuss modern symmetric-key ciphers based on algebraic structures. This chapter has several objectives:

☞   To review the concept of algebraic structures
☞   To define and give some examples of groups
☞   To define and give some examples of rings
☞   To define and give some examples of fields
☞   To emphasize the finite fields of type GF($2^n$) that make it possible to perform operations such as addition, subtraction, multiplication, and division on $n$-bit words in modern block ciphers

The next few chapters will discuss modern symmetric-key block ciphers that perform some operations on $n$-bit words. Understanding and analyzing these ciphers requires some knowledge of a branch of modern algebra called algebraic structures. This chapter first reviews the topic of algebraic structures, and then it shows how to perform operations such as addition or multiplication on $n$-bit words.

## 4.1                                      ALGEBRAIC STRUCTURES

Chapter 2 discussed some sets of numbers, such as $\mathbf{Z}$, $\mathbf{Z}_n$, $\mathbf{Z}_n^*$, $\mathbf{Z}_p$ and $\mathbf{Z}_p^*$. Cryptography requires sets of integers and specific operations that are defined for those sets. The combination of the set and the operations that are applied to the elements of the set is called an **algebraic structure.** In this chapter, we will define three common algebraic structures: *groups, rings,* and *fields* (Fig. 4.1).

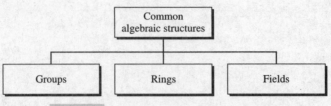

**Fig. 4.1** *Common algebraic structures*

## 4.1.1 Groups

A **group (G)** is a set of elements with a binary operation "•" that satisfies four properties (or axioms). A **commutative group,** also called an **abelian group,** is a group in which the operator satisfies the four properties for groups plus an extra property, commutativity. The four properties for groups plus commutativity are defined as follows:

❑ **Closure:** If $a$ and $b$ are elements of **G**, then $c = a \bullet b$ is also an element of **G**. This means that the result of applying the operation on any two elements in the set is another element in the set.

❑ **Associativity:** If $a$, $b$, and $c$ are elements of **G**, then $(a \bullet b) \bullet c = a \bullet (b \bullet c)$. In other words, it does not matter in which order we apply the operation on more than two elements.

❑ **Commutativity:** For all $a$ and $b$ in **G**, we have $a \bullet b = b \bullet a$. Note that this property needs to be satisfied only for a commutative group.

❑ **Existence of identity:** For all $a$ in **G**, there exists an element $e$, called the identity element, such that $e \bullet a = a \bullet e = a$.

❑ **Existence of inverse:** For each $a$ in **G**, there exists an element $a'$, called the inverse of $a$, such that $a \bullet a' = a' \bullet a = e$.

Figure 4.2 shows the concept of a group.

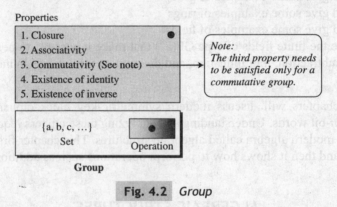

**Fig. 4.2** *Group*

## *Application*

Although a group involves a single operation, the properties imposed on the operation allow the use of a pair of operations as long as they are inverses of each other. For example, if the defined operation is addition, the group supports both addition and subtraction, because subtraction is addition using the additive inverse. This is also true for multiplication and division. However, a group can support only addition/subtraction or multiplication/division operations, but not the both at the same time.

**Example 4.1**   The set of residue integers with the addition operator, G = <$Z_n$, + >, is a commutative group. We can perform addition and subtraction on the elements of this set without moving out of the set. Let us check the properties.

1. Closure is satisfied. The result of adding two integers in $Z_n$ is another integer in $Z_n$.
2. Associativity is satisfied. The result of 4 + (3 + 2) is the same as (4 + 3) + 2.
3. Commutativity is satisfied. We have 3 + 5 = 5 + 3.
4. The identify element is 0. We have 3 + 0 = 0 + 3 = 3.
5. Every element has an additive inverse. The inverse of an element is its complement. For example, the inverse of 3 is -3 ($n$ - 3 in $Z_n$) and the inverse of -3 is 3. The inverse allows us to perform subtraction on the set.

**Example 4.2**   The set $Z_n^*$ with the multiplication operator, G = <$Z_{n^*}$, × >, is also an abelian group. We can perform multiplication and division on the elements of this set without moving out of the set. It is easy to check the first three properties. The identity element is 1. Each element has an inverse that can be found according to the extended Euclidean algorithm.

**Example 4.3**   Although we normally think about a group as the set of numbers with the regular operations such as addition or subtraction, the definition of the group allows us to define any set of objects and an operation that satisfies the above-mentioned properties. Let us define a set G = < {$a$, $b$, $c$, $d$}, •> and the operation as shown in Table 4.1.

**Table 4.1**   *Operation table for Example 4.3*

| • | $a$ | $b$ | $c$ | $d$ |
|---|-----|-----|-----|-----|
| $a$ | $a$ | $b$ | $c$ | $d$ |
| $b$ | $b$ | $c$ | $d$ | $a$ |
| $c$ | $c$ | $d$ | $a$ | $b$ |
| $d$ | $d$ | $a$ | $b$ | $c$ |

This is an abelian group. All five properties are satisfied:

1. Closure is satisfied. Applying the operation on any pair of elements result in another elements in the set.
2. Associativity is also satisfied. To prove this we need to check the property for any combination of three elements. For example, ($a$ + $b$) + $c$ = $a$ + ($b$ + $c$) = $d$.
3. The operation is commutative. We have $a$ + $b$ = $b$ + $a$.
4. The group has an identity element, which is $a$.
5. Each element has an inverse. The inverse pairs can be found by finding the identity in each row (shaded). The pairs are ($a$, $a$), ($b$, $d$), ($c$, $c$).

**Example 4.4**   In a group, the elements in the set do not have to be numbers or objects; they can be rules, mappings, functions, or even actions. A very interesting group is the **permutation group**. The set is the set of all permutations, and the operation is composition: applying one permutation after another. Figure 4.3 shows composition of two permutations that transpose three inputs to create three outputs.

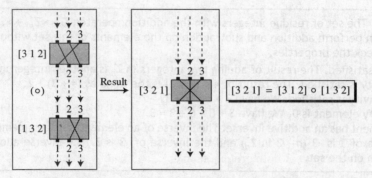

**Fig. 4.3**  *Composition of permutations (Example 4.4)*

The inputs and outputs can be characters (Chapter 2) or can be bits (Chapter 5). We have shown each permutation by a table in which the content shows where the input comes from and the index (not shown) defines the output. Composition involve applying two permutations, one after the other. Note that the expression in Fig. 4.3 is read from right to left: the first permutation is [1 3 2] followed by [3 1 2]; the result is [3 2 1]. With three inputs and three outputs, there can be 3! or 6 different permutations. Table 4.2 shows how the operation is defined. The first row is the first permutation; the first column is the second permutation. The result is the cross-section element.

In this case, only four properties are satisfied; the group is non-abelian.
1. Closure is satisfied.
2. Associativity is also satisfied. To prove this we need to check the property for any combination of three elements.
3. The commutative property is not satisfied. This can be easily checked, but we leave it as an exercise.

**Table 4.2**  *Operation table for permutation group*

| ∘ | [1 2 3] | [1 3 2] | [2 1 3] | [2 3 1] | [3 1 2] | [3 2 1] |
|---|---|---|---|---|---|---|
| [1 2 3] | [1 2 3] | [1 3 2] | [2 1 3] | [2 3 1] | [3 1 2] | [3 2 1] |
| [1 3 2] | [1 3 2] | [1 2 3] | [2 3 1] | [2 1 3] | [3 2 1] | [3 1 2] |
| [2 1 3] | [2 1 3] | [3 1 2] | [1 2 3] | [3 2 1] | [1 3 2] | [2 3 1] |
| [2 3 1] | [2 3 1] | [3 2 1] | [1 3 2] | [3 1 2] | [1 2 3] | [2 1 3] |
| [3 1 2] | [3 1 2] | [2 1 3] | [3 2 1] | [1 2 3] | [2 3 1] | [1 3 2] |
| [3 2 1] | [3 2 1] | [2 3 1] | [3 1 2] | [1 3 2] | [2 1 3] | [1 2 3] |

4. The set has an identity element, which is [1 2 3] (no permutation). These are shaded.
5. Each element has an inverse. The inverse pairs can be found using the identity elements.

**Example 4.5**  In the previous example, we showed that a set of permutations with the composition operation is a group. This implies that using two permutations one after another cannot strengthen the security of a cipher, because we can always find a permutation that can do the same job because of the closure property.

*Finite Group*  A group is called a **finite group** if the set has a finite number of elements; otherwise, it is an **infinite group.**

*Order of a Group*  The **order of a group,** |G|, is the number of elements in the group. If the group is not finite, its order is infinite; if the group is finite, the order is finite.

*Subgroups*  A subset **H** of a group **G** is a **subgroup** of **G** if **H** itself is a group with respect to the operation on **G**. In other words, if **G** = <**S**, • > is a group, **H** = <**T**, •> is a group under the same operation, and **T** is a nonempty subset of **S**, then **H** is a subgroup of **G**. The above definition implies that:

1.  If $a$ and $b$ are members of both groups, then $c = a • b$ is also a member of both groups.
2.  The group share the same identity element.
3.  If $a$ is a member of both groups, the inverse of $a$ is also a member of both groups.
4.  The group made of the identity element of **G**, **H** = <{e}, •>, is a subgroup of **G**.
5.  Each group is a subgroup of itself.

**Example 4.6**  Is the group **H** = <$Z_{10}$, +> a subgroup of the group **G** = <$Z_{12}$, +>?

*Solution*  The answer is no. Although **H** is a subset of **G**, the operations defined for these two groups are different. The operation in **H** is addition modulo 10; the operation in **G** is addition modulo 12.

*Cyclic Subgroups*  If a subgroup of a group can be generated using the power of an element, the subgroup is called the **cyclic subgroup.** The term *power* here means repeatedly applying the group operation to the element:

$$a^n \rightarrow a • a • \dots • a \quad (n \text{ times})$$

The set made from this process is referred to as <$a$>. Note that the duplicate elements must be discarded. Note also that $a^0 = e$.

**Example 4.7**  Four cyclic subgroups can be made from the group **G** = <$Z_6$, +>. They are $H_1$ = <{0}, +>, $H_2$ = <{0, 2, 4}, +>, $H_3$ = <{0, 3}, +>, and $H_4$ = **G**. Note that when the operation is addition, $a^n$ means multiplying $n$ by $a$. Note also that in all of these groups, the operation is addition modulo 6. The following show how we find the elements of these cyclic subgroups.

a.  The cyclic subgroup generated from 0 is $H_1$, which has only one element, the identity element.

   $0^0 \bmod 6 = 0$                       (stop: the process will be repeated)

b.  The cyclic subgroup generated from 1 is $H_4$, which is **G** itself.

   $1^0 \bmod 6 = 0$
   $1^1 \bmod 6 = 1$
   $1^2 \bmod 6 = (1 + 1) \bmod 6 = 2$
   $1^3 \bmod 6 = (1 + 1 + 1) \bmod 6 = 3$
   $1^4 \bmod 6 = (1 + 1 + 1 + 1) \bmod 6 = 4$
   $1^5 \bmod 6 = (1 + 1 + 1 + 1 + 1) \bmod 6 = 5$    (stop: the process will be repeated)

c.  The cyclic subgroup generated from 2 is $H_2$, which has three elements: 0, 2, and 4.

   $2^0 \bmod 6 = 0$
   $2^1 \bmod 6 = 2$
   $2^2 \bmod 6 = (2 + 2) \bmod 6 = 4$           (stop: the process will be repeated)

d. The cyclic subgroup generated from 3 is $H_3$, which has two elements: 0 and 3.

> $3^0 \bmod 6 = 0$
> $3^1 \bmod 6 = 3$              (stop: the process will be repeated)

e. The cyclic subgroup generated from 4 is $H_2$; this is not a new subgroup.

> $4^0 \bmod 6 = 0$
> $4^1 \bmod 6 = 4$
> $4^2 \bmod 6 = (4 + 4) \bmod 6 = 2$      (stop: the process will be repeated)

f. The cyclic subgroup generated from 5 is $H_4$, which is **G** itself.

> $5^0 \bmod 6 = 0$
> $5^1 \bmod 6 = 5$
> $5^2 \bmod 6 = 4$
> $5^3 \bmod 6 = 3$
> $5^4 \bmod 6 = 2$
> $5^5 \bmod 6 = 1$              (stop: the process will be repeated)

---

**Example 4.8** Three cyclic subgroups can be made from the group $G = <Z_{10}{}^{*}, \times>$. **G** has only four elements: 1, 3, 7, and 9. The cyclic subgroups are $H_1 = <\{1\}, \times>$, $H_2 = <\{1, 9\}, \times>$, and $H_3 = G$. The following show how we find the elements of these subgroups.

a. The cyclic subgroup generated from 1 is $H_1$. The subgroup has only one element, the identity element.

> $1^0 \bmod 10 = 1$           (stop: the process will be repeated)

b. The cyclic subgroup generated from 3 is $H_3$, which is **G** itself.

> $3^0 \bmod 10 = 1$
> $3^1 \bmod 10 = 3$
> $3^2 \bmod 10 = 9$
> $3^3 \bmod 10 = 7$           (stop: the process will be repeated)

c. The cyclic subgroup generated from 7 is $H_3$, which is **G** itself.

> $7^0 \bmod 10 = 1$
> $7^1 \bmod 10 = 7$
> $7^2 \bmod 10 = 9$
> $7^3 \bmod 10 = 3$           (stop: the process will be repeated)

d. The cyclic subgroup generated from 9 is $H_2$. The subgroup has only two elements.

> $9^0 \bmod 10 = 1$
> $9^1 \bmod 10 = 9$           (stop: the process will be repeated)

## Cyclic Groups

A **cyclic group** is a group that is its own cyclic subgroup. In Example 4.7, the group **G** has a cyclic subgroup $H_5 = G$. This means that the group **G** is a cyclic group. In this case, the element that generates the cyclic subgroup can also generate the group itself. This element is referred to as a generator. If $g$ is a generator, the elements in a finite cyclic group can be written as

$\{e, g, g^2, \dots, g^{n-1}\}$, where $g^n = e$.
Note that a cyclic group can have many generators.

---

**Example 4.9**

   a.   The group $G = <Z_6, +>$ is a cyclic group with two generators, $g = 1$ and $g = 5$.
   b.   The group $G = <Z_{10}, \times>$ is a cyclic group with two generators, $g = 3$ and $g = 7$.

---

## Lagrange's Theorem

**Lagrange's theorem** relates the order of a group to the order of its subgroup. Assume that **G** is a group, and **H** is a subgroup of **G**. If the order of **G** and **H** are $|G|$ and $|H|$, respectively, then, based on this theorem, $|H|$ divides $|G|$. In Example 4.7, $|G| = 6$. The order of the subgroups are $|H_1| = 1$, $|H_2| = 3$, $|H_3| = 2$, and $|H_4| = 6$. Obviously all of these orders divide 6.

    Lagrange's theorem has a very interesting application. Given a group **G** of order $|G|$, the orders of the potential subgroups can be easily determined if the divisors of $|G|$ can be found. For example, the order of the group $G = <Z_{17}, +>$ is 17. The only divisors of 17 are 1 and 17. This means that this group can have only two subgroups, $H_1$ with the identity element and $H_2 = G$.

## Order of an Element

The **order of an element** $a$ in a group, $\text{ord}(a)$, is the smallest integer $n$ such that $a^n = e$. The definition can be paraphrased: the order of an element is the order of the cyclic group it generates.

---

**Example 4.10**

   a.   In the group $G = <Z_6, +>$, the orders of the elements are: $\text{ord}(0) = 1$, $\text{ord}(1) = 6$, $\text{ord}(2) = 3$, $\text{ord}(3) = 2$, $\text{ord}(4) = 3$, $\text{ord}(5) = 6$.
   b.   In the group $G = <Z_{10}^*, \times>$, the orders of the elements are: $\text{ord}(1) = 1$, $\text{ord}(3) = 4$, $\text{ord}(7) = 4$, $\text{ord}(9) = 2$.

---

### 4.1.2 Ring

A **ring**, denoted as $R = <\{\dots\}, \bullet, \square>$, is an algebraic structure with two operations. The first operation must satisfy all five properties required for an abelian group. The second operation must satisfy only the first two. In addition, the second operation must be distributed over the first. **Distributivity** means that for all $a$, $b$, and $c$ elements of **R**, we have $a \square (b \bullet c) = (a \square b) \bullet (a \square c)$ and $(a \bullet b) \square c = (a \square c) \bullet (b \square c)$. A **commutative ring** is a ring in which the commutative property is also satisfied for the second the operation. Figure 4.4 shows a ring and a commutative ring.

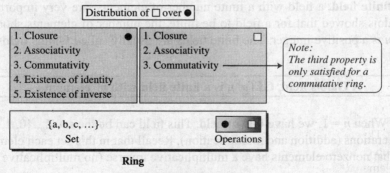

**Fig. 4.4** *Ring*

***Application***   A ring involves two operations. However, the second operation can fail to satisfy the third and fourth properties. In other words, the first operation is actually a pair of operation such as addition and subtraction; the second operation is a single operation, such as multiplication, but not division.

---

**Example 4.11**   The set Z with two operations, addition and multiplication, is a commutative ring. We show it by R = <Z, +, ×>. Addition satisfies all of the five properties; multiplication satisfies only three properties. Multiplication also distributes over addition. For example, $5 \times (3 + 2) = (5 \times 3) + (5 \times 2) = 25$. Although, we can perform addition and subtraction on this set, we can perform only multiplication, but not division. Division is not allowed in this structure because it yields an element out of the set. The result of dividing 12 by 5 is 2.4, which is not in the set.

---

### 4.1.3   Field

A **field,** denoted by $\mathbf{F} = <\{...\}, \bullet, \square >$ is a commutative ring in which the second operation satisfies all five properties defined for the first operation except that the identity of the first operation (sometimes called the zero element) has no inverse. Figure 4.5 shows the field.

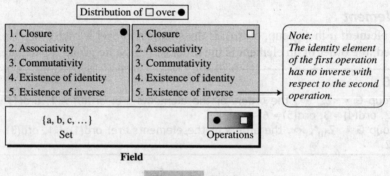

**Fig. 4.5**   *Field*

***Application***   A field is a structure that supports two pairs of operations that we have used in mathematics: addition/subtraction and multiplication/division. There is one exception: division by zero is not allowed.

***Finite Fields***   Although we have fields of infinite order, only finite fields extensively used in cryptography. A **finite field,** a field with a finite number of elements, are very important structures in cryptography. Galois showed that for a field to be finite, the number of elements should be $p^n$, where $p$ is a prime and $n$ is a positive integer. The finite fields are usually called **Galois fields** and denoted as $\mathbf{GF}(p^n)$.

---

**A Galois field, GF($p^n$), is a finite field with $p^n$ elements.**

---

***GF(p) Fields***   When $n = 1$, we have **GF**($p$) field. This field can be the set $\mathbf{Z}_p$, $\{0, 1, ..., p - 1\}$, with two arithmetic operations (addition and multiplication). Recall that in this set each element has an additive inverse and that nonzero elements have a multiplicative inverse (no multiplicative inverse for 0).

**Example 4.12**   A very common field in this category is **GF**(2) with the set {0, 1} and two operations, addition and multiplication, as shown in Fig. 4.6.

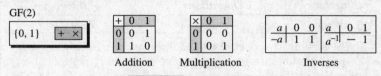

**Fig. 4.6**  *GF(2) field*

There are several things to notice about this field. First, the set has only two elements, which are binary digits or bits (0 and 1). Second, the addition operation is actually the exclusive-or (XOR) operation we use on two binary digits. Third, the multiplication operation is the AND operation we use on two binary digits. Fourth, addition and subtraction operations are the same (XOR operation). Fifth, multiplication and division operations are the same (AND operation).

---

**Addition/subtraction in GF(2) is the same as the XOR operation; multiplication/division is the same as the AND operation.**

---

**Example 4.13**   We can define **GF**(5) on the set $Z_5$ (5 is a prime) with addition and multiplication operators as shown in Fig. 4.7.

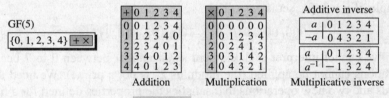

**Fig. 4.7**  *GF(5) field*

Although we can use the extended Euclidean algorithm to find the multiplicative inverses of elements in **GF**(5), it is simpler to look at the multiplication table and find each pair with the product equal to 1. They are (1,1), (2, 3), (3, 2), and (4, 4). Note that we can apply addition/subtraction and multiplication/division on the set except that division by 0 is not allowed.

### *GF(pⁿ) Fields*

***GF($p^n$) Fields***   In addition to GF($p$) fields, we are also interested in GF($p^n$) fields in cryptography. However, the set **Z**, **Z**$_n$, **Z**$_n$* and **Z**$_p$, which we have used so far with operations such as addition and multiplication, cannot satisfy the requirement of a field. Some new sets and some new operations on those sets must be defined. The next section, we shows how **GF($2^n$)** is a very useful field in cryptography.

## Conclusion

The study of three algebraic structures allows us to use sets in which operations similar to addition subtraction and multiplication/division can be used with the set. We need to distinguish between the three structures. The first structure, the group, supports one related pair of operations. The second structure, the ring, supports one related pair of operations and one single operation. The third structure, the field, supports two pairs of operations. Table 4.3 may help us to see the difference.

**Table 4.3**  *Summary of algebraic structures*

| Algebraic Structure | Supported Typical Operations | Supported Typical Sets of Integers |
|---|---|---|
| Group | $(+\;-)$ or $(\times \div)$ | $\mathbf{Z}_n$ or $\mathbf{Z}_n^*$ |
| Ring | $(+\;-)$ and $(\times)$ | $\mathbf{Z}$ |
| Field | $(+\;-)$ and $(\times \div)$ | $\mathbf{Z}_p$ |

## 4.2  GF($2^n$) FIELDS

In cryptography, we often need to use four operations (addition, subtraction, multiplication, and division). In other words, we need to use fields. However, when we work with computers, the positive integers are stored in the computer as $n$-bit words in which $n$ is usually 8, 16, 32, 64, and so on. This means that the range of integers is 0 to $2^n - 1$. The modulus is $2^n$. So we have two choices if we want to use a field:

1.  We can use **GF**($p$) with the set $\mathbf{Z}_p$, where $p$ is the largest prime number less than $2^n$. Although this scheme works, it is inefficient because we cannot use the integers from $p$ to $2^n - 1$. For example, if $n = 4$, the largest prime less than $2^4$ is 13. This means that we cannot use integers 13, 14, and 15. If $n = 8$, the largest prime less than $2^8$ is 251, so we cannot use 251, 252, 253, 254, and 255.

2.  We can work in GF($2^n$) and uses a set of $2^n$ elements. The elements in this set are $n$-bit words. For example, if $n = 3$, the set is

$$\{000, 001, 010, 011, 100, 101, 110, 111\}$$

However, we cannot interpret each element as an integer between 0 to 7 because the regular four operations cannot be applied (the modulus $2^n$ is not a prime). We need to define a set of $n$-bit words and two new operations that satisfies the properties defined for a field.

---

**Example 4.14**  Let us define a GF($2^2$) field in which the set has four 2-bit words: {00, 01, 10, 11}. We can redefine addition and multiplication for this field in such a way that all properties of these operations are satisfied, as shown in Fig. 4.8.

| $\oplus$ | 00 | 01 | 10 | 11 |
|---|---|---|---|---|
| 00 | 00 | 01 | 10 | 11 |
| 01 | 01 | 00 | 11 | 10 |
| 10 | 10 | 11 | 00 | 01 |
| 11 | 11 | 10 | 01 | 00 |

Addition — Identity: 00

| $\otimes$ | 00 | 01 | 10 | 11 |
|---|---|---|---|---|
| 00 | 00 | 00 | 00 | 00 |
| 01 | 00 | 01 | 10 | 11 |
| 10 | 00 | 10 | 11 | 01 |
| 11 | 00 | 11 | 01 | 10 |

Multiplication — Identity: 01

**Fig. 4.8**  *An example of a GF($2^2$) field*

Each word is the additive inverse of itself. Every word (except 00) has a multiplicative inverse. The multiplicative inverse pairs are (01, 01) and (10, 11). Addition and multiplication are defined in terms of polynomials.

## 4.2.1 Polynomials

Although we can directly define the rules for addition and multiplication operations on $n$-bit words that satisfy the properties in $GF(2^n)$, it is easier to work with a representation of $n$-bit words, a polynomial of degree $n - 1$. A **polynomial** of degree $n - 1$ is an expression of the form

$$f(x) = a_{n-1}x^{n-1} + a_{n-2}x^{n-2} + \cdots + a_1x^1 + a_0x^0$$

where $x^i$ is called the $i$th term and $a_i$ is called coefficient of the $i$th term. Although we are familiar with polynomials in algebra, to represent an $n$-bit word by a polynomial we need to follow some rules:

a. The power of $x$ defines the position of the bit in the $n$-bit word. This means the leftmost bit is at position zero (related to $x^0$); the rightmost bit is at position $n - 1$ (related to $x^{n-1}$).

b. The coefficients of the terms define the value of the bits. Because a bit can have only a value of 0 or 1, our polynomial coefficients can be either 0 or 1.

---

**Example 4.15** Figure 4.9 shows how we can represent the 8-bit word (10011001) using a polynomials.

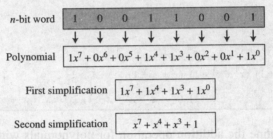

**Fig. 4.9** *Representation of an 8-bit word by a polynomial*

Note that the term is totally omitted if the coefficient is 0, and the coefficient is omitted if it is 1. Also note that $x^0$ is 1.

---

**Example 4.16** To find the 8-bit word related to the polynomial $x^5 + x^2 + x$, we first supply the omitted terms. Since $n = 8$, it means the polynomial is of degree 7. The expanded polynomial is

$$0x^7 + 0x^6 + 1x^5 + 0x^4 + 0x^3 + 1x^2 + 1x^1 + 0x^0$$

This is related to the 8-bit word 00100110.

---

***Operations*** Note that any operation on polynomials actually involves two operations: operations on coefficients and operations on two polynomials. In other words, we need to define two fields: one for the coefficients and one for the polynomials. Coefficients are made of 0 or 1; we can use the **GF(2)** field for this purpose. We discusses this field before (see Example 4.14). For the polynomials we need the field $GF(2^n)$, which we will discuss shortly.

---

**Polynomials representing $n$-bit words use two fields: GF(2) and $GF(2^n)$.**

---

***Modulus*** Before defining the operations on polynomials, we need to talk about the modulus polynomials. Addition of two polynomials never creates a polynomial out of the set. However, multiplication of two polynomials may create a polynomial with degrees more than $n - 1$. This means we need to divide the result by a modulus and keep only the remainder, as we did in modular arithmetic. For the sets of polynomials in $\mathbf{GF}(2^n)$, a group of polynomials of degree $n$ is defined as the modulus. The modulus in this case acts as a *prime polynomial,* which means that no polynomials in the set can divide this polynomial. A prime polynomial cannot be factored into a polynomial with degree of less than $n$. Such polynomials are referred to as *irreducible polynomials.* Table 4.4 shows irreducible polynomials of degrees 1 to 5. It may be noted that the number of terms in an irreducible polynomial is odd (so we have trinomials, pentanomials). Why? Consider an irreducible polynomial with even terms, $f(x)$. Thus $f(1) = 0$ (as there are even terms, so $f(1)$ is the XOR of even one-values). Thus $(x + 1)$ is a factor of $f(x)$, and hence $f(x)$ is not irreducible.

For each degree, there is often more than one irreducible polynomial, which means when we define our $GF(2^n)$ we need to declare which irreducible polynomial we are using as the modulus.

**Table 4.4**     *List of irreducible polynomials*

| Degree | Irreducible Polynomials |
|---|---|
| 1 | $(x + 1), (x)$ |
| 2 | $(x^2 + x + 1)$ |
| 3 | $(x^3 + x^2 + 1), (x^3 + x + 1)$ |
| 4 | $(x^4 + x^3 + x^2 + x + 1), (x^4 + x^3 + 1), (x^4 + x + 1)$ |
| 5 | $(x^5 + x^2 + 1), (x^5 + x^3 + x^2 + x + 1), (x^5 + x^4 + x^3 + x + 1), (x^5 + x^4 + x^3 + x^2 + 1), (x^5 + x^4 + x^2 + x + 1)$ |

**Addition**     Now let us define the addition operation for polynomials with coefficient in GF(2). Addition is very easy: we add the coefficients of the corresponding terms in GF(2). Note that adding two polynomials of degree $n - 1$ always create a polynomial with degree $n - 1$, which means that we do not need to reduce the result using the modulus.

**Example 4.17**     Let us do $(x^5 + x^2 + x) \oplus (x^3 + x^2 + 1)$ in $GF(2^8)$. We use the symbol $\oplus$ to show that we mean polynomial addition. The following shows the procedure:

$$0x^7 + 0x^6 + 1x^5 + 0x^4 + 0x^3 + 1x^2 + 1x^1 + 0x^0 \quad \oplus$$
$$0x^7 + 0x^6 + 0x^5 + 0x^4 + 1x^3 + 1x^2 + 0x^1 + 1x^0$$
$$\overline{\hspace{8cm}}$$
$$0x^7 + 0x^6 + 1x^5 + 0x^4 + 1x^3 + 0x^2 + 1x^1 + 1x^0 \quad \rightarrow \quad x^5 + x^3 + x + 1$$

There is a short cut: keeps the uncommon terms and delete the common terms. In other words, $x^5$, $x^3$, $x$, and 1 are kept and $x^2$, which is common in the two polynomials, is deleted.

**Example 4.18**     There is also another short cut. Because the addition in **GF(2)** means the exclusive-or (XOR) operation. So we can exclusive-or the two words, bits by bits, to get the result. In the previous example, $x^5 + x^2 + x$ is 00100110 and $x^3 + x^2 + 1$ is 00001101. The result is 00101011 or in polynomial notation $x^5 + x^3 + x + 1$.

**Additive Identity**     The additive identity in a polynomial is a zero polynomial (a polynomial with all coefficients set to zero) because adding a polynomial with itself results in a zero polynomial.

*Additive Inverse*   The additive inverse of a polynomial with coefficients in GF(2) is the polynomial itself. This means that the subtraction operation is the same as the addition operation.

---

**Addition and subtraction operations on polynomials are the same operation.**

---

*Multiplication*   Multiplication in polynomials is the sum of the multiplication of each term of the first polynomial with each term of the second polynomial. However, we need to remember three points. First, the coefficient multiplication is done in GF(2). Second, multiplying $x^i$ by $x^j$ results in $x^{i+j}$. Third, the multiplication may create terms with degree more than $n - 1$, which means the result needs to be reduced using a modulus polynomial. We first show how to multiply two polynomials according to the above definition. Later we will see a more efficient algorithm that can be used by a computer program.

> **Example 4.19**   Find the result of $(x^5 + x^2 + x) \otimes (x^7 + x^4 + x^3 + x^2 + x)$ in $GF(2^8)$ with irreducible polynomial $(x^8 + x^4 + x^3 + x + 1)$. Note that we use the symbol $\otimes$ to show the multiplication of two polynomials.

*Solution*   We first multiply the two polynomials as we have learned in algebra. Note that in this process, a pair of terms with equal power of $x$ are deleted. For example, $x^9 + x^9$ is totally deleted because the result is a zero polynomial, as we discussed above.

$$P_1 \otimes P_2 = x^5(x^7 + x^4 + x^3 + x^2 + x) + x^2(x^7 + x^4 + x^3 + x^2 + x) + x(x^7 + x^4 + x^3 + x^2 + x)$$
$$P_1 \otimes P_2 = x^{12} + x^9 + x^8 + x^7 + x^6 + x^9 + x^6 + x^5 + x^4 + x^3 + x^8 + x^5 + x^4 + x^3 + x^2$$
$$P_1 \otimes P_2 = (x^{12} + x^7 + x^2) \bmod (x^8 + x^4 + x^3 + x + 1) = x^5 + x^3 + x^2 + x + 1$$

To find the final result, divide the polynomial of degree 12 by the polynomial of degree 8 (the modulus) and keep only the remainder. The process is the same as we have learned in algebra, but we need to remember that subtraction is the same as addition here. Figure 4.10 shows the process of division.

$$
\begin{array}{r}
x^4 + 1 \\
x^8 + x^4 + x^3 + x + 1 \overline{\smash{\big)}\ x^{12} + x^7 + x^2} \\
x^{12} + x^8 + x^7 + x^5 + x^4 \\
\hline
x^8 + x^5 + x^4 + x^2 \\
x^8 + x^4 + x^3 + x + 1 \\
\hline
\end{array}
$$

Remainder $\boxed{x^5 + x^3 + x^2 + x + 1}$

**Fig. 4.10**   *Polynomial division with coefficients in GF(2)*

*Multiplicative Identity*   The multiplicative identity is always 1. For example, in $GF(2^8)$, the multiplicative inverse is the bit pattern 00000001.

*Multiplicative Inverse*   Finding the multiplicative inverse is a little more involved. The extended Euclidean algorithm must be applied to the modulus and the polynomial. The process is exactly the same as for integers.

**Example 4.20**   In GF$(2^4)$, find the inverse of $(x^2 + 1)$ modulo $(x^4 + x + 1)$.

**Solution**   We use the extended Euclidean algorithm as in Table 4.5:

**Table 4.5**   *Euclidean algorithm for Exercise 4.20*

| $q$ | $r_1$ | $r_2$ | $r$ | $t_1$ | $t_2$ | $t$ |
|---|---|---|---|---|---|---|
| $(x^2 + 1)$ | $(x^4 + x + 1)$ | $(x^2 + 1)$ | $(x)$ | $(0)$ | $(1)$ | $(x^2 + 1)$ |
| $(x)$ | $(x^2 + 1)$ | $(x)$ | $(1)$ | $(1)$ | $(x^2 + 1)$ | $(x^3 + x + 1)$ |
| $(x)$ | $(x)$ | $(1)$ | $(0)$ | $(x^2 + 1)$ | $(x^3 + x + 1)$ | $(0)$ |
| | $(1)$ | $(0)$ | | $(x^3 + x + 1)$ | $(0)$ | |

This means that $(x^2 + 1)^{-1}$ modulo $(x^4 + x + 1)$ is $(x^3 + x + 1)$. The answer can be easily proved by multiplying the two polynomials and finding the remainder when the result is divided by the modulus.

$$[(x^2 + 1) \otimes (x^3 + x + 1)] \bmod (x^4 + x + 1) = 1$$

**Example 4.21**   In GF$(2^8)$, find the inverse of $(x^5)$ modulo $(x^8 + x^4 + x^3 + x + 1)$.

**Solution**   Use the Extended Euclidean algorithm as shown in Table 4.6:

**Table 4.6**   *Euclidean algorithm for Example 4.21*

| $q$ | $r_1$ | $r_2$ | $r$ | $t_1$ | $t_2$ | $t$ |
|---|---|---|---|---|---|---|
| $(x^3)$ | $(x^8 + x^4 + x^3 + x + 1)$   $(x^5)$ | $(x^4 + x^3 + x + 1)$ | | $(0)$ | $(1)$ | $(x^3)$ |
| $(x + 1)$ | $(x^5)$   $(x^4 + x^3 + x + 1)$ | $(x^3 + x^2 + 1)$ | | $(1)$ | $(x^3)$ | $(x^4 + x^3 + 1)$ |
| $(x)$ | $(x^4 + x^3 + x + 1)$   $(x^3 + x^2 + 1)$ | $(1)$ | | $(x^3)$   $(x^4 + x^3 + 1)$ | | $(x^5 + x^4 + x^3 + x)$ |
| $(x^3 + x^2 + 1)$ | $(x^3 + x^2 + 1)$   $(1)$ | $(0)$ | | $(x^4 + x^3 + 1)$   $(x^5 + x^4 + x^3 + x)$ | | $(0)$ |
| | $(1)$   $(0)$ | | | $(x^5 + x^4 + x^3 + x)$   $(0)$ | | |

This means that $(x^5)^{-1}$ modulo $(x^8 + x^4 + x^3 + x + 1)$ is $(x^5 + x^4 + x^3 + x)$. The answer can be easily proved by multiplying the two polynomials and finding the remainder when the result is divided by the modulus.

$$[(x^5) \otimes (x^5 + x^4 + x^3 + x)] \bmod (x^8 + x^4 + x^3 + x + 1) = 1$$

**Multiplication Using a Computer**   Because of the division operation, there is an efficiency problem involved in writing a program to multiply two polynomials. The computer implementation uses a better algorithm, repeatedly multiplying a reduced polynomial by $x$. For example, instead of finding the result of $(x^2 \otimes P_2)$, the program finds the result of $(x \otimes (x \otimes P_2))$. The benefit of this strategy will be discussed shortly, but first let us use an example to show the process.

**Example 4.22**  Find the result of multiplying $P_1 = (x^5 + x^2 + x)$ by $P_2 = (x^7 + x^4 + x^3 + x^2 + x)$ in $GF(2^8)$ with irreducible polynomial $(x^8 + x^4 + x^3 + x + 1)$ using the algorithm described above.

**Solution**  The process is shown in Table 4.7. We first find the partial result of multiplying $x^0$, $x^1$, $x^2$, $x^3$, $x^4$, and $x^5$ by $P_2$. Note that although only three terms are needed, the product of $x^m \otimes P_2$ for $m$ from 0 to 5 because each calculation depends on the previous result.

**Table 4.7**  *An efficient algorithm for multiplication using polynomials (Example 4.22)*

| Powers | Operation | New Result | Reduction |
|--------|-----------|-----------|-----------|
| $x^0 \otimes P_2$ | | $x^7 + x^4 + x^3 + x^2 + x$ | No |
| $x^1 \otimes P_2$ | $x \otimes (x^7 + x^4 + x^3 + x^2 + x)$ | $x^5 + x^2 + x + 1$ | **Yes** |
| $x^2 \otimes P_2$ | $x \otimes (x^5 + x^2 + x + 1)$ | $x^6 + x^3 + x^2 + x$ | No |
| $x^3 \otimes P_2$ | $x \otimes (x^6 + x^3 + x^2 + x)$ | $x^7 + x^4 + x^3 + x^2$ | No |
| $x^4 \otimes P_2$ | $x \otimes (x^7 + x^4 + x^3 + x^2)$ | $x^5 + x + 1$ | **Yes** |
| $x^5 \otimes P_2$ | $x \otimes (x^5 + x + 1)$ | $x^6 + x^2 + x$ | No |
| $\mathbf{P_1 \times P_2 = (x^6 + x^2 + x) + (x^6 + x^3 + x^2 + x) + (x^5 + x^2 + x + 1) = x^5 + x^3 + x^2 + x + 1}$ | | | |

The above algorithm has two benefits. First, multiplication of a polynomial by $x$ can be easily achieved by one-bit shifting of the $n$-bit word; an operation provided by common programming languages. Second, the result needed to be reduced only if the polynomial maximum power is $n - 1$. In this case, reduction can be easily done by an XOR operation with the modulus because the highest power in the result is only 8. We can then design a simple algorithm to find each partial result:

1. If the most significant bit of the previous result is 0, just shift the previous result one bit to the left.
2. If the most significant bit of the previous result is 1,
   a. shift it one bit to the left, and
   b. exclusive-or it with the modulus without the most significant bit

**Example 4.23**  Repeat Example 4.22 using bit patterns of size 8.

**Solution**  We have $P_1 = 000100110$, $P_2 = 10011110$, modulus $= 100011010$ (nine bits). We show the exclusive-or operation by $\oplus$. See Table 4.8.

**Table 4.8**  *An efficient algorithm for multiplication using n-bit words*

| Powers | Shift-Left Operation | Exclusive-Or |
|--------|---------------------|--------------|
| $x^0 \otimes P_2$ | | 10011110 |
| $x^1 \otimes P_2$ | 00111100 | $(00111100) \oplus (00011010) =$ **00100111** |
| $x^2 \otimes P_2$ | 01001110 | **01001110** |
| $x^3 \otimes P_2$ | 10011100 | 10011100 |
| $x^4 \otimes P_2$ | 00111000 | $(00111000) \oplus (00011010) = 00100011$ |
| $x^5 \otimes P_2$ | 01000110 | **01000110** |
| $\mathbf{P_1 \otimes P_2 = (00100111) \oplus (01001110) \oplus (01000110) = 00101111}$ | | |

In this case, we need only five shift-left operations and four exclusive-or operations to multiply the two polynomials. In general, a maximum of $n-1$ shift-left operations and $2n$ exclusive-or operations are needed to multiply two polynomial of degree $n-1$.

---

**Multiplication of polynomials in GF($2^n$) can be achieved using shift-left and exclusive-or operations.**

---

**Example 4.24**  The GF($2^3$) field has 8 elements. We use the irreducible polynomial ($x^3 + x^2 + 1$) and show the addition and multiplication tables for this field. We show both 3-bit words and the polynomials. Note that there are two irreducible polynomials for degree 3. The other one, ($x^3 + x + 1$), yields a totally different table for multiplication. Table 4.9 shows addition. The shaded boxes easily give us the additive inverses pairs.

**Table 4.9**  *Addition table for GF($2^3$)*

| $\oplus$ | 000 (0) | 001 (1) | 010 ($x$) | 011 ($x+1$) | 100 ($x^2$) | 101 ($x^2+1$) | 110 ($x^2+x$) | 111 ($x^2+x+1$) |
|---|---|---|---|---|---|---|---|---|
| 000 (0) | 000 (0) | 001 (1) | 010 ($x$) | 011 ($x+1$) | 100 ($x^2$) | 101 ($x^2+1$) | 110 ($x^2+x$) | 111 ($x^2+x+1$) |
| 001 (1) | 001 (1) | 000 (0) | 011 ($x+1$) | 010 ($x^2$) | 101 ($x^2+1$) | 100 ($x^2+x$) | 111 ($x^2+x+1$) | 110 ($x^2+x$) |
| 010 ($x$) | 010 ($x$) | 011 ($x+1$) | 000 (0) | 001 (1) | 110 ($x^2+x$) | 111 ($x^2+x+1$) | 100 ($x^2+x$) | 101 ($x^2+1$) |
| 011 ($x+1$) | 011 ($x+1$) | 010 ($x$) | 001 (1) | 000 (0) | 111 ($x^2+x+1$) | 110 ($x^2+x$) | 101 ($x^2+1$) | 100 ($x^2$) |
| 100 ($x^2$) | 100 ($x^2$) | 101 ($x^2+1$) | 110 ($x^2+x$) | 111 ($x^2+x+1$) | 000 (0) | 001 (1) | 010 ($x$) | 011 ($x+1$) |
| 101 ($x^2+1$) | 101 ($x^2+1$) | 100 ($x^2$) | 111 ($x^2+x+1$) | 110 ($x^2+x$) | 001 (1) | 000 (0) | 011 ($x+1$) | 010 ($x$) |
| 110 ($x^2+x$) | 110 ($x^2+x$) | 111 ($x^2+x+1$) | 100 ($x^2$) | 101 ($x^2+1$) | 010 ($x$) | 011 ($x+1$) | 000 (0) | 001 (1) |
| 111 ($x^2+x+1$) | 111 ($x^2+x+1$) | 110 ($x^2+x$) | 101 ($x^2+1$) | 100 ($x^2$) | 011 ($x+1$) | 010 ($x$) | 001 (1) | 000 (0) |

Table 4.10 shows multiplication. The shaded boxes easily give us the multiplicative inverse pairs.

## Multiplication Using a Generator

Sometimes it is easier to define the elements of the **GF($2^n$)** field using a generator. In this field with the irreducible polynomial $f(x)$, an element in the field, $a$, must satisfy the relation $f(a) = 0$. In particular, if $g$ is a generator of the field, then $f(g) = 0$. It can be proved that the elements of the field can be generated as

$$\{0, g, g, g^2, ..., g^N\}, \text{ where } N = 2^n - 2$$

**Table 4.10**  *Multiplication table for GF($2^3$) with irreducible polynomial ($x^3 + x^2 + 1$)*

| $\otimes$ | 000 (0) | 001 (1) | 010 (x) | 011 (x + 1) | 100 ($x^2$) | 101 ($x^2 + 1$) | 110 ($x^2 + x$) | 111 ($x^2 + x + 1$) |
|---|---|---|---|---|---|---|---|---|
| 000 (0) | 000 (0) | 000 (0) | 000 (0) | 000 (0) | 000 (0) | 000 (0) | 000 (0) | 000 (0) |
| 001 (1) | 000 (0) | 001 (1) | 010 (x) | 011 (x + 1) | 100 ($x^2$) | 101 ($x^2 + 1$) | 110 ($x^2 + x$) | 111 ($x^2 + x + 1$) |
| 010 (x) | 000 (0) | 010 (x) | 100 (x) | 110 ($x^2 + x$) | 101 ($x^2 + 1$) | 111 ($x^2 + x + 1$) | 001 (1) | 011 (x + 1) |
| 011 (x + 1) | 000 (0) | 011 (x + 1) | 110 ($x^2 + x$) | 101 ($x^2 + 1$) | 001 (1) | 010 (x) | 111 ($x^2 + x + 1$) | 100 (x) |
| 100 ($x^2$) | 000 (0) | 100 ($x^2$) | 101 ($x^2 + 1$) | 001 (1) | 111 ($x^2 + x + 1$) | 011 (x + 1) | 010 (x) | 110 ($x^2 + x$) |
| 101 ($x^2 + 1$) | 000 (0) | 101 ($x^2 + 1$) | 111 ($x^2 + x + 1$) | 010 (x) | 011 (x + 1) | 110 ($x^2 + x$) | 100 ($x^2$) | 001 (1) |
| 110 ($x^2 + x$) | 000 (0) | 110 ($x^2 + x$) | 001 (1) | 111 ($x^2 + x + 1$) | 010 (x) | 100 ($x^2$) | 011 (x + 1) | 101 ($x^2 + 1$) |
| 111 ($x^2 + x + 1$) | 000 (0) | 111 ($x^2 + x + 1$) | 011 (x + 1) | 100 ($x^2$) | 110 ($x^2 + x$) | 001 (1) | 101 ($x^2 + 1$) | 010 (x) |

---

**Example 4.25**  Generate the elements of the field **GF($2^4$)** using the irreducible polynomial $f(x) = x^4 + x + 1$.

***Solution***  The elements $0, g^0, g^1, g^2$, and $g^3$ can be easily generated, because they are the 4-bit representations of $0, 1, x^2$, and $x^3$ (there is no need for polynomial division). Elements $g^4$ through $g^{14}$, which represent $x^4$ though $x^{14}$ need to be divided by the irreducible polynomial. To avoid the polynomial division, the relation $f(g) = g^4 + g + 1 = 0$ can be used. Using this relation, we have $g^4 = -g - 1$. Because in this field addition and subtraction are the same operation, $g^4 = g + 1$. We use this relation to find the value of all elements as 4-bit words:

$$
\begin{array}{ccccccccc}
0 & = & 0 & = & 0 & = & 0 & \longrightarrow & 0 & = & (0000) \\
g^0 & = & g^0 & = & g^0 & = & g^0 & \longrightarrow & g^0 & = & (0001) \\
g^1 & = & g^1 & = & g^1 & = & g^1 & \longrightarrow & g^1 & = & (0010) \\
g^2 & = & g^2 & = & g^2 & = & g^2 & \longrightarrow & g^2 & = & (0100) \\
g^3 & = & g^3 & = & g^3 & = & g^3 & \longrightarrow & g^3 & = & (1000) \\
g^4 & = & g^4 & = & g^4 & = & g + 1 & \longrightarrow & g^4 & = & (0011) \\
g^5 & = & g(g^4) & = & g(g + 1) & = & g^2 + g & \longrightarrow & g^5 & = & (0110) \\
g^6 & = & g(g^5) & = & g(g^2 + g) & = & g^3 + g^2 & \longrightarrow & g^6 & = & (1100) \\
g^7 & = & g(g^6) & = & g(g^3 + g) & = & g^3 + g + 1 & \longrightarrow & g^7 & = & (1011) \\
g^8 & = & g(g^7) & = & g(g^3 + g + 1) & = & g^2 + 1 & \longrightarrow & g^8 & = & (0101) \\
g^9 & = & g(g^8) & = & g(g^2 + 1) & = & g^3 + g & \longrightarrow & g^9 & = & (1010) \\
g^{10} & = & g(g^9) & = & g(g^3 + g) & = & g^2 + g + 1 & \longrightarrow & g^{10} & = & (0111) \\
g^{11} & = & g(g^{10}) & = & g(g^2 + g + 1) & = & g^3 + g^2 + g & \longrightarrow & g^{11} & = & (1110) \\
g^{12} & = & g(g^{11}) & = & g(g^3 + g^2 + g) & = & g^3 + g^2 + g + 1 & \longrightarrow & g^{12} & = & (1111) \\
g^{13} & = & g(g^{12}) & = & g(g^3 + g^2 + g + 1) & = & g^3 + g^2 + 1 & \longrightarrow & g^{13} & = & (1101) \\
g^{14} & = & g(g^{13}) & = & g(g^3 + g^2 + 1) & = & g^3 + 1 & \longrightarrow & g^{14} & = & (1001)
\end{array}
$$

The main idea is to reduce terms $g^4$ to $g^{14}$ to a combination of the terms 1, $g$, $g^2$, and $g^3$, using the relation $g^4 = g + 1$. For example,

$$g^{12} = g\,(g^{11}) = g\,(g^3 + g^2 + g) = g^4 + g^3 + g^2 = g^3 + g^2 + g + 1$$

After the reduction, it is easy to transform the powers into an $n$-bit word. For example, $g^3 + 1$ is equivalent to 1001, because only the powers 0 and 3 are present. Note that two equal terms cancel each other in this process. For example, $g^2 + g^2 = 0$.

### Inverses

Finding inverses using the above representation is simple.

*Additive Inverses*  The additive inverse of each element is the element itself because addition and subtraction in this field are the same: $-g^3 = g^3$

*Multiplicative Inverses*  Finding the multiplicative inverse of each element is also very simple. For example, we can find the multiplicative inverse of $g^3$ as shown below:

$$(g^3)^{-1} = g^{-3} = g^{12} = g^3 + g^2 + g + 1 \rightarrow (1111)$$

Note that the exponents are calculated modulo $2^n - 1$, 15 in this case. Therefore, the exponent $-3$ mod $15 = 12$ mod 15. It can be easily proved that $g^3$ and $g^{12}$ are inverses of each other because $g^3 \times g^{12} = g^{15} = g^0 = 1$.

*Operations*  The four operations defined for the field can also be performed using this representation.

*Addition and Subtraction*  Addition and subtraction are the same operation. The intermediate results can be simplified as shown in the following example.

---

**Example 4.26**  The following show the results of addition and subtraction operations:
a.  $g^3 + g^{12} + g^7 = g^3 + (g^3 + g^2 + g + 1) + (g^3 + g + 1) = g^3 + g^2 \rightarrow (1100)$
b.  $g^3 - g^6 = g^3 + g^6 = g^3 + (g^3 + g^2) = g^2 \rightarrow (0100)$

---

*Multiplication and Division*  Multiplication is the addition of powers modulo $2^n - 1$. Division is multiplication using the multiplicative inverse.

---

**Example 4.27**  The following show the result of multiplication and division operations:
a.  $g^9 \times g^{11} = g^{20} = g^{20 \bmod 15} = g^5 = g^2 + g \rightarrow (0110)$
b.  $g^3 / g^8 = g^3 \times g^7 = g^{10} = g^2 + g + 1 \rightarrow (0111)$

---

### Conclusion

The finite field $GF(2^n)$ can be used to define four operations of addition, subtraction, multiplication and division over $n$-bit words. The only restriction is that division by zero is not defined. Each $n$-bit word can also be represented as a polynomial of degree $n - 1$ with coefficients in $GF(2)$, which means that the operations on $n$-bit words are the same as the operations on this polynomial. To make it modular, we need to define an irreducible polynomial of degree $n$ when we multiply two polynomials. The extended Euclidean algorithm can be applied to polynomials to find the multiplicative inverses.

## 4.3             RECOMMENDED READING

The following books and Web sites provide more details about subjects discussed in this chapter. The items enclosed in brackets refer to the reference list at the end of the book.

### Books

[Dur05], [Ros06], [Bla03], [BW00], and [DF04] discuss algebraic structures thoroughly.

### WebSites

The following websites give more information about topics discussed in this chapter.

http://en.wikipedia.org/wiki/Algebraic_structure
http://en.wikipedia.org/wiki/Ring_%28mathematics%29
http://en.wikipedia.org/wiki/Polynomials
http://www.math.niu.edu/~rusin/known-math/index/20-XX.html
http://www.math.niu.edu/~rusin/known-math/index/13-XX.html
http://www.hypermaths.org/quadibloc/math/abaint.htm
http://en.wikipedia.org/wiki/Finite_field

## *Key Terms*

| | |
|---|---|
| abelian group | field |
| algebraic structure | finite field |
| associativity | finite group |
| closure | Galois field |
| commutative group | group |
| commutative ring | irreducible polynomial |
| commutativity | Lagrange's theorem |
| composition | order of an element |
| cyclic group | order of a group |
| cyclic subgroup | permutation group |
| distributivity | polynomial |
| existence of identity | ring |
| existence of inverse | subgroup |

## *Summary*

★    Cryptography requires sets and specific operations defined on those sets. The combination of the set and the operations applied to elements of the set is called an algebraic structure. Three algebraic structures were introduced in this chapter: groups, rings, and fields.

★    A group is an algebraic structure with a binary operation shown as that satisfies four properties: closure, associativity, existence of identity, and existence of inverse. A commutative group, also called an abelian group, is a group in which the operator satisfies an extra property: commutativity.

★    A subset **H** of a group **G** is a subgroup of **G** if **H** itself is a group with respect to the operation on **G**. If a subgroup of a group can be generated using the power of an element, the subgroup is called the cyclic subgroup. A cyclic group is a group that is its own cyclic subgroup.

★ Lagrange's theorem relates the order of a group to the order of its subgroup. If the order of **G** and **H** are |**G**| and |**H**|, respectively, then, |**H**| divides |**G**|.

★ The order of an element $a$ in a group is the smallest positive integer $n$ such that $a^n = e$.

★ A ring is an algebraic structure with two operations. The first operation needs to satisfy all five properties required for an abelian group. The second operation needs to satisfy only the first two. In addition, the second operation must be distributed over the first. A commutative ring is a ring in which the commutative property is also satisfied for the second the operation.

★ A field is a commutative ring in which the second operation satisfies all five properties defined for the first operation except that the identity of the first operation has no inverse. A finite field, also called a Galois field, is a field with $p^n$ elements, where $p$ is a prime and $n$ is a positive integer. GF($p^n$) fields are used to allow operations on $n$-bit words in cryptography.

★ Polynomials with coefficients in GF(2) are used to represent $n$-bit words. Addition and multiplication on $n$-bit words can be defined as addition and multiplication of polynomials.

★ Sometimes it is easier to define the elements of the **GF**($2^n$) field using a generator. If $g$ is a generator of the field, then $f(g) = 0$. Finding inverses and performing operations on the elements of the field become simpler when the elements are represented as the powers of the generator.

## Practice Set

### Review Questions

**4.1** Define an algebraic structure and list three algebraic structures discussed in this chapter.

**4.2** Define a group and distinguish between a group and a commutative group.

**4.3** Define a ring and distinguish between a ring and a commutative ring.

**4.4** Define a field and distinguish between an infinite field and a finite field.

**4.5** Show the number of elements in Galois fields in terms of a prime number.

**4.6** Give one example of a group using a set of residues.

**4.7** Give one example of a ring using a set of residues.

**4.8** Give one example of a field using a set of residues.

**4.9** Show how a polynomial can represent an $n$-bit word.

**4.10** Define an irreducible polynomial.

### Exercises

**4.11** For the group $\mathbf{G} = <\mathbf{Z}_4, +>$:
  a.  Prove that it is an abelian group.
  b.  Show the result of $3 + 2$ and $3 - 2$.

**4.12** For the group $\mathbf{G} = <\mathbf{Z}_6^*, \times>$:
  a.  Prove that it is an abelian group.
  b.  Show the result of $5 \times 1$ and $1 \div 5$.
  c.  Show that why we should not worry about division by zero in this group.

**4.13** Only one operation was defined for the group in Table 4.1. Assume that this operation is addition. Show the table for the subtraction operation (the inverse operation).

**4.14** Prove that the permutation group in Table 4.2 is not commutative.

**4.15** Partially prove that the permutation group in Table 4.2 satisfies associativity by giving a few cases.

**4.16** Create a permutation table for two inputs and two outputs similar to Table 4.2.

**4.17** Alice uses three consecutive permutations [1 3 2], [3 2 1], and [2 1 3]. Show how Bob can use only one permutation to reverse the process. Use Table 4.2.

**4.18** Find all subgroups of the following groups:
  a.  $G = <Z_{16}, +>$
  b.  $G = <Z_{23}, +>$
  c.  $G = <Z_{16}*, \times>$
  d.  $G = <Z_{17}*, \times>$

**4.19** Using Lagrange's theorem, find the orders of all the potential subgroups of the following groups:
  a.  $G = <Z_{18}, +>$
  b.  $G = <Z_{29}, +>$
  c.  $G = <Z_{12}*, \times>$
  d.  $G = <Z_{19}*, \times>$

**4.20** Find the orders of all elements in the following groups:
  a.  $G = <Z_8, +>$
  b.  $G = <Z_7, +>$
  c.  $G = <Z_9*, \times>$
  d.  $G = <Z_7*, \times>$

**4.21** Redo Example 4.25 using the irreducible polynomial $f(x) = x^4 + x^3 + 1$.

**4.22** Redo Example 4.26 using the irreducible polynomial $f(x) = x^4 + x^3 + 1$.

**4.23** Redo Example 4.27 using the irreducible polynomial $f(x) = x^4 + x^3 + 1$.

**4.24** Which of the following is a valid Galois field?
  a.  GF(12)
  b.  GF(13)
  c.  GF(16)
  d.  GF(17)

**4.25** For each of the following *n*-bit words, find the polynomial that represent that word:
  a.  10010
  b.  10
  c.  100001
  d.  00011

**4.26** Find the *n*-bit word that is represented by each of the following polynomials.
  a.  $x^2 + 1$ in GF($2^4$)
  b.  $x^2 + 1$ in GF($2^5$)
  c.  $x + 1$ in GF($2^3$)
  d.  $x^7$ in GF($2^8$)

**4.27** In the field GF(7), find the result of
  a.  $5 + 3$
  b.  $5 - 4$

    c.   $5 \times 3$

    d.   $5 \div 3$

**4.28**  Prove that $(x)$ and $(x + 1)$ are irreducible polynomials of degree 1.

**4.29**  Prove that $(x^2 + x + 1)$ is an irreducible polynomials of degree 2.

**4.30**  Prove that $(x^3 + x^2 + 1)$ is an irreducible polynomials of degree 3.

**4.31**  Multiply the following *n*-bit words using polynomials.

    a.   $(11) \times (10)$

    b.   $(1010) \times (1000)$

    c.   $(11100) \times (10000)$

**4.32**  Find the multiplicative inverse of the following polynomials in $GF(2^2)$. Note that there is only one modulus for this field.

    a.   1

    b.   $x$

    c.   $x + 1$

**4.33**  Use the extended Euclidean algorithm to find the inverse of $(x^4 + x^3 + 1)$ in $GF(2^5)$ using the modulus $(x^5 + x^2 + 1)$.

**4.34**  Create a table for addition and multiplication for $GF(2^4)$, using $(x^4 + x^3 + 1)$ as the modulus.

**4.35**  Using Table 4.10, perform the following operations:

    a.   $(100) \div (010)$

    b.   $(100) \div (000)$

    c.   $(101) \div (011)$

    d.   $(000) \div (111)$

**4.36**  Show how to multiply $(x^3 + x^2 + x + 1)$ by $(x^2 + 1)$ in $GF(2^4)$ using the algorithm in Table 4.7. Use $(x^4 + x^3 + 1)$ as modulus.

**4.37**  Show how to multiply $(10101)$ by $(10000)$ in $GF(2^5)$ using the algorithm in Table 4.8. Use $(x^5 + x^2 + 1)$ as modulus.

# 5

# Introduction to Modern Symmetric-Key Ciphers

## Objectives

This chapter has several objectives:

- ☞ To distinguish between traditional and modern symmetric-key ciphers.
- ☞ To introduce modern block ciphers and discuss their characteristics.
- ☞ To explain why modern block ciphers need to be designed as substitution ciphers.
- ☞ To introduce components of block ciphers such as D-boxes and S-boxes.
- ☞ To discuss product ciphers and distinguish between two classes of product ciphers: Feistel and non-Feistel ciphers.
- ☞ To discuss two kinds of attacks particularly designed for modern block ciphers: differential and linear cryptanalysis.
- ☞ To introduce stream ciphers and to distinguish between synchronous and non-synchronous stream ciphers.
- ☞ To discuss linear and nonlinear feedback shift registers for implementing stream ciphers.
- ☞ To introduce why a single linear feedback shift register is not suitable for cryptography.

The traditional symmetric-key ciphers that we have studied so far are **character-oriented ciphers**. With the advent of the computer, we need **bit-oriented ciphers.** This is because the information to be encrypted is not just text; it can also consist of numbers, graphics, audio, and video data. It is convenient to convert these types of data into a stream of bits, to encrypt the stream, and then to send the encrypted stream. In addition, when text is treated at the bit level, each character is replaced by 8 (or 16) bits, which means that the number of symbols becomes 8 (or 16) times larger. Mixing a larger number of symbols increases security.

This chapter provides the necessary background for the study of the modern block and stream ciphers discussed in the next three chapters. Most of this chapter is devoted to discussion of the general ideas behind modern block ciphers; the last part is dedicated to discussion on the principles of modern stream ciphers with a special focus on linear feedback shift registers.

## 5.1             MODERN BLOCK CIPHERS

A symmetric-key **modern block cipher** encrypts an $n$-bit block of plaintext or decrypts an $n$-bit block of ciphertext. The encryption or decryption algorithm uses a $k$-bit key. The decryption algorithm must be the inverse of the encryption algorithm, and both operations must use the same secret key so that Bob can retrieve the message sent by Alice. Figure 5.1 shows the general idea of encryption and decryption in a modern block cipher.

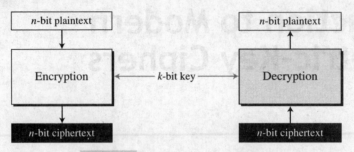

**Fig. 5.1**    *A modern block cipher*

If the message has fewer than $n$ bits, padding must be added to make it an $n$-bit block; if the message has more than $n$ bits, it should be divided into $n$-bit blocks and the appropriate padding must be added to the last block if necessary. The common values for $n$ are 64, 128, 256, or 512 bits.

> **Example 5.1**    How many padding bits must be added to a message of 100 characters if 8-bit ASCII is used for encoding and the block cipher accepts blocks of 64 bits?

**Solution**    Encoding 100 characters using 8-bit ASCII results in an 800-bit message. The plaintext must be divisible by 64. If |M| and |Pad| are the length of the message and the length of the padding,

$$|M| + |Pad| = 0 \bmod 64 \rightarrow |Pad| = -\,800 \bmod 64 \rightarrow 32 \bmod 64$$

This means that 32 bits of padding (for example, 0's) need to be added to the message. The plaintext then consists of 832 bits or thirteen 64-bit blocks. Note that only the last block contains padding. The cipher uses the encryption algorithm thirteen times to create thirteen ciphertext blocks.

### 5.1.1   Substitution or Transposition

A modern block cipher can be designed to act as a substitution cipher or a transposition cipher. This is the same idea as is used in traditional ciphers, except that the symbols to be substituted or transposed are bits instead of characters.

If the cipher is designed as a substitution cipher, a 1-bit or a 0-bit in the plaintext can be replaced by either a 0 or a 1. This means that the plaintext and the ciphertext can have a different number of 1's. A 64-bit plaintext block of 12 0's and 52 1's can be encrypted to a ciphertext of 34 0's and 30 1's. If the cipher is designed as a transposition cipher, the bits are only reordered (transposed); there is the same number of 1's in the plaintext and in the ciphertext. In either case, the number of $n$-bit possible plaintexts or ciphertexts is $2^n$, because each of the $n$ bits in the block can have one of the two values, 0 or 1.

Modern block ciphers are designed as substitution ciphers because the inherent characteristics of transposition (preserving the number of 1's or 0's) makes the cipher vulnerable to exhaustive-search attacks, as the next example shows.

**Example 5.2**  Suppose that we have a block cipher where $n = 64$. If there are 10 1's in the ciphertext, how many trial-and-error tests does Eve need to do to recover the plaintext from the intercepted ciphertext in each of the following cases?

  a.  The cipher is designed as a substitution cipher.
  b.  The cipher is designed as a transposition cipher.

**Solution**

  a.  In the first case (substitution), Eve has no idea how many 1's are in the plaintext. Eve needs to try all possible $2^{64}$ 64-bit blocks to find one that makes sense. If Eve could try 1 billion blocks per second, it would still take hundreds of years, on average, before she could be successful.

  b.  In the second case (transposition), Eve knows that there are exactly 10 1's in the plaintext, because transposition does not change the number of 1's (or 0's) in the ciphertext. Eve can launch an exhaustive-search attack using only those 64-bit blocks that have exactly 10 1's. There are only $(64!) / [(10!)(54!)] = 151{,}473{,}214{,}816$ out of $2^{64}$ 64-bit words that have exactly 10 1's. Eve can test all of them in less than 3 minutes if she can do 1 billion tests per second.

**To be resistant to exhaustive-search attack, a modern block cipher needs to be designed as a substitution cipher.**

## 5.1.2  Block Ciphers as Permutation Groups

As we will see in later chapters, we need to know whether a modern block cipher is a group (see Chapter 4). To answer this question, first assume that the key is long enough to choose every possible mapping from the input to the output. Call this a full-size key cipher. In practice, however, the key is smaller; only some mappings from the input to the output are possible. Although a block cipher needs to have a key that is a secret between the sender and the receiver, there are also keyless components that are used inside a cipher.

### Full-Size Key Ciphers

Although full-size key ciphers are not used in practice, we first discuss this category to make the discussion of partial-size key ciphers understandable.

### Full-Size Key Transposition Block Ciphers

A full-size key transposition cipher only transposes bits without changing their values, so it can be modeled as an *n*-object permutation with a set of *n*! permutation tables in which the key defines which table is used by Alice and Bob. We need to have *n*! possible keys, so the key should have $\lceil \log_2 n! \rceil$ bits.

**Example 5.3**  Show the model and the set of permutation tables for a 3-bit block transposition cipher where the block size is 3 bits.

**Solution**  The set of permutation tables has 3! = 6 elements, as shown in Fig. 5.2. The key should be $\lceil \log_2 6 \rceil = 3$ bits long. Note that, although a 3-bit key can select $2^3 = 8$ different mappings, we use only 6 of them.

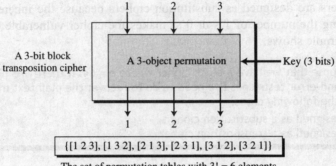

The set of permutation tables with 3! = 6 elements

**Fig. 5.2** *A transposition block cipher modeled as a permutation*

*Full-Size Key Substitution Block Ciphers* A full-size key substitution cipher does not transpose bits; it substitutes bits. At first glance, it appears that a full-size key substitution cipher cannot be modeled as a permutation. However, we can model the substitution cipher as a permutation if we can decode the input and encode the output. **Decoding** means transforming an $n$-bit integer into a $2^n$-bit string with only a single 1 and $2^n - 1$ 0's. The position of the single 1 is the value of the integer, in which the positions range from 0 to $2^n - 1$. **Encoding** is the reverse process. Because the new input and output have always a single 1, the cipher can be modeled as a permutation of $2^n!$ objects.

**Example 5.4** Show the model and the set of permutation tables for a 3-bit block substitution cipher.

*Solution* The three-input plaintext can be an integer between 0 to 7. This can be decoded as an 8-bit string with a single 1. For example, 000 can be decoded as 00000001; 101 can be decoded as 00100000. Figure 5.3 shows the model and the set of permutation tables. Note that the number of elements in the set is much bigger than the number of elements in the transposition cipher (8! = 40,320). The key is also much longer, $\lceil \log_2 40,320 \rceil = 16$ bits. Although a 16-bit key can define 65,536 different mappings, only 40,320 are used.

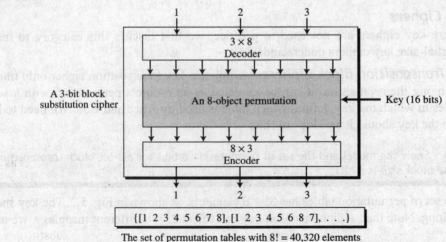

The set of permutation tables with 8! = 40,320 elements

**Fig. 5.3** *A substitution block cipher model as a permutation*

---

**A full-size key *n*-bit transposition cipher or a substitution block cipher can be modeled as a permutation, but their key sizes are different:**
**For a transposition cipher, the key is $\lceil \log_2 n! \rceil$ bits long.**
**For a substitution cipher, the key is $\lceil \log_2(2^n)! \rceil$ bits long.**

---

***Permutation Group***   The fact that a full-size key transposition or substitution cipher is a permutation shows that, if encryption (or decryption) uses more than one stage of any of these ciphers, the result is equivalent to a permutation group under the composition operation. As discussed in Chapter 4, two or more cascaded permutations can be always replaced with a single permutation. This means that it is useless to have more than one stage of full-size key ciphers, because the effect is the same as having a single stage.

### Partial-Size Key Ciphers

Actual ciphers cannot use full-size keys because the size of the key becomes so large, especially for a substitution block cipher. For example, a common substitution cipher is DES (see Chapter 6), which uses a 64-bit block cipher. If the designers of DES had used a full-size key, the key would have been $\log_2(2^{64}!) \approx 2^{70}$ bits. The key size for DES is only 56 bits, which is a very small fraction of the full-size key. This means that DES uses only $2^{56}$ mappings out of approximately $2^{2^{70}}$ possible mappings.

***Permutation Group***   Now the question is whether a multi-stage partial-key transposition or substitution is a permutation group under the composition operation. This question is extremely important because it tells us whether a multi-stage version of the same cipher can be made to achieve more security (see the discussion of multiple DES in Chapter 6). A partial-key cipher is a group if it is a subgroup of the corresponding full-size key cipher. In other words, if the full-size key cipher makes a group $\mathbf{G} = \langle \mathbf{M}, \circ \rangle$, where $\mathbf{M}$ is a set of mappings and the operation is the composition ($\circ$), then the partial-size key cipher must make a subgroup $\mathbf{H} = \langle \mathbf{N}, \circ \rangle$, where $\mathbf{N}$ is a subset of $\mathbf{M}$ and the operation is the same.

For example, it has been proved that the multi-stage DES with a 56-bit key is not a group because no subgroup with $2^{56}$ mappings can be created from the corresponding group with $2^{64}!$ mappings.

---

**A partial-key cipher is a group under the composition operation if it is a subgroup of the corresponding full-size key cipher.**

---

### Keyless Ciphers

Although a keyless cipher is practically useless by itself, keyless ciphers are used as components of keyed ciphers.

***Keyless Transposition Ciphers***   A keyless (or fixed-key) transposition cipher (or unit) can be thought of as a prewired transposition cipher when implemented in hardware. The fixed key (single permutation rule) can be represented as a table when the unit is implemented in software. The next section of this chapter discusses keyless transposition ciphers, called D-boxes, which are used as building blocks of modern block ciphers.

***Keyless Substitution Ciphers***   A keyless (or fixed-key) substitution cipher (or unit) can be thought of as a predefined mapping from the input to the output. The mapping can be defined as a table, a mathematical function, and so on. The next section of this chapter discusses keyless substitution ciphers, called S-boxes, which are used as building blocks of modern block ciphers.

### 5.1.3 Components of a Modern Block Cipher

Modern block ciphers normally are keyed substitution ciphers in which the key allows only partial mappings from the possible inputs to the possible outputs. However, modern block ciphers normally are not designed as a single unit. To provide the required properties of a modern block cipher, such as diffusion and confusion (discussed shortly), a modern block cipher is made of a combination of transposition units for diffusion (called D-boxes), substitution units (called S-boxes), and some other units (discussed shortly).

#### D-boxes

A **D-box** (diffusion box) parallels the traditional transposition cipher for characters. It transposes bits. We can find three types of D-boxes in modern block ciphers: straight D-boxes, expansion D-boxes, and compression D-boxes, as shown in Fig. 5.4. It helps in the spreading or diffusion of the input disturbances.

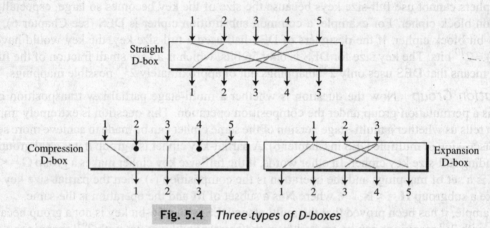

**Fig. 5.4** *Three types of D-boxes*

Figure 5.4 shows a $5 \times 5$ straight D-box, a $5 \times 3$ compression D-box, and a $3 \times 5$ expansion D-box. We will discuss each of them in more detail.

#### Straight D-boxes
A **straight D-box** with $n$ inputs and $n$ outputs is a permutation. There are $n!$ possible mappings.

---

**Example 5.5**    Figure 5.5 shows all 6 possible mappings of a $3 \times 3$ D-box.

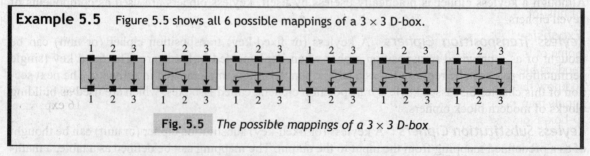

**Fig. 5.5** *The possible mappings of a $3 \times 3$ D-box*

---

Although a D-box can use a key to define one of the $n!$ mappings, D-boxes are normally keyless, which means that the mapping is predetermined. If the D-box is implemented in hardware, it is prewired; if it is implemented in software, a permutation table shows the rule of mapping. In the second case, the entries in the table are the inputs and the positions of the entries are the outputs. Table 5.1 shows an example of a straight permutation table when *n* is 64.

**Table 5.1**  *Example of a permutation table for a straight D-box*

| | | | | | | | | | | | | | | | |
|--|--|--|--|--|--|--|--|--|--|--|--|--|--|--|--|
| 58 | 50 | 42 | 34 | 26 | 18 | 10 | 02 | 60 | 52 | 44 | 36 | 28 | 20 | 12 | 04 |
| 62 | 54 | 46 | 38 | 30 | 22 | 14 | 06 | 64 | 56 | 48 | 40 | 32 | 24 | 16 | 08 |
| 57 | 49 | 41 | 33 | 25 | 17 | 09 | 01 | 59 | 51 | 43 | 35 | 27 | 19 | 11 | 03 |
| 61 | 53 | 45 | 37 | 29 | 21 | 13 | 05 | 63 | 55 | 47 | 39 | 31 | 23 | 15 | 07 |

Table 5.1 has 64 entries, corresponding to the 64 inputs. The position (index) of the entry corresponds to the output. Because the first entry contains the number 58, we know that the first output comes from the 58th input. Because the last entry is 7, we know that the 64th output comes from the 7th input, and so on.

**Example 5.6**  Design an 8 × 8 permutation table for a straight D-box that moves the two middle bits (bits 4 and 5) in the input word to the two ends (bits 1 and 8) in the output words. Relative positions of other bits should not be changed.

*Solution*  We need a straight D-box with the table [4 1 2 3 6 7 8 5]. The relative positions of input bits 1, 2, 3, 6, 7, and 8 have not been changed, but the first output takes the fourth input and the eighth output takes the fifth input.

*Compression D-boxes*  A **compression D-box** is a D-box with *n* inputs and *m* outputs where *m* < *n*. Some of the inputs are blocked and do not reach the output (see Fig. 5.4 ). The compression D-boxes used in modern block ciphers normally are keyless with a table showing the rule for transposing bits. We need to know that a table for a compression D-box has *m* entries, but the content of each entry is from 1 to *n* with some missing values (those inputs that are blocked). Table 5.2 shows an example of a table for a 32 × 24 compression D-box. Note that inputs 7, 8, 9, 15, 16, 23, 24, and 25 are blocked.

**Table 5.2**  *Example of a 32 × 24 D-box*

| | | | | | | | | | | | |
|--|--|--|--|--|--|--|--|--|--|--|--|
| 01 | 02 | 03 | 21 | 22 | 26 | 27 | 28 | 29 | 13 | 14 | 17 |
| 18 | 19 | 20 | 04 | 05 | 06 | 10 | 11 | 12 | 30 | 31 | 32 |

Compression D-boxes are used when we need to permute bits and the same time decrease the number of bits for the next stage.

*Expansion D-boxes*  An **expansion D-box** is a D-box with *n* inputs and *m* outputs where *m* > *n*. Some of the inputs are connected to more than one input (see Fig. 5.4). The expansion D-boxes used in modern block ciphers normally are keyless, where a table shows the rule for transposing bits. We need to know that a table for an expansion D-box has *m* entries, but *m* − *n* of the entries are repeated (those inputs mapped to more than one output). Table 5.3 shows an example of a table for a 12 × 16 expansion D-box. Note that each of the inputs 1, 3, 9, and 12 is mapped to two outputs.

**Table 5.3**  *Example of a 12 × 16 D-box*

| | | | | | | | | | | | | | | | |
|--|--|--|--|--|--|--|--|--|--|--|--|--|--|--|--|
| 01 | 09 | 10 | 11 | 12 | 01 | 02 | 03 | 03 | 04 | 05 | 06 | 07 | 08 | 09 | 12 |

Expansion D-boxes are used when we need to transpose bits and the same time increase the number of bits for the next stage.

*Invertibility*   A straight D-box is invertible. This means that we can use a straight D-box in the encryption cipher and its inverse in the decryption cipher. The mapping defined by a straight D-box is a permutation, and thus may be referred to as P-box. The permutation tables, however, need to be the inverses of each other. In Chapter 3, we saw how we can make the inverse of a permutation table.

**Example 5.7**   Figure 5.6 shows how to invert a permutation table represented as a one-dimensional table.

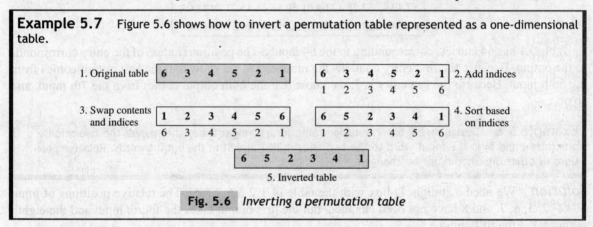

**Fig. 5.6**   *Inverting a permutation table*

Compression and expansion D-boxes have no inverses. In a compression D-box, an input can be dropped during encryption; the decryption algorithm does not have a clue how to replace the dropped bit (a choice between a 0-bit or a 1-bit). In an expansion D-box, an input may be mapped to more than one output during encryption; the decryption algorithm does not have a clue which of the several inputs are mapped to an output. Figure 5.7 demonstrates both cases.

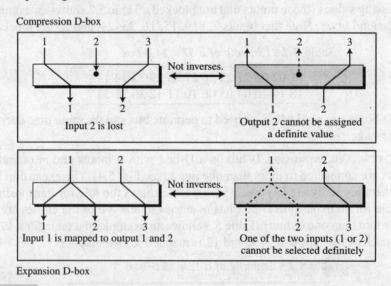

**Fig. 5.7**   *Compression and expansion D-boxes as non-invertible components*

Figure 5.7 also shows that a compression D-box is not the inverse of an expansion D-box or vice versa. This means that if we use a compression D-box in the encryption cipher, we cannot use an expansion D-box in the decryption cipher; or vice versa. However, as will be shown later in this chapter, there are ciphers that use compression or expansion D-boxes in the encryption cipher; the effects of these are canceled in some other ways in the decryption cipher.

---

**A straight D-box is invertible, but compression and expansion D-boxes are not.**

---

### 5.1.4 S-Boxes

An **S-box** (substitution box) can be thought of as a miniature substitution cipher. However, an S-box can have a different number of inputs and outputs. In other words, the input to an S-box could be an $n$-bit word, but the output can be an $m$-bit word, where $m$ and $n$ are not necessarily the same. Although an S-box can be keyed or keyless, modern block ciphers normally use keyless S-boxes, where the mapping from the inputs to the outputs is predetermined.

---

**An S-box is an $m \times n$ substitution unit, where $m$ and $n$ are not necessarily the same.**

---

### *Linear Versus Nonlinear S-Boxes*

In an S-box with $n$ inputs and $m$ outputs, we call the inputs $x_1, ..., x_n$ and the outputs $y_1, ..., y_m$. The relationship between the inputs and the outputs can be represented as a set of equations

$$y_1 = f_1(x_1, x_2, ..., x_n)$$
$$y_2 = f_2(x_1, x_2, ..., x_n)$$
$$...$$
$$y_m = f_m(x_1, x_2, ..., x_n)$$

In a **linear S-box,** the above relations can be expressed as

$$y_1 = a_{1,1}x_1 \oplus a_{1,2}x_1 \oplus ... \oplus a_{1,n}x_n$$
$$y_2 = a_{2,1}x_1 \oplus a_{2,2}x_1 \oplus ... \oplus a_{2,n}x_n$$
$$...$$
$$y_m = a_{m,1}x_1 \oplus a_{m,2}x_1 \oplus ... \oplus a_{m,n}x_n$$

In a **nonlinear S-box** we cannot have the above relations for every output. Such an S-box will have 'and' terms, like $x_1x_2$, $x_3x_7$ etc. in their expressions.

---

**Example 5.8**   In an S-box with three inputs and two outputs, we have

$$y_1 = x_1 \oplus x_2 \oplus x_3 \quad y_2 = x_1$$

The S-box is linear because $a_{1,1} = a_{1,2} = a_{1,3} = a_{2,1} = 1$ and $a_{2,2} = a_{2,3} = 0$. The relationship can be represented by matrices, as shown below:

$$\begin{bmatrix} y_1 \\ y_2 \end{bmatrix} = \begin{bmatrix} 1 & 1 & 1 \\ 1 & 0 & 0 \end{bmatrix} \times \begin{bmatrix} x_1 \\ x_2 \\ x_3 \end{bmatrix}$$

---

**Example 5.9** In an S-box with three inputs and two outputs, we have

$$y_1 = x_1 x_2 \qquad y_2 = x_1 + x_2 x_3$$

where multiplication and addition is in **GF**(2). The S-box is nonlinear because there is no linear relationship between the inputs and the outputs. Note the 'and' term(s) $x_1 x_2$ and $x_2 x_3$.

**Example 5.10** The following table defines the input/output relationship for an S-box of size $3 \times 2$. The leftmost bit of the input defines the row; the two rightmost bits of the input define the column. The two output bits are values on the cross section of the selected row and column.

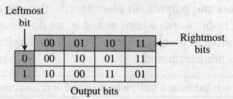

Based on the table, an input of 010 yields the output 01. An input of 101 yields the output of 00.

*Invertibility* S-boxes are substitution ciphers in which the relationship between input and output is defined by a table or mathematical relation. An S-box may or may not be invertible. In an invertible S-box, the number of input bits should be the same as the number of output bits.

**Example 5.11** Figure 5.8 shows an example of an invertible S-box. One of tables is used in the encryption algorithm; the other table is used in the decryption algorithm. In each table, the leftmost bit of the input defines the row; the next two bits define the column. The output is the value where the input row and column meet.

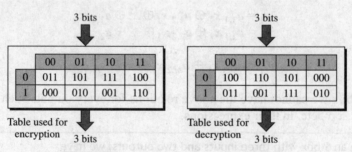

**Fig. 5.8** *S-box tables for Example 5.11*

For example, if the input to the left box is 001, the output is 101. The input 101 in the right table creates the output 001, which shows that the two tables are inverses of each other.

### Exclusive-Or

An important component in most block ciphers is the *exclusive-or* operation. As we discussed in Chapter 4, addition and subtraction operations in the **GF**($2^n$) field are performed by a single operation called the *exclusive-or* (XOR).

***Properties*** The five properties of the exclusive-or operation in the $\mathbf{GF}(2^n)$ field makes this operation a very interesting component for use in a block cipher.

1. *Closure:* This property guarantees that the result of exclusive-oring two $n$-bit words is another $n$-bit word.
2. *Associativity:* This property allows us to use more than one exclusive-or operator in any order.

$$x \oplus (y \oplus z) \;\leftrightarrow\; (x \oplus y) \oplus z$$

3. *Commutativity:* This property allows us to swap the inputs without affecting the output.

$$x \oplus y \;\leftrightarrow\; y \oplus x$$

4. *Existence of identity:* The identity element for the exclusive-or operation is an $n$-bit word that consists of all 0's, or $(00\ldots0)$. This implies that exclusive-oring of a word with the identity element does not change that word.

$$x \oplus (00\ldots0) = x$$

We use this property in the Feistel cipher discussed later in this chapter.

5. *Existence of inverse:* In the $\mathbf{GF}(2^n)$ field, each word is the additive inverse of itself. This implies that exclusive-oring of a word with itself yields the identity element.

$$x \oplus x = (00\ldots0)$$

We also use this property in the Feistel cipher discussed later in this chapter.

***Complement*** The complement operation is a unary operation (one input and one output) that flips each bit in a word. A 0-bit is changed to a 1-bit; a 1-bit is changed to a 0-bit. We are interested in the complement operation in relation to the exclusive-or operation. If $\bar{x}$ is the complement of $x$, then the following two relations hold:

$$x \oplus \bar{x} = (11\ldots1) \qquad \text{and} \qquad x \oplus (11\ldots1) = \bar{x}$$

We also use these properties later in this chapter when we discuss the security of some ciphers.

***Inverse*** The inverse of a component in a cipher makes sense if the component represents a unary operation (one input and one output). For example, a keyless D-box or a keyless S-box can be made invertible because they have one input and one output. An exclusive operation is a binary operation. The inverse of an exclusive-or operation can make sense only if one of the inputs is fixed (is the same in encryption and decryption). For example, if one of the inputs is the key, which normally is the same in encryption and decryption, then an exclusive-or operation is self-invertible, as shown in Fig. 5.9.

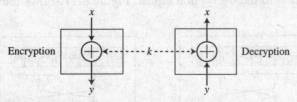

**Fig. 5.9** *Invertibility of the exclusive-or operation*

In Fig. 5.9, the additive inverse property implies that

$$y = x \oplus k \qquad \rightarrow \qquad x = k \oplus y$$

We will use this property when we discuss the structure of block ciphers later in this chapter.

## Circular Shift

Another component found in some modern block ciphers is the **circular shift operation.** Shifting can be to the left or to the right. The circular left-shift operation shifts each bit in an $n$-bit word $k$ positions to the left; the leftmost $k$ bits are removed from the left and become the rightmost bits. The circular right-shift operation shifts each bit in an $n$-bit word $k$ positions to the right; the rightmost $k$ bits are removed from the right and become the leftmost bits. Figure 5.10 shows both left and right operations in the case where $n = 8$ and $k = 3$.

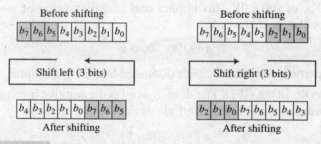

**Fig. 5.10** *Circular shifting an 8-bit word to the left or right*

The circular shift operation mixes the bits in a word and helps hide the patterns in the original word. Although the number of positions to be shifted can be used as a key, the circular shift operation normally is keyless; the value of $k$ is fixed and predetermined.

*Invertibility*  A circular left-shift operation is the inverse of the circular right-shift operation. If one is used in the encryption cipher, the other can be used in the decryption cipher.

*Property*  The circular shift operation has two properties that we need to be aware of. First, the shifting is modulo $n$. In other words, if $k = 0$ or $k = n$, there is no shifting. If $k$ is larger than $n$, then the input is shifted $k \bmod n$ bits. Second, the circular shift operation under the composition operation is a group. This means that shifting a word more than once is the same as shifting it only once.

*Swap*  The **swap operation** is a special case of the circular shift operation where $k = n/2$. This means this operation is valid only if $n$ is an even number. Because left-shifting $n/2$ bits is the same as right-shifting $n/2$, this component is self-invertible. A swap operation in the encryption cipher can be totally canceled by a swap operation in the decryption cipher. Figure 5.11 shows the swapping operation for an 8-bit word.

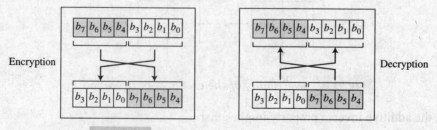

**Fig. 5.11** *Swap operation on an 8-bit word*

***Split and Combine*** Two other operations found in some block ciphers are split and combine. The **split operation** normally splits an *n*-bit word in the middle, creating two equal-length words. The **combine operation** normally concatenates two equal-length words to create an *n*-bit word. These two operations are inverses of each other and can be used as a pair to cancel each other out. If one is used in the encryption cipher, the other is used in the decryption cipher. Figure 5.12 shows the two operations in the case where $n = 8$.

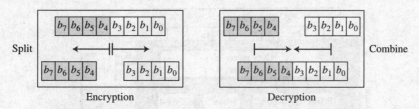

**Fig. 5.12** *Split and combine operations on an 8-bit word*

## 5.1.5 Product Ciphers

Shannon introduced the concept of a **product cipher.** A product cipher is a complex cipher combining substitution, permutation, and other components discussed in previous sections.

***Diffusion and Confusion*** Shannon's idea in introducing the product cipher was to enable the block ciphers to have two important properties: diffusion and confusion. The idea of **diffusion** is to hide the relationship between the ciphertext and the plaintext. This will frustrate the adversary who uses ciphertext statistics to find the plaintext. Diffusion implies that each symbol (character or bit) in the ciphertext is dependent on some or all symbols in the plaintext. In other words, if a single symbol in the plaintext is changed, several or all symbols in the ciphertext will also be changed.

---

**Diffusion hides the relationship between the ciphertext and the plaintext.**

---

The idea of **confusion** is to hide the relationship between the ciphertext and the key. This will frustrate the adversary who tries to use the ciphertext to find the key. In other words, if a single bit in the key is changed, most or all bits in the ciphertext will also be changed.

---

**Confusion hides the relationship between the ciphertext and the key.**

---

***Rounds*** Diffusion and confusion can be achieved using iterated product ciphers where each iteration is a combination of S-boxes, D-boxes, and other components. Each iteration is referred to as a **round.** The block cipher uses a **key schedule** or **key generator** that creates different keys for each round from the cipher key. In an *N*-round cipher, the plaintext is encrypted *N* times to create the ciphertext; the ciphertext is decrypted *N* times to create the plaintext. We refer to the text created at the intermediate levels (between two rounds) as the middle text. Figure 5.13 shows a simple product cipher with two rounds. In practice, product ciphers have more than two rounds.

In Fig. 5.13, three transformations happen at each round:

a. The 8-bit text is mixed with the key to whiten the text (hide the bits using the key). This is normally done by exclusive-oring the 8-bit word with the 8-bit key.

b.   The outputs of the whitener are organized into four 2-bit groups and are fed into four S-boxes. The values of bits are changed based on the structure of the S-boxes in this transformation.

c.   The outputs of S-boxes are passed through a D-box to transpose the bits so that in the next round each box receives different inputs. Since this is a straight D-box and has to be invertible (for the purpose of decryption), so it is referred to as a permutation (P-box) and is denoted as P in Fig. 5.14.

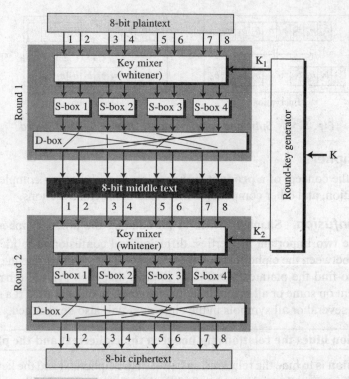

**Fig. 5.13**   *A product cipher made of two rounds*

*Diffusion*   The primitive design of Fig. 5.13 shows how a product with the combination of S-boxes and D-boxes can guarantee diffusion. Figure 5.14 shows how changing a single bit in the plaintext affects many bits in the ciphertext.

a.   In the first round, bit 8, after being exclusive-ored with the corresponding bit of $K_1$, affects two bits (bits 7 and 8) through S-box 4. Bit 7 is permuted and becomes bit 2; bit 8 is permuted and becomes bit 4. After the first round, bit 8 has affected bits 2 and 4. In the second round, bit 2, after being exclusive-ored with the corresponding bit of $K_2$, affects two bits (bits 1 and 2) through S-box 1. Bit 1 is permuted and becomes bit 6; bit 2 is permuted and becomes bit 1. Bit 4, after being exclusive-ored with the corresponding bit in $K_2$, affects bits 3 and 4. Bit 3 remains the same; bit 4 is permuted and becomes bit 7. After the second round, bit 8 has affected bits 1, 3, 6, and 7.

b.   Going through these steps in the other direction (from ciphertext to the plaintext) shows that each bit in the ciphertext is affected by several bits in the plaintext.

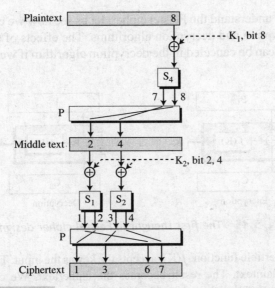

**Fig. 5.14** *Diffusion and confusion in a block cipher*

***Confusion*** Figure 5.14 also shows us how the confusion property can be achieved through the use of a product cipher. The four bits of ciphertext, bits 1, 3, 6, and 7, are affected by three bits in the key (bit 8 in $K_1$ and bits 2 and 4 in $K_2$). Going through the steps in the other direction shows that each bit in each round key affects several bits in the ciphertext. The relationship between ciphertext bits and key bits is obscured.

***Practical Ciphers*** To improve diffusion and confusion, practical ciphers use larger data blocks, more S-boxes, and more rounds. With some thought, it can be seen that increasing the number of rounds using more S-boxes may create a better cipher in which the ciphertext looks more and more like a random *n*-bit word. In this way, the relationship between ciphertext and plaintext is totally hidden (diffusion). Increasing the number of rounds increases the number of round keys, which better hides the relationship between the ciphertext and the key.

### 5.1.6 Two Classes of Product Ciphers

Modern block ciphers are all product ciphers, but they are divided into two classes. The ciphers in the first class use both invertible and noninvertible components. The ciphers in this class are normally referred to as Feistel ciphers. The block cipher DES discussed in Chapter 6 is a good example of a Feistel cipher. The ciphers in the second class use only invertible components. We refer to ciphers in this class as non-Feistel ciphers (for the lack of another name). The block cipher AES discussed in Chapter 7 is a good example of a non-Feistel cipher.

### *Feistel Ciphers*

Feistel designed a very intelligent and interesting cipher that has been used for decades. A **Feistel cipher** can have three types of components: self-invertible, invertible, and noninvertible. A Feistel cipher combines all noninvertible elements in a unit and uses the same unit in the encryption and decryption algorithms. The question is how the encryption and decryption algorithms are inverses of each other if each has a non-invertible unit. Feistel showed that they can be canceled out.

*First Thought* To better understand the Feistel cipher, let us see how we can use the same noninvertible component in the encryption and decryption algorithms. The effects of a noninvertible component in the encryption algorithm can be canceled in the decryption algorithm if we use an exclusive-or operation, as shown in Fig. 5.15.

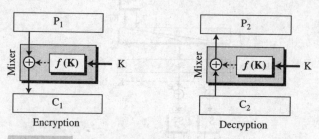

**Fig. 5.15** *The first thought in Feistel cipher design*

In the encryption, a noninvertible function, $f(K)$, accepts the key as the input. The output of this component is exclusive-ored with the plaintext. The result becomes the ciphertext. We call the combination of the function and the exclusive-or operation the **mixer** (for lack of another name). The mixer plays an important role in the later development of the Feistel cipher.

Because the key is the same in encryption and decryption, we can prove that the two algorithms are inverses of each other. In other words, if $C_2 = C_1$ (no change in the ciphertext during transmission), then $P_2 = P_1$.

**Encryption:** $C_1 = P_1 \oplus f(K)$

**Decryption:** $P_2 = C_2 \oplus f(K) = C_1 \oplus f(K) = P_1 \oplus f(K) \oplus f(K) = P_1 \oplus (00...0) = P_1$

Note that two properties of exclusive-or operation have been used (existence of inverse and existence of identity).

The above argument proves that, although the mixer has a noninvertible element, the mixer itself is self-invertible.

**The mixer in the Feistel design is self-invertible.**

**Example 5.12** This is a trivial example. The plaintext and ciphertext are each 4 bits long and the key is 3 bits long. Assume that the function takes the first and third bits of the key, interprets these two bits as a decimal number, squares the number, and interprets the result as a 4-bit binary pattern. Show the results of encryption and decryption if the original plaintext is 0111 and the key is 101.

*Solution* The function extracts the first and second bits to get 11 in binary or 3 in decimal. The result of squaring is 9, which is 1001 in binary.

**Encryption:** $C = P \oplus f(K) = 0111 \oplus 1001 = 1110$

**Decryption:** $P = C \oplus f(K) = 1110 \oplus 1001 = 0111$    Same as the original P

The function $f(101) = 1001$ is noninvertible, but the exclusive-or operation allows us to use the function in both encryption and decryption algorithms. In other words, the function is noninvertible, but the mixer is self-invertible.

*Improvement*   Let us improve on our first thought to get closer to the Feistel cipher. We know that we need to use the same input to the noninvertible element (the function), but we don't want to use only the key. We want the input to the function to also be part of the plaintext in the encryption and part of the ciphertext in the decryption. The key can be used as the second input to the function. In this way, our function can be a complex element with some keyless elements and some keyed elements. To achieve this goal, divide the plaintext and the ciphertext into two equal-length blocks, left and right. We call the left block L and the right block R. Let the right block be the input to the function, and let the left block be exclusive-ored with the function output. We need to remember one important point: the inputs to the function must be exactly the same in encryption and decryption. This means that the right section of plaintext in the encryption and the right section of the ciphertext in the decryption must be the same. In other words, the right section must go into and come out of the encryption and decryption processes unchanged. Figure 5.16 shows the idea.

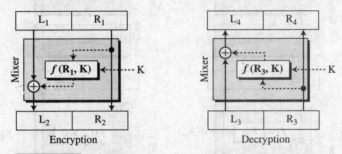

**Fig. 5.16**   *Improvement of the previous Feistel design*

The encryption and decryption algorithms are still inverses of each other. Assume that $L_3 = L_2$ and $R_3 = R_2$ (no change in the ciphertext during transmission).

$$R_4 = R_3 = R_2 = R_1$$
$$L_4 = L_3 \oplus f(R_3, K) = L_2 \oplus f(R_2, K) = L_1 \oplus f(R_1, K) \oplus f(R_1, K) = L_1$$

The plaintext used in the encryption algorithm is correctly regenerated by the decryption algorithm.

*Final Design*   The preceding improvement has one flaw. The right half of the plaintext never changes. Eve can immediately find the right half of the plaintext by intercepting the ciphertext and extracting the right half of it. The design needs more improvement. First, increase the number of rounds. Second, add a new element to each round: a **swapper.** The effect of the swapper in the encryption round is canceled by the effect of the swapper in the decryption round. However, it allows us to swap the left and right halves in each round. Figure 5.17 shows the new design with two rounds.

Note that there are two round keys, $K_1$ and $K_2$. The keys are used in reverse order in the encryption and decryption.

Because the two mixers are inverses of each other, and the swappers are inverses of each other, it should be clear that the encryption and decryption ciphers are inverses of each other. However, let us see if we can prove this fact using the relationship between the left and right sections in each cipher. In other words, let us see if $L_6 = L_1$ and $R_6 = R_1$, assuming that $L_4 = L_3$ and $R_4 = R_3$ (no change in the ciphertext during transmission). We first prove the equality for the middle text.

$$L_5 = R_4 \oplus f(L_4, K_2) = R_3 \oplus f(R_2, K_2) = L_2 \oplus f(R_2, K_2) \oplus f(R_2, K_2) = L_2$$

$$R_5 = L_4 = L_3 = R_2$$

Then it is easy to prove that the equality holds for two plaintext blocks.

$$L_6 = R_5 \oplus f(L_5, K_1) = R_2 \oplus f(L_2, K_1) = L_1 \oplus f(R_1, K_1) \oplus f(R_1, K_1) = L_1$$

$$R_6 = L_5 = L_2 = R_1$$

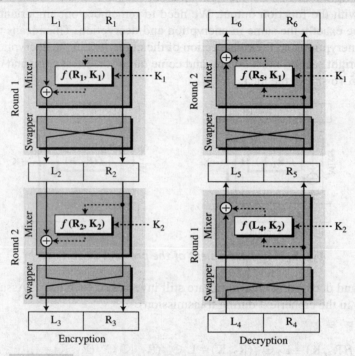

**Fig. 5.17**  *Final design of a Feistel cipher with two rounds*

## Non-Feistel Ciphers

A **non-Feistel cipher** uses only invertible components. A component in the plaintext has the corresponding component in the cipher. For example, S-boxes need to have an equal number of inputs and outputs to be compatible. No compression or expansion D-boxes are allowed, because they are not invertible. In a non-Feistel cipher, there is no need to divide the plaintext into two halves as we saw in the Feistel ciphers. Figure 5.13 can be thought of as a non-Feistel cipher because the only components in each round are the exclusive-or operation (self-invertible), $2 \times 2$ S-boxes that can be designed to be invertible, and a straight D-box that is invertible using the appropriate permutation table. Because each component is invertible, it can be shown that each round is invertible. We only need to use the round keys in the reverse order. The encryption uses round keys $K_1$ and $K_2$. The decryption algorithm needs to use round keys $K_2$ and $K_1$.

## 5.1.7  Attacks on Block Ciphers

Attacks on traditional ciphers can also be used on modern block ciphers, but today's block ciphers resist most of the attacks discussed in Chapter 3. For example, brute-force attack on the key is usually infeasible because the keys normally are very large. However, new attacks on block ciphers have been devised that are based on the structure of the modern block ciphers. These attacks use differential and linear cryptanalysis techniques.

### Differential Cryptanalysis

Eli Biham and Adi Shamir introduced the idea of **differential cryptanalysis.** This is a *chosen-plaintext* attack; Eve can somehow access Alice's computer, submitting chosen plaintext and obtaining the corresponding ciphertext. The goal is to find Alice's cipher key.

**Algorithm Analysis**   Before Eve uses the chosen-plaintext attack, she needs to analyze the encryption algorithm in order to collect some information about plaintext-ciphertext relationships. Obviously, Eve does not know the cipher key. However, some ciphers have weaknesses in their structures that can allow Eve to find a relationship between the plaintext differences and ciphertext differences leaking information about the key.

---

**Example 5.13**   (The key has no effect on differential values). Assume that the cipher performs key mixing by the exclusive-or operation, as shown in Fig. 5.18. Without knowing the value of the key, Eve can easily find the relationship between plaintext differences (differential) and ciphertext differences (differential). By plaintext difference we mean $P_1 \oplus P_2$ and by ciphertext difference, we mean $C_1 \oplus C_2$. The following proves that $C_1 \oplus C_2 = P_1 \oplus P_2$:

$$C_1 = P_1 \oplus K \quad C_2 = P_2 \oplus K \rightarrow C_1 \oplus C_2 = P_1 \oplus K \oplus P_2 \oplus K = P_1 \oplus P_2$$

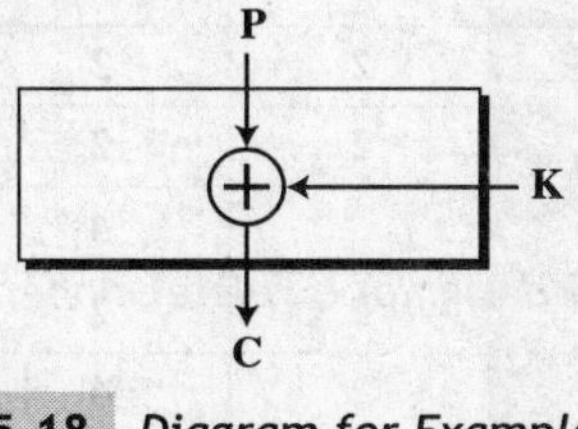

**Fig. 5.18**   *Diagram for Example 5.13*

---

Now consider the S-box which is present in the cipher. Figure 5.19 shows a cipher with a single XOR of key and one S-box. It may be noted that we are not attacking the cipher. As the cipher has no security in a known plaintext or chosen plaintext setting. This is easy to see as if we know the cipher, C, for a plaintext, P, we can easily obtain X (see Fig. 5.19) from C and use it to obtain possible K values from P. Thus, only linear transformations like XOR-ing or a single round of S-Box is naively insecure against a known or chosen plaintext attack. However, we study this example to show that while non-linearty of the S-boxes are much needed for the security of ciphers (refer to the discussion on linear cryptanalysis), they introduce certain "properties" which help to develop further attacks. We observe this property in the next example.

**Example 5.14**   We add one S-box to Example 5.13, as shown in Fig. 5.19.

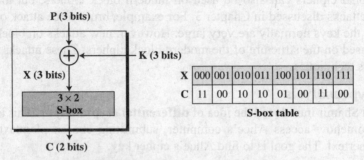

| X | 000 | 001 | 010 | 011 | 100 | 101 | 110 | 111 |
|---|-----|-----|-----|-----|-----|-----|-----|-----|
| C | 11  | 00  | 10  | 10  | 01  | 00  | 11  | 00  |

S-box table

**Fig. 5.19**   *Diagram for Example 5.14*

Although the effect of the key is still canceled, when we use differences between two X's and two P's $(X_1 \oplus X_2 = P_1 \oplus P_2)$, the existence of the S-box prevents Eve from finding a definite relationship between the plaintext differences and the ciphertext differences. However, she can create a probabilistic relationship. Eve can make Table 5.4, which shows, for each plaintext difference, how many ciphertext differences the cipher may create. Note that the table is made from information about the S-box input/output table in Fig. 5.19 because $P_1 \oplus P_2 = X_1 \oplus X_2$.

**Table 5.4**   *Differential input/output for the cipher in Example 5.14*

|               |     | $C_1 \oplus C_2$ |      |      |      |
|---------------|-----|------|------|------|------|
|               |     | *00* | *01* | *10* | *11* |
|               | 000 | 8    |      |      |      |
|               | 001 | 2    | 2    |      | 4    |
|               | 010 | 2    | 2    | 4    |      |
| $P_1 \oplus P_2$ | 011 |      | 4    | 2    | 2    |
|               | 100 | 2    | 2    | 4    |      |
|               | 101 |      | 4    | 2    | 2    |
|               | 110 | 4    |      | 2    | 2    |
|               | 111 |      |      | 2    | 6    |

Because the key size is 3 bits, there can be eight cases for each difference in the input. The table shows that if the input difference is $(000)_2$, the output difference is always $(00)_2$. On the other hand, the table shows that if the input difference is $(100)_2$, there are two cases of $(00)_2$ output difference, two cases of $(01)_2$ output difference, and four cases of $(01)_2$ output difference.

**Example 5.15**   The heuristic result of Example 5.14 can create probabilistic information for Eve as shown in Table 5.5. The entries in the table show the probabilities of occurrences. Those with zero probability will never occur.

**Table 5.5** *Differential distribution table (XOR Profile) for Example 5.15*

| | | $C_1 \oplus C_2$ | | | |
|---|---|---|---|---|---|
| | | *00* | *01* | *10* | *11* |
| | 000 | 1 | 0 | 0 | 0 |
| | 001 | 0.25 | 0.25 | 0 | 0.50 |
| | 010 | 0.25 | 0.25 | 0.50 | 0 |
| $P_1 \oplus P_2$ | 011 | 0 | 0.50 | 0.25 | 0.25 |
| | 100 | 0.25 | 0.25 | 0.50 | 0 |
| | 101 | 0 | 0.50 | 0.25 | 0.25 |
| | 110 | 0.50 | 0 | 0.25 | 0.25 |
| | 111 | 0 | 0 | 0.25 | 0.75 |

Note that when there was no S-box $C_1 \oplus C2 = P_1 \oplus P_2$, thus for every input difference, there is an output difference or the input/output differential profile has a uniform distribution. However, with the introduction of the S-box this uniformity is distributed. This serves as a distinguishing property which is exploited in the differential property which is exploited in the Differential Cryptanalysis method.

***Launching a Chosen-Plaintext Attack***   After the analysis, which can be done once and kept for future uses as long as the structure of the cipher does not change, Eve can choose the plaintexts for attacks. The differential probability distribution table (Table 5.5) helps Eve choose plaintexts that have the highest probability in the table.

***Guessing the Key Value***   After launching some attacks with appropriate chosen plaintexts, Eve can find some plaintext-ciphertext pairs that allow her to guess the value of the key. This step starts from C and makes toward P.

**Example 5.16**   Consider a 2-round structure in the cipher. It may be mentioned that this alone cannot be the cipher as it is not invertible. But it may form a part or branch of a cipher as shown in case of Feistel ciphers. However for differential analysis it does not really matter whether the S-boxes are invertible. Eve chooses plaintexts such that they maintain a fixed XOR. Like the XOR profile of the S-box suggests that a differential path of 001→11 occurs with a high probability of 0.5. Eve thus chooses $P_1$, $P_2$ (two plaintexts) such that $P_1 \oplus P_2 = 011$ and expects $x_1 \oplus X_2 = 11$ (see figure) with a high probability.

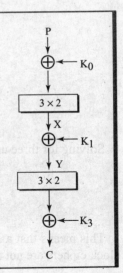

Now, she considers $C_1$ and $C_2$, the two corresponding ciphertexts and guesses $K_3$ values. For $C_1 \oplus K_3$ there are two values of Y, say $Y_1$, (see figure) and for $C_1 \oplus K_3$ there are two values of $Y_1$, say $Y_2$, possible. Note that $Y_1 \oplus Y_2 = X_1 \oplus X_2$ and thus Eve then checks whether $Y_1 \oplus Y_2 = 11$.

Because of the non-uniformity in the XOR profile, the possible values of $K_3$ get vastly reduced.

Thus Eve is able to ascertain portions of the round key, K3.

*General Procedure* Modern block ciphers have more complexity than we discussed in this section. In addition, they are made from different rounds. Eve can use the following strategy:

1. Because each round is the same, Eve can create a differential distribution table (XOR profile) for each S-box and combine them to create the distribution for each round.
2. Assuming that each round is independent (a fair assumption), Eve can create a distribution table for the whole cipher by multiplying the corresponding probabilities.
3. Eve now can make a list of plaintexts for attacks based on the distribution table in step 2. Note that the table in step 2 only helps Eve choose a smaller number of ciphertext-plaintext pairs.

---

**Differential cryptanalysis is based on a nonuniform differential distribution table of the S-boxes in a block cipher.**

**A more detailed differential cryptanalysis is given in Appendix N.**

---

## Linear Cryptanalysis

**Linear cryptanalysis** was presented by Mitsuru Matsui in 1993. The analysis uses *known-plaintext* attacks (versus the chosen-plaintext attacks in differential cryptanalysis). To see the main idea behind the attack, assume that the cipher is made of a single round, as shown in Fig. 5.20, where $c_0$, $c_1$, and $c_2$ represent the three bits in the output and $x_0$, $x_1$, and $x_2$ represent the three bits in the input of the S-box.

The S-box is a linear transformation in which each output is a linear function of input, as we discussed earlier in this chapter. With this linear component, we can create three linear equations between plaintext and ciphertext bits, as shown below:

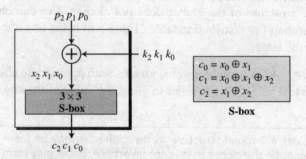

**Fig. 5.20** *A simple cipher with a linear S-box*

$$c_0 = p_0 \oplus k_0 \oplus p_1 \oplus k_1$$
$$c_1 = p_0 \oplus k_0 \oplus p_1 \oplus k_1 \oplus p_2 \oplus k_2$$
$$c_2 = p_1 \oplus k_1 \oplus p_2 \oplus k_2$$

Solving for three unknowns, we get

$$k_1 = (p_1) \oplus (c_0 \oplus c_1 \oplus c_2)$$
$$k_2 = (p_2) \oplus (c_0 \oplus c_1)$$
$$k_0 = (p_0) \oplus (c_1 \oplus c_2)$$

This means that a single known-plaintext value can find the values of $k_0$, $k_1$, and $k_2$. However, real block ciphers are not as simple as this one; they have more components and the S-boxes are not linear.

*Linear Approximation*  In some modern block ciphers, it may happen that some S-boxes are not totally nonlinear; they can be approximated, probabilistically, by some linear functions. In general, given a cipher with plaintext and ciphertext of $n$ bits and a key of $m$ bits, we are looking for some equations of the form:

$$(k_0 \oplus k_1 \oplus \cdots \oplus k_x) = (p_0 \oplus p_1 \oplus \cdots \oplus p_y) \oplus (c_0 \oplus c_1 \oplus \cdots \oplus c_z)$$

where $1 \le x \le m$, $1 \le y \le n$, and $1 \le z \le n$. The bits in the intercepted plaintext and ciphertext can be used to find the key bits. To be effective, each equation should hold with probability $1/2 \pm \varepsilon$, where $\varepsilon$ is called the *bias*. An equation with larger $\varepsilon$ is more effective than one with smaller $\varepsilon$.

---

**A more detailed linear cryptanalysis is given in Appendix N.**

---

## 5.2　　　　　　　　　　MODERN STREAM CIPHERS

In Chapter 3 we briefly discussed the difference between traditional stream ciphers and tradition block ciphers. Similar differences exist between modern stream ciphers and modern block ciphers. In a **modern stream cipher,** encryption and decryption are done $r$ bits at a time. We have a plaintext bit stream $P = p_n \ldots p_2 p_1$, a ciphertext bit stream $C = c_n \ldots c_2 c_1$, and a key bit stream $K = k_n \ldots k_2 k_1$, in which $p_i$, $c_i$, and $k_i$ are $r$-bit words. Encryption is $c_i = \text{E}(k_i, p_i)$, and decryption is $p_i = \text{D}(k_i, c_i)$, as shown in Fig. 5.21.

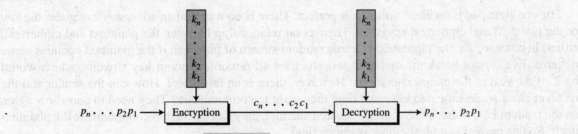

**Fig. 5.21** *Stream cipher*

Stream ciphers are faster than block ciphers. The hardware implementation of a stream cipher is also easier. When we need to encrypt binary streams and transmit them at a constant rate, a stream cipher is the better choice to use. Stream ciphers are also more immune to the corruption of bits during transmission.

---

**In a modern stream cipher, each $r$-bit word in the plaintext stream is enciphered using an $r$-bit word in the key stream to create the corresponding $r$-bit word in the ciphertext stream.**

---

Looking at Fig. 5.21, one can suggest that the main issue in modern stream ciphers is how to generate the key stream $K = k_n \ldots k_2 k_1$. Modern stream ciphers are divided into two broad categories: synchronous and nonsynchronous.

### 5.2.1　Synchronous Stream Ciphers

In a **synchronous stream cipher,** the key stream is independent of the plaintext or ciphertext stream. The key stream is generated and used with no relationship between key bits and the plaintext or ciphertext bits.

**In a synchronous stream cipher the key is independent of the plaintext or ciphertext.**

*One-Time Pad* The simplest and the most secure type of synchronous stream cipher is called the **one-time pad,** which was invented and patented by Gilbert Vernam. A one-time pad cipher uses a key stream that is randomly chosen for each encipherment. The encryption and decryption algorithms each use a single exclusive-or operation. Based on properties of the exclusive-or operation discussed earlier, the encryption and decryption algorithms are inverses of each other. It is important to note that in this cipher the exclusive-or operation is used one bit at a time. In other words, the operation is over 1-bit word and the field is **GF**(2). Note also that there must be a secure channel so that Alice can send the key stream sequence to Bob (Fig. 5.22).

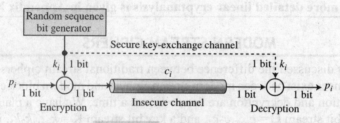

**Fig. 5.22** *One-time pad*

The one-time pad is an ideal cipher. It is perfect. There is no way that an adversary can guess the key or the plaintext and ciphertext statistics. There is no relationship between the plaintext and ciphertext, either. In other words, the ciphertext is a true random stream of bits even if the plaintext contains some patterns. Eve cannot break the cipher unless she tries all possible random key streams, which would be $2^n$ if the size of the plaintext is $n$ bits. However, there is an issue here. How can the sender and the receiver share a one-time pad key each time they want to communicate? They need to somehow agree on the random key. If there exists such a secured channel, they can use that to communicate the plaintext itself. So this perfect and ideal cipher is impractical.

**Example 5.17** What is the pattern in the ciphertext of a one-time pad cipher in each of the following cases?
a. The plaintext is made of $n$ 0's.
b. The plaintext is made of $n$ 1's.
c. The plaintext is made of alternating 0's and 1's.
d. The plaintext is a random string of bits.

**Solution**
a. Because $0 \oplus k_i = k_i$, the ciphertext stream is the same as the key stream. If the key stream is random, the ciphertext is also random. The patterns in the plaintext are not preserved in the ciphertext.
b. Because $1 \oplus k_i = \overline{k}_i$ where $\overline{k}_i$ is the complement of $k_i$, the ciphertext stream is the complement of the key stream. If the key stream is random, the ciphertext is also random. Again the patterns in the plaintext are not preserved in the ciphertext.

c. In this case, each bit in the ciphertext stream is either the same as the corresponding bit in the key stream or the complement of it. Therefore, the result is also a random string if the key stream is random.

d. In this case, the ciphertext is definitely random because the exclusive-or of two random bits also results in a random bit.

*Feedback Shift Register*    One compromise to the one-time-pad is the **feedback shift register** **(FSR).** An FSR can be implemented in either software or hardware, but the hardware implementation is easier to discuss. A feedback shift register is made of a **shift register** and a **feedback function,** as shown in Fig. 5.23.

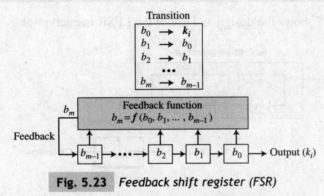

**Fig. 5.23**    *Feedback shift register (FSR)*

The shift register is a sequence of $m$ cells, $b_0$ to $b_{m-1}$, where each cell holds a single bit. The cells are initialized to an $m$-bit word, called the initial value or the **seed.** Whenever an output bit is needed (for example, in a click of time), every bit is shifted one cell to the right, which means that each cell gives its value to the cell to its right and receives the value of the cell to its left. The rightmost cell, $b_0$, gives its value as output ($k_i$); the leftmost cell, $b_{m-1}$, receives its value from the feedback function. We call the output of the feedback function $b_m$. The feedback function defines how the values of cells are combined to calculate $b_m$. A feedback shift register can be linear or nonlinear.

*Linear Feedback Shift Register*    In a **linear feedback shift register (LFSR)**, $b_m$ is a linear function of $b_0, b_1, ..., b_{m-1}$.

$$b_m = c_{m-1}\, b_{m-1} + \cdots + c_2\, b_2 + c_1\, b_1 + c_0\, b_0\ (c_0 \neq 0)$$

However, we are dealing with binary digits because the multiplication and addition are in the **GF**(2) field, so the value of $c_i$ is either 1 or 0, but $c_0$ should be 1 to get a feedback from the output. The addition operation is also the exclusive-or operation. In other words,

$$b_m = c_{m-1}\, b_{m-1} \oplus \quad \cdots \quad \oplus c_2\, b_2 \oplus c_1\, b_1 \oplus c_0\, b_0\ (c_0 \neq 0)$$

**Example 5.18**    Create a linear feedback shift register with 5 cells in which $b_5 = b_4 \oplus b_2 \oplus b_0$.

***Solution***    If $c_i = 0$, $b_i$ has no role in calculation of $b_m$. This means that $b_i$ is not connected to the feedback function. If $c_i = 1$, $b_i$ is involved in calculation of $b_m$. In this example, $c_1$ and $c_3$ are 0's, which means that we have only three connections. Figure 5.24 shows the design.

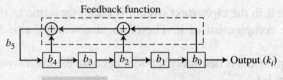

**Fig. 5.24**  *LFSR for Example 5.18*

**Example 5.19**  Create a linear feedback shift register with 4 cells in which $b_4 = b_1 \oplus b_0$. Show the value of output for 20 transitions (shifts) if the seed is $(0001)_2$.

**Solution**  Figure 5.25 shows the design and use of the LFSR in encryption.

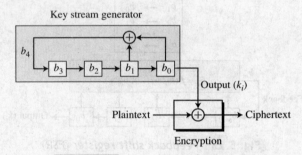

**Fig. 5.25**  *LFSR for Example 5.19*

Table 5.6 shows the values of the key stream. For each transition, first the value of $b_4$ is calculated and then each bit is shifted one cell to the right.

**Table 5.6**  *Cell values and key sequence for Example 5.19*

| States | $b_4$ | $b_3$ | $b_2$ | $b_1$ | $b_0$ | $k_i$ |
|--------|-------|-------|-------|-------|-------|-------|
| Initial | 1 | 0 | 0 | 0 | 1 | |
| 1 | 0 | 1 | 0 | 0 | 0 | 1 |
| 2 | 0 | 0 | 1 | 0 | 0 | 0 |
| 3 | 1 | 0 | 0 | 1 | 0 | 0 |
| 4 | 1 | 1 | 0 | 0 | 1 | 0 |
| 5 | 0 | 1 | 1 | 0 | 0 | 1 |
| 6 | 1 | 0 | 1 | 1 | 0 | 0 |
| 7 | 0 | 1 | 0 | 1 | 1 | 0 |
| 8 | 1 | 0 | 1 | 0 | 1 | 1 |
| 9 | 1 | 1 | 0 | 1 | 0 | 1 |
| 10 | 1 | 1 | 1 | 0 | 1 | 0 |
| 11 | 1 | 1 | 1 | 1 | 0 | 1 |
| 12 | 0 | 1 | 1 | 1 | 1 | 0 |

| 13 | 0 | 0 | 1 | 1 | 1 | 1 |
|----|---|---|---|---|---|---|
| 14 | 0 | 0 | 0 | 1 | 1 | 1 |
| 15 | 1 | 0 | 0 | 0 | 1 | 1 |
| 16 | 0 | 1 | 0 | 0 | 0 | 1 |
| 17 | 0 | 0 | 1 | 0 | 0 | 0 |
| 18 | 1 | 0 | 0 | 1 | 0 | 0 |
| 19 | 1 | 1 | 0 | 0 | 1 | 0 |
| 20 | 1 | 1 | 1 | 0 | 0 | 1 |

Note that the key stream is 100010011010111 10001.... This looks like a random sequence at first glance, but if we go through more transitions, we see that the sequence is periodic. It is a repetition of 15 bits as shown below:

100010011010111 **100010011010111** 100010011010111 **100010011010111** ...

The key stream generated from a LFSR is a pseudorandom sequence in which the sequence is repeated after $N$ bits. The stream has a period, but the period is not 4, the size of the seed. Based on the design and the seed, the period can be up to $2^m - 1$. The reason is that the $m$-bit seed can create up to $2^m$ different patterns, from all 0's to all 1's. However, if the seed is all 0's the result is useless; the plaintext would be a continuous stream of 0's, so this is excluded. However, one can slightly modify the LFSR to include all the zero states in its state transition, thus resulting in a periodicity of $2^n$. The details are left as an exercise to the reader.

---

**The maximum period of an LFSR is $2^m - 1$.**

---

In the previous example, the period is the maximum ($2^4 - 1 = 15$). To achieve this maximum period (a better randomness), we need first to think about the feedback function as a **characteristic polynomial** with coefficients in the **GF**(2) field.

$$b_m = c_{m-1} b_{m-1} + ... + c_1 b_1 + c_0 b_0 \quad \rightarrow \quad x^m = c_{m-1} x^{m-1} + ... + c_1 x^1 + c_0 x^0$$

Because addition and subtraction are the same in this field, all terms can be moved to one side, which creates a polynomial of degree $m$ (referred to as the *characteristic polynomial*).

$$x^m + c_{m-1} x^{m-1} + \quad ... \quad + c_1 x^1 + c_0 x^0 = 0$$

An LFSR has a maximum period of $2^m - 1$ if it has an even number of cells and the characteristic polynomial is a **primitive polynomial.** A primitive polynomial is an irreducible polynomial that divides $x^e + 1$, where $e$ is the least integer in the form $e = 2^k - 1$ and $k \geq 2$. It is not easy to generate a primitive polynomial. A polynomial is chosen randomly and then checked to see if it is primitive. However, there are many already tested primitive polynomials to choose from (see Appendix G).

**Example 5.20** The characteristic polynomial for the LFSR in Example 5.19 is $(x^4 + x + 1)$, which is a primitive polynomial. Table 4.4 (Chapter 4) shows that it is an irreducible polynomial. This polynomial also divides $(x^7 + 1) = (x^4 + x + 1) (x^3 + 1)$, which means $e = 2^3 - 1 = 7$.

## Attacks on Stream Ciphers Using One LFSR

Consider a stream cipher built using a single LFSR as shown in Fig. 5.26.

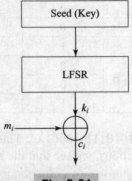

**Fig. 5.26**

The LFSR generates a sequence of key streams which are xored with the message to produce the ciphertext stream. Consider an attacker who knows the structure of the LFSR and its length $n$. Suppose she engages in a known plaintext kind of attack, where she obtains pairs of the type $(m_i, c_i)$ for $n$-bit values. These values provide the attacker $n$ successive key stream bits generated by the LFSR, which she can use to obtain the state of the LFSR at a time instance $n$ clock cycles before. Since the adversary is also aware of the connection of the LFSR, she can obtain future key streams by clocking the LFSR with the found out state.

The other more interesting scenario is when the adversary is unaware of the length of the LFSR or its connection polynomial. There is a famous algorithm propounded in 1965, called *Berlekamp Massey (BM)* algorithm which solves the problem efficiently. We present a discussion on the algorithm.

Consider an $n$ length LFSR as depicted in the Fig. 5.27, when it is generating the $j$th output bit $s_j$. The LFSR registers clearly holds the previous $n$ output bits, $s_{j-1}, s_{j-2}, \ldots, s_{j-n}$.

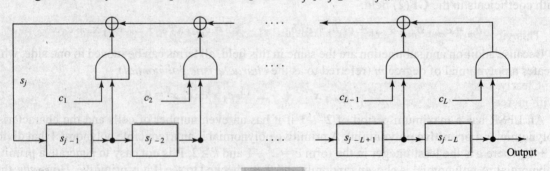

**Fig. 5.27**

An LFSR is said to generate a finite sequence $s_0, s_1, \ldots, s_{N-1}$ when this sequence coincides with the first $N$ output digits of the LFSR for some initial loading.

Consider a sequence $s_0, s_1, \ldots, s_{N-1}$ which is being generated by an LFSR with length $L$. Clearly, if $L \geq N$ then the LFSR always generates the sequence. However if $L < N$, the LFSR generates the sequence if and only if:

$$s_j = \sum_{i=1}^{L} c_i s_{j-i}, j = L,\ L+1,...,N-1$$

We state first a theorem.

**Theorem 1** If some LFSR of length $L$ generates the sequence $s_0, s_1, ..., s_{N-1}$ but not the sequence $s_0$, $s_1, ..., s_{N-1}, s_N$ then any LFSR that generates the latter sequence has length $L'$, satisfying:

$$s_1, ..., s_{N-1}, s_N$$

$$L' \geq N + 1 - L$$

*Proof:* A simple proof follows by contradiction. Contradicting, we have $L' < N + 1 - L$ or, $L' \leq N - L$.

Note that if $L \geq N$, then $L' \leq 0$. Thus we have an impossible outcome, thus proving the theorem trivially true.

In the scenario when $L < N$, let $c_1, ..., c_L$ and $c_1', ..., c_L'$ denote the two LFSRs. Thus we have the following facts:

$$\sum_{i=1}^{L} c_i s_{j-i} = s_j, j = L, L+1, ..., N-1$$

$$\neq s_N, j = N$$

and, $$\sum_{i=1}^{L'} c'_k s_{j-k} = s_j, j = L', L'+1, ..., N-1, N$$

Now consider, $\sum_{i=1}^{L} c_i s_{N-i}$ Note that $\{s_{N-L}, s_{N-L+1}, ..., s_{N-1}\}$ is a subset of $\{s_{L'}, s_{L'+1}, ..., s_{N-1}\}$, as $L' \leq N - L$.

$$\therefore \quad \sum_{i=1}^{L} c_i s_{N-i} = \sum_{i=1}^{L} c_i \sum_{k=1}^{L'} c'_k s_{N-i-k} = \sum_{k=1}^{L'} c'_k \sum_{i=1}^{L} c_i s_{N-i-k} = \sum_{k=1}^{L'} c'_k s_{N-k} = s_N$$

This violates the fact that $s_N$ is not generated by the first LFSR. Next we define an important term in context to LFSRs called *Linear Complexity* ($L_N(s)$) as the minimum length of all LFSRs that generates $s = s_0, s_1, ..., s_{N-1}$.

Clearly, $L_N(s) \leq N$ as any N length LFSR can generate s. Also $L_N(s)$ is monotonically non-decreasing with increasing N. Also the following conventions hold trivially:

1. Any 0 sequence can be generated by an LFSR of length, $L = 0$.
2. When $s_0, s_1, ..., s_{N-1}$ are all 0's but $s_N = 1$, then $L = N + 1$.

Thus using Theorem 1 and the monotonicity of $L_N(s)$, the following result holds:

**Lemma 1** If some LFSR of length $L$ generates the sequence $s_0, s_1, ... s_{N-1}$ but not the sequence $s_0$, $s_1, ... s_{N-1}, s_N$ then:

$$L_{N+1}(s) \geq \max [L_N(s), N + 1 - L_N(s)]$$

Hence an update of $L_N(s)$ is needed only if $N + 1 - L_N(s) > L_N(s)$ or, $N \geq 2 L_N(s)$.

Next we present the Berlekamp Massey Algorithm. It is a recursive algorithm for producing one of the LFSRs of length $L_N(s)$, which generates $s_0, \ldots, s_{N-1}$ for $N = 1, 2, 3, \ldots$

The algorithm takes a sequence $s_0, \ldots, s_{N-1}$ and returns the corresponding Linear Complexity $L_N(s)$ and also the connection polynomial $C(D) = 1 + c_1 D + \ldots + c_L D^L$, which has degree at most $L$ in the indeterminate $D$. The convention is $C(D) = 1$ for the LFSR of length $L = 0$.

For a given $s$, let $C^N(D) = 1 + C_1^{(N)}(D) + \ldots + C_{L_N(s)}^{(N)}(D)^{L_N(s)}$ denote the connection polynomial of a minimal length $L_N(s)$ LFSR that generates $s_0, s_1 \ldots, s_{N-1}$.

The BMA presents a constructive algorithm to generate $C^N(D)$ and $L_N(s)$ of a LFSR which generates $s$. Consider an example of a sequence 0011. Clearly an LFSR with $L = 0$ and $C(D) = 1$ can generate the subsequence 00. However the sequence 001 can be generated by an LFSR of length $2 + 1 - 0 = 3$, and the corresponding feedback polynomial is $1 + D$. Although the above LFSR generates 001, it does not generate 0011, as the $4^{\text{th}}$ streamed out bit is 0, while we are expecting a 1. Hence we need to correct this "discrepancy" by either changing the connection polynomial or going to a higher length LFSR. In this case, we change the LFSR to have the connection polynomial $C(D) = 1 + D + D^3$ to make the correction. Next we shall address to the rationale behind such a change by formalizing the notion of discrepancy.

We show inductively that the inequality in Lemma 1 is an equality. We note this in the base case from the above example. Assume that the inductive hypothesis holds for $n$ and lesser values. We show the validity for $n + 1$. The corresponding parameters of the LFSR are $L_N(s)$ and $C^N(D)$.

$$\therefore \quad s_j \oplus \sum_{i=1}^{L_m(s)} c_i^{(n)} s_{j-i} = \begin{cases} 0, j = L_{n(s)}, \ldots, n-1 \\ d_n, j = n \end{cases}$$

Here $d_n$ is the discrepancy between $s_n$ and the $(n + 1)^{\text{st}}$ bit generated by the minimal length LFSR, which we have found to generate the first $n$ bits of $s$.

Clearly if $d_n = 0$, there is no connection necessary and the LFSR also generates the $(n + 1)^{\text{st}}$ bit of $s$. Therefore, $L_{n+1}(s) = L_n(s)$, $C^{(n+1)}(D) = C^n(D)$.

The other case is when $d_n = 1$. Let $m$ be the sequence length before the last change in the minimal length, i.e., $L_m(s) < L_n(s)$ and $L_{m+1}(s) = L_n(s)$.

Since a length change was required, the LFSR with parameters $\langle L_m(s), C^m(D) \rangle$ could not generate $s_0$, $s_1, \ldots, s_m$.

$$\therefore \quad s_j \oplus \sum_{i=1}^{L_m(s)} c_i^{(n)} s_{j-i} = \begin{cases} 0, j = L_{m(s)}, \ldots, m-1 \\ d_m, j = m \end{cases}$$

By induction hypothesis, $L_{m+1}(s) = L_n(s) = \max [L_m(s), m + 1 - L_m(s)]$

$\because \quad L_m(s) < L_n(s)$, we have $L_n(s) = m + 1 - L_m(s)$

We make a claim at this point. $C(D) = C^n(D) \oplus D^{n-m} C^m(D)$ is a valid next choice for $C^{n+1}(D)$. Note that the degree of $C(D) = \max [L_n(s), n - m + L_m(s)] = \max [L_n(s), n + 1 - L_n(s)]$

$\therefore C(D)$ is an allowable connection polynomial for an LFSR of length

$$L = \max [L_n(s), n + 1 - L_n(s)]$$

Next we need to argue that the LFSR with connection polynomial $C(D)$ indeed generates the sequence $s_0, \ldots, s_N$.

Since, $C^n(D) = 1 + c_1^n(D) + \ldots + c_{L_n(s)}^n D^{L_n(s)}$ and, $C^m(D) = 1 + c_1^m(D) + \cdots + c_{L_m(s)}^m D^{L_m(s)}$

we have $D^{n-m}C^m(D) = D^{n-m} + c_1^m(D^{n-m+1}) + \cdots + c_{L_m(s)}^m D^{L_m(s)+n-m}$.

$\therefore$ the coefficient of $C(D) = C^n(D) + D^{n-m}C^m(D)$ can be enumerated as follows:

$$c_1 = c_1^n$$

$$\ldots$$

$$c_{n-m} = c_{n-m}^n \oplus 1$$

$$c_{n-m+1} = c_{n-m+1}^n \oplus c_1^m$$

$$\ldots$$

Hence the discrepancy for all the $n$ values generated by the LFSR can be determined as follows using the above enumeration of the coefficients.

$$\therefore \quad s_j \oplus \sum_{i=1}^{L} c_i s_{j-i} = s_j \oplus \sum_{i=1}^{L_n(s)} c_i^{(n)} s_{j-i} \oplus$$

$$[s_{j-n+m} \oplus \sum_{i=1}^{L_m(s)} c_i^{(m)} s_{j-n+m-i}]$$

$$= \begin{cases} 0, j = L, L+1, \ldots, n-1 \\ 1 \oplus 1 = 0, j = n \end{cases}$$

Note that the terms in the square bracket comes from the state variables corresponding to the coefficients $c_{n-m}, \ldots$ . Also note we have used the fact that the first part of the discrepancy:

$$s_j \oplus \sum_{i=1}^{L_n(s)} c_i^{(n)} s_{j-i} \text{ is 0 when } j = L, L+1, \ldots, n-1.$$

This is because the LFSR generates the sequence till $s_{n-1}$.
Likewise the second term denoted by:

$$s_{j-n+m} \oplus \sum_{i=1}^{L_m(s)} c_i^{(m)} s_{j-n+m-i} \text{ is also 0,}$$

as this LFSR can generate the sequence till $s_{m-1}$.

When $j = n$, both the LFSRs generate a 1 as discrepancy and hence cancels out each other. This makes the LFSR with connection polynomial C(D) generate the sequence till $s_n$

We summarize the above discussion in the form of an algorithm:

---

### Algorithm 5.1           Berlekamp-Massey Algorithm

INPUT: a binary sequence $s_n = s_0, s_1, s_2 \ldots, s_{n-1}$ of length $n$.

OUTPUT: the linear complexity $L(s^n)$ of $s^n$, $0 \le L(s^n) \le n$.

1. *Initialization.* $C(D) \leftarrow 1, L \leftarrow 0, m \leftarrow -1, B(D) \leftarrow 1, N \leftarrow 0$.
2. While $(N < n)$ do the following:
   - 2.1 *Compute the next discrepancy d.* $d \leftarrow (s_N + \sum_{i=1}^{L} c_i s_{N-i}) \bmod 2$.
   - 2.2 If $d = 1$ then do the following:
     $$T(D) \leftarrow C(D), C(D) \leftarrow C(D) + B(D) \cdot D^{N-m}.$$
     If $L \le N/2$ then $L \leftarrow N + 1 - L, m \leftarrow N, B(D) \leftarrow T(D)$.
   - 2.3 $N \leftarrow N + 1$.
3. Return $(L)$.

---

**Example 5.21**   Reconstruct an LFSR (of the shortest length) which generates the sequence 00111011.

The following table shows the working of the BMA algorithm to solve the problem.

| $S_n$ | $d$ | $T(D)$ | $C(D)$ | $L$ | $m$ | $B(D)$ | $N$ |
|-------|-----|--------|--------|-----|-----|--------|-----|
| – | – | – | $1$ | $0$ | $-1$ | $1$ | $0$ |
| $0$ | $0$ | – | $1$ | $0$ | $-1$ | $1$ | $1$ |
| $0$ | $0$ | – | $1$ | $0$ | $-1$ | $1$ | $2$ |
| $1$ | $1$ | $1$ | $1 + D^3$ | $3$ | $2$ | $1$ | $3$ |
| $1$ | $1$ | $1 + D^3$ | $1 + D + D^3$ | $3$ | $2$ | $1$ | $4$ |
| $1$ | $0$ | $1 + D^3$ | $1 + D + D^3$ | $3$ | $2$ | $1$ | $5$ |
| $0$ | $0$ | $1 + D^3$ | $1 + D + D^3$ | $3$ | $2$ | $1$ | $6$ |
| $1$ | $0$ | $1 + D^3$ | $1 + D + D^3$ | $3$ | $2$ | $1$ | $7$ |
| $1$ | $1$ | $1 + D + D^3$ | $1 + D + D^3 + D^5$ | $5$ | $7$ | $1 + D + D^3$ | $8$ |

*Nonlinear Feedback Shift Register*   The linear feedback shift register is vulnerable to attacks mainly because of its linearity. A better stream cipher can be achieved using a **nonlinear feedback shift register (NLFSR)**. An NLFSR has the same structure as an LFSR except that the $b_m$ is the nonlinear function of $b_0, b_1, \ldots, b_m$. For example, in a 4-bit NLFSR, the relation can be as shown below where AND means bit-wise *and* operation, OR means bit-wise *or* operation:

$$b_4 = (b_3 \text{ AND } b_2) \text{ OR } (b_1 \text{ AND } \overline{b}_0)$$

However, NLFSRs are not common because it is difficult to mathematically construct NLFSR with the maximum period.

*Combination*   A stream cipher can use a combination of linear and nonlinear structures. Some LFSRs can be made with the maximum period and then combined through a nonlinear function.

## Nonsynchronous Stream Ciphers

In a **nonsynchronous stream cipher,** each key in the key stream depends on previous plaintext or ciphertext.

---

**In a nonsynchronous stream cipher, the key depends on either the plaintext or ciphertext.**

---

Two methods that are used to create different modes of operation for block ciphers (*output feedback mode* and *counter mode*) actually create stream ciphers (see Chapter 8).

## 5.3                                    RECOMMENDED READING

The following books and websites provide more details about subjects discussed in this chapter. The items enclosed in brackets refer to the reference list at the end of the book.

### Books

[Sti06] and [PHS03] give a complete discussion of D-boxes and S-boxes. Stream ciphers are elaborated in [Sch99] and [Sal03]. [Sti06], [PHS03], and [Vau06] present thorough and interesting discussions of differential and linear cryptanalysis.

### References

- James Massey, "*Shift-Register Synthesis and BCH Decoding*", IEEE Transactions on Information Theory, 1969
- D. Stinson, *Cryptography: Theory and Practice*, Chapman & Hall/CRC
- A. Menezes, P. Van Oorschot, Scott Vanstone, "*Handbook of Applied Cryptography*" (Available online)

### WebSites

The following websites give more information about topics discussed in this chapter.
  http://en.wikipedia.org/wiki/Feistel_cipher
  http://www.quadibloc.com/crypto/co040906.htm
  tigger.uic.edu/~jleon/mcs425-s05/handouts/feistal-diagram.pdf

## *Key Terms*

| | |
|---|---|
| bit-oriented cipher | compression D-box |
| characteristic polynomial | confusion |
| character-oriented cipher | decoding |
| circular shift operation | differential cryptanalysis |
| combine operation | differential distribution table |
| diffusion | nonlinear S-box |

encoding

expansion D-box

feedback function

feedback shift register (FSR)

Feistel cipher

key generator

key schedule

linear cryptanalysis

linear feedback shift register (LFSR)

linear S-box

mixer

modern block cipher

modern stream cipher

non-Feistel cipher

nonlinear feedback shift register (NLFSR)

nonsynchronous stream cipher

one-time pad

D-box

primitive polynomial

product cipher

round

S-box

seed

shift register

split operation

straight D-box

swap operation

swapper

synchronous stream cipher

XOR profile

## Summary

★ The traditional symmetric-key ciphers are character-oriented ciphers. With the advent of the computer, we need bit-oriented ciphers.

★ A symmetric-key modern block cipher encrypts an $n$-bit block of plaintext or decrypts an $n$-bit block of ciphertext. The encryption or decryption algorithm uses a $k$-bit key.

★ A modern block cipher can be designed to act as a substitution cipher or a transposition cipher. However, to be resistant to exhaustive-search attack, a modern block cipher needs to be designed as a substitution cipher.

★ Modern block ciphers normally are keyed substitution ciphers in which the key allows only practical mapping from the possible inputs to possible outputs.

★ A modern block cipher is made of a combination of D-boxes, substitution units, S-boxes, and some other units.

★ A D-box (diffusion box) parallels the traditional transposition cipher for characters. There are three types of D-boxes: straight D-boxes, expansion D-boxes, and compression D-boxes.

★ An S-box (substitution box) can be thought of as a miniature of a substitution cipher. However, there can be a different number of inputs and outputs in an S-box.

★ An important component in most block ciphers is the exclusive-or operation, which can be thought of as an addition or subtraction operation in the $\mathbf{GF}(2^n)$ field.

★ An operation found in some modern block ciphers is the circular shift operation, in which shifting can be to the left or to the right. The swap operation is a special case of the circular shift operation where $k = n/2$. Two other operations found in some block ciphers are split and combine.

★ Shannon introduced the concept of a product cipher. A product cipher is a complex cipher combining S-boxes, D-boxes, and other components to achieve diffusion and confusion. Diffusion hides the relationship between the plaintext and the ciphertext; confusion hides the relationship between the cipher key and the ciphertext.

★ Modern block ciphers are all product ciphers, but they are divided into two classes: Feistel ciphers and non-Feistel ciphers. Feistel ciphers use both invertible and noninvertible components. Non-Feistel ciphers use only invertible components.

★ Some new attacks on block ciphers are based on the structure of modern block ciphers. These attacks use differential and linear cryptanalysis techniques.

★ In a modern stream cipher, each *r*-bit word in the plaintext stream is enciphered using an *r*-bit word in the key stream to create the corresponding *r*-bit word in the ciphertext stream. Modern stream ciphers can be divided into two broad categories: synchronous stream ciphers and nonsynchronous stream ciphers. In a synchronous stream cipher, the key stream is independent of the plaintext or ciphertext stream. In a nonsynchronous stream cipher, the key stream depends on the plaintext or ciphertext stream.

★ The simplest and most secure type of synchronous stream cipher is called the one-time pad. A one-time pad cipher uses a key stream that is randomly chosen for each encipherment. The encryption and decryption algorithm are each an exclusive-or operation. The one-time pad cipher is not practical because the key needs to be changed for each communication. One compromise to the one-time-pad is the feedback shift register (FSR), which can be implemented in hardware or software.

# *Practice Set*

## Review Questions

**5.1** Distinguish between a modern and a traditional symmetric-key cipher.

**5.2** Explain why modern block ciphers are designed as substitution ciphers instead of transposition ciphers.

**5.3** Explain why both substitution and transposition ciphers can be thought of as permutations.

**5.4** List some components of a modern block cipher.

**5.5** Define a D-box and list its three variations. Which variation is invertible?

**5.6** Define an S-box and mention the necessary condition for an S-box to be invertible.

**5.7** Define a product cipher and list the two classes of product ciphers.

**5.8** Distinguish between diffusion and confusion.

**5.9** Distinguish between a Feistel and a non-Feistel block cipher.

**5.10** Distinguish between differential and linear cryptanalysis. Which one is a chosen-plaintext attack? Which one is a known-plaintext attack?

**5.11** Distinguish between a synchronous and a nonsynchronous stream cipher.

**5.12** Define a feedback shift register and list the two variations used in stream ciphers.

## Exercises

**5.13** A transposition block has 10 inputs and 10 outputs. What is the order of the permutation group? What is the key size?

**5.14** A substitution block has 10 inputs and 10 outputs. What is the order of the permutation group? What is the key size?

**5.15** a. Show the result of 3-bit circular left shift on word $(10011011)_2$.

b. Show the result of 3-bit circular right shift on the word resulting from Part a.

c. Compare the result of Part b with the original word in Part a.

**5.16**  a.  Swap the word $(10011011)_2$.

  b.  Swap the word resulting from Part a.

  c.  Compare the result of Part a and Part b to show that swapping is a self-invertible operation.

**5.17**  Find the result of the following operations:

  a.  $(01001101) \oplus (01001101)$

  b.  $(01001101) \oplus (10110010)$

  c.  $(01001101) \oplus (00000000)$

  d.  $(01001101) \oplus (11111111)$

**5.18**  a.  Decode the word 010 using a $3 \times 8$ decoder.

  b.  Encode the word 00100000 using a $8 \times 3$ encoder.

**5.19**  A message has 2000 characters. If it is supposed to be encrypted using a block cipher of 64 bits, find the size of the padding and the number of blocks.

**5.20**  Show the table for the straight D-box in Fig. 5.4.

**5.21**  Show the table for the compression D-box in Fig. 5.4.

**5.22**  Show the table for the expansion D-box in Fig. 5.4.

**5.23**  Show the D-box defined by the following table:

$$8\ 1\ 2\ 3\ 4\ 5\ 6\ 7$$

**5.24**  Determine whether the D-box with the following table is a straight D-box, a compression D-box, or an expansion D-box.

$$1\ 1\ 2\ 3\ 4\ 4$$

**5.25**  Determine whether the D-box with the following table is a straight D-box, a compression D-box, or an expansion D-box.

$$1\ 3\ 5\ 6\ 7$$

**5.26**  Determine whether the D-box with the following permutation table is a straight D-box, a compression D-box, or an expansion D-box.

$$1\ 2\ 3\ 4\ 5\ 6$$

**5.27**  The input/output relation in a $2 \times 2$ S-box is shown by the following table. Show the table for the inverse S-box.

|  |  | Input: right bit | |
|---|---|---|---|
|  |  | 0 | 1 |
| Input: left bit | 0 | 01 | 11 |
|  | 1 | 10 | 00 |

**5.28**  Show an LFSR with the characteristic polynomial $x^5 + x^2 + 1$. What is the period?

**5.29**  What is the characteristic polynomial of the following LFSR? What is the maximum period?

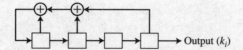

**5.30**  Show the 20-bit key stream generated from the LFSR in Fig. 5.25 if the seed is 1110.

**5.31**  The maximum period length of an LFSR is 32. How many bits does the shift register have?

**5.32**  A $6 \times 2$ S-box exclusive-ors the odd-numbered bits to get the left bit of the output and exclusive-ors the even-numbered bits to get the right bit of the output. If the input is 110010, what is the output? If the input is 101101, what is the output?

**5.33**  The leftmost bit of a $4 \times 3$ S-box rotates the other three bits. If the leftmost bit is 0, the three other bits are rotated to the right one bit. If the leftmost bit is 1, the three other bits are rotated to the left one bit. If the input is 1011, what is the output? If the input is 0110, what is the output?

**5.34**  Write a routine in pseudocode that splits an $n$-bit word to two words, each of $n/2$ bits.

**5.35**  Write a routine in pseudocode that combines two $n/2$-bit words into an $n$-bit word.

**5.36**  Write a routine in pseudocode that swaps the left and right halves of an $n$-bit word.

**5.37**  Write a routine in pseudocode that circular-shifts an $n$-bit word $k$ bits to the left or right based on the first parameter passed to the routine.

**5.38**  Write a routine in pseudocode for a D-box in which the mapping is defined by a table.

**5.39**  Write a routine in pseudocode for an S-box in which the input/output is defined by a table.

**5.40**  Write a routine in pseudocode that simulates each round of a non-Feistel cipher described in Fig. 5.13.

**5.41**  Write a routine in pseudocode that simulates each round of the Feistel cipher described in Fig. 5.17.

**5.42**  Write a routine in pseudocode that simulates an $n$-bit LFSR.

**5.43**  Apply Berlekamp-Massey algorithm to deduce the linear complexity for the sequence 01010101.

**5.44**  What is the complexity of Berlekamp-Massey algorithm in terms of the number of bits in the sequence?

**5.45**  Write a program in C to implement the Berlekamp-Massey algorithm.

# 6

# Data Encryption Standard (DES)

## Objectives

In this chapter, we discuss the Data Encryption Standard (DES), the modern symmetric-key block cipher. The following are our main objectives for this chapter:

☞ To review a short history of DES
☞ To define the basic structure of DES
☞ To describe the details of building elements of DES
☞ To describe the round keys generation process
☞ To analyze DES

The emphasis is on how DES uses a Feistel cipher to achieve confusion and diffusion of bits from the plaintext to the ciphertext.

## 6.1                          INTRODUCTION

The **Data Encryption Standard (DES)** is a symmetric-key block cipher published by the **National Institute of Standards and Technology (NIST)**.

### 6.1.1   History

In 1973, NIST published a request for proposals for a national symmetric-key cryptosystem. A proposal from IBM, a modification of a project called Lucifer, was accepted as DES. DES was published in the *Federal Register* in March 1975 as a draft of the **Federal Information Processing Standard (FIPS)**.

After the publication, the draft was criticized severely for two reasons. First, critics questioned the small key length (only 56 bits), which could make the cipher vulnerable to brute-force attack. Second, critics were concerned about some hidden design behind the internal structure of DES. They were suspicious that some part of the structure (the S-boxes) may have some hidden trapdoor that would allow the **National Security Agency (NSA)** to decrypt the messages without the need for the key. Later IBM designers mentioned that the internal structure was designed to prevent differential cryptanalysis.

DES was finally published as FIPS 46 in the *Federal Register* in January 1977. NIST, however, defines DES as the standard for use in unclassified applications. DES has been the most widely used symmetric-key block cipher since its publication. NIST later issued a new standard (FIPS 46-3) that recommends the use of triple DES (repeated DES cipher three times) for future applications. As we will see in Chapter 7, AES, the recent standard, is supposed to replace DES in the long run.

### 6.1.2 Overview

DES is a block cipher, as shown in Fig. 6.1.

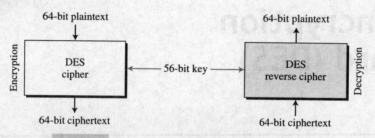

**Fig. 6.1** *Encryption and decryption with DES*

At the encryption site, DES takes a 64-bit plaintext and creates a 64-bit ciphertext; at the decryption site, DES takes a 64-bit ciphertext and creates a 64-bit block of plaintext. The same 56-bit cipher key is used for both encryption and decryption.

## 6.2    DES STRUCTURE

Let us concentrate on encryption; later we will discuss decryption. The encryption process is made of two permutations (P-boxes), which we call initial and final permutations, and sixteen Feistel rounds. Each round uses a different 48-bit round key generated from the cipher key according to a predefined algorithm described later in the chapter. Figure 6.2 shows the elements of DES cipher at the encryption site.

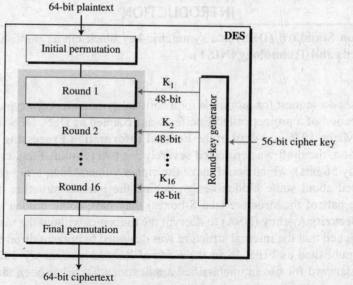

**Fig. 6.2** *General structure of DES*

## 6.2.1 Initial and Final Permutations

Figure 6.3 shows the initial and final permutations (P-boxes). Each of these permutations takes a 64-bit input and permutes them according to a predefined rule. We have shown only a few input ports and the corresponding output ports. These permutations are keyless straight permutations that are the inverse of each other. For example, in the initial permutation, the 58th bit in the input becomes the first bit in the output. Similarly, in the final permutation, the first bit in the input becomes the 58th bit in the output. In other words, if the rounds between these two permutations do not exist, the 58th bit entering the initial permutation is the same as the 58th bit leaving the final permutation.

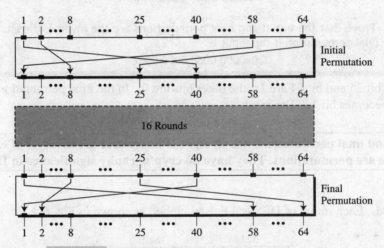

**Fig. 6.3** *Initial and final permutation steps in DES*

The permutation rules for these P-boxes are shown in Table 6.1. Each side of the table can be thought of as a 64-element array. Note that, as with any permutation table we have discussed so far, the value of each element defines the input port number, and the order (index) of the element defines the output port number.

**Table 6.1** *Initial and final permutation tables*

| Initial Permutation | Final Permutation |
|---|---|
| 58 50 42 34 26 18 10 02 | 40 08 48 16 56 24 64 32 |
| 60 52 44 36 28 20 12 04 | 39 07 47 15 55 23 63 31 |
| 62 54 46 38 30 22 14 06 | 38 06 46 14 54 22 62 30 |
| 64 56 48 40 32 24 16 08 | 37 05 45 13 53 21 61 29 |
| 57 49 41 33 25 17 09 01 | 36 04 44 12 52 20 60 28 |
| 59 51 43 35 27 19 11 03 | 35 03 43 11 51 19 59 27 |
| 61 53 45 37 29 21 13 05 | 34 02 42 10 50 18 58 26 |
| 63 55 47 39 31 23 15 07 | 33 01 41 09 49 17 57 25 |

These two permutations have no cryptography significance in DES. Both permutations are keyless and predetermined. The reason they are included in DES is not clear and has not been revealed by the DES designers. The guess is that DES was designed to be implemented in hardware (on chips) and that these two complex permutations may thwart a software simulation of the mechanism.

**Example 6.1**  Find the output of the initial permutation box when the input is given in hexadecimal as:

$$0x0002\ 0000\ 0000\ 0001$$

**Solution**  The input has only two 1s (bit 15 and bit 64); the output must also have only two 1s (the nature of straight permutation). Using Table 6.1, we can find the output related to these two bits. Bit 15 in the input becomes bit 63 in the output. Bit 64 in the input becomes bit 25 in the output. So the output has only two 1s, bit 25 and bit 63. The result in hexadecimal is

$$0x0000\ 0080\ 0000\ 0002$$

**Example 6.2**  Prove that the initial and final permutations are the inverse of each other by finding the output of the final permutation if the input is

$$0x0000\ 0080\ 0000\ 0002$$

**Solution**  Only bit 25 and bit 64 are 1s; the other bits are 0s. In the final permutation, bit 25 becomes bit 64 and bit 63 becomes bit 15. The result

$$0x0002\ 0000\ 0000\ 0001$$

**The initial and final permutations are straight D-boxes that are inverses of each other and hence are permutations. They have no cryptography significance in DES.**

### 6.2.2  Rounds

DES uses 16 rounds. Each round of DES is a Feistel cipher, as shown in Fig. 6.4.

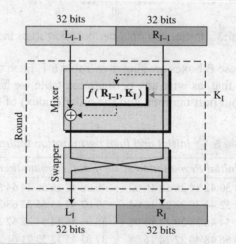

**Fig. 6.4**  *A round in DES (encryption site)*

The round takes $L_{I-1}$ and $R_{I-1}$ from previous round (or the initial permutation box) and creates $L_I$ and $R_I$, which go to the next round (or final permutation box). As we discussed in Chapter 5, we can assume that each round has two cipher elements (mixer and swapper). Each of these elements is invertible. The swapper is obviously invertible. It swaps the left half of the text with the right half. The mixer is invertible because of the XOR operation. All noninvertible elements are collected inside the function $f(R_{I-1}, K_I)$.

## DES Function

The heart of DES is the DES function. The DES function applies a 48-bit key to the rightmost 32 bits ($R_{I-1}$) to produce a 32-bit output. This function is made up of four sections: an expansion D-box, a whitener (that adds key), a group of S-boxes, and a straight D-box as shown in Fig. 6.5.

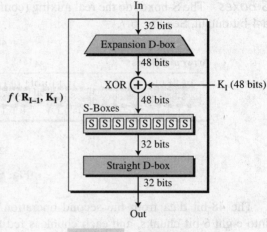

**Fig. 6.5** *DES function*

### Expansion D-box

Since $R_{I-1}$ is a 32-bit input and $K_I$ is a 48-bit key, we first need to expand $R_{I-1}$ to 48 bits. $R_{I-1}$ is divided into 8 4-bit sections. Each 4-bit section is then expanded to 6 bits. This expansion permutation follows a predetermined rule. For each section, input bits 1, 2, 3, and 4 are copied to output bits 2, 3, 4, and 5, respectively. Output bit 1 comes from bit 4 of the previous section; output bit 6 comes from bit 1 of the next section. If sections 1 and 8 can be considered adjacent sections, the same rule applies to bits 1 and 32. Fig. 6.6 shows the input and output in the expansion permutation.

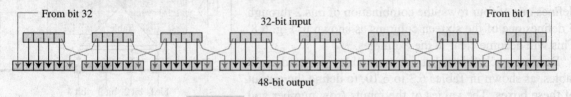

**Fig. 6.6** *Expansion permutation*

Although the relationship between the input and output can be defined mathematically, DES uses Table 6.2 to define this D-box. Note that the number of output ports is 48, but the value range is only 1 to 32. Some of the inputs go to more than one output. For example, the value of input bit 5 becomes the value of output bits 6 and 8.

**Table 6.2** *Expansion D-box table*

| 32 | 01 | 02 | 03 | 04 | 05 |
|----|----|----|----|----|----|
| 04 | 05 | 06 | 07 | 08 | 09 |
| 08 | 09 | 10 | 11 | 12 | 13 |
| 12 | 13 | 14 | 15 | 16 | 17 |
| 16 | 17 | 18 | 19 | 20 | 21 |
| 20 | 21 | 22 | 23 | 24 | 25 |
| 24 | 25 | 26 | 27 | 28 | 29 |
| 28 | 29 | 31 | 31 | 32 | 01 |

### Whitener (XOR)

After the expansion permutation, DES uses the XOR operation on the expanded right section and the round key. Note that both the right section and the key are 48-bits in length. Also note that the round key is used only in this operation.

***S-Boxes*** The S-boxes do the real mixing (confusion). DES uses 8 S-boxes, each with a 6-bit input and a 4-bit output. See Fig. 6.7.

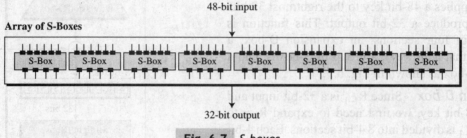

**Fig. 6.7** *S-boxes*

The 48-bit data from the second operation is divided into eight 6-bit chunks, and each chunk is fed into a box. The result of each box is a 4-bit chunk; when these are combined the result is a 32-bit text. The substitution in each box follows a pre-determined rule based on a 4-row by 16-column table. The combination of bits 1 and 6 of the input defines one of four rows; the combination of bits 2 through 5 defines one of the sixteen columns as shown in Fig. 6.8. This will become clear in the examples.

Because each S-box has its own table, we need eight tables, as shown in Tables 6.3 to 6.10, to define the output of these boxes. The values of the inputs (row number and column number) and the values of the outputs are given as decimal numbers to save space. These need to be changed to binary.

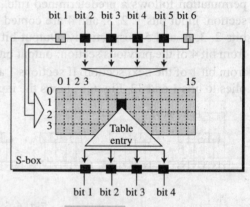

**Fig. 6.8** *S-box rule*

**Table 6.3** *S-box 1*

|   | 0 | 1 | 2 | 3 | 4 | 5 | 6 | 7 | 8 | 9 | 10 | 11 | 12 | 13 | 14 | 15 |
|---|---|---|---|---|---|---|---|---|---|---|----|----|----|----|----|----|
| *0* | 14 | 04 | 13 | 01 | 02 | 15 | 11 | 08 | 03 | 10 | 06 | 12 | 05 | 09 | 00 | 07 |
| *1* | 00 | 15 | 07 | 04 | 14 | 02 | 13 | 10 | 03 | 06 | 12 | 11 | 09 | 05 | 03 | 08 |
| *2* | 04 | 01 | 14 | 08 | 13 | 06 | 02 | 11 | 15 | 12 | 09 | 07 | 03 | 10 | 05 | 00 |
| *3* | 15 | 12 | 08 | 02 | 04 | 09 | 01 | 07 | 05 | 11 | 03 | 14 | 10 | 00 | 06 | 13 |

**Table 6.4** *S-box 2*

|   | 0 | 1 | 2 | 3 | 4 | 5 | 6 | 7 | 8 | 9 | 10 | 11 | 12 | 13 | 14 | 15 |
|---|---|---|---|---|---|---|---|---|---|---|----|----|----|----|----|----|
| *0* | 15 | 01 | 08 | 14 | 06 | 11 | 03 | 04 | 09 | 07 | 02 | 13 | 12 | 00 | 05 | 10 |
| *1* | 03 | 13 | 04 | 07 | 15 | 02 | 08 | 14 | 12 | 00 | 01 | 10 | 06 | 09 | 11 | 05 |
| *2* | 00 | 14 | 07 | 11 | 10 | 04 | 13 | 01 | 05 | 08 | 12 | 06 | 09 | 03 | 02 | 15 |
| *3* | 13 | 08 | 10 | 01 | 03 | 15 | 04 | 02 | 11 | 06 | 07 | 12 | 00 | 05 | 14 | 09 |

**Table 6.5**   *S-box 3*

|   | 0 | 1 | 2 | 3 | 4 | 5 | 6 | 7 | 8 | 9 | 10 | 11 | 12 | 13 | 14 | 15 |
|---|---|---|---|---|---|---|---|---|---|---|----|----|----|----|----|----|
| 0 | 10 | 00 | 09 | 14 | 06 | 03 | 15 | 05 | 01 | 13 | 12 | 07 | 11 | 04 | 02 | 08 |
| 1 | 13 | 07 | 00 | 09 | 03 | 04 | 06 | 10 | 02 | 08 | 05 | 14 | 12 | 11 | 15 | 01 |
| 2 | 13 | 06 | 04 | 09 | 08 | 15 | 03 | 00 | 11 | 01 | 02 | 12 | 05 | 10 | 14 | 07 |
| 3 | 01 | 10 | 13 | 00 | 06 | 09 | 08 | 07 | 04 | 15 | 14 | 03 | 11 | 05 | 02 | 12 |

**Table 6.6**   *S-box 4*

|   | 0 | 1 | 2 | 3 | 4 | 5 | 6 | 7 | 8 | 9 | 10 | 11 | 12 | 13 | 14 | 15 |
|---|---|---|---|---|---|---|---|---|---|---|----|----|----|----|----|----|
| 0 | 07 | 13 | 14 | 03 | 00 | 6 | 09 | 10 | 1 | 02 | 08 | 05 | 11 | 12 | 04 | 15 |
| 1 | 13 | 08 | 11 | 05 | 06 | 15 | 00 | 03 | 04 | 07 | 02 | 12 | 01 | 10 | 14 | 09 |
| 2 | 10 | 06 | 09 | 00 | 12 | 11 | 07 | 13 | 15 | 01 | 03 | 14 | 05 | 02 | 08 | 04 |
| 3 | 03 | 15 | 00 | 06 | 10 | 01 | 13 | 08 | 09 | 04 | 05 | 11 | 12 | 07 | 02 | 14 |

**Table 6.7**   *S-box 5*

|   | 0 | 1 | 2 | 3 | 4 | 5 | 6 | 7 | 8 | 9 | 10 | 11 | 12 | 13 | 14 | 15 |
|---|---|---|---|---|---|---|---|---|---|---|----|----|----|----|----|----|
| 0 | 02 | 12 | 04 | 01 | 07 | 10 | 11 | 06 | 08 | 05 | 03 | 15 | 13 | 00 | 14 | 09 |
| 1 | 14 | 11 | 02 | 12 | 04 | 07 | 13 | 01 | 05 | 00 | 15 | 10 | 03 | 09 | 08 | 06 |
| 2 | 04 | 02 | 01 | 11 | 10 | 13 | 07 | 08 | 15 | 09 | 12 | 05 | 06 | 03 | 00 | 14 |
| 3 | 11 | 08 | 12 | 07 | 01 | 14 | 02 | 13 | 06 | 15 | 00 | 09 | 10 | 04 | 05 | 03 |

**Table 6.8**   *S-box 6*

|   | 0 | 1 | 2 | 3 | 4 | 5 | 6 | 7 | 8 | 9 | 10 | 11 | 12 | 13 | 14 | 15 |
|---|---|---|---|---|---|---|---|---|---|---|----|----|----|----|----|----|
| 0 | 12 | 01 | 10 | 15 | 09 | 02 | 06 | 08 | 00 | 13 | 03 | 04 | 14 | 07 | 05 | 11 |
| 1 | 10 | 15 | 04 | 02 | 07 | 12 | 09 | 05 | 06 | 01 | 13 | 14 | 00 | 11 | 03 | 08 |
| 2 | 09 | 14 | 15 | 05 | 02 | 08 | 12 | 03 | 07 | 00 | 04 | 10 | 01 | 13 | 11 | 06 |
| 3 | 04 | 03 | 02 | 12 | 09 | 05 | 15 | 10 | 11 | 14 | 01 | 07 | 10 | 00 | 08 | 13 |

**Table 6.9**   *S-box 7*

|   | 0 | 1 | 2 | 3 | 4 | 5 | 6 | 7 | 8 | 9 | 10 | 11 | 12 | 13 | 14 | 15 |
|---|---|---|---|---|---|---|---|---|---|---|----|----|----|----|----|----|
| 0 | 4 | 11 | 2 | 14 | 15 | 00 | 08 | 13 | 03 | 12 | 09 | 07 | 05 | 10 | 06 | 01 |
| 1 | 13 | 00 | 11 | 07 | 04 | 09 | 01 | 10 | 14 | 03 | 05 | 12 | 02 | 15 | 08 | 06 |
| 2 | 01 | 04 | 11 | 13 | 12 | 03 | 07 | 14 | 10 | 15 | 06 | 08 | 00 | 05 | 09 | 02 |
| 3 | 06 | 11 | 13 | 08 | 01 | 04 | 10 | 07 | 09 | 05 | 00 | 15 | 14 | 02 | 03 | 12 |

**Table 6.10**   *S-box 8*

|   | 0 | 1 | 2 | 3 | 4 | 5 | 6 | 7 | 8 | 9 | 10 | 11 | 12 | 13 | 14 | 15 |
|---|---|---|---|---|---|---|---|---|---|---|----|----|----|----|----|----|
| 0 | 13 | 02 | 08 | 04 | 06 | 15 | 11 | 01 | 10 | 09 | 03 | 14 | 05 | 00 | 12 | 07 |
| 1 | 01 | 15 | 13 | 08 | 10 | 03 | 07 | 04 | 12 | 05 | 06 | 11 | 10 | 14 | 09 | 02 |
| 2 | 07 | 11 | 04 | 01 | 09 | 12 | 14 | 02 | 00 | 06 | 10 | 10 | 15 | 03 | 05 | 08 |
| 3 | 02 | 01 | 14 | 07 | 04 | 10 | 8 | 13 | 15 | 12 | 09 | 09 | 03 | 05 | 06 | 11 |

---

**Example 6.3**   The input to S-box 1 is <u>1</u>0001<u>1</u>. What is the output?

---

*Solution*   If we write the first and the sixth bits together, we get 11 in binary, which is 3 in decimal. The remaining bits are 0001 in binary, which is 1 in decimal. We look for the value in row 3, column 1, in Table 6.3 (S-box 1). The result is 12 in decimal, which in binary is 1100. So the input 100011 yields the output 1100.

---

**Example 6.4**   The input to S-box 8 is <u>0</u>0000<u>0</u>. What is the output?

---

*Solution*   If we write the first and the sixth bits together, we get 00 in binary, which is 0 in decimal. The remaining bits are 0000 in binary, which is 0 in decimal. We look for the value in row 0, column 0, in Table 6.10 (S-box 8). The result is 13 in decimal, which is 1101 in binary. So the input 000000 yields the output 1101.

*Final Permutation*   The last operation in the DES function is a permutation with a 32-bit input and a 32-bit output. The input/output relationship for this operation is shown in Table 6.11 and follows the same general rule as previous tables. For example, the seventh bit of the input becomes the second bit of the output.

**Table 6.11**   *Straight permutation table*

| 16 | 07 | 20 | 21 | 29 | 12 | 28 | 17 |
|----|----|----|----|----|----|----|----|
| 01 | 15 | 23 | 26 | 05 | 18 | 31 | 10 |
| 02 | 08 | 24 | 14 | 32 | 27 | 03 | 09 |
| 19 | 13 | 30 | 06 | 22 | 11 | 04 | 25 |

### 6.2.3   Cipher and Reverse Cipher

Using mixers and swappers, we can create the cipher and reverse cipher, each having 16 rounds. The cipher is used at the encryption site; the reverse cipher is used at the decryption site. The whole idea is to make the cipher and the reverse cipher algorithms similar.

*First Approach*   To achieve this goal, one approach is to make the last round (round 16) different from the others; it has only a mixer and no swapper. This is done in Figure 6.9.

Although the rounds are not aligned, the elements (mixer or swapper) are aligned. We proved in Chapter 5 that a mixer is a self-inverse; so is a swapper. The final and initial permutations are also inverses of each other. The left section of the plaintext at the encryption site, $L_0$, is enciphered as $L_{16}$ at the encryption site; $L_{16}$ at the decryption is deciphered as $L_0$ at the decryption site. The situation is the same with $R_0$ and $R_{16}$.

A very important point we need to remember about the ciphers is that the round keys ($K_1$ to $K_{16}$) should be applied in the reverse order. At the encryption site, round 1 uses $K_1$ and round 16 uses $K_{16}$; at the decryption site, round 1 uses $K_{16}$ and round 16 uses $K_1$.

---

**In the first approach, there is no swapper in the last round.**

---

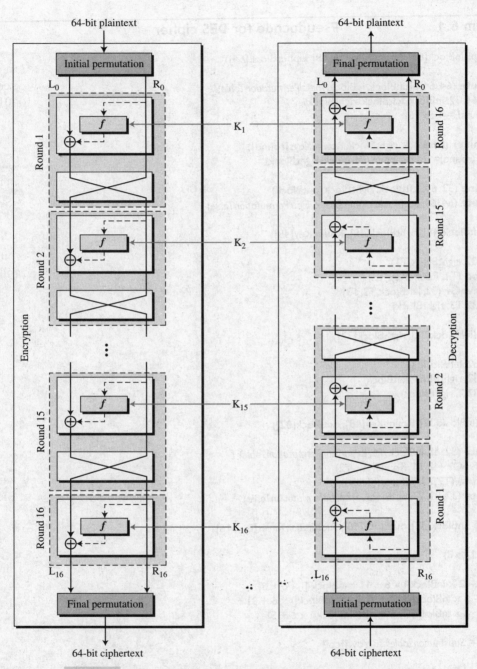

**Fig. 6.9** *DES cipher and reverse cipher for the first approach*

## Algorithm

Algorithm 6.1 gives the pseudocode for the cipher and four corresponding routines in the first approach. The codes for the rest of the routines are left as exercises.

## Algorithm 6.1         Pseudocode for DES cipher

```
Cipher (plainBlock[64], RoundKeys[16, 48], cipherBlock[64])
{
    permute (64, 64, plainBlock, inBlock, InitialPermutationTable)
    split (64, 32, inBlock, leftBlock, rightBlock)
    for (round = 1 to 16)
    {
        mixer (leftBlock, rightBlock, RoundKeys[round])
        if (round!=16) swapper (leftBlock, rightBlock)
    }
    combine (32, 64, leftBlock, rightBlock, outBlock)
    permute (64, 64, outBlock, cipherBlock, FinalPermutationTable)
}
mixer (leftBlock[48], rightBlock[48], RoundKey[48])
{
    copy (32, rightBlock, T1)
    function (T1, RoundKey, T2)
    exclusiveOr (32, leftBlock, T2, T3)
    copy (32, T3, rightBlock)
}
swapper (leftBlock[32], rigthBlock[32])
{
    copy (32, leftBlock, T)
    copy (32, rightBlock, leftBlock)
    copy (32, T, rightBlock)
}
function (inBlock[32], RoundKey[48], outBlock[32])
{
    permute (32, 48, inBlock, T1, ExpansionPermutationTable)
    exclusiveOr (48, T1, RoundKey, T2)
    substitute (T2, T3, SubstituteTables)
    permute (32, 32, T3, outBlock, StraightPermutationTable)
}
substitute (inBlock[32], outBlock[48], SubstitutionTables[8, 4, 16])
{
    for (i = 1 to 8)
    {
        row ← 2 × inBlock[i × 6 + 1] + inBlock [i × 6 + 6]
        col ← 8 × inBlock[i × 6 + 2] + 4 × inBlock[i × 6 + 3] +
              2 × inBlock[i × 6 + 4] + inBlock[i × 6 + 5]

        value = SubstitutionTables [i][row][col]

        outBlock[[i × 4 + 1] ← value / 8;   value ← value mod 8
        outBlock[[i × 4 + 2] ← value / 4;   value ← value mod 4
        outBlock[[i × 4 + 3] ← value / 2;   value ← value mod 2
        outBlock[[i × 4 + 4] ← value
    }
}
```

***Alternative Approach*** In the first approach, round 16 is different from other rounds; there is no swapper in this round. This is needed to make the last mixer in the cipher and the first mixer in the reverse cipher aligned. We can make all 16 rounds the same by including one swapper to the 16th round and add an extra swapper after that (two swappers cancel the effect of each other). We leave the design for this approach as an exercise.

***Key Generation*** The **round-key generator** creates sixteen 48-bit keys out of a 56-bit cipher key. However, the cipher key is normally given as a 64-bit key in which 8 extra bits are the parity bits, which are dropped before the actual key-generation process, as shown in Fig. 6.10.

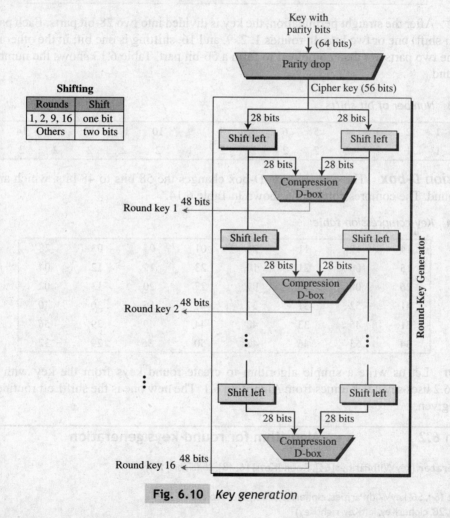

| Shifting | |
|---|---|
| **Rounds** | **Shift** |
| 1, 2, 9, 16 | one bit |
| Others | two bits |

**Fig. 6.10** *Key generation*

***Parity Drop*** The preprocess before key expansion is a compression transposition step that we call **parity bit drop.** It drops the parity bits (bits 8, 16, 24, 32, ..., 64) from the 64-bit key and permutes the rest of the bits according to Table 6.12. The remaining 56-bit value is the actual cipher key which is used to generate round keys. The parity drop step (a compression D-box) is shown in Table 6.12.

**Table 6.12** *Parity-bit drop table*

| | | | | | | | |
|---|---|---|---|---|---|---|---|
| 57 | 49 | 41 | 33 | 25 | 17 | 09 | 01 |
| 58 | 50 | 42 | 34 | 26 | 18 | 10 | 02 |
| 59 | 51 | 43 | 35 | 27 | 19 | 11 | 03 |
| 60 | 52 | 44 | 36 | 63 | 55 | 47 | 39 |
| 31 | 23 | 15 | 07 | 62 | 54 | 46 | 38 |
| 30 | 22 | 14 | 06 | 61 | 53 | 45 | 37 |
| 29 | 21 | 13 | 05 | 28 | 20 | 12 | 04 |

***Shift Left*** After the straight permutation, the key is divided into two 28-bit parts. Each part is shifted left (circular shift) one or two bits. In rounds 1, 2, 9, and 16, shifting is one bit; in the other rounds, it is two bits. The two parts are then combined to form a 56-bit part. Table 6.13 shows the number of shifts for each round.

**Table 6.13** *Number of bit shifts*

| Round | 1 | 2 | 3 | 4 | 5 | 6 | 7 | 8 | 9 | 10 | 11 | 12 | 13 | 14 | 15 | 16 |
|---|---|---|---|---|---|---|---|---|---|---|---|---|---|---|---|---|
| Bit shifts | 1 | 1 | 2 | 2 | 2 | 2 | 2 | 2 | 1 | 2 | 2 | 2 | 2 | 2 | 2 | 1 |

***Compression D-box*** The compression D-box changes the 58 bits to 48 bits, which are used as a key for a round. The compression step is shown in Table 6.14.

**Table 6.14** *Key-compression table*

| | | | | | | | |
|---|---|---|---|---|---|---|---|
| 14 | 17 | 11 | 24 | 01 | 05 | 03 | 28 |
| 15 | 06 | 21 | 10 | 23 | 19 | 12 | 04 |
| 26 | 08 | 16 | 07 | 27 | 20 | 13 | 02 |
| 41 | 52 | 31 | 37 | 47 | 55 | 30 | 40 |
| 51 | 45 | 33 | 48 | 44 | 49 | 39 | 56 |
| 34 | 53 | 46 | 42 | 50 | 36 | 29 | 32 |

***Algorithm*** Let us write a simple algorithm to create round keys from the key with parity bits. Algorithm 6.2 uses several routines from Algorithm 6.1. The new one is the shiftLeft routine, for which the code is given.

---

**Algorithm 6.2**          **Algorithm for round-keys generation**

---

```
Key_Generator (keyWithParities[64], RoundKeys[16, 48], ShiftTable[16])
{
    permute (64, 56, keyWithParities, cipherKey, ParityDropTable)
    split (56, 28, cipherKey, leftKey, rightKey)
    for (round = 1 to 16)
    {
        shiftLeft (leftKey, ShiftTable[round])
        shiftLeft (rightKey, ShiftTable[round])
```

*Algorithm 6.2   (Contd.)*

```
        combine (28, 56, leftKey, rightKey, preRoundKey)
        permute (56, 48, preRoundKey, RoundKeys[round], KeyCompressionTable)
    }
}
shiftLeft (block[28], numOfShifts)
{
    for (i = 1 to numOfShifts)
    {
        T ← block[1]
        for (j = 2 to 28)
        {
            block [j–1] ← block [j]
        }
        block[28] ← T
    }
}
```

## 6.2.4   Examples

Before analyzing DES, let us look at some examples to see the how encryption and decryption change the value of bits in each round.

**Example 6.5**   We choose a random plaintext block and a random key, and determine what the ciphertext block would be (all in hexadecimal):

Plaintext: 123456ABCD132536                     Key: AABB09182736CCDD
CipherText: C0B7A8D05F3A829C

Let us show the result of each round and the text created before and after the rounds. Table 6.15 first shows the result of steps before starting the round.

**Table 6.15**   *Trace of data for Example 6.5*

| Plaintext: 123456ABCD132536 | | | |
|---|---|---|---|
| *After initial permutation:*14A7D67818CA18AD | | | |
| After splitting: $L_0$=14A7D678 $R_0$=18CA18AD | | | |
| *Round* | *Left* | *Right* | *Round Key* |
| *Round 1* | 18CA18AD | 5A78E394 | 194CD072DE8C |
| *Round 2* | 5A78E394 | 4A1210F6 | 4568581ABCCE |
| *Round 3* | 4A1210F6 | B8089591 | 06EDA4ACF5B5 |
| *Round 4* | B8089591 | 236779C2 | DA2D032B6EE3 |
| *Round 5* | 236779C2 | A15A4B87 | 69A629FEC913 |
| *Round 6* | A15A4B87 | 2E8F9C65 | C1948E87475E |
| *Round 7* | 2E8F9C65 | A9FC20A3 | 708AD2DDB3C0 |
| *Round 8* | A9FC20A3 | 308BEE97 | 34F822F0C66D |
| *Round 9* | 308BEE97 | 10AF9D37 | 84BB4473DCCC |

*Table 6.15   (Contd.)*

| Round 10 | 10AF9D37 | 6CA6CB20 | 02765708B5BF |
|----------|----------|----------|--------------|
| Round 11 | 6CA6CB20 | FF3C485F | 6D5560AF7CA5 |
| Round 12 | FF3C485F | 22A5963B | C2C1E96A4BF3 |
| Round 13 | 22A5963B | 387CCDAA | 99C31397C91F |
| Round 14 | 387CCDAA | BD2DD2AB | 251B8BC717D0 |
| Round 15 | BD2DD2AB | CF26B472 | 3330C5D9A36D |
| Round 16 | 19BA9212 | CF26B472 | 181C5D75C66D |

*After combination:* 19BA9212CF26B472

*Ciphertext:* C0B7A8D05F3A829C                                   *(after final permutation)*

The plaintext goes through the initial permutation to create completely different 64 bits (16 hexadecimal digit). After this step, the text is split into two halves, which we call $L_0$ and $R_0$. The table shows the result of 16 rounds that involve mixing and swapping (except for the last round). The results of the last rounds ($L_{16}$ and $R_{16}$) are combined. Finally the text goes through final permutation to create the ciphertext.

Some points are worth mentioning here. First, the right section out of each round is the same as the left section out of the next round. The reason is that the right section goes through the mixer without change, but the swapper moves it to the left section. For example, $R_1$ passes through the mixer of the second round without change, but then it becomes $L_2$ because of the swapper. The interesting point is that we do not have a swapper at the last round. That is why $R_{15}$ becomes $R_{16}$ instead of becoming $L_{16}$.

**Example 6.6**   Let us see how Bob, at the destination, can decipher the ciphertext received from Alice using the same key. We have shown only a few rounds to save space. Table 6.16 shows some interesting points. First, the round keys should be used in the reverse order. Compare Table 6.15 and Table 6.16. The round key for round 1 is the same as the round key for round 16. The values of $L_0$ and $R_0$ during decryption are the same as the values of $L_{16}$ and $R_{16}$ during encryption. This is the same with other rounds. This proves not only that the cipher and the reverse cipher are inverses of each other in the whole, but also that each round in the cipher has a corresponding reverse round in the reverse cipher. The result proves that the initial and final permutation steps are also inverses of each other.

**Table 6.16**   *Trace of data for Example 6.6*

*Ciphertext:* C0B7A8D05F3A829C

*After initial permutation:* 19BA9212CF26B472
After splitting: $L_0$=19BA9212    $R_0$=CF26B472

| Round | Left | Right | Round Key |
|-------|------|-------|-----------|
| Round 1 | CF26B472 | BD2DD2AB | 181C5D75C66D |
| Round 2 | BD2DD2AB | 387CCDAA | 3330C5D9A36D |
| ... | ... | ... | ... |
| Round 15 | 5A78E394 | 18CA18AD | 4568581ABCCE |
| Round 16 | 14A7D678 | 18CA18AD | 194CD072DE8C |

After combination: 14A7D67818CA18AD

Plaintext:123456ABCD132536                                   *(after final permutation)*

## 6.3 DES ANALYSIS

Critics have used a strong magnifier to analyze DES. Tests have been done to measure the strength of some desired properties in a block cipher. The elements of DES have gone through scrutinies to see if they have met the established criteria. We discuss some of these in this section.

### 6.3.1 Properties

Two desired properties of a block cipher are the avalanche effect and the completeness.

***Avalanche Effect*** **Avalanche effect** means a small change in the plaintext (or key) should create a significant change in the ciphertext. DES has been proved to be strong with regard to this property.

---

**Example 6.7**   To check the avalanche effect in DES, let us encrypt two plaintext blocks (with the same key) that differ only in one bit and observe the differences in the number of bits in each round.

Plaintext: 0000000000000000          Key: 22234512987ABB23
Ciphertext: 4789FD476E82A5F1

Plaintext: 0000000000000001          Key: 22234512987ABB23
Ciphertext: 0A4ED5C15A63FEA3

  Although the two plaintext blocks differ only in the rightmost bit, the ciphertext blocks differ in 29 bits. This means that changing approximately 1.5 percent of the plaintext creates a change of approximately 45 percent in the ciphertext. Table 6.17 shows the change in each round. It shows that significant changes occur as early as the third round.

**Table 6.17**   *Number of bit differences for Example 6.7*

| Rounds | 1 | 2 | 3 | 4 | 5 | 6 | 7 | 8 | 9 | 10 | 11 | 12 | 13 | 14 | 15 | 16 |
|---|---|---|---|---|---|---|---|---|---|---|---|---|---|---|---|---|
| Bit differences | 1 | 6 | 20 | 29 | 30 | 33 | 32 | 29 | 32 | 39 | 33 | 28 | 30 | 31 | 30 | 29 |

---

***Completeness Effect*** **Completeness effect** means that each bit of the ciphertext needs to depend on many bits on the plaintext. The diffusion and confusion produced by D-boxes and S-boxes in DES, show a very strong completeness effect.

### 6.3.2 Design Criteria

The design of DES was revealed by IBM in 1994. Many tests on DES have proved that it satisfies some of the required criteria as claimed. We briefly discuss some of these design issues.

***S-Boxes***   We have discussed the general design criteria for S-boxes in Chapter 5; we only discuss the criteria selected for DES here. The design provides confusion and diffusion of bits from each round to the next. According to this revelation and some research, we can mention several properties of S-boxes.

1.  The entries of each row are permutations of values between 0 and 15.
2.  S-boxes are nonlinear. In other words, the output is not an affine transformation of the input. See Chapter 5 for discussion on the linearity of S-boxes.
3.  If we change a single bit in the input, two or more bits will be changed in the output.

4. If two inputs to an S-box differ only in two middle bits (bits 3 and 4), the output must differ in at least two bits. In other words, S(x) and S(x ⊕ 001100) must differ in at least two bits where x is the input and S(x) is the output.

5. If two inputs to an S-box differ in the first two bits (bits 1 and 2) and are the same in the last two bits (5 and 6), the two outputs must be different. In other words, we need to have the following relation S(x) ≠ S(x ⊕ 11bc00), in which b and c are arbitrary bits.

6. There are only 32 6-bit input-word pairs ($x_i$ and $x_j$), in which $x_i \oplus x_j \neq (000000)_2$. These 32 input pairs create 32 4-bit output-word pairs. If we create the difference between the 32 output pairs, $d = y_i \oplus y_j$, no more than 8 of these $d$'s should be the same.

7. A criterion similar to # 6 is applied to three S-boxes.

8. In any S-box, if a single input bit is held constant (0 or 1) and the other bits are changed randomly, the differences between the number of 0s and 1s are minimized.

## D-Boxes

Between two rows of S-boxes (in two subsequent rounds), there are one straight D-box (32 to 32) and one expansion D-box (32 to 48). These two D-boxes together provide diffusion of bits. We have discussed the general design principle of D-boxes in Chapter 5. Here we discuss only the ones applied to the D-boxes used inside the DES function. The following criteria were implemented in the design of D-boxes to achieve this goal:

1. Each S-box input comes from the output of a different S-box (in the previous round).

2. No input to a given S-box comes from the output from the same box (in the previous round).

3. The four outputs from each S-box go to six different S-boxes (in the next round).

4. No two output bits from an S-box go to the same S-box (in the next round).

5. If we number the eight S-boxes, $S_1, S_2, \ldots, S_8$,

   a. An output of $S_{j-2}$ goes to one of the first two bits of $S_j$ (in the next round).

   b. An output bit from $S_{j-1}$ goes to one of the last two bits of $S_j$ (in the next round).

   c. An output of $S_{j+1}$ goes to one of the two middle bits of $S_j$ (in the next round).

6. For each S-box, the two output bits go to the first or last two bits of an S-box in the next round. The other two output bits go to the middle bits of an S-box in the next round.

7. If an output bit from $S_j$ goes to one of the middle bits in $S_k$ (in the next round), then an output bit from $S_k$ cannot go to the middle bit of $S_j$. If we let $j = k$, this implies that none of the middle bits of an S-box can go to one of the middle bits of the same S-box in the next round.

**Number of Rounds**  DES uses sixteen rounds of Feistel ciphers. It has been proved that after eight rounds, each ciphertext is a function of every plaintext bit and every key bit; the ciphertext is thoroughly a random function of plaintext and ciphertext. Therefore, it looks like eight rounds should be enough. However, experiments have found that DES versions with less than sixteen rounds are even more vulnerable to known-plaintext attacks than brute-force attack, which justifies the use of sixteen rounds by the designers of DES.

### 6.3.3  DES Weaknesses

During the last few years critics have found some weaknesses in DES.

### Weaknesses in Cipher Design

We will briefly mention some weaknesses that have been found in the design of the cipher.

*S-boxes*  At least three weaknesses are mentioned in the literature for S-boxes.
1. In S-box 4, the last three output bits can be derived in the same way as the first output bit by complementing some of the input bits.
2. Two specifically chosen inputs to an S-box array can create the same output.
3. It is possible to obtain the same output in a single round by changing bits in only three neighboring S-boxes.

*D-boxes*  One mystery and one weakness were found in the design of D-boxes:
1. It is not clear why the designers of DES used the initial and final permutations; these have no security benefits.
2. In the expansion permutation (inside the function), the first and fourth bits of every 4-bit series are repeated.

### Weakness in the Cipher Key

Several weaknesses have been found in the cipher key.

*Key Size*  Critics believe that the most serious weakness of DES is in its key size (56 bits). To do a brute-force attack on a given ciphertext block, the adversary needs to check $2^{56}$ keys.
- a. With available technology, it is possible to check one million keys per second. This means that we need more than two thousand years to do brute-force attacks on DES using only a computer with one processor.
- b. If we can make a computer with one million chips (parallel processing), then we can test the whole key domain in approximately 20 hours. When DES was introduced, the cost of such a computer was over several million dollars, but the cost has dropped rapidly. A special computer was built in 1998 that found the key in 112 hours.
- c. Computer networks can simulate parallel processing. In 1977 a team of researchers used 3500 computers attached to the Internet to find a key challenged by RSA Laboratories in 120 days. The key domain was divided among all of these computers, and each computer was responsible to check the part of the domain.
- d. If 3500 networked computers can find the key in 120 days, a secret society with 42,000 members can find the key in 10 days.

The above discussion shows that DES with a cipher key of 56 bits is not safe enough to be used comfortably. We will see later in the chapter that one solution is to use triple DES (3DES) with two keys (112 bits) or triple DES with three keys (168 bits).

*Weak Keys*  Four out of $2^{56}$ possible keys are called **weak keys.** A weak key is the one that, after parity drop operation (using Table 6.12), consists either of all 0s, all 1s, or half 0s and half 1s. These keys are shown in Table 6.18.

**Table 6.18**  *Weak keys*

| Keys before parities drop (64 bits) | | | | Actual key (56 bits) | |
| --- | --- | --- | --- | --- | --- |
| 0101 | 0101 | 0101 | 0101 | 0000000 | 0000000 |
| 1F1F | 1F1F | 0E0E | 0E0E | 0000000 | FFFFFFF |
| E0E0 | E0E0 | F1F1 | F1F1 | FFFFFFF | 0000000 |
| FEFE | FEFE | FEFE | FEFE | FFFFFFF | FFFFFFF |

The round keys created from any of these weak keys are the same and have the same pattern as the cipher key. For example, the sixteen round keys created from the first key is all made of 0s; the one from the second is made of half 0s and half 1s. The reason is that the key-generation algorithm first divides the cipher key into two halves. Shifting or permutation of a block does not change the block if it is made of all 0s or all 1s.

What is the disadvantage of using a weak key? If we encrypt a block with a weak key and subsequently encrypt the result with the same weak key, we get the original block. The process creates the same original block if we decrypt the block twice. In other words, each weak key is the inverse of itself $E_k(E_k(P)) = P$, as shown in Fig. 6.11.

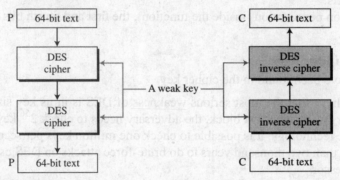

**Fig. 6.11** *Double encryption and decryption with a weak key*

Weak keys should be avoided because the adversary can easily try them on the intercepted ciphertext. If after two decryptions the result is the same, the adversary has found the key.

**Example 6.8** Let us try the first weak key in Table 6.18 to encrypt a block two times. After two encryptions with the same key the original plaintext block is created. Note that we have used the encryption algorithm two times, not one encryption followed by another decryption.

> Key: 0x0101010101010101
> Plaintext: *0x1234567887654321*    Ciphertext: 0x814FE938589154F7
>
> Key: 0x0101010101010101
> Plaintext: 0x814FE938589154F7    Ciphertext: *0x1234567887654321*

*Semi-weak Keys* There are six key pairs that are called **semi-weak keys.** These six pairs are shown in Table 6.19 (64-bit format before dropping the parity bits).

**Table 6.19** *Semi-weak keys*

| First key in the pair | | | | Second key in the pair | | | |
|---|---|---|---|---|---|---|---|
| 01FE | 01FE | 01FE | 01FE | FE01 | FE01 | FE01 | FE01 |
| 1FE0 | 1FE0 | 0EF1 | 0EF1 | E01F | E01F | F10E | F10E |
| 01E0 | 01E1 | 01F1 | 01F1 | E001 | E001 | F101 | F101 |
| 1FFE | 1FFE | 0EFE | 0EFE | FE1F | FE1F | FE0E | FE0E |
| 011F | 011F | 010E | 010E | 1F01 | 1F01 | 0E01 | 0E01 |
| E0FE | E0FE | F1FE | F1FE | FEE0 | FEE0 | FEF1 | FEF1 |

A semi-weak key creates only two different round keys and each of them is repeated eight times. In addition, the round keys created from each pair are the same with different orders. To show the idea, we have created the round keys from the first pairs as shown below:

| | | |
|---|---|---|
| *Round key 1* | **9153E54319BD** | 6EAC1ABCE642 |
| *Round key 2* | **6EAC1ABCE642** | 9153E54319BD |
| *Round key 3* | **6EAC1ABCE642** | 9153E54319BD |
| *Round key 4* | **6EAC1ABCE642** | 9153E54319BD |
| *Round key 5* | **6EAC1ABCE642** | 9153E54319BD |
| *Round key 6* | **6EAC1ABCE642** | 9153E54319BD |
| *Round key 7* | **6EAC1ABCE642** | 9153E54319BD |
| *Round key 8* | **6EAC1ABCE642** | 9153E54319BD |
| *Round key 9* | **9153E54319BD** | 6EAC1ABCE642 |
| *Round key 10* | **9153E54319BD** | 6EAC1ABCE642 |
| *Round key 11* | **9153E54319BD** | 6EAC1ABCE642 |
| *Round key 12* | **9153E54319BD** | 6EAC1ABCE642 |
| *Round key 13* | **9153E54319BD** | 6EAC1ABCE642 |
| *Round key 14* | **9153E54319BD** | 6EAC1ABCE642 |
| *Round key 15* | **9153E54319BD** | 6EAC1ABCE642 |
| *Round key 16* | **6EAC1ABCE642** | 9153E54319BD |

As the list shows, there are eight equal round keys in each semi-weak key. In addition, round key 1 in the first set is the same as round key 16 in the second; round key 2 in the first is the same as round key 15 in the second; and so on. This means that the keys are inverses of each other $E_{k_2}(E_{k_1}(P)) = P$, as shown in Fig. 6.12.

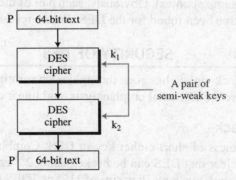

**Fig. 6.12** *A pair of semi-weak keys in encryption and decryption*

***Possible Weak Keys*** There are also 48 keys that are called **possible weak keys.** A possible weak key is a key that creates only four distinct round keys; in other words, the sixteen round keys are divided into four groups and each group is made of four equal round keys.

**Example 6.9** What is the probability of randomly selecting a weak, a semi-weak, or a possible weak key?

*Solution* DES has a key domain of $2^{56}$. The total number of the above keys are 64 (4 + 12 + 48). The probability of choosing one of these keys is $8.8 \times 10^{-16}$, almost impossible.

*Key Complement* In the key domain ($2^{56}$), definitely half of the keys are *complement* of the other half. A **key complement** can be made by inverting (changing 0 to 1 or 1 to 0) each bit in the key. Does a key complement simplify the job of the cryptanalysis? It happens that it does. Eve can use only half of the possible keys ($2^{55}$) to perform brute-force attack. This is because

$$C = E (K, P) \rightarrow \overline{C} = E (\overline{K}, \overline{P})$$

In other words, if we encrypt the complement of plaintext with the complement of the key, we get the complement of the ciphertext. Eve does not have to test all $2^{56}$ possible keys, she can test only half of them and then complement the result.

**Example 6.10** Let us test the claim about the complement keys. We have used an arbitrary key and plaintext to find the corresponding ciphertext. If we have the key complement and the plaintext, we can obtain the complement of the previous ciphertext (Table 6.20).

Table 6.20 *Results for Example 6.10*

|  | *Original* | *Complement* |
|---|---|---|
| Key | 1234123412341234 | EDCBEDCBEDCBEDCB |
| Plaintext | 12345678ABCDEF12 | EDCBA987543210ED |
| Ciphertext | E112BE1DEFC7A367 | 1EED41E210385C98 |

*Key Clustering* Key clustering refers to the situation in which two or more different keys can create the same ciphertext from the same plaintext. Obviously, each pair of the semi-weak keys is a key cluster. However, no more clusters have been found for the DES. Future research may reveal some more.

## 6.4                                       SECURITY OF DES

DES, as the first important block cipher, has gone through much scrutiny. Among the attempted attacks, three are of interest: brute-force, differential cryptanalysis, and linear cryptanalysis.

### 6.4.1 Brute-Force Attack

We have discussed the weakness of short cipher key in DES. Combining this weakness with the key complement weakness, it is clear that DES can be broken using $2^{55}$ encryptions. However, today most applications use either 3DES with two keys (key size of 112) or 3DES with three keys (key size of 168). These two multiple-DES versions make DES resistant to brute-force attacks.

## 6.4.2 Differential Cryptanalysis

We discussed the technique of differential cryptanalysis on modern block ciphers in Chapter 5. DES is not immune to that kind of attack. However, it has been revealed that the designers of DES already knew about this type of attack and designed S-boxes and chose 16 as the number of rounds to make DES specifically resistant to this type of attack. Today, it has been shown that DES can be broken using differential cryptanalysis if we have $2^{47}$ chosen plaintexts or $2^{55}$ known plaintexts. Although this looks more efficient than a brute-force attack, finding $2^{47}$ chosen plaintexts or $2^{55}$ know plaintexts is impractical. Therefore, we can say that DES is resistant to differential cryptanalysis. It has also been shown that increasing the number of rounds to 20 require more than $2^{64}$ chosen plaintexts for this attack, which is impossible because the possible number of plaintext blocks in DES is only $2^{64}$.

---

**We show an example of DES differential cryptanalysis in Appendix N.**

---

## 6.4.3 Linear Cryptanalysis

We discussed the technique of linear cryptanalysis on modern block ciphers in Chapter 5. Linear cryptanalysis is newer than differential cryptanalysis. DES is more vulnerable to linear cryptanalysis than to differential cryptanalysis, probably because this type of attack was not known to the designers of DES. S-boxes are not very resistant to linear cryptanalysis. It has been shown that DES can be broken using $2^{43}$ pairs of known plaintexts. However, from the practical point of view, finding so many pairs is very unlikely.

---

**We show an example of DES linear cryptanalysis in Appendix N.**

---

# 6.5 MULTIPLE DES—CONVENTIONAL ENCRYPTION ALGORITHMS

If a block cipher has a key size, which is small in context to the present day computation power, then a natural way out may be to perform multiple encryptions by the block cipher. As an example, consider the DES algorithm which has a key size of 56 bits, which is short in context to the modern computation capability. The threat is that such a key value can be evaluated by brute force key search. Hence two DES applications give what is known as 2-DES.

## 6.5.1 2-DES and Meet in the Middle Attack

Consider a message m, which is to be encrypted. The corresponding block cipher for one application of the DES applications is represented by $E_k$, where $k$ is the corresponding DES key. The output of 2-DES is $c = E_{k_2}(E_{k_1}(m))$. To decrypt similarly, $m = D_{k_1}(D_{k_2}(c))$. This cipher, 2-DES should offer additional security, equivalent to both $k_1$ and $k_2$. The cipher 2-DES obtained by the repeated application of DES is called, $2 - DES = DES \times DES$. This is called a product cipher obtained by the composition of two ciphers. Such an idea can similarly be extended to multiple ciphers.

It may be noted that such a product on the DES cipher is expected to provide additional security, because DES does not form a group under the composition operation. That is the composition (application) of two ciphers with two different keys cannot be obtained by a single application of DES with a key. Thus 2-DES is expected to provide security equivalent to $56 \times 2 = 112$ bits. However it can be shown that such a cipher can be attacked by an attack method which is called Meet-in-the-Middle attack.

## 6.5.2 Meet-in-the-Middle (MIM) Attack and 3-DES

Consider the cipher 2-DES as defined above. The plaintext and the ciphertext of the cipher is $P=\{0,1\}^m$. The key space of DES is $K=\{0,1\}^n$, the key size of the product cipher is expected to be $K_1 \times K_2$, where the key is represented as the ordered pair $(k_1, k_2)$, where $k_1$ belongs to $K_1$ and $k_2$ belongs to $K_2$.

The attacker obtains $l$ pairs of plaintexts and ciphertexts: $(p_1, c_1), \ldots, (p_l, c_1)$. The key is say $(K_1, K_2)$ but unknown to the attacker (obviously, else why will he/she be an attacker).

It is easy to prove that for all $1 \le i \le l$, $DES_{K_1}(p_i) = DES_{K_2}^{-1}(c)$. There are in total $2^{2n}$ keys. The probability of a key satisfying this equation for a particular value of i is $2^{-m}$, as that is the block size of the cipher. Since all the $i$ values of the plaintext, ciphertext pairs are independent, the probability of a key satisfying the above equation for all the $l$ values of i, is $2^{-ml}$.

Thus the reduced key space which satisfies the above test is expected to be $2^{2n}.2^{-ml} = 2^{2n-ml}$.

Suppose $l \ge 2n/m$, hence the number of keys passing the above test is $\le 1$. Thus if for a key $(K_1, K_2)$, for all $1 \le i \le l$, $DES_{K_i}(p_i) = DES_{K_i}^{-1}(c)$ is satisfied, there is a high probability that the key is the correct key.

The attacker maintains two lists $L_1$ and $L_2$ as follows:

$L_1$ contains $2^n$ rows, where each row stores one round DES encryptions of the $l$ plaintexts, $p_1, \ldots, p_l$. $L_2$ contains also $2^n$ rows where each row stores one round DES decryptions of the $l$ ciphertexts, $c_1, \ldots, c_l$. The lists are sorted in lexicographical order with respect to the plaintexts and ciphertexts. The lists look like as shown in the Fig. 6.13.

| $L_1$:Plain Texts | Key |
|---|---|
| $DES_{K_1^1}(p_1)DES_{K_1^1}(p_2)...DES_{K_1^1}(p_l)$ | $K_1^1$ |
| $DES_{K_1^{2^n}}(p_1)DES_{K_1^{2^n}}(p_2)...DES_{K_1^{2^n}}(p_l)$ | $K_1^{2^n}$ |

| $L_2$: Cipher Texts | Key |
|---|---|
| $DES_{K_1^1}^{-1}(c_1)DES_{K_1^1}^{-1}(c_2)...DES_{K_1^1}^{-1}(c_l)$ | $K_2^1$ |
| $DES_{K_1^{2^n}}^{-1}(c_1)DES_{K_1^{2^n}}^{-1}(c_2)...DES_{K_1^{2^n}}^{-1}(c_l)$ | $K_2^{2^n}$ |

(a)                          (b)

**Fig. 6.13**

The attacker now searches the lists $L_1$ and $L_2$ and looks for a row $i$ in $L_1$ which matches with a row $j$ in $L_2$. Then by the above discussion, if $l \ge 2n/m$ there is a high probability that the key is $(K_1^i, K_2^j)$. What is the complexity of the attack? Each table has $2^n$ rows. Each row has $l$ blocks of size m bits each plus an additional n bits for the key. Hence each row of the table has ml+n bits. Thus the memory required by the attacker per table is $2^n(ml + n)$, and for the two tables it is equal to $2^{n+1}(ml + n)$. The time complexity of the attack is proportional to the number of encryptions or decryptions required. This works out to $2.l.2^n = l.2^{n+1}$.

This is an example of known plaintext attack, because the plaintext is known but not chosen.

Thus we see that for typical values of DES, where $n = m = 56$, the security provided by DES against a meet-in-the-middle attack is that of 57 bits, as opposed to the expected security of 112 bits. Also it may be noted that the attack works with a high probability of success if $l \ge 2$, which means that only two plaintexts needs to be known for the attack.

Since double DES or 2-DES has a problem of this meet-in-the-middle attack, Triple-DES or 3-DES was developed. The expected security of 3-DES is 112 bits (why?).

There are in general two flavors of 3-DES. There are at least two flavors of implementation of 3-DES. The first implementation uses three keys, namely $K_1$, $K_2$, $K_3$. The ciphertext of $m$ is thus obtained by $C = DES_{k_1}[DES_{k_2}(DES_{k_3}(m))]$. The second way to implement 3-DES is using two keys, thus $C = DES_{k_1}[DES_{k_2}^{-1}(DES_{k_1}(m))]$. Thus if the keys $K_1$ and $K_2$ are the same then we obtain a single DES. This backward compatibility of the two key version of 3-DES is the reason why the middle layer is a decryption. It has otherwise no security implications.

## 6.6      EXAMPLES OF BLOCK CIPHERS INFLUENCED BY DES

### 6.6.1   The CAST Block Cipher

The CAST Block Cipher is an improvement of the DES block cipher, invented in Canada by Carlisle Adams and Stafford Tavares. The name of the cipher seems to be after the initials of the inventors. The CAST algorithm has 64 bit block size and has a key of size 64 bits.

CAST is based on the Feistel structure to implement the substitution permutation network. The authors state that they use the Feistel structure, as it is well studied and free of basic structural weaknesses.

***S-Boxes of CAST***   CAST uses S-Boxes of dimension $m \times n$ $(m < n)$. The typical dimension of the S-Boxes of CAST is $8 \times 32$. The principle behind the construction is as follows: choose $n$ distinct binary bent functions of length $2^m$, such that the linear combinations of these functions sum to highly non-linear, Boolen functions. Bent function are Boolean functions with even input variables having the highest possible non-linearity. The resultant functions also satisfy Strict Avalanche Criteria (SAC). SAC states that S-Box output bit $j$ should change with probability ½ when any single input bit is changed, for all $i, j$. Note that the probability is computed over the set of all pairs of input vectors which differ only in bit i. Half of the bent functions have a weight of $(2^{m-1} + 2^{(m/2)-1})$ and the other have a weight of $(2^{m-1} - 2^{(m/2)-1})$.

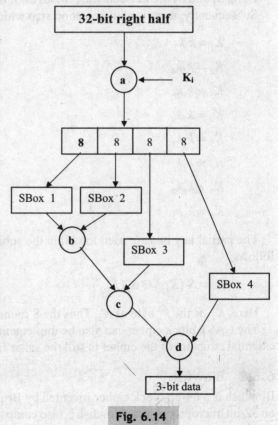

***Encryption Function***   The plaintext block is divided into a left half and a right half. The algorithm has 8 rounds. Each round is essentially a Feistel structure. In each round the right half is combined with the round key using a function $f$ and then XOR-ed with the left half. The new left half after the round is the same as the right half before the round. After 8 iterations of the rounds, the left and the right half are concatenated to form the ciphertext.

***The Round Function f***   The round function in CAST can be realized as follows. The 32 bit input can be combined with 32 bits of the round key through a function, denoted by "a" (refer Fig. 6.14).

**Fig. 6.14**

The 32-bit data half is combined using operation "*a*" and the 32-bit result is split into 8 bit pieces. Each piece is input into a 8 × 32 S-Box. The output of S-Box 1 and 2 are combined using the operation "*b*"; the 32 bit output is combined with the output of S-Box 3, the output is combined in turn with the output of S-Box 4. The combining functions are denoted in the figure by "*c*" and "*d*". A simple way would be where all the combining functions are XOR functions, however more complex operations may also be used.

**Key Scheduling of CAST**    The key scheduling in CAST has three main components:

1.  A key transformation step which converts the primary key (input key) to an intermediate key.
2.  A relatively simple bit-selection algorithm mapping the primary key and the intermediate key to a form, referred as partial key bits.
3.  A set of key-schedule S-Boxes which are used to create subkeys from the partial key bits.

Let, the input key be denoted by KEY = $k_1 k_2 k_3 k_4 k_5 k_6 k_7 k_8$, where $k_i$ is the $i^{th}$ byte of the primary key. The key transformation step generates the intermediate key, KEY' = $k'_1 k'_2 k'_3 k'_4 k'_5 k'_6 k'_7 k'_8$ as follows:

$$k'_1 k'_2 k'_3 k'_4 = k_1 k_2 k_3 k_4 \oplus S_1[k_5] \oplus S_2[k_7]$$

$$k'_5 k'_6 k'_7 k'_8 = k_5 k_6 k_7 k_8 \oplus S_1[k'_2] \oplus S_2[k'_4]$$

Here, $S_1$ and $S_2$ are key-schedule $S$-Boxes of dimension 8 × 32.

Subsequently, there is a bit-selection step which operates as shown below:

$$K'_1 = k_1 k_2$$
$$K'_2 = k_3 k_4$$
$$K'_3 = k_5 k_6$$
$$K'_4 = k_7 k_8$$
$$K'_5 = k'_4 k'_3$$
$$K'_6 = k'_2 k'_1$$
$$K'_7 = k'_8 k'_7$$
$$K'_8 = k'_6 k'_5$$

The partial key bits are used to obtain the subkeys, $K_i$. The subkeys are 32 bits, and are obtained as follows:

$$K_i = S_1(K'_{i,1}) \oplus S_2(K'_{i,2})$$

Here, $K'_{i,j}$ is the $j^{th}$ byte of $K'_i$. Thus the 8 round subkeys are obtained.

The CAST block cipher can also be implemented with 128 bits, and is referred to as CAST-128. The essential structure of the cipher is still the same as discussed above.

## 6.6.2   Blowfish

Blowfish is a 64-bit block cipher invented by Bruce Schneier. Blowfish was designed for fast ciphering on 32-bit microprocessors. Blowfish is also compact and has a variable key length which can be increased to 448 bits.

Blowfish is suitable for applications where the key does not change frequently like communication links or file encryptors. However for applications like packet switching or as an one-way hash function, it is unsuitable. Blowfish is not ideal for smart cards, which requires even more compact ciphers. Blowfish is faster than DES when implemented on 32-bit microprocessors. Next we discuss on the round structure of Blowfish.

**Round Structure** The algorithm is based on the Feistel structure and has two important parts: the round structure and the key expansion function.

There are 16 rounds, and each round are made of simple transformations which are iterated. Each round consists of a key-dependent permutation, and a key and data-dependent substitution. All the operations are additions and XORs on 32 bit words, and lookups in 4 32-bit S-Boxes. Blowfish has a P-array, $P_0, P_1, \ldots, P_{18}$ each of which are 32 bit subkeys. There are 4 S-Boxes, each of which maps an 8-bit input to 32-bits. The round structure of Blowfish is illustrated in Fig. 6.15.

The round function is also explained underneath with a pseudo-code.

Divide x into two 32-bit halves: $x_L, x_R$

For $i = 1$ to 16:

$x_L = x_L \oplus P_i$

$x_R = F[x_L] \oplus x_R$

Swap $x_L$ and $x_R$

(undo the last swap)

$x_R = x_R \oplus P_{17}$

$x_L = x_L \oplus P_{18}$

Ciphertext = Concatenation of $x_L$ and $x_R$

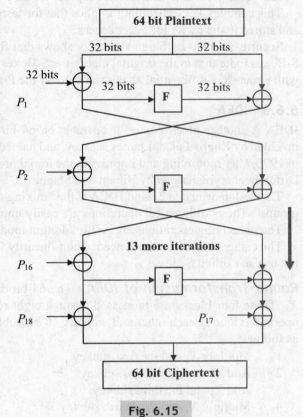

Fig. 6.15

The function F is central to the security of the block cipher and is defined as below:

Divide $x_L$ into four 8-bit parts: $a, b, c, d$

$$F[x_L] = ((S_1[a] + S_2[b] \bmod 2^{32}) \oplus S_3[c]) + S_4[d] \bmod 2^{32}$$

**Key Scheduling Algorithm** The subkeys are computed using the following method:
1. The P-array and then the four S-Boxes are initialized with a fixed string. The string is the hexadecimal digits of $\pi$.
2. $P_1$ is XOR-ed with 32 bits of the key, $P_2$ is XOR-ed with the next 32 bits of the key, and so on for all the bits of the key. If needed the key bits are cycled to ensure that all the P-array elements are XOR-ed.

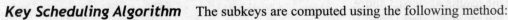

3. An all-zero string is encrypted with the Blowfish algorithm, with the subkeys $P_1$ to $P_{18}$ obtained so far in steps 1 and 2.
4. $P_1$ and $P_2$ are replaced by the 64 bit output of step 3.
5. The output of step 3 is now encrypted with the updated subkeys to replace $P_3$ and $P_4$ with the ciphertext of step 4.
6. This process is continued to replace all the *P*-arrays and the *S*-Boxes in order.

This complex key-scheduling implies that for faster operations the subkeys should be precomputed and stored in the cache for faster access.

Security analysis by Serge Vaudenay shows that for a Blowfish algorithm implemented with known S-Boxes (note that in the original cipher the S-Boxes are generated during the encryption process) and with r-rounds, a differential attack can recover the P-array with $2^{8r+1}$ chosen plaintexts.

### 6.6.3 IDEA

IDEA is another block cipher. It operates on 64 bit data blocks and the key is 128 bit long. It was invented by Xuejia Lai and James Massey, and named IDEA (International Data Encryption Algorithm) in 1990, after modifying and improving the initial proposal of the cipher based on the seminal work on Differential cryptanalysis by Biham and Shamir.

The design principle behind IDEA is the "mixing of arithmetical operations from different algebraic groups". These arithmetical operations are easily implemented both in hardware and software.

The underlying operations are XOR, addition modulo $2^{16}$, multiplication modulo $2^{16}+1$.

The cipher obtains the much needed non-linearity from the later two arithmetical operations and does not use an explicit S-Box.

***Round Transformation of IDEA*** The 64-bit data is divided into four 16 bit blocks: $X_1, X_2, X_3, X_4$. These four blocks are processed through eight rounds and transformed by the above arithmetical operations among each other and with six 16 bit subkeys. In each round the sequence of operations is as follows:

1. Multiply $X_1$ and the first subkey.
2. Add $X_2$ and the second subkey.
3. Add $X_3$ and the third subkey.
4. Multiply $X_4$ and the fourth subkey.
5. XOR the results of step 1 and 3.
6. XOR the results of step 2 and 4.
7. Multiply the results of steps 5 with the fifth subkey.
8. Add the results of steps 6 and 7.
9. Multiply the results of steps 8 with the sixth subkey.
10. Add the results of steps 7 and 9.
11. XOR the results of steps 1 and 9.
12. XOR the results of steps 3 and 9.
13. XOR the results of steps 2 and 10.
14. XOR the results of steps 4 and 10.

The outputs of steps 11, 12, 13 and 14 are stored in four words of 16 bits each, namely $Y_1$, $Y_2$, $Y_3$ and $Y_4$. The blocks $Y_2$ and $Y_3$ are swapped, and the resultant four blocks are the output of a round of IDEA. It may be noted that the last round of IDEA does not have the swap step.

Instead the last round has the following additional transformations:

1. Multiply $Y_1$ and the first subkey.

2. Add $Y_2$ and the second subkey.
3. Add $Y_3$ and the third subkey.
4. Multiply $Y_4$ and the fourth subkey.

Finally, the ciphertext is the concatenation of the blocks $Y_1$, $Y_2$, $Y_3$ and $Y_4$.

**Key Scheduling of IDEA** IDEA has a very simple key scheduling. It takes the 128 bit key and divides it into eight 16 bit blocks. The first six blocks are used for the first round, while the remaining two are to be used for the second round. Then the entire 128 bit key is given a rotation for 25 steps to the left and again divided into eight blocks. The first four blocks are used as the remaining subkeys for the second round, while the last four blocks are to be used for the third round. The key is then again given a left shift by 25 bits, and the other subkeys are obtained. The process is continued till the end of the algorithm.

For decryption, the subkeys are reversed and are either the multiplicative or additive inverse of the encryption subkeys. The all zero subkey is considered to represent $2^{16}=-1$ for the modular multiplication operation, mod $2^{16}+1$. Thus the multiplicative inverse of 0 is itself, as $-1$ multiplied with $-1$ gives 1, the multiplicative identity in the group. Computing these keys may have its overhead, but it is a one time operation, at the beginning of the decryption process.

IDEA has resisted several cryptanalytic efforts. The designers gave argument to justify that only 4 rounds of the cipher makes it immune to differential cryptanalysis.

Joan Daemen, Rene Govaerts and Joos Vandewalle showed that the cipher had certain keys which can be easily discovered in a chosen plaintext attack.

They used the fact that the use of multiplicative subkeys with the value of 1 or -1 gives rise to linear factors in the round function. A linear factor is a linear equation in the key, input and output bits that hold for all possible input bits. The linear factors can be revealed by expressing the modulo 2 sum of LSBs of the output subblocks of an IDEA round in terms of inputs and key bits.

From the round structure of IDEA, the XOR of the LSBs of the first and second output subblock of a round are represented by $y_1$ and $y_2$.

$$y_1 \oplus y_2 = (X_1.Z_1)|_0 \oplus 1 \oplus x_3 \oplus z_3$$

If $Z_1=(-)1=0\ldots01$ (i,e if the 15 MSB bits of the $Z_1$ are 0), we have the following linear equation:

$$y_1 \oplus y_2 = x_1 \oplus x_3 \oplus z_1 \oplus z_3 \oplus 1$$

If the key bits are considered as constants, this linear factor can be interpreted as the propagation of knowledge from to $x_1 \oplus x_3$ to $y_1 \oplus y_2$. This is indicated by $(1,0,1,0) \rightarrow (1,1,0,0)$.

Similar factors and their corresponding conditions on subkey blocks can be found for all 15 combinations of LSB output bits and are listed in the following table:

**Table 6.21** *Linear Factors in the round function with conditions on the subkeys*

| Linear Factor | $Z_1$ | $Z_4$ | $Z_5$ | $Z_6$ |
|---|---|---|---|---|
| $(0,0,0,1)\rightarrow(0,0,1,0)$ | – | $(-)1$ | – | $(-)1$ |
| $(0,0,1,0)\rightarrow(1,0,1,1)$ | – | – | $(-)1$ | $(-)1$ |
| $(0,0,1,1)\rightarrow(1,0,0,1)$ | – | $(-)1$ | $(-)1$ | – |
| $(0,1,0,0)\rightarrow(0,0,0,1)$ | – | – | – | $(-)1$ |
| $(0,1,0,1)\rightarrow(0,0,1,1)$ | – | $(-)1$ | – | – |

| | | | | |
|---|---|---|---|---|
| $(0,1,1,0) \rightarrow (1,0,1,0)$ | – | – | (–)1 | – |
| $(0,1,1,1) \rightarrow (1,0,0,0)$ | – | (–)1 | (–)1 | (–)1 |
| $(1,0,0,0) \rightarrow (0,1,1,1)$ | (–)1 | – | (–)1 | (–)1 |
| $(1,0,0,1) \rightarrow (0,1,0,1)$ | (–)1 | (–)1 | (–)1 | – |
| $(1,0,1,0) \rightarrow (1,1,0,0)$ | (–)1 | – | – | – |
| $(1,0,1,1) \rightarrow (1,1,1,0)$ | (–)1 | (–)1 | – | (–)1 |
| $(1,1,0,0) \rightarrow (0,1,1,0)$ | (–)1 | – | (–)1 | – |
| $(1,1,0,1) \rightarrow (0,1,0,0)$ | (–)1 | (–)1 | (–)1 | (–)1 |
| $(1,1,1,0) \rightarrow (1,1,0,1)$ | (–)1 | – | – | (–)1 |
| $(1,1,1,1) \rightarrow (1,1,1,1)$ | (–)1 | (–)1 | – | – |

The linear factors in the rounds can be combined to obtain multiple round linear factors, by combining linear factors such that the intermediate terms cancel out. For every round they impose conditions on subkeys that can be converted into conditions on global keys, using the following table (which follows from the key scheduling algorithm of IDEA):

**Table 6.22** *Derivation of encryption subkeys from the global key of size 128 bits*

| $r$ | $Z_1$ | $Z_2$ | $Z_3$ | $Z_4$ | $Z_5$ | $Z_6$ |
|---|---|---|---|---|---|---|
| 1 | 0–15 | 16–31 | 32–47 | 48–63 | 64–79 | 80–95 |
| 2 | 96–111 | 112–127 | 25–40 | 41–56 | 57–72 | 73–88 |
| 3 | 89–104 | 105–120 | 121–8 | 9–24 | 50–65 | 66–81 |
| 4 | 82–97 | 98–113 | 114–1 | 2–17 | 18–33 | 34–49 |
| 5 | 75–90 | 91–106 | 107–122 | 123–10 | 11–26 | 27–42 |
| 6 | 43–58 | 59–74 | 100–115 | 116–3 | 4–19 | 20–35 |
| 7 | 36–51 | 52–67 | 68–83 | 84–99 | 125–12 | 13–28 |
| 8 | 29–44 | 45–60 | 61–76 | 77–92 | 93–108 | 109–124 |
| 9 | 22–37 | 38–53 | 54–69 | 70–85 | – | – |

A possible combination for a multiple round linear factor for IDEA is shown in the underlying table. The conditions on the global key bits are also mentioned. The global key bits whose indices are there in the table should be zero. Since key bits with indices 26-28, 72-74 or 111-127 do not appear, there are $2^{23}$ global keys that can have this linear factor. This is called a class of weak keys as they can be detected by checking the satisfaction of linear factors by some plaintext-ciphertext combinations.

**Table 6.23** *Conditions on key bits for linear factor (1,0,1,0)->(0,1,1,0)*

| Round | Input Term | $Z_1$ | $Z_5$ |
|---|---|---|---|
| 1 | (1,0,1,0) | 0–14 | – |
| 2 | (1,1,0,0) | 96–110 | 57–71 |
| 3 | (0,1,1,0) | – | 50–64 |
| 4 | (1,0,1,0) | 82–96 | – |

| | | | | |
|---|---|---|---|---|
| 5 | (1,1,0,0) | 75–89 | 11–25 |
| 6 | (0,1,1,0) | – | 4–18 |
| 7 | (1,0,1,0) | 36–50 | – |
| 8 | (1,1,0,0) | 29–44 | 93–107 |
| 9 | (0,1,1,1) | – | – |

## 6.7 RECOMMENDED READING

The following books and websites provide more details about subjects discussed in this chapter. The items enclosed in brackets […] refer to the reference list at the end of the book.

### Books

[Sta06], [Sti06], [Rhe03], [Sal03], [Mao04], and [TW06] discuss DES.

### WebSites

The following websites give more information about topics discussed in this chapter.

http://www.itl.nist.gov/fipspubs/fip46-2.htm
www.nist.gov/director/prog-ofc/report01-2.pdf
www.engr.mun.ca/~howard/PAPERS/ldc_tutorial.ps
islab.oregonstate.edu/koc/ece575/notes/dc1.pdf
homes.esat.kuleuven.be/~abiryuko/Cryptan/matsui_des
http://nsfsecurity.pr.erau.edu/crypto/lincrypt.html

## *Key Terms*

| | |
|---|---|
| avalanche effect | National Security Agency (NSA) |
| completeness effect | parity bit drop |
| Data Encryption Standard (DES) | possible weak keys |
| double DES (2DES) | round-key generator |
| Federal Information Processing | Standard semi-weak keys |
| (FIPS) | triple DES (3DES) |
| key complement | triple DES with three keys |
| meet-in-the-middle attack | triple DES with two keys |
| National Institute of Standards and Technology (NIST) | weak keys |

## *Summary*

★ The Data Encryption Standard (DES) is a symmetric-key block cipher published by the National Institute of Standards and Technology (NIST) as FIPS 46 in the *Federal Register*.

★ At the encryption site, DES takes a 64-bit plaintext and creates a 64-bit ciphertext. At the decryption site, DES takes a 64-bit ciphertext and creates a 64-bit block of plaintext. The same 56-bit cipher key is used for both encryption and decryption.

★ The encryption process is made of two permutations (P-boxes), which we call initial and final permutations, and sixteen Feistel rounds. Each round of DES is a Feistel cipher with two elements (mixer and swapper). Each of these elements is invertible.

★ The heart of DES is the DES function. The DES function applies a 48-bit key to the rightmost 32 bits to produce a 32-bit output. This function is made up of four operations: an expansion permutation, a whitener (that adds key), a group of S-boxes, and a straight permutation.

★ The round-key generator creates sixteen 48-bit keys out of a 56-bit cipher key. However, the cipher key is normally presented as a 64-bit key in which 8 extra bits are the parity bits, which are dropped before the actual key-generation process.

★ DES has shown a good performance with respect to avalanche and completeness effects. Areas of weaknesses in DES include cipher design (S-boxes and P-boxes) and cipher key (length, weak keys, semi-weak keys, possible weak keys, and key complements).

★ Since DES is not a group, one solution to improve the security of DES is to use multiple DES (double and triple DES). Double DES is vulnerable to meet-in-the-middle attack, so triple DES with two keys or three keys is common in applications.

★ The design of S-boxes and number of rounds makes DES almost immune from the differential cryptanalysis. However, DES is vulnerable to linear cryptanalysis if the adversary can collect enough known plaintexts.

## *Practice Set*

### Review Questions

**6.1** What is the block size in DES? What is the cipher key size in DES? What is the round-key size in DES?

**6.2** What is the number of rounds in DES?

**6.3** How many mixers and swappers are used in the first approach of making encryption and decryption inverses of each other? How many are used in the second approach?

**6.4** How many permutations are used in a DES cipher algorithm? How many permutations are used in the round-key generator?

**6.5** How many exclusive-or operations are used in the DES cipher?

**6.6** Why does the DES function need an expansion permutation?

**6.7** Why does the round-key generator need a parity drop permutation?

**6.8** What is the difference between a weak key, a semi-weak key, and a possible weak key?

**6.9** What is double DES? What kind of attack on double DES makes it useless?

**6.10** What is triple DES? What is triple DES with two keys? What is triple DES with three keys?

### Exercises

**6.11** Answer the following questions about S-boxes in DES:
   a.   Show the result of passing 110111 through S-box 3.
   b.   Show the result of passing 001100 through S-box 4.
   c.   Show the result of passing 000000 through S-box 7.
   d.   Show the result of passing 111111 through S-box 2.

**6.12** Draw the table to show the result of passing 000000 through all 8 S-boxes. Do you see a pattern in the outputs?

**6.13** Draw the table to show the result of passing 111111 through all 8 S-boxes. Do you see a pattern in the outputs?

**6.14** Check the third criterion for S-box 3 using the following pairs of inputs.
- a.   000000 and 000001
- b.   111111 and 111011

**6.15** Check the fourth design criterion for S-box 2 using the following pairs of inputs.
- a.   001100 and 110000
- b.   110011 and 001111

**6.16** Check the fifth design criterion for S-box 4 using the following pairs of inputs.
- a.   001100 and 110000
- b.   110011 and 001111

**6.17** Create 32 6-bit input pairs to check the sixth design criterion for S-box 5.

**6.18** Show how the eight design criteria for S-box 7 are fulfilled.

**6.19** Prove the first design criterion for P-boxes by checking the input to S-box 2 in round 2.

**6.20** Prove the second design criterion for P-boxes by checking inputs to S-box 3 in round 4.

**6.21** Prove the third design criterion for P-boxes by checking the output of S-box 4 in round 3.

**6.22** Prove the fourth design criterion for P-boxes by checking the output of S-box 6 in round 12.

**6.23** Prove the fifth design criteria for P-boxes by checking the relationship between S-boxes 3, 4, and 5 in rounds 10 and 11.

**6.24** Prove the sixth design criteria for P-boxes by checking the destination of an arbitrary S-box.

**6.25** Prove the seventh design criterion for P-boxes by checking the relationship between S-box 5 in round 4 and S-box 7 in round 5.

**6.26** Redraw Fig. 6.9 using the alternate approach.

**6.27** Prove that the reverse cipher in Fig. 6.9 is in fact the inverse of the cipher for a three-round DES. Start with a plaintext at the beginning of the cipher and prove that you can get the same plaintext at the end of the reverse cipher.

**6.28** Carefully study the key compression permutation of Table 6.14.
- a.   Which input ports are missing in the output?
- b.   Do all left 24 output bits come from all left 28 input bits?
- c.   Do all right 24 output bits come from all right 28 input bits?

**6.29** Show the results of the following hexadecimal data

$$0110\ 1023\ 4110\ 1023$$

after passing it through the initial permutation box.

**6.30** Show the results of the following hexadecimal data

$$AAAA\ BBBB\ CCCC\ DDDD$$

after passing it through the final permutation box.

**6.31** If the key with parity bit (64 bits) is 0123 ABCD 2562 1456, find the first round key.

**6.32** Using a plaintext block of all 0s and a 56-bit key of all 0s, prove the key-complement weakness assuming that DES is made only of one round.

**6.33** Can you devise a meet-in-the- middle attack for a triple DES?

**6.34** Write pseudocode for the *permute* routine used in Algorithm 6.1

**permute (n, m, inBlock[n], outBlock[m], *permutationTable[m]*)**

**6.35** Write pseudocode for the *split* routine used in Algorithm 6.1

**split (n, m, inBlock[n], leftBlock[m], rightBlock[m])**

**6.36** Write pseudocode for the *combine* routine used in Algorithm 6.1

**combine (n, m, leftBlock[n], rightBlock[n], outBlock[m])**

**6.37** Write pseudocode for the *exclusiveOr* routine used in Algorithm 6.1

**exclusiveOr (n, firstInBlock[n], secondInBlock[n], outBlock[n])**

**6.38** Change Algorithm 6.1 to represent the alternative approach.

**6.39** Augment Algorithm 6.1 to be used for both encryption and decryption.

# 7

# Advanced Encryption Standard (AES)

## Objectives

In this chapter, we discuss the Advanced Encryption Standard (AES), the modern symmetric-key block cipher that may replace DES. This chapter has several objectives:

☞ To review a short history of AES
☞ To define the basic structure of AES
☞ To define the transformations used by AES
☞ To define the key expansion process
☞ To discuss different implementations

The emphasis is on how the algebraic structures discussed in Chapter 4 achieve the AES security goals.

## 7.1        INTRODUCTION

The **Advanced Encryption Standard (AES)** is a symmetric-key block cipher published by the **National Institute of Standards and Technology (NIST)** in December 2001.

### 7.1.1   History

In 1997, NIST started looking for a replacement for DES, which would be called the *Advanced Encryption Standard* or *AES*. The NIST specifications required a block size of 128 bits and three different key sizes of 128, 192, and 256 bits. The specifications also required that AES be an open algorithm, available to the public worldwide. The announcement was made internationally to solicit responses from all over the world.

After the *First AES Candidate Conference,* NIST announced that 15 out of 21 received algorithms had met the requirements and been selected as the first candidates (August 1998). Algorithms were submitted from a number of countries; the variety of these proposals demonstrated the openness of the process and worldwide participation.

After the *Second AES Candidate Conference,* which was held in Rome, NIST announced that 5 out of 15 candidates—*MARS, RC6, Rijndael, Serpent*, and *Twofish*—were selected as the finalists (August 1999).

After the *Third AES Candidate Conference,* NIST announced that **Rijndael,** (pronounced like "Rain Doll"), designed by Belgian researchers Joan Daemen and Vincent Rijment, was selected as *Advanced Encryption Standard* (October 2000).

In February 2001, NIST announced that a draft of the **Federal Information Processing Standard (FIPS)** was available for public review and comment.

Finally, AES was published as FIPS 197 in the *Federal Register* in December 2001.

### 7.1.2 Criteria

The criteria defined by NIST for selecting AES fall into three areas: security, cost, and implementation. At the end, *Rijndael* was judged the best at meeting the combination of these criteria.

*Security* The main emphasis was on security. Because NIST explicitly demanded a 128-bit key, this criterion focused on resistance to cryptanalysis attacks other than brute-force attack.

*Cost* The second criterion was cost, which covers the computational efficiency and storage requirement for different implementations such as hardware, software, or smart cards.

*Implementation* This criterion included the requirement that the algorithm must have flexibility (be implementable on any platform) and simplicity.

### 7.1.3 Rounds

AES is a non-Feistel cipher that encrypts and decrypts a data block of 128 bits. It uses 10, 12, or 14 rounds. The key size, which can be 128, 192, or 256 bits, depends on the number of rounds. Figure 7.1 shows the general design for the encryption algorithm (called cipher); the decryption algorithm (called inverse cipher) is similar, but the round keys are applied in the reverse order.

In Fig. 7.1, $N_r$ defines the number of rounds. The figure also shows the relationship between the number of rounds and the key size, which means that we can have three different AES versions; they are referred as AES-128, AES-192, and AES-256. However, the round keys, which are created by the key-expansion algorithm are always 128 bits, the same size as the plaintext or ciphertext block.

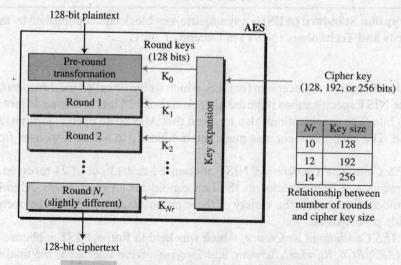

**Fig. 7.1** *General design of AES encryption cipher*

**AES has defined three versions, with 10, 12, and 14 rounds.**
**Each version uses a different cipher key size (128, 192, or 256), but the round keys are always 128 bits.**

The number of round keys generated by the key-expansion algorithm is always one more than the number of rounds. In other words, we have

**Number of round keys = $N_r + 1$**

We refer to the round keys as $K_0, K_1, K_2, ..., K_{N_r}$.

## 7.1.4 Data Units

AES uses five units of measurement to refer to data: bits, bytes, words, blocks, and state. The bit is the smallest and atomic unit; other units can be expressed in terms of smaller ones. Figure 7.2 shows the non-atomic data units: byte, word, block, and state.

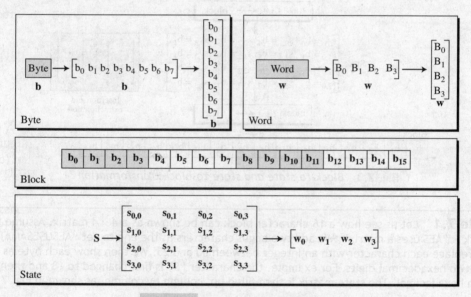

**Fig. 7.2** *Data units used in AES*

***Bit***   In AES, a **bit** is a binary digit with a value of 0 or 1. We use a lowercase letter to refer to a bit.

***Byte***   A **byte** is a group of eight bits that can be treated as a single entity, a row matrix ($1 \times 8$) of eight bits, or a column matrix ($8 \times 1$) of eight bits. When treated as a row matrix, the bits are inserted to the matrix from left to right; when treated as a column matrix, the bits are inserted into the matrix from top to bottom. We use a lowercase bold letter to refer to a byte.

***Word***   A **word** is a group of 32 bits that can be treated as a single entity, a row matrix of four bytes, or a column matrix of four bytes. When it is treated as a row matrix, the bytes are inserted into the matrix from left to right; when it is considered as a column matrix, the bytes are inserted into the matrix from top to bottom. We use the lowercase bold letter **w** to show a word.

***Block***   AES encrypts and decrypts data blocks. A **block** in AES is a group of 128 bits. However, a block can be represented as a row matrix of 16 bytes.

***State*** AES uses several rounds in which each round is made of several stages. Data block is transformed from one stage to another. At the beginning and end of the cipher, AES uses the term *data block;* before and after each stage, the data block is referred to as a **state.** We use an uppercase bold letter to refer to a state. Although the states in different stages are normally called **S,** we occasionally use the letter **T** to refer to a temporary state. States, like blocks, are made of 16 bytes, but normally are treated as matrices of $4 \times 4$ bytes. In this case, each element of a state is referred to as $s_{r,c}$, where $r$ (0 to 3) defines the row and the $c$ (0 to 3) defines the column. Occasionally, a state is treated as a row matrix ($1 \times 4$) of words. This makes sense, if we think of a word as a column matrix. At the beginning of the cipher, bytes in a data block are inserted into a state column by column, and in each column, from top to bottom. At the end of the cipher, bytes in the state are extracted in the same way, as shown in Fig. 7.3.

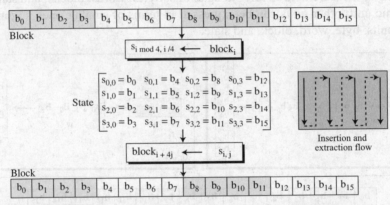

**Fig. 7.3** *Block-to-state and state-to-block transformation*

**Example 7.1** Let us see how a 16-character block can be shown as a $4 \times 4$ matrix. Assume that the text block is "AES uses a matrix". We add two bogus characters at the end to get "AESUSESAMATRIXZZ". Now we replace each character with an integer between 00 and 25. We then show each byte as an integer with two hexadecimal digits. For example, the character "S" is first changed to 18 and then written as $12_{16}$ in hexadecimal. The state matrix is then filled up, column by column, as shown in Fig. 7.4.

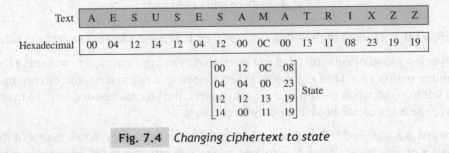

**Fig. 7.4** *Changing ciphertext to state*

### 7.1.5 Structure of Each Round

Figure 7.5 shows the structure of each round at the encryption side. Each round, except the last, uses four transformations that are invertible. The last round has only three transformations.

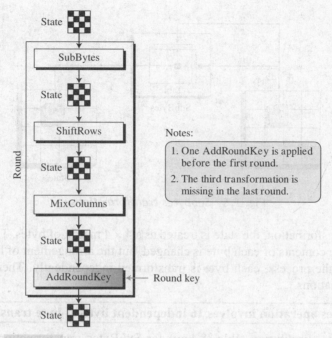

**Fig. 7.5** *Structure of each round at the encryption site*

As Fig. 7.5 shows, each transformation takes a state and creates another state to be used for the next transformation or the next round. The pre-round section uses only one transformation (AddRoundKey); the last round uses only three transformations (MixColumns transformation is missing).

At the decryption site, the inverse transformations are used: InvSubByte, -InvShiftRows, InvMixColumns, and AddRoundKey (this one is self-invertible).

## 7.2 TRANSFORMATIONS

To provide security, AES uses four types of transformations: substitution, permutation, mixing, and key-adding. We will discuss each here.

### 7.2.1 Substitution

AES, like DES, uses substitution. However, the mechanism is different. First, the substitution is done for each byte. Second, only one table is used for transformation of every byte, which means that if two bytes are the same, the transformation is also the same. Third, the transformation is defined by either a table lookup process or mathematical calculation in the $GF(2^8)$ field. AES uses two invertible transformations.

**SubBytes** The first transformation, **SubBytes,** is used at the encryption site. To substitute a byte, we interpret the byte as two hexadecimal digits. The left digit defines the row and the right digit defines the column of the substitution table. The two hexadecimal digits at the junction of the row and the column are the new byte. Figure 7.6 shows the idea.

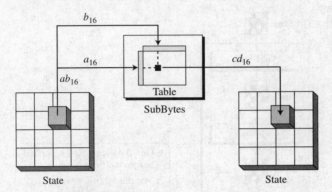

**Fig. 7.6** *SubBytes transformations*

In the SubBytes transformation, the state is treated as a $4 \times 4$ matrix of bytes. Transformation is done one byte at a time. The contents of each byte is changed, but the arrangement of the bytes in the matrix remains the same. In the process, each byte is transformed independently. There are sixteen distinct byte-to-byte transformations.

---

**The SubBytes operation involves 16 independent byte-to-byte transformations.**

---

Table 7.1 shows the substitution table (S-box) for SubBytes transformation. The transformation definitely provides confusion effect. For example, two bytes, $5A_{16}$ and $5B_{16}$, which differ only in one bit (the rightmost bit) are transformed to $BE_{16}$ and $39_{16}$, which differ in four bits.

**Table 7.1** *SubBytes transformation table*

| | *0* | *1* | *2* | *3* | *4* | *5* | *6* | *7* | *8* | *9* | *A* | *B* | *C* | *D* | *E* | *F* |
|---|---|---|---|---|---|---|---|---|---|---|---|---|---|---|---|---|
| *0* | 63 | 7C | 77 | 7B | F2 | 6B | 6F | C5 | 30 | 01 | 67 | 2B | FE | D7 | AB | 76 |
| *1* | CA | 82 | C9 | 7D | FA | 59 | 47 | F0 | AD | D4 | A2 | AF | 9C | A4 | 72 | C0 |
| *2* | B7 | FD | 93 | 26 | 36 | 3F | F7 | CC | 34 | A5 | E5 | F1 | 71 | D8 | 31 | 15 |
| *3* | 04 | C7 | 23 | C3 | 18 | 96 | 05 | 9A | 07 | 12 | 80 | E2 | EB | 27 | B2 | 75 |
| *4* | 09 | 83 | 2C | 1A | 1B | 6E | 5A | A0 | 52 | 3B | D6 | B3 | 29 | E3 | 2F | 84 |
| *5* | 53 | D1 | 00 | ED | 20 | FC | B1 | 5B | 6A | CB | BE | 39 | 4A | 4C | 58 | CF |
| *6* | D0 | EF | AA | FB | 43 | 4D | 33 | 85 | 45 | F9 | 02 | 7F | 50 | 3C | 9F | A8 |
| *7* | 51 | A3 | 40 | 8F | 92 | 9D | 38 | F5 | BC | B6 | DA | 21 | 10 | FF | F3 | D2 |
| *8* | CD | 0C | 13 | EC | 5F | 97 | 44 | 17 | C4 | A7 | 7E | 3D | 64 | 5D | 19 | 73 |
| *9* | 60 | 81 | 4F | DC | 22 | 2A | 90 | 88 | 46 | EE | B8 | 14 | DE | 5E | 0B | DB |
| *A* | E0 | 32 | 3A | 0A | 49 | 06 | 24 | 5C | C2 | D3 | AC | 62 | 91 | 95 | E4 | 79 |
| *B* | E7 | CB | 37 | 6D | 8D | D5 | 4E | A9 | 6C | 56 | F4 | EA | 65 | 7A | AE | 08 |
| *C* | BA | 78 | 25 | 2E | 1C | A6 | B4 | C6 | E8 | DD | 74 | 1F | 4B | BD | 8B | 8A |
| *D* | 70 | 3E | B5 | 66 | 48 | 03 | F6 | 0E | 61 | 35 | 57 | B9 | 86 | C1 | 1D | 9E |
| *E* | E1 | F8 | 98 | 11 | 69 | D9 | 8E | 94 | 9B | 1E | 87 | E9 | CE | 55 | 28 | DF |
| *F* | 8C | A1 | 89 | 0D | BF | E6 | 42 | 68 | 41 | 99 | 2D | 0F | B0 | 54 | BB | 16 |

**InvSubBytes**   **InvSubBytes** is the inverse of SubBytes. The transformation is done using Table 7.2. We can easily check that the two transformations are inverse of each other.

**Table 7.2**   *InvSubBytes transformation table*

|   | 0 | 1 | 2 | 3 | 4 | 5 | 6 | 7 | 8 | 9 | A | B | C | D | E | F |
|---|---|---|---|---|---|---|---|---|---|---|---|---|---|---|---|---|
| 0 | 52 | 09 | 6A | D5 | 30 | 36 | A5 | 38 | BF | 40 | A3 | 9E | 81 | F3 | D7 | FB |
| 1 | 7C | E3 | 39 | 82 | 9B | 2F | FF | 87 | 34 | 8E | 43 | 44 | C4 | DE | E9 | CB |
| 2 | 54 | 7B | 94 | 32 | A6 | C2 | 23 | 3D | EE | 4C | 95 | 0B | 42 | FA | C3 | 4E |
| 3 | 08 | 2E | A1 | 66 | 28 | D9 | 24 | B2 | 76 | 5B | A2 | 49 | 6D | 8B | D1 | 25 |
| 4 | 72 | F8 | F6 | 64 | 86 | 68 | 98 | 16 | D4 | A4 | 5C | CC | 5D | 65 | B6 | 92 |
| 5 | 6C | 70 | 48 | 50 | FD | ED | B9 | DA | 5E | 15 | 46 | 57 | A7 | 8D | 9D | 84 |
| 6 | 90 | D8 | AB | 00 | 8C | BC | D3 | 0A | F7 | E4 | 58 | 05 | B8 | B3 | 45 | 06 |
| 7 | D0 | 2C | 1E | 8F | CA | 3F | 0F | 02 | C1 | AF | BD | 03 | 01 | 13 | 8A | 6B |
| 8 | 3A | 91 | 11 | 41 | 4F | 67 | DC | EA | 97 | F2 | CF | CE | F0 | B4 | E6 | 73 |
| 9 | 96 | AC | 74 | 22 | E7 | AD | 35 | 85 | E2 | F9 | 37 | E8 | 1C | 75 | DF | 6E |
| A | 47 | F1 | 1A | 71 | 1D | 29 | C5 | 89 | 6F | B7 | 62 | 0E | AA | 18 | BE | 1B |
| B | FC | 56 | 3E | 4B | C6 | D2 | 79 | 20 | 9A | DB | C0 | FE | 78 | CD | 5A | F4 |
| C | 1F | DD | A8 | 33 | 88 | 07 | C7 | 31 | B1 | 12 | 10 | 59 | 27 | 80 | EC | 5F |
| D | 60 | 51 | 7F | A9 | 19 | B5 | 4A | 0D | 2D | E5 | 7A | 9F | 93 | C9 | 9C | EF |
| E | A0 | E0 | 3B | 4D | AE | 2A | F5 | B0 | C8 | EB | BB | 3C | 83 | 53 | 99 | 61 |
| F | 17 | 2B | 04 | 7E | BA | 77 | D6 | 26 | E1 | 69 | 14 | 63 | 55 | 21 | 0C | 7D |

**Example 7.2**   Figure 7.7 shows how a state is transformed using the SubBytes transformation. The figure also shows that the InvSubBytes transformation creates the original one. Note that if the two bytes have the same values, their transformation is also the same. For example, the two bytes $04_{16}$ and $04_{16}$ in the left state are transformed to $F2_{16}$ and $F2_{16}$ in the right state and vice versa. The reason is that every byte uses the same table. In contrast, we saw that DES (Chapter 6) uses eight different S-boxes.

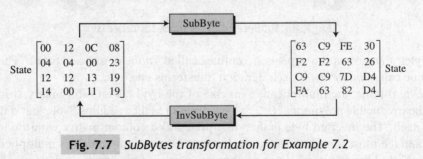

**Fig. 7.7**   *SubBytes transformation for Example 7.2*

## Transformation Using the GF($2^8$) Field

Although we can use Table 7.1 or Table 7.2 to find the substitution for each byte, AES also defines the transformation algebraically using the GF($2^8$) field with the irreducible polynomials ($x^8 + x^4 + x^3 + x + 1$), as shown in Fig. 7.8.

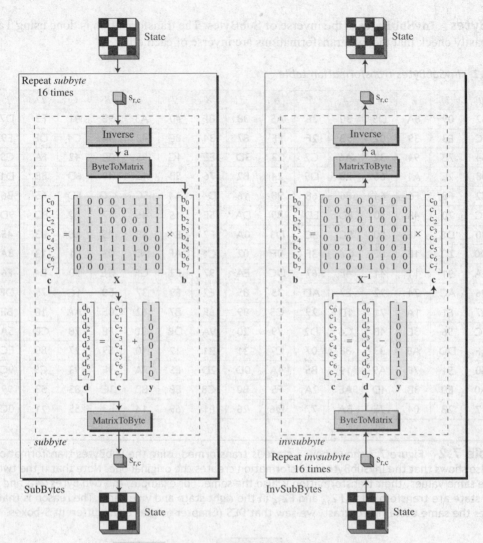

**Fig.7.8** *SubBytes and InvSubBytes processes*

The SubBytes transformation repeats a routine, called *subbyte,* sixteen times. The InvSubBytes repeats a routine called *invsubbyte.* Each iteration transforms one byte.

In the *subbyte* routine, the multiplicative inverse of the byte (as an 8-bit binary string) is found in $GF(2^8)$ with the irreducible polynomial $(x^8 + x^4 + x^3 + x + 1)$ as the modulus. Note that if the byte is $00_{16}$, its inverse is itself. The inverted byte is then interpreted as a column matrix with the least significant bit at the top and the most significant bit at the bottom. This column matrix is multiplied by a constant square matrix, $\mathbf{X}$, and the result, which is a column matrix, is added with a constant column matrix, $\mathbf{y}$, to give the new byte. Note that multiplication and addition of bits are done in GF(2). The *invsubbyte* is doing the same thing in reverse order.

After finding the multiplicative inverse of the byte, the process is similar to the affine ciphers we discussed in Chapter 3. In the encryption, multiplication is first and addition is second; in the decryption, subtraction (addition by inverse) is first and division (multiplication by inverse) is second. We can easily prove that the two transformations are inverses of each other because addition or subtraction in GF(2) is actually the XOR operation.

$$\text{subbyte:} \quad \rightarrow \quad \mathbf{d} = \mathbf{X} \, (s_{r,c})^{-1} \oplus \mathbf{y}$$

$$\text{invsubbyte:} \rightarrow \; [\mathbf{X}^{-1}(\mathbf{d} \oplus \mathbf{y})]^{-1} = [\mathbf{X}^{-1}(\mathbf{X} \, (s_{r,c})^{-1} \oplus \mathbf{y} \oplus \mathbf{y})]^{-1} = [(s_{r,c})^{-1}]^{-1} = s_{r,c}$$

---

**The SubBytes and InvSubBytes transformations are inverses of each other.**

---

**Example 7.3**  Let us show how the byte 0C is transformed to FE by *subbyte* routine and transformed back to 0C by the *invsubbyte* routine.

1. *subbyte:*
   a. The multiplicative inverse of 0C in $GF(2^8)$ field is B0, which means **b** is (10110000).
   b. Multiplying matrix **X** by this matrix results in **c** = (10011101)
   c. The result of XOR operation is **d** = (11111110), which is FE in hexadecimal.
2. *invsubbyte:*
   a. The result of XOR operation is **c** = (10011101)
   b. The result of multiplying by matrix $\mathbf{X}^{-1}$ is (11010000) or B0
   c. The multiplicative inverse of B0 is 0C.

*Algorithm*  Although we have shown matrices to emphasize the nature of substitution (affine transformation), the algorithm does not necessarily use multiplication and addition of matrices because most of the elements in the constant square matrix are only 0 or 1. The value of the constant column matrix is 0x63. We can write a simple algorithm to do the SubBytes. Algorithm 7.1 calls the subbyte routine 16 time, one for each byte in the state.

---

**Algorithm 7.1**  **Pseudocode for SubBytes transformation**

```
SubBytes (S)
{
    for (r = 0 to 3)
     for (c = 0 to 3)
          S_r,c = subbyte (S_r,c)
}
subbyte (byte)
{
    a ← byte⁻¹          // Multiplicative inverse in GF(2⁸) with inverse of 00 to be 00
    ByteToMatrix (a, b)
    for (i = 0 to 7)
    {
        c_i ← b_i ⊕ b_(i+4)mod 8 ⊕ b_(i+5)mod 8 ⊕ b_(i+6)mod 8 ⊕ b_(i+7)mod 8
        d_i ← c_i ⊕ ByteToMatrix (0x63)
    }
    MatrixToByte (d, d)
    byte ← d
}
```

The ByteToMatrix routine transforms a byte to an $8 \times 1$ column matrix. The MatrixToByte routine transforms an $8 \times 1$ column matrix to a byte. The expansion of these routines and the algorithm for InvSubBytes are left as exercises.

**Nonlinearity** Although the multiplication and addition of matrices in the *subbyte* routine are an affine-type transformation and linear, the replacement of the byte by its multiplicative inverse in $GF(2^8)$ is nonlinear. This step makes the whole transformation -nonlinear.

## 7.2.2 Permutation

Another transformation found in a round is shifting, which permutes the bytes. Unlike DES, in which permutation is done at the bit level, shifting transformation in AES is done at the byte level; the order of the bits in the byte is not changed.

**ShiftRows** In the encryption, the transformation is called **ShiftRows** and the shifting is to the left. The number of shifts depends on the row number (0, 1, 2, or 3) of the state matrix. This means the row 0 is not shifted at all and the last row is shifted three bytes. Figure 7.9 shows the shifting transformation.

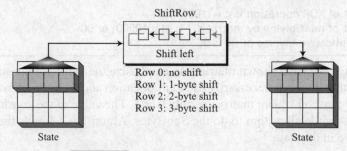

**Fig. 7.9** *ShiftRows transformation*

Note that the ShiftRows transformation operates one row at a time.

**InvShiftRows** In the decryption, the transformation is called **InvShiftRows** and the shifting is to the right. The number of shifts is the same as the row number (0, 1, 2, and 3) of the state matrix.

---

**The ShiftRows and InvShiftRows transformations are inverses of each other.**

---

**Algorithm** Algorithm 7.2 for ShiftRows transformation is very simple. However, to emphasize that the transformation is one row at a time, we use a routine called *shiftrow* that shifts the byte in a single row. We call this routine three times. The shiftrow routine first copies the row into a temporary row matrix, **t.** It then shifts the row.

**Example 7.4** Figure 7.10 shows how a state is transformed using ShiftRows transformation. The figure also shows that InvShiftRows transformation creates the original state.

| Algorithm 7.2 | Pseudocode for ShiftRows transformation |
|---|---|

```
ShiftRows (S)
{
    for (r = 1 to 3)
        shiftrow (s_r, r)               // s_r is the rth row
}
shiftrow (row, n)                        // n is the number of bytes to be shifted
{
    CopyRow (row, t)                     // t is a temporary row
    for (c = 0 to 3)
        row_(c − n) mod 4 ← t_c
}
```

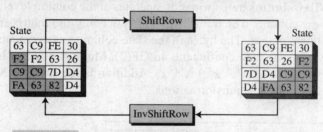

State

| 63 | C9 | FE | 30 |
|---|---|---|---|
| F2 | F2 | 63 | 26 |
| C9 | C9 | 7D | D4 |
| FA | 63 | 82 | D4 |

ShiftRow

State

| 63 | C9 | FE | 30 |
|---|---|---|---|
| F2 | 63 | 26 | F2 |
| 7D | D4 | C9 | C9 |
| D4 | FA | 63 | 82 |

InvShiftRow

**Fig. 7.10** *ShiftRows transformation in Example 7.4*

## 7.2.3 Mixing

The substitution provided by the SubBytes transformation changes the value of the byte based only on original value and an entry in the table; the process does not include the neighboring bytes. We can say that SubBytes is an *intrabyte* transformation. The permutation provided by the ShiftRows transformation exchanges bytes without permuting the bits inside the bytes. We can say that ShiftRows is a *byte-exchange* transformation. We also need an *interbyte* transformation that changes the bits inside a byte, based on the bits inside the neighboring bytes. We need to mix bytes to provide diffusion at the bit level.

The mixing transformation changes the contents of each byte by taking four bytes at a time and combining them to recreate four new bytes. To guarantee that each new byte is different (even if all four bytes are the same), the combination process first multiplies each byte with a different constant and then mixes them. The mixing can be provided by matrix multiplication. As we discussed in Chapter 2, when we multiply a square matrix by a column matrix, the result is a new column matrix. Each element in the new matrix depends on all four elements of the old matrix after they are multiplied by row values in the constant matrix. Figure 7.11 shows the idea.

$$
\begin{bmatrix}
ax + by + cz + dt \\
ex + fy + gz + ht \\
ix + jy + kz + lt \\
mx + ny + oz + pt
\end{bmatrix}
=
\begin{bmatrix}
a & b & c & d \\
e & f & g & h \\
i & j & k & l \\
m & n & o & p
\end{bmatrix}
\times
\begin{bmatrix}
x \\
y \\
z \\
t
\end{bmatrix}
$$

New matrix          Constant matrix          Old matrix

**Fig. 7.11** *Mixing bytes using matrix multiplication*

AES defines a transformation, called MixColumns, to achieve this goal. There is also an inverse transformation, called InvMixColumns. Figure 7.12 shows the constant matrices used for these transformations. These two matrices are inverses of each other when the elements are interpreted as 8-bit words (or polynomials) with coefficients in $GF(2^8)$. The proof is left as an exercise.

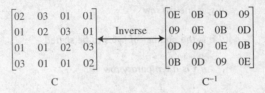

$$\begin{bmatrix} 02 & 03 & 01 & 01 \\ 01 & 02 & 03 & 01 \\ 01 & 01 & 02 & 03 \\ 03 & 01 & 01 & 02 \end{bmatrix} \xleftrightarrow{\text{Inverse}} \begin{bmatrix} 0E & 0B & 0D & 09 \\ 09 & 0E & 0B & 0D \\ 0D & 09 & 0E & 0B \\ 0B & 0D & 09 & 0E \end{bmatrix}$$

C $\qquad\qquad\qquad$ C$^{-1}$

**Fig. 7.12** *Constant matrices used by MixColumns and InvMixColumns*

**MixColumns** The **MixColumns** transformation operates at the column level; it transforms each column of the state to a new column. The transformation is actually the matrix multiplication of a state column by a constant square matrix. The bytes in the state column and constants matrix are interpreted as 8-bit words (or polynomials) with coefficients in GF(2). Multiplication of bytes is done in $GF(2^8)$ with modulus (10001101) or $(x^8 + x^4 + x^3 + x + 1)$. Addition is the same as XORing of 8-bit words. Figure 7.13 shows the MixColumns transformations.

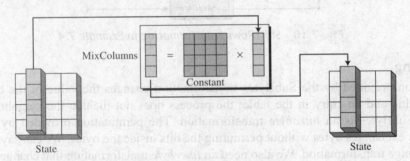

**Fig.7.13** *MixColumns transformation*

**InvMixColumns** The **InvMixColumns** transformation is basically the same as the MixColumns transformation. If the two constant matrices are inverses of each other, it is easy to prove that the two transformations are inverses of each other.

**The MixColumns and InvMixColumns transformations are inverses of each other.**

**Algorithm** Algorithm 7.3 shows the code for MixColumns transformation.

Algorithms for MixColumns and InvMixColumns involve multiplication and addition in the $GF(2^8)$ field. As we saw in Chapter 4, there is a simple and efficient algorithm for multiplication and addition in this field. However, to show the nature of the algorithm (transformation of a column at a time), we use a routine, called *mixcolumn*, to be called four times by the algorithm. The routine *mixcolumn* simply multiplies the rows of the constant matrix by a column in the state. In the above algorithm, the operator (•) used in the mixcolumn routine is multiplication in the $GF(2^8)$ field. It can be replaced with a simple routine as discussed in Chapter 4. The code for InvMixColumns is left as an exercise.

## Algorithm 7.3        Pseudocode for MixColumns transformation

```
MixColumns (S)
{
   for (c = 0 to 3)
      mixcolumn (s_c)
}
mixcolumn (col)
{

   CopyColumn (col, t)              // t is a temporary column

   col_0 ← (0x02) • t_0 ⊕ (0x03 • t_1) ⊕ t_2  ⊕ t_3

   col_1 ← t_0 ⊕ (0x02) • t_1 ⊕  (0x03) • t_2  ⊕ t_3

   col_2 ← t_0 ⊕ t_1 ⊕ (0x02) • t_2 ⊕   (0x03) • t_3

   col_3 ← (0x03 • t_0) ⊕ t_1 ⊕ t_2 ⊕ (0x02) • t_3
}
```

**Example 7.5**    Figure 7.14 shows how a state is transformed using the MixColumns transformation. The figure also shows that the InvMixColumns transformation creates the original one.

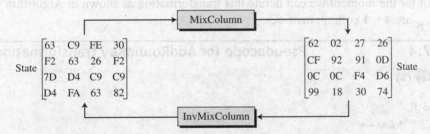

**Fig. 7.14**  *The MixColumns transformation in Example 7.5*

Note that equal bytes in the old state are not equal any more in the new state. For example, the two bytes F2 in the second row are changed to CF and 0D.

### 7.2.4   Key Adding

Probably the most important transformation is the one that includes the cipher key. All previous transformations use known algorithms that are invertible. If the cipher key is not added to the state at each round, it is very easy for the adversary to find the plaintext, given the ciphertext. The cipher key is the only secret between Alice and Bob in this case.

AES uses a process called key expansion (discussed later in the Chapter) that creates $N_r + 1$ round keys from the cipher key. Each round key is 128 bits long—it is treated as four 32-bit words. For the purpose of adding the key to the state, each word is considered as a column matrix.

***AddRoundKey***    **AddRoundKey** also proceeds one column at a time. It is similar to MixColumns in this respect. MixColumns multiplies a constant square matrix by each state column; AddRoundKey adds a round key word with each state column matrix. The operation in MixColumns is matrix multiplication;

the operation in AddRoundKey is matrix addition. Since addition and subtraction in this field are the same, the AddRoundKey transformation is the inverse of itself. Figure 7.15 shows the AddRoundKey transformation.

**The AddRoundKey transformation is the inverse of itself.**

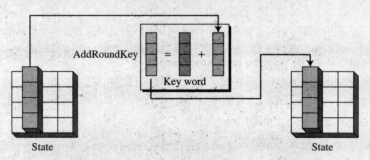

**Fig. 7.15** *AddRoundKey transformation*

*Algorithm* The AddRoundKey transformation can be thought as XORing of each column of the state, with the corresponding key word. We will discuss how the cipher key is expanded into a set of key words, but for the moment we can define this transformation as shown in Algorithm 7.4. Note that $s_c$ and $w_{round+4c}$ are $4 \times 1$ column matrices.

| **Algorithm 7.4** | **Pseudocode for AddRoundKey transformation** |
|---|---|

```
AddRoundKey (S)
{
    for (c = 0 to 3)
        sc ← sc ⊕ wround + 4c
}
```

We need to remember, however, that the $\oplus$ operator here means XORing two column matrices, each of 4 bytes. Writing a simple routine to do that is left as an exercise.

## 7.3                                    KEY EXPANSION

To create round key for each round, AES uses a key-expansion process. If the number of rounds is $N_r$, the **key-expansion** routine creates $N_r + 1$ 128-bit round keys from one single 128-bit cipher key. The first round key is used for pre-round transformation (AddRoundKey); the remaining round keys are used for the last transformation (AddRoundKey) at the end of each round.

The key-expansion routine creates round keys word by word, where a word is an array of four bytes. The routine creates $4 \times (N_r + 1)$ words that are called

$$w_0, w_1, w_2, \ldots, w_{4(Nr+1)-1}$$

In other words, in the AES-128 version (10 rounds), there are 44 words; in the AES-192 version (12 rounds), there are 52 words; and in the AES-256 version (with 14 rounds), there are 60 words. Each round key is made of four words. Table 7.3 shows the relationship between rounds and words.

**Table 7.3** *Words for each round*

| Round | Words | | | |
|-------|-------|-------|-------|-------|
| Pre-round | $\mathbf{w}_0$ | $\mathbf{w}_1$ | $\mathbf{w}_2$ | $\mathbf{w}_3$ |
| 1 | $\mathbf{w}_4$ | $\mathbf{w}_5$ | $\mathbf{w}_6$ | $\mathbf{w}_7$ |
| 2 | $\mathbf{w}_8$ | $\mathbf{w}_9$ | $\mathbf{w}_{10}$ | $\mathbf{w}_{11}$ |
| . . . | . . . | | | |
| $N_r$ | $\mathbf{w}_{4N_r}$ | $\mathbf{w}_{4N_r+1}$ | $\mathbf{w}_{4N_r+2}$ | $\mathbf{w}_{4N_r+3}$ |

## 7.3.1 Key Expansion in AES-128

Let us show the creation of words for the AES-128 version; the processes for the other two versions are the same with some slight changes. Figure 7.16 shows how 44 words are made from the original key.

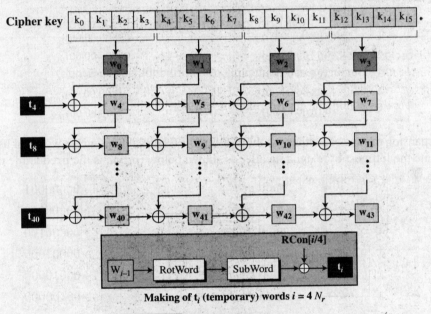

Making of $\mathbf{t}_i$ (temporary) words $i = 4\,N_r$

**Fig. 7.16** *Key expansion in AES*

The process is as follows:

1. The first four words ($\mathbf{w}_0$, $\mathbf{w}_1$, $\mathbf{w}_2$, $\mathbf{w}_3$) are made from the cipher key. The cipher key is thought of as an array of 16 bytes ($k_0$ to $k_{15}$). The first four bytes ($k_0$ to $k_3$) become $\mathbf{w}_0$; the next four bytes ($k_4$ to $k_7$) become $\mathbf{w}_1$; and so on. In other words, the concatenation of the words in this group replicates the cipher key.

2. The rest of the words ($\mathbf{w}_i$ for $i = 4$ to $43$) are made as follows:

   a. If $(i \bmod 4) \neq 0$, $\mathbf{w}_i = \mathbf{w}_{i-1} \oplus \mathbf{w}_{i-4}$. Referring to Figure 7.16, this means each word is made from the one at the left and the one at the top.

   b. If $(i \bmod 4) = 0$, $\mathbf{w}_i = \mathbf{t} \oplus \mathbf{w}_{i-4}$. Here $\mathbf{t}$, a temporary word, is the result of applying two routines, SubWord and RotWord, on $\mathbf{w}_{i-1}$ and XORing the result with a round constants, RCon. In other words, we have,

$$t = \text{SubWord (RotWord } (\mathbf{w}_{i-1})) \oplus \text{RCon}_{i/4}$$

**RotWord**    The **RotWord** (rotate word) routine is similar to the ShiftRows transformation, but it is applied to only one row. The routine takes a word as an array of four bytes and shifts each byte to the left with wrapping.

**SubWord**    The **SubWord** (substitute word) routine is similar to the SubBytes transformation, but it is applied only to four bytes. The routine takes each byte in the word and substitutes another byte for it.

**Round Constants**    Each round constant, RCon, is a 4-byte value in which the rightmost three bytes are always zero. Table 7.4 shows the values for AES-128 version (with 10 rounds).

**Table 7.4**    *RCon constants*

| Round | Constant (RCon) | Round | Constant (RCon) |
|-------|-----------------|-------|-----------------|
| 1 | $(\mathbf{01}\ 00\ 00\ 00)_{16}$ | 6 | $(\mathbf{20}\ 00\ 00\ 00)_{16}$ |
| 2 | $(\mathbf{02}\ 00\ 00\ 00)_{16}$ | 7 | $(\mathbf{40}\ 00\ 00\ 00)_{16}$ |
| 3 | $(\mathbf{04}\ 00\ 00\ 00)_{16}$ | 8 | $(\mathbf{80}\ 00\ 00\ 00)_{16}$ |
| 4 | $(\mathbf{08}\ 00\ 00\ 00)_{16}$ | 9 | $(\mathbf{1B}\ 00\ 00\ 00)_{16}$ |
| 5 | $(\mathbf{10}\ 00\ 00\ 00)_{16}$ | 10 | $(\mathbf{36}\ 00\ 00\ 00)_{16}$ |

The key-expansion routine can either use the above table when calculating the words or use the $\text{GF}(2^8)$ field to calculate the leftmost byte dynamically, as shown below (*prime* is the irreducible polynomial):

| | | | | | | | | |
|---|---|---|---|---|---|---|---|---|
| $RC_1$ | $\rightarrow$ | $x^{1-1}$ | $= x^0$ | mod *prime* | $= 1$ | | $\rightarrow 00000001$ | $\rightarrow 01_{16}$ |
| $RC_2$ | $\rightarrow$ | $x^{2-1}$ | $= x^1$ | mod *prime* | $= x$ | | $\rightarrow 00000010$ | $\rightarrow 02_{16}$ |
| $RC_3$ | $\rightarrow$ | $x^{3-1}$ | $= x^2$ | mod *prime* | $= x^2$ | | $\rightarrow 00000100$ | $\rightarrow 04_{16}$ |
| $RC_4$ | $\rightarrow$ | $x^{4-1}$ | $= x^3$ | mod *prime* | $= x^3$ | | $\rightarrow 00001000$ | $\rightarrow 08_{16}$ |
| $RC_5$ | $\rightarrow$ | $x^{5-1}$ | $= x^4$ | mod *prime* | $= x^4$ | | $\rightarrow 00010000$ | $\rightarrow 10_{16}$ |
| $RC_6$ | $\rightarrow$ | $x^{6-1}$ | $= x^5$ | mod *prime* | $= x^5$ | | $\rightarrow 00100000$ | $\rightarrow 20_{16}$ |
| $RC_7$ | $\rightarrow$ | $x^{7-1}$ | $= x^6$ | mod *prime* | $= x^6$ | | $\rightarrow 01000000$ | $\rightarrow 40_{16}$ |
| $RC_8$ | $\rightarrow$ | $x^{8-1}$ | $= x^7$ | mod *prime* | $= x^7$ | | $\rightarrow 10000000$ | $\rightarrow 80_{16}$ |
| $RC_9$ | $\rightarrow$ | $x^{9-1}$ | $= x^8$ | mod *prime* | $= x^4 + x^3 + x + 1$ | $\rightarrow 00011011$ | $\rightarrow 1B_{16}$ |
| $RC_{10}$ | $\rightarrow$ | $x^{10-1}$ | $= x^9$ | mod *prime* | $= x^5 + x^4 + x^2 + x$ | $\rightarrow 00110110$ | $\rightarrow 36_{16}$ |

The leftmost byte, which is called $RC_i$ is actually $x^{i-1}$, where $i$ is the round number. AES uses the irreducible polynomial $(x^8 + x^4 + x^3 + x + 1)$.

**Algorithm**    Algorithm 7.5 is a simple algorithm for the key-expansion routine (version AES-128).

## Algorithm 7.5             Pseudocode for key expansion in AES-128

**KeyExpansion ([$key_0$ to $key_{15}$], [$w_0$ to $w_{43}$])**
```
{
    for (i = 0 to 3)
        w_i ← key_4i + key_4i+1 + key_4i+2 + key_4i+3
    for (i = 4 to 43)
    {
        if (i mod 4 ≠ 0) w_1 ← w_i−1 + w_i−4
        else
        {
            t ← SubWord (RotWord (w_i−1)) ⊕ RCon_i/4        // t is a temporary word
            w_i ← t + w_i−4
        }
    }
}
```

---

**Example 7.6**    Table 7.5 shows how the keys for each round are calculated assuming that the 128-bit cipher key agreed upon by Alice and Bob is $(24\ 75\ A2\ B3\ 34\ 75\ 56\ 88\ 31\ E2\ 12\ 00\ 13\ AA\ 54\ 87)_{16}$.

**Table 7.5**    *Key expansion example*

| Round | Values of $t$'s | First word in the round | Second word in the round | Third word in the round | Fourth word in the round |
|-------|------------------|--------------------------|---------------------------|--------------------------|---------------------------|
| — | | $w_{00} = 2475A2B3$ | $w_{01} = 34755688$ | $w_{02} = 31E21200$ | $w_{03} = 13AA5487$ |
| 1 | AD20177D | $w_{04} = 8955B5CE$ | $w_{05} = BD20E346$ | $w_{06} = 8CC2F146$ | $w_{07} = 9F68A5C1$ |
| 2 | 470678DB | $w_{08} = CE53CD15$ | $w_{09} = 73732E53$ | $w_{10} = FFB1DF15$ | $w_{11} = 60D97AD4$ |
| 3 | 31DA48D0 | $w_{12} = FF8985C5$ | $w_{13} = 8CFAAB96$ | $w_{14} = 734B7483$ | $w_{15} = 2475A2B3$ |
| 4 | 47AB5B7D | $w_{16} = B822deb8$ | $w_{17} = 34D8752E$ | $w_{18} = 479301AD$ | $w_{19} = 54010FFA$ |
| 5 | 6C762D20 | $w_{20} = D454F398$ | $w_{21} = E08C86B6$ | $w_{22} = A71F871B$ | $w_{23} = F31E88E1$ |
| 6 | 52C4F80D | $w_{24} = 86900B95$ | $w_{25} = 661C8D23$ | $w_{26} = C1030A38$ | $w_{27} = 321D82D9$ |
| 7 | E4133523 | $w_{28} = 62833EB6$ | $w_{29} = 049FB395$ | $w_{30} = C59CB9AD$ | $w_{31} = F7813B74$ |
| 8 | 8CE29268 | $w_{32} = EE61ACDE$ | $w_{33} = EAFE1F4B$ | $w_{34} = 2F62A6E6$ | $w_{35} = D8E39D92$ |
| 9 | 0A5E4F61 | $w_{36} = E43FE3BF$ | $w_{37} = 0EC1FCF4$ | $w_{38} = 21A35A12$ | $w_{39} = F940C780$ |
| 10 | 3FC6CD99 | $w_{40} = DBF92E26$ | $w_{41} = D538D2D2$ | $w_{42} = F49B88C0$ | $w_{43} = 0DDB4F40$ |

In each round, the calculation of the last three words are very simple. For the calculation of the first word we need to first calculate the value of temporary word (**t**). For example, the first **t** (for round 1) is calculated as

**RotWord** (13AA5487) = AA548713     →     **SubWord** (AA548713) = AC20177D
**t** = AC20177D ⊕ **RCon$_1$** = AC20 17 7D ⊕ $01000000_{16}$ = AD20177D

> **Example 7.7**   Each round key in AES depends on the previous round key. The dependency, however, is nonlinear because of SubWord transformation. The addition of the round constants also guarantees that each round key will be different from the previous one.

> **Example 7.8**   The two sets of round keys can be created from two cipher keys that are different only in one bit.

> Cipher Key 1: 12 45 A2 A1 23 31 A4 A3 B2 CC A**A** 34 C2 BB 77 23
> Cipher Key 2: 12 45 A2 A1 23 31 A4 A3 B2 CC A**B** 34 C2 BB 77 23

As Table 7.6 shows, there are significant differences between the two corresponding round keys (*R.* means *round* and *B. D.* means *bit difference*).

**Table 7.6**   *Comparing two sets of round keys*

| R. | Round keys for set 1 | | | | Round keys for set 2 | | | | B. D. |
|---|---|---|---|---|---|---|---|---|---|
| — | 1245A2A1 | 2331A4A3 | B2CCA<u>A</u>34 | C2BB7723 | 1245A2A1 | 2331A4A3 | B2CCA<u>B</u>34 | C2BB7723 | 01 |
| 1 | F9B08484 | DA812027 | 684D8<u>A</u>13 | AAF6F<u>D</u>30 | F<u>9</u>B08484 | DA812027 | 684D8<u>B</u>13 | AAF6F<u>C</u>30 | 02 |
| 2 | B9E48028 | 6365A00F | 0B282A1C | A1DED72C | B9008028 | 6381A00F | 0BCC2B1C | A13AD72C | 17 |
| 3 | A0EAF11A | C38F5115 | C8A77B09 | 6979AC25 | 3D0EF11A | 5E8F5115 | 55437A09 | F479AD25 | 30 |
| 4 | 1E7BCEE3 | DDF49FF6 | 1553E4FF | 7C2A48DA | 839BCEA5 | DD149FB0 | 8857E5B9 | 7C2E489C | 31 |
| 5 | EB2999F3 | 36DD0605 | 238EE2FA | 5FA4AA20 | A2C910B5 | 7FDD8F05 | F78A6ABC | 8BA42220 | 34 |
| 6 | 82852E3C | B4582839 | 97D6CAC3 | C87260E3 | CB5AA788 | B487288D | 430D4231 | C8A96011 | 56 |
| 7 | 82553FD4 | 360D17ED | A1DBDD2E | 69A9BDCD | 588A2560 | EC0D0DED | AF004FDC | 67A92FCD | 50 |
| 8 | D12F822D | E72295C0 | 46F948EE | 2F50F523 | 0B9F98E5 | E7929508 | 4892DAD4 | 2F3BF519 | 44 |
| 9 | 99C9A438 | 7EEB31F8 | 38127916 | 17428C35 | F2794CF0 | 15EBD9F8 | 5D79032C | 7242F635 | 51 |
| 10 | 83AD32C8 | FD460330 | C5547A26 | D216F613 | E83BDAB0 | FDD00348 | A0A90064 | D2EBF651 | 52 |

> **Example 7.9**   The concept of weak keys, as we discussed for DES in Chapter 6, does not apply to AES. Assume that all bits in the cipher key are 0s. The following shows the words for some rounds:
>
> | Pre-round: | 00000000 | 00000000 | 00000000 | 00000000 |
> |---|---|---|---|---|
> | Round 01: | 62636363 | 62636363 | 62636363 | 62636363 |
> | Round 02: | 9B9898C9 | F9FBFBAA | 9B9898C9 | F9FBFBAA |
> | Round 03: | 90973450 | 696CCFFA | F2F45733 | 0B0FAC99 |
> | . . . | . . . | . . . | . . . | . . . |
> | Round 10: | B4EF5BCB | 3E92E211 | 23E951CF | 6F8F188E |
>
> The words in the pre-round and the first round are all the same. In the second round, the first word matches with the third; the second word matches with the fourth. However, after the second round the pattern disappears; every word is different.

## 7.3.2   Key Expansion in AES-192 and AES-256

Key-expansion algorithms in the AES-192 and AES-256 versions are very similar to the key expansion algorithm in AES-128, with the following differences:

1.  In AES-192, the words are generated in groups of six instead of four.
    a.  The cipher key creates the first six words ($\mathbf{w}_0$ to $\mathbf{w}_5$).
    b.  If $i \bmod 6 \neq 0$, $\mathbf{w}_i = \mathbf{w}_{i-1} + \mathbf{w}_{i-6}$; otherwise, $\mathbf{w}_i = \mathbf{t} + \mathbf{w}_{i-6}$.
2.  In AES-256, the words are generated in groups of eight instead of four.
    a.  The cipher key creates the first eight words ($\mathbf{w}_0$ to $\mathbf{w}_7$).
    b.  If $i \bmod 8 \neq 0$, $\mathbf{w}_i = \mathbf{w}_{i-1} + \mathbf{w}_{i-8}$; otherwise, $\mathbf{w}_i = \mathbf{t} + \mathbf{w}_{i-8}$.
    c.  If $i \bmod 4 = 0$, but $i \bmod 8 \neq 0$, then $\mathbf{w}_i = \text{SubWord}(\mathbf{w}_{i-1}) + \mathbf{w}_{i-8}$.

### 7.3.3  Key-Expansion Analysis

The key-expansion mechanism in AES has been designed to provide several features that thwart the cryptanalyst.

1.  Even if Eve knows only part of the cipher key or the values of the words in some round keys, she still needs to find the rest of the cipher key before she can find all round keys. This is because of the nonlinearity produced by SubWord transformation in the key-expansion process.
2.  Two different cipher keys, no matter how similar to each other, produce two expansions that differ in at least a few rounds.
3.  Each bit of the cipher key is diffused into several rounds. For example, changing a single bit in the cipher key, will change some bits in several rounds.
4.  The use of the constants, the RCons, removes any symmetry that may have been created by the other transformations.
5.  There are no serious weak keys in AES, unlike in DES.
6.  The key-expansion process can be easily implemented on all platforms.
7.  The key-expansion routine can be implemented without storing a single table; all calculations can be done using the $GF(2^8)$ and $FG(2)$ fields.

## 7.4                                    THE AES CIPHER

Now let us see how AES uses four types of transformations for encryption and decryption. In the standard, the encryption algorithm is referred to as the **cipher** and the decryption algorithm as the **inverse cipher.**

As we mentioned before, AES is a non-Feistel cipher, which means that each transformation or group of transformations must be invertible. In addition, the cipher and the inverse cipher must use these operations in such a way that cancel each other. The round keys must also be used in the reverse order. Two different designs are given to be used for different implementation. We discuss both designs for AES-128; the designs for other versions are the same.

### 7.4.1  Original Design

In the original design, the order of transformations in each round is not the same in the cipher and reverse cipher. Figure 7.17 shows this version.

First, the order of SubBytes and ShiftRows is changed in the reverse cipher. Second, the order of MixColumns and AddRoundKey is changed in the reverse cipher. This difference in ordering is needed to make each transformation in the cipher aligned with its inverse in the reverse cipher. Consequently, the decryption algorithm as a whole is the inverse of the encryption algorithm. We have shown only three rounds, but the rest is the same. Note that the round keys are used in the reverse order. Note that the encryption and decryption algorithms in the original design are not similar.

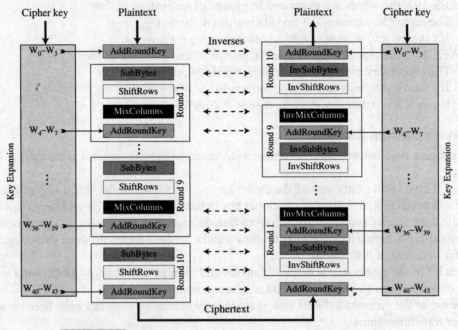

**Fig. 7.17** *Cipher and inverse cipher of the original design*

***Algorithm*** The code for the AES-128 version of this design is shown in Algorithm 7.6. The code for the inverse cipher is left as an exercise.

| Algorithm 7.6 | Pseudocode for cipher in the original design |
|---|---|

```
Cipher (InBlock [16], OutBlock[16], w[0 ... 43])
{
    BlockToState (InBlock, S)
    S ← AddRoundKey (S, w[0...3])
    for (round = 1 to 10)
    {
        S ← SubBytes (S)
        S ← ShiftRows (S)
        if (round ≠ 10) S ← MixColumns (S)
        S ← AddRoundKey (S, w[4 × round, 4 × round + 3])
    }
    StateToBlock (S, OutBlock);
}
```

## 7.4.2 Alternative Design

For those applications that prefer similar algorithms for encryption and decryption, a different inverse cipher was developed. In this version, the transformations in the reverse cipher are rearranged to make the order of transformations the same in the cipher and reverse cipher. In this design, invertibility is provided for a pair of transformations, not for each single transformation.

**SubBytes/ShiftRows Pairs**   SubBytes change the contents of each byte without changing the order of the bytes in the state; ShiftRows change the order of the bytes in the state without changing the contents of the bytes. This implies that we can change the order of these two transformations in the inverse cipher without affecting the invertibility of the whole algorithm. Figure 7.18 shows the idea. Note that the combination of two transformations in the cipher and inverse cipher are the inverses of each other.

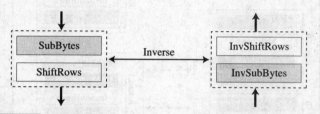

**Fig. 7.18**   *Invertibility of SubBytes and ShiftRows combinations*

**MixColumns/AddRoundKey Pair**   Here the two involved transformations are of different nature. However, the pairs can become inverses of each other if we multiply the key matrix by the inverse of the constant matrix used in MixColumns transformation. We call the new transformation **InvAddRoundKey**. Figure 7.19 shows the new configuration.

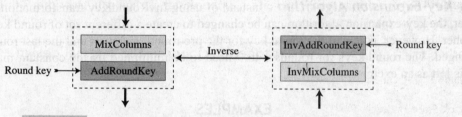

**Fig. 7.19**   *Invertibility of MixColumns and AddRoundKey combinations*

It can be proved that the two combinations are now inverses of each other. In the cipher we call the input state to the combination S and the output state T. In the reverse cipher the input state to the combination is T. The following shows that the output state is also S. Note that the MixColumns transformation is actually multiplication of the C matrix (constant matrix by the state).

**Cipher:** $T = CS \oplus K$
**Inverse Cipher:** $C^{-1}T \oplus C^{-1}K = C^{-1}(CS \oplus K) \oplus C^{-1}K = C^{-1}CS \oplus C^{-1}K \oplus C^{-1}K = S$

Now we can show the cipher and inverse cipher for the alternate design. Note that we still need to use two AddRoundKey transformations in the decryption. In other words, we have nine InvAddRoundKey and two AddRoundKey transformations as shown in Fig. 7.20.

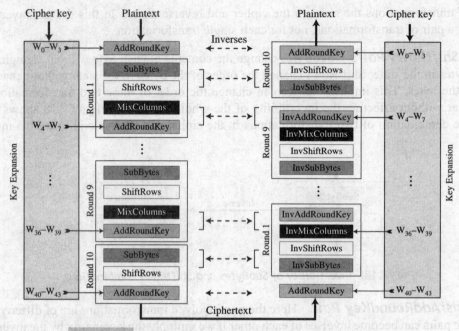

**Fig. 7.20** *Cipher and reverse cipher in alternate design*

***Changing Key-Expansion Algorithm*** Instead of using InvRoundKey transformation in the reverse cipher, the key-expansion algorithm can be changed to create a different set of round keys for the inverse cipher. However, note that the round key for the pre-round operation and the last round should not be changed. The round keys for rounds 1 to 9 need to be multiplied by the constant matrix. This algorithm is left as an exercise.

## 7.5                                    EXAMPLES

In this section, some examples of encryption/decryption and key generation are given to emphasize some points discussed in the two previous sections.

**Example 7.10**   The following shows the ciphertext block created from a plaintext block using a randomly selected cipher key.

> **Plaintext:**    00 04 12 14 12 04 12 00 0C 00 13 11 08 23 19 19
>
> **Cipher Key:** 24 75 A2 B3 34 75 56 88 31 E2 12 00 13 AA 54 87
>
> **Ciphertext:** BC 02 8B D3 E0 E3 B1 95 55 0D 6D FB E6 F1 82 41

Table 7.7 shows the values of state matrices and round keys for this example.

**Table 7.7** *Example of encryption*

| Round | Input State | Output State | Round Key |
|-------|-------------|--------------|-----------|
| Pre-round | 00 12 0C 08<br>04 04 00 23<br>12 12 13 19<br>14 00 11 19 | 24 26 3D 1B<br>71 71 E2 89<br>B0 44 01 4D<br>A7 88 11 9E | 24 34 31 13<br>75 75 E2 AA<br>A2 56 12 54<br>B3 88 00 87 |
| 1 | 24 26 3D 1B<br>71 71 E2 89<br>B0 44 01 4D<br>A7 88 11 9E | 6C 44 13 BD<br>B1 9E 46 35<br>C5 B5 F3 02<br>5D 87 FC 8C | 89 BD 8C 9F<br>55 20 C2 68<br>B5 E3 F1 A5<br>CE 46 46 C1 |
| 2 | 6C 44 13 BD<br>B1 9E 46 35<br>C5 B5 F3 02<br>5D 87 FC 8C | 1A 90 15 B2<br>66 09 1D FC<br>20 55 5A B2<br>2B CB 8C 3C | CE 73 FF 60<br>53 73 B1 D9<br>CD 2E DF 7A<br>15 53 15 D4 |
| 3 | 1A 90 15 B2<br>66 09 1D FC<br>20 55 5A B2<br>2B CB 8C 3C | F6 7D A2 B0<br>1B 61 B4 B8<br>67 09 C9 45<br>4A 5C 51 09 | FF 8C 73 13<br>89 FA 4B 92<br>85 AB 74 0E<br>C5 96 83 57 |
| 4 | F6 7D A2 B0<br>1B 61 B4 B8<br>67 09 C9 45<br>4A 5C 51 09 | CA E5 48 BB<br>D8 42 AF 71<br>D1 BA 98 2D<br>4E 60 9E DF | B8 34 47 54<br>22 D8 93 01<br>DE 75 01 0F<br>B8 2E AD FA |
| 5 | CA E5 48 BB<br>D8 42 AF 71<br>D1 BA 98 2D<br>4E 60 9E DF | 90 35 13 60<br>2C FB 82 3A<br>9E FC 61 ED<br>49 39 CB 47 | D4 E0 A7 F3<br>54 8C 1F 1E<br>F3 86 87 88<br>98 B6 1B E1 |
| 6 | 90 35 13 60<br>2C FB 82 3A<br>9E FC 61 ED<br>49 39 CB 47 | 18 0A B9 B5<br>64 68 6A FB<br>5A EF D7 79<br>8E B2 10 4D | 86 66 C1 32<br>90 1C 03 1D<br>0B 8D 0A 82<br>95 23 38 D9 |
| 7 | 18 0A B9 B5<br>64 68 6A FB<br>5A EF D7 79<br>8E B2 10 4D | 01 63 F1 96<br>55 24 3A 62<br>F4 8A DE 4D<br>CC BA 88 03 | 62 04 C5 F7<br>83 9F 9C 81<br>3E B3 B9 3B<br>B6 95 AD 74 |
| 8 | 01 63 F1 96<br>55 24 3A 62<br>F4 8A DE 4D<br>CC BA 88 03 | 2A 34 D8 46<br>2D 6B A2 D6<br>51 64 CF 5A<br>87 A8 F8 28 | EE EA 2F D8<br>61 FE 62 E3<br>AC 1F A6 9D<br>DE 4B E6 92 |

*Table 7.7   (Contd.)*

| 9 | 2A 34 D8 46<br>2D 6B A2 D6<br>51 64 CF 5A<br>87 A8 F8 28 | 0A D9 F1 3C<br>95 63 9F 35<br>2A 80 29 00<br>16 76 09 77 | E4 0E 21 F9<br>3F C1 A3 40<br>E3 FC 5A C7<br>BF F4 12 80 |
|---|---|---|---|
| 10 | 0A D9 F1 3C<br>95 63 9F 35<br>2A 80 29 00<br>16 76 09 77 | BC E0 55 E6<br>02 E3 0D F1<br>8B B1 6D 82<br>D3 95 F8 41 | DB D5 F4 0D<br>F9 38 9B DB<br>2E D2 88 4F<br>26 D2 C0 40 |

---

**Example 7.11**   Figure 7.21 shows the state entries in one round, round 7, in Example 7.10.

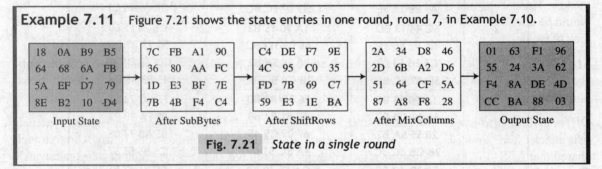

**Fig. 7.21**   *State in a single round*

---

**Example 7.12**   One may be curious to see the result of encryption when the plaintext is made of all 0s. Using the cipher key in Example 7.10 yields the ciphertext.

> Plaintext:   00 00 00 00 00 00 00 00 00 00 00 00 00 00 00 00
>
> Cipher Key: 24 75 A2 B3 34 75 56 88 31 E2 12 00 13 AA 54 87
>
> Ciphertext: 63 2C D4 5E 5D 56 ED B5 62 04 01 A0 AA 9C 2D 8D

---

**Example 7.13**   Let us check the avalanche effect that we discussed in Chapter 6. Let us change only one bit in the plaintext and compare the results. We changed only one bit in the last byte. The result clearly shows the effect of diffusion and confusion. Changing a single bit in the plaintext has affected many bits in the ciphertext.

> Plaintext 1:   00 00 00 00 00 00 00 00 00 00 00 00 00 00 00 00
>
> Plaintext 2:   00 00 00 00 00 00 00 00 00 00 00 00 00 00 00 01
>
> Ciphertext 1: 63 2C D4 5E 5D 56 ED B5 62 04 01 A0 AA 9C 2D 8D
>
> Ciphertext 2: 26 F3 9B BC A1 9C 0F B7 C7 2E 7E 30 63 92 73 13

---

**Example 7.14**   The following shows the effect of using a cipher key in which all bits are 0s.

> Plaintext:   00 04 12 14 12 04 12 00 0c 00 13 11 08 23 19 19
>
> Cipher Key: 00 00 00 00 00 00 00 00 00 00 00 00 00 00 00 00
>
> Ciphertext: 5A 6F 4B 67 57 B7 A5 D2 C4 30 91 ED 64 9A 42 72

## 7.6                    ANALYSIS OF AES

Following is a brief review of the three characteristics of AES.

### 7.6.1   Security

AES was designed after DES. Most of the known attacks on DES were already tested on AES; none of them has broken the security of AES so far.

***Brute-Force Attack***     AES is definitely more secure than DES due to the larger-size key (128, 192, and 256 bits). Let us compare DES with 56-bit cipher key and AES with 128-bit cipher key. For DES we need $2^{56}$ (ignoring the key complement issue) tests to find the key; for AES we need $2^{128}$ tests to find the key. This means that if we can break DES in $t$ seconds, we need $(2^{72} \times t)$ seconds to break AES. This would be almost impossible. In addition, AES provides two other versions with longer cipher keys. The lack of weak keys is another advantage of AES over DES.

***Statistical Attacks***     The strong diffusion and confusion provided by the combination of the Sub-Bytes, ShiftRows, and MixColumns transformations removes any frequency pattern in the plaintext. Numerous tests have failed to do statistical analysis of the ciphertext.

***Differential and Linear Attacks***     AES was designed after DES. Differential and linear cryptanalysis attacks were no doubt taken into consideration. Recently Alex Biryukov and Dmitry Khovratovich shared that AES–192 and 256 can be attacked using a technique known as "related key cryptanalysis". The attack was published in 2009, however, there have been no known attacks on AES–128 as yet.

### 7.6.2   Implementation

AES can be implemented in software, hardware, and firmware. The implementation can use table lookup process or routines that use a well-defined algebraic structure. The transformation can be either byte-oriented or word-oriented. In the byte-oriented version, the whole algorithm can use an 8-bit processor; in the word-oriented version, it can use a 32-bit processor. In either case, the design of constants makes processing very fast.

### 7.6.3   Simplicity and Cost

The algorithms used in AES are so simple that they can be easily implemented using cheap processors and a minimum amount of memory.

## 7.7                    RECOMMENDED READING

The following books and websites give more details about subjects discussed in this chapter. We recommend the following books and sites. The items enclosed in brackets refer to the reference list at the end of the book.

### Books

[Sta06], [Sti06], [Rhe03], [Sal03], [Mao04], and [TW06] discuss AES.

### WebSites

The following websites give more information about topics discussed in this chapter.
    csrc.nist.gov/publications/fips/fips197/fips-197.pdf

http://www.quadibloc.com/crypto/co040401.htm
http://www.ietf.org/rfc/rfc3394.txt

## Key Terms

| | |
|---|---|
| AddRoundKey | key expansion |
| Advanced Encryption Standard (AES) | MixColumns |
| bitblock | National Institute of Standards and Technology (NIST) |
| byte | Rijndael |
| cipher | RotWord |
| InvAddRoundKey | ShiftRows |
| inverse cipher | state |
| InvMixColumns | SubBytes |
| InvShiftRows | SubWord |
| InvSubBytes | word |

## Summary

★ The Advanced Encryption Standard (AES) is a symmetric-key block cipher published by NIST as FIPS 197. AES is based on the Rijndael algorithm.

★ AES is a non-Feistel cipher that encrypts and decrypts a data block of 128 bits. It uses 10, 12, or 14 number of rounds. The key size, which can be 128, 192, or 256 bits depends on the number of rounds.

★ AES is byte-oriented. The 128-bit plaintext or ciphertext is considered as sixteen 8-bit bytes. To be able to perform some mathematical transformations on bytes, AES has defined the concept of a state. A state is a $4 \times 4$ matrix in which each entry is a byte.

★ To provide security, AES uses four types of transformations: substitution, permutation, mixing, and key-adding. Each round of AES, except the last, uses the four transformations. The last round uses only three of the four transformations.

★ Substitution is defined by either a table lookup process or mathematical calculation in the $GF(2^8)$ field. AES uses two invertible transformations, SubBytes and InvSubBytes, which are inverses of each other.

★ The second transformation in a round is shifting, which permutes the bytes. In the encryption, the transformation is called ShiftRows. In the decryption, the transformation is called InvShiftRows. The ShiftRows and InvShiftRows transformations are inverses of each other.

★ The mixing transformation changes the contents of each byte by taking four bytes at a time and combining them to recreate four new bytes. AES defines two transformations, MixColumns and InvMixColumns, to be used in the encryption and decryption. MixColumns multiplies the state matrix by a constant square matrix; the InvMixColumns does the same using the inverse constant matrix. The MixColumns and InvMixColumns transformations are inverses of each other.

★ The transformation that performs whitening is called AddRoundKey. The previous state is added (matrix addition) with the round matrix key to create the new state. Addition of individual elements in the two matrices is done in $GF(2^8)$, which means that 8-bit words are XORed. The AddRoundKey transformation is the inverse of itself.

★ In the first configuration (10 rounds with 128-bit keys), the key generator creates eleven 128-bit round keys out of the 128-bit cipher key. AES uses the concept of a word for key generation. A word is made of four bytes. The round keys are generated word by word. AES numbers the words from $w_0$ to $w_{43}$. The process is referred to as key expansion.

★ AES cipher uses two algorithms for decryption. In the original design, the order of transformations in each round is not the same in the encryption and decryption. In the alternative design, the transformations in the decryption algorithms are rearranged to make ordering the same in encryption and decryption. In the second version, the invertibility is provided for a pair of transformations.

# *Practice Set*

## Review Questions

**7.1**  List the criteria defined by NIST for AES.

**7.2**  List the parameters (block size, key size, and the number of rounds) for the three AES versions.

**7.3**  How many transformations are there in each version of AES? How many round keys are needed for each version?

**7.4**  Compare DES and AES. Which one is bit-oriented? Which one is byte-oriented?

**7.5**  Define a state in AES. How many states are there in each version of AES?

**7.6**  Which of the four transformations defined for AES change the contents of bytes? Which one does not change the contents of the bytes?

**7.7**  Compare the substitution in DES and AES. Why do we have only one substitution table (S-box) in AES, but several in DES?

**7.8**  Compare the permutations in DES and AES. Why do we need expansion and compression permutations in DES, but not in AES?

**7.9**  Compare the round keys in DES and AES. In which cipher is the size of the round key the same as the size of the block?

**7.10**  Why do you think the mixing transformation (MixColumns) is not needed in DES, but is needed in AES?

## Exercises

**7.11**  In a cipher, S-boxes can be either *static* or *dynamic*. The parameters in a static S-box do not depend on the key.

    a.  State some advantages and some disadvantages of static and dynamic S-boxes.

    b.  Are the S-boxes (substitution tables) in AES static or dynamic?

**7.12**  AES has a larger block size than DES (128 versus 64). Is this an advantage or disadvantage? Explain.

**7.13**  AES defines different implementations with three different numbers of rounds (10, 12, and 14); DES defines only implementation with 16 rounds. What are the advantages and disadvantages of AES over DES with respect to this difference?

**7.14**  AES defines three different cipher-key sizes (128, 192, and 256); DES defines only one cipher-key size (56). What are the advantages and disadvantages of AES over DES with respect to this difference?

**7.15**  In AES, the size of the block is the same as the size of the round key (128 bits); in DES, the size of the block is 64 bits, but the size of the round key is only 48 bits. What are the advantages and disadvantages of AES over DES with respect to this difference?

**7.16**  Prove that the ShiftRows and InvShiftRows transformations are permutations by doing the following:

    a.  Show the permutation table for ShiftRows. The table needs to have 128 entries, but since the contents of a byte do not change, the table can have only 16 entries with the assumption that each entry represents a byte.

    b.    Repeat Part a for InvShiftRows transformation.

    c.    Using the results of Parts *a* and *b*, prove that the ShiftRows and InvShiftRows transformations are inverses of each other.

**7.17**    Using the same cipher key, apply each of the following transformations on two plaintexts that differ only in the first bit. Find the number of bits changed after each transformation. Each transformation is applied independently.

    a.    SubBytes

    b.    ShiftRows

    c.    MixColumns

    d.    AddRoundKey (with the same round keys of your choice)

**7.18**    To see the nonlinearity of the SubBytes transformation, show that if *a* and *b* are two bytes, we have

$$\text{SubBytes } (a \oplus b) \neq \text{SubBytes } (a) \oplus \text{SubBytes } (b)$$

Use $a = 0x57$ and $b = 0xA2$ as an example.

**7.19**    Give a general formula to calculate the number of each kind of transformation (SubBytes, ShiftRows, MixColumns, and AddRoundKey) and the number of total transformations for each version of AES. The formula should be parametrized on the number of rounds.

**7.20**    Redraw Fig. 7.5 for AES-192 and AES-256.

**7.21**    Create two new tables that show RCons constants for the AES-192 and AES-256 implementations (see Table 7.4).

**7.22**    In AES-128, the round key used in the pre-round operation is the same as the cipher key. Is this the case for AES-192? Is this the case for AES-256?

**7.23**    In Fig. 7.8, multiply the X and $X^{-1}$ matrices to prove that they are inverses of each other.

**7.24**    Using Fig. 7.12, rewrite the square matrices C and $C^{-1}$ using polynomials with coefficients in GF(2). Multiply the two matrices and prove that they are inverse of each other.

**7.25**    Prove that the code in Algorithm 7.1 (SubBytes transformation) matches the process shown in Fig. 7.8.

**7.26**    Using Algorithm 7.1 (SubBytes transformation), do the following:

    a.    Write the code for a routine that calculates the inverse of a byte in $GF(2^8)$.

    b.    Write the code for ByteToMatrix.

    c.    Write the code for MatrixToByte.

**7.27**    Write an algorithm for the InvSubBytes transformation.

**7.28**    Prove that the code in Algorithm 7.2 (ShiftRows transformation) matches the process shown in Fig. 7.9.

**7.29**    Using Algorithm 7.2 (ShiftRows transformation), write the code for CopyRow routine.

**7.30**    Write an algorithm for the InvShiftRows transformation.

**7.31**    Prove that the code in Algorithm 7.3 (MixColumns transformation) matches with the process shown in Fig. 7.13.

**7.32**    Using Algorithm 7.3 (MixColumns transformation), write the code for the CopyColumn routine.

**7.33**    Rewrite Algorithm 7.3 (MixColumns transformation) replacing the operators (.) with a routine called MultField to calculate the multiplication of two bytes in the $GF(2^8)$ field.

**7.34**    Write an algorithm for InvMixColumn transformation.

**7.35**   Prove that the code in Algorithm 7.4 (AddRoundKey transformation) matches the process shown in Fig. 7.15.

**7.36**   In Algorithm 7.5 (Key Expansion),
   a.   Write the code for the SubWord routine.
   b.   Write the code for the RotWord routine.

**7.37**   Give two new algorithms for key expansion in AES-192 and AES-256 (see Algorithm 7.5).

**7.38**   Write the key-expansion algorithm for alternate reverse cipher.

**7.39**   Write the algorithm for inverse cipher in the original design.

**7.40**   Write the algorithm for the inverse cipher in the alternative design.

# 8

# Encipherment Using Modern Symmetric-Key Ciphers

## Objectives

This chapter has several objectives:

- ☞ To show how modern standard ciphers, such as DES or AES, can be used to encipher long messages.
- ☞ To discuss five modes of operation designed to be used with modern block ciphers.
- ☞ To define which mode of operation creates stream ciphers out of the underlying block ciphers.
- ☞ To discuss the security issues and the error propagation of different modes of operation.
- ☞ To discuss two stream ciphers used for real-time processing of data.

This chapter shows how the concepts discussed in Chapter 5 and two modern block ciphers discussed in Chapters 6 and 7 can be used to encipher long messages. It also introduces two stream ciphers.

## 8.1 USE OF MODERN BLOCK CIPHERS

Symmetric-key encipherment can be done using modern block ciphers. The two modern block ciphers discussed in Chapters 6 and 7, namely DES and AES, are designed to encipher and decipher a block of text of fixed size. DES encrypts and decrypts a block of 64 bits; AES encrypts and decrypts a block of 128 bits. In real-life applications, the text to be enciphered is of variable size and normally much larger than 64 or 128 bits. **Modes of operation** have been devised to encipher text of any size employing either DES or AES. Figure 8.1 shows the five modes of operation that will be discussed here.

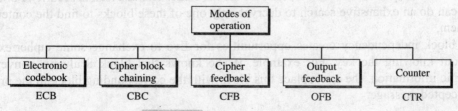

**Fig. 8.1** *Modes of operation*

## 8.1.1 Electronic Codebook (ECB) Mode

The simplest mode of operation is called the **electronic codebook (ECB) mode.** The plaintext is divided into $N$ blocks. The block size is $n$ bits. If the plaintext size is not a multiple of the block size, the text is padded to make the last block the same size as the other blocks. The same key is used to encrypt and decrypt each block. Figure 8.2 shows the encryption and decryption in this mode.

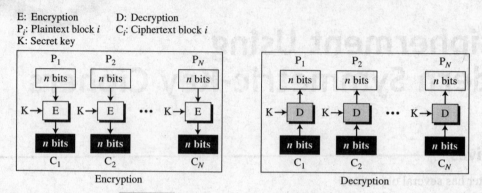

E: Encryption     D: Decryption
$P_i$: Plaintext block $i$     $C_i$: Ciphertext block $i$
K: Secret key

**Fig. 8.2** *Electronic codebook (ECB) mode*

The relation between plaintext and ciphertext block is shown below:

Encryption: $C_i = E_K(P_i)$            Decryption: $P_i = D_K(C_i)$

**Example 8.1** It can be proved that each plaintext block at Alice's site is exactly recovered at Bob's site. Because encryption and decryption are inverses of each other,

$$P_i = D_K(C_i) = D_K(E_K(P_i)) = P_i$$

**Example 8.2** This mode is called *electronic codebook* because one can precompile $2^K$ codebooks (one for each key) in which each codebook has $2^n$ entries in two columns. Each entry can list the plaintext and the corresponding ciphertext blocks. However, if $K$ and $n$ are large, the codebook would be far too large to precompile and maintain.

*Security Issues* Following are security issues in CBC mode:

1. Patterns at the block level are preserved. For example, equal blocks in the plaintext become equal blocks in the ciphertext. If Eve finds out that ciphertext blocks 1, 5, and 10 are the same, she knows that plaintext blocks 1, 5, and 10 are the same. This is a leak in security. For example, Eve can do an exhaustive search to decrypt only one of these blocks to find the contents of all of them.

2. The block independency creates opportunities for Eve to exchange some ciphertext blocks without knowing the key. For example, if she knows that block 8 always conveys some specific information, she can replace this block with the corresponding block in the previously intercepted message.

> **Example 8.3** Assume that Eve works in a company a few hours per month (her monthly payment is very low). She knows that the company uses several blocks of information for each employee in which the seventh block is the amount of money to be deposited in the employee's account. Eve can intercept the ciphertext sent to the bank at the end of the month, replace the block with the information about her payment with a copy of the block with the information about the payment of a full-time colleague. Each month Eve can receive more money than she deserves.

**Error Propagation** A single bit error in transmission can create errors in several (normally half of the bits or all of the bits) in the corresponding block. However, the error does not have any effect on the other blocks.

**Algorithm** Simple algorithms can be written for encryption or decryption. Algorithm 8.1 gives the pseudocode routine for encryption; the routine for decryption is left as an exercise. $E_K$ encrypts a single block and can be one of the ciphers discussed in Chapters 6 or 7 (DES or AES).

---

**Algorithm 8.1**                 **Encryption for ECB mode**

---

```
ECB_Encryption (K, Plaintext blocks)
{
    for (i = 1 to N )
    {
        Ci ← EK (Pi)
    }
    return Ciphertext blocks
}
```

**Ciphertext Stealing** In ECB mode, padding must be added to the last block if it is not $n$ bits long. Padding is not always possible. For example, when the ciphertext needs to be stored in the buffer where the plaintext was previously stored, plaintext and ciphertext must be the same. A technique called **ciphertext stealing (CTS)** can make it possible to use ECB mode without padding. In this technique the last two plaintext blocks, $P_{N-1}$ and $P_N$, are encrypted differently and out of order, as shown below, assuming that $P_{N-1}$ has $n$ bits and $P_N$ has $m$ bits, where $m \leq n$.

$$X = E_K (P_{N-1}) \quad \rightarrow \quad C_N = head_m (X)$$
$$Y = P_N \mid tail_{n-m} (X) \rightarrow \quad C_{N-1} = E_K (Y)$$

The $head_m$ function selects the leftmost $m$ bits; the $tail_{n-m}$ function selects the rightmost $n - m$ bits. The detailed diagram and the procedure of the encryption and decryption are left as exercises.

**Applications** The ECB mode of operation is not recommended for encryption of messages of more than one block to be transferred through an insecure channel. If the message is short enough to fit in one block, the security issues and propagation errors are tolerable.

One area where the independency of the ciphertext block is useful is where records need to be encrypted before they are stored in a database or decrypted before they are retrieved. Because the order of encryption and decryption of blocks is not important in this mode, access to the database can be random if each record is a block or multiple blocks. A record can be retrieved from the middle, decrypted, and encrypted after modification without affecting other records.

Another advantage of this mode is that we can use parallel processing if we need to create, for example, a very huge encrypted database.

## 8.1.2 Cipher Block Chaining (CBC) Mode

The next evolution in the operation mode is the **cipher block chaining (CBC) mode.** In CBC mode, each plaintext block is exclusive-ored with the previous ciphertext block before being encrypted. When a block is enciphered, the block is sent, but a copy of it is kept in memory to be used in the encryption of the next block. The reader may wonder about the initial block. There is no ciphertext block before the first block. In this case, a phony block called the **initialization vector (IV)** is used. The sender and receiver agree upon a specific predetermined IV. In other words, an IV is used instead of the nonexistent $C_0$. Figure 8.3 shows CBC mode. At the sender side, exclusive-oring is done before encryption; at the receiver site, decryption is done before exclusive-oring.

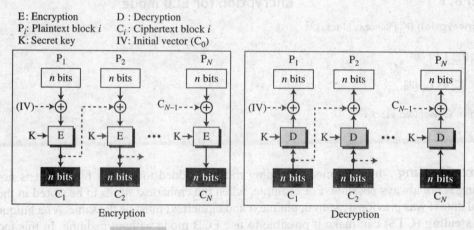

**Fig. 8.3** *Cipher block chaining (CBC) mode*

The relation between plaintext and ciphertext blocks is shown below:

| **Encryption:** | **Decryption:** |
|---|---|
| $C_0 = IV$ | $C_0 = IV$ |
| $C_i = E_K (P_i \oplus C_{i-1})$ | $P_i = D_K (C_i) \oplus C_{i-1}$ |

**Example 8.4** It can be proved that each plaintext block at Alice's site is recovered exactly at Bob's site. Because encryption and decryption are inverses of each other,

$$P_i = D_K (C_i) \oplus C_{i-1} = D_K (E_K (P_i \oplus C_{i-1})) \oplus C_{i-1} = P_i \oplus C_{i-1} \oplus C_{i-1} = P_i$$

*Initialization Vector (IV)*  The initialization vector (IV) should be known by the sender and the receiver. Although keeping the vector secret is not necessary, the integrity of the vector plays an important role in the security of CBC mode; IV should be kept safe from change. If Eve can change the bit values of the IV, it can change the bit values of the first block.

Several methods have been recommended for using IV. A pseudorandom number can be selected by the sender and transmitted through a secure channel (using ECB mode for example). A fixed value can be agreed upon by Alice and Bob as the IV when the secret key is established. It can be part of the secret key, and so on.

***Security Issues*** Following are two of the security issues in CBC mode:
1. In CBC mode, equal plaintext blocks belonging to the same message are enciphered into different ciphertext blocks. In other words, the patterns at the block levels are not preserved. However, if two messages are equal, their encipherment is the same if they use the same IV. As a matter of fact, if the first M blocks in two different messages are equal, they are enciphered into equal blocks unless different IVs are used. For this reason, some people recommend the use of a timestamp as an IV.
2. Eve can add some ciphertext blocks to the end of the ciphertext stream.

***Error Propagation*** In CBC mode, a single bit error in ciphertext block $C_j$ during transmission may create error in most bits in plaintext block $P_j$ during decryption. However, this single error toggles only one bit in plaintext block $P_{j+1}$ (the bit in the same location). The proof of this fact is left as an exercise. Plaintext blocks $P_{j+2}$ to $P_N$ are not affected by this single bit error. A single bit error in ciphertext is *self-recovered*.

***Algorithm*** Algorithm 8.2 gives the pseudocode for encryption. The algorithm calls the *encrypt* routine that encrypts a single block (DES or AES, for example). The decryption algorithm is left as an exercise.

| Algorithm 8.2 | Encryption algorithm for ECB mode |
| --- | --- |

```
CBC_Encryption (IV, K, Plaintext blocks)
{
    C₀ ← IV
    for ( i = 1 to N )
    {
        Temp ← Pᵢ ⊕ Cᵢ₋₁
        Cᵢ ← E_K (Temp)
    }
    return Ciphertext blocks
}
```

***Ciphertext Stealing*** The ciphertext stealing technique described for ECB mode can also be applied to CBC mode, as shown below

$$U = P_{N-1} \oplus C_{N-2} \rightarrow X = E_K (U) \rightarrow C_N = head_m (X).$$
$$V = P_N \,|\, pad_{n-m} (0) \rightarrow Y = X \oplus V \rightarrow C_{N-1} = E_K (Y)$$

The *head* function is the same as described in ECB mode; the *pad* function inserts 0's.

***Applications*** The CBC mode of operation can be used to encipher messages. However, because of chaining mechanism, parallel processing is not possible. CBC mode is not used to encrypt and decrypt random-access files records because encryption and decryption require access to the previous records. As we will see in Chapter 11, CBC mode is also used for authentication.

### 8.1.3 Cipher Feedback (CFB) Mode

ECB and CBC modes encrypt and decrypt blocks of the message. The block size, $n$, is predetermined by the underlying cipher; for example, $n = 64$ for DES and $n = 128$ for AES. In some situations, we need to use DES or AES as secure ciphers, but the plaintext or ciphertext block sizes are to be smaller. For example, to encrypt and decrypt ASCII 8-bit characters, you would not want to use one of the traditional ciphers discussed in Chapter 3 because they are insecure. The solution is to use DES or AES in **cipher feedback (CFB) mode.** In this mode the size of the block used in DES or AES is $n$, but the size of the plaintext or ciphertext block is $r$, where $r \leq n$.

The idea is to use DES or AES, not for encrypting the plaintext or decrypting the ciphertext, but to encrypt or decrypt the contents of a shift register, S, of size $n$. Encryption is done by exclusive-oring an $r$-bit plaintext block with $r$ bits of the shift register. Decryption is done by exclusive-oring an $r$-bit ciphertext block with $r$ bits of the shift register. For each block, the shift register $S_i$ is made by shifting the shift register $S_{i-1}$ (previous shift register) $r$ bits to the left and filling the rightmost $r$ bits with $C_{i-1}$. $S_i$ is then encrypted to $T_i$. Only the rightmost $r$ bits of $T_i$ are exclusive-ored with the plaintext block $P_i$ to make the $C_i$. Note that $S_1$, which is not shifted, is set to the IV for the first block.

Figure 8.4 shows the CFB mode for enciphering; deciphering is the same, but the roles of plaintext blocks ($P_i$'s) and ciphertext blocks ($C_i$'s) are switched. Note that both encipherment and decipherment use the encryption function of the underlying block cipher (DES or AES, for example).

E : Encryption     D : Decryption     $S_i$: Shift register
$P_i$: Plaintext block $i$     $C_i$: Ciphertext block $i$     $T_i$: Temporary register
K : Secret key     IV: Initial vector ($S_1$)

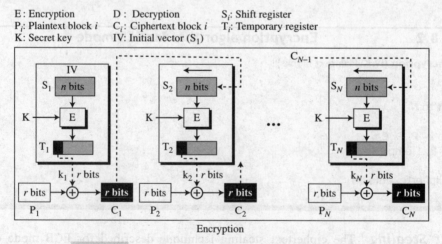

**Fig. 8.4** *Encryption in cipher feedback (CFB) mode*

> **In CFB mode, encipherment and decipherment use the encryption function of the underlying block cipher.**

The relation between plaintext and ciphertext blocks is shown below:

**Encryption:** $C_i = P_i \oplus$ SelectLeft$_r$ {$E_K$ [ShiftLeft$_r$ ($S_{i-1}$) | $C_{i-1}$)]}

**Decryption:** $P_i = C_i \oplus$ SelectLeft$_r$ {$E_K$ [ShiftLeft$_r$ ($S_{i-1}$) | $C_{i-1}$)]}

where the ShiftLeft$_r$ routine shifts the contents of its argument $r$ bits to the left (the leftmost $r$ bits are dropped). The operator | shows the concatenation. The SelectLeft$_r$ routine selects only the leftmost $r$ bits from the argument. It can be proven that each plaintext block at Alice's site is recovered exactly at Bob's site, but the proof is left as an exercise.

One interesting point about this mode is that no padding is required because the size of the blocks, $r$, is normally chosen to fit the data unit to be encrypted (a character, for example). Another interesting point is that the system does not have to wait until it has received a large block of data (64 bits or 128 bits) before starting the encryption. The encrypting process is done for a small block of data (such as a character). These two advantages come with a disadvantage. CFB is less efficient than CBC or ECB, because it needs to apply the encryption function of underlying block cipher for each small block of size $r$.

**CFB as a Stream Cipher**  Although CFB is an operation mode for using block ciphers such as DES or AES, the result is a stream cipher. In fact, it is a nonsynchronous stream cipher in which the key stream is dependent on the ciphertext. Figure 8.5 shows the point of the encryption and decryption where the key generator is conspicuous.

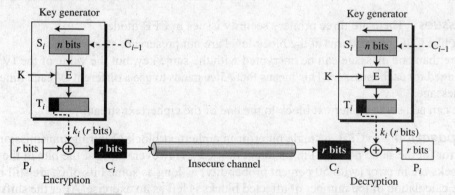

**Fig. 8.5** *Cipher feedback (CFB) mode as a stream cipher*

Figure 8.5 shows that the underlying cipher (DES or AES), the cipher key (K), and the previous cipher block ($C_i$) are used only to create the key streams ($k_1, k_2, ..., k_N$).

**Algorithm**  Algorithm 8.3 gives the routine for encryption. The algorithm calls several other routines whose details are left as exercises. Note that we have written the algorithm in such a way to show the stream nature of the mode (real-time situation). The algorithm runs as long as there are plaintext blocks to be encrypted.

---

**Algorithm 8.3**                    **Encryption algorithm for CFB**

```
CFB_Encryption (IV, K, r)
{
    i ← 1
    while (more blocks to encrypt)
    {
        input (Pᵢ)
        if (i = 1)
            S ← IV
        else
        {
            Temp ← shiftLeftᵣ (S)
            S ← concatenate (Temp, Cᵢ₋₁)
        }
        T ← E_K(S)
        kᵢ ← selectLeftᵣ (T)
        Cᵢ ← Pᵢ ⊕ kᵢ
        output (Cᵢ)
        i ← i + 1
    }
}
```

**Security Issues**    There are three primary security issues in CFB mode:

1.  Just like CBC, the patterns at the block level are not preserved.
2.  More than one message can be encrypted with the same key, but the value of the IV should be changed for each message. This means that Alice needs to use a different IV each time she sends a message.
3.  Eve can add some ciphertext block to the end of the ciphertext stream.

**Error Propagation**    In CFB, a single bit error in ciphertext block $C_j$ during transmission creates a single bit error (at the same position) in plaintext block $P_j$. However, most of the bits in the following plaintext blocks are in error (with 50 percent probability) as long as some bits of $C_j$ are still in the shift register. The calculation of the number of affected blocks is left as an exercise. After the shift register is totally refreshed, the system recovers from the error.

**Application**    The CFB mode of operation can be used to encipher blocks of small size such as one character or bit at a time. There is no need for padding because the size of the plaintext block is normally fixed (8 for a character or 1 for a bit).

**Special Case**    If the blocks in the text and in the underlying cipher are the same size ($n = r$), the encryption/decryption becomes simpler, but discovery of the diagram and the algorithm are left as an exercise.

### 8.1.4  Output Feedback (OFB) Mode

**Output feedback (OFB) mode** is very similar to CFB mode, with one difference: each bit in the ciphertext is independent of the previous bit or bits. This avoids error propagation. If an error occurs in transmission, it does not affect the bits that follow. Note that, like CFB, both the sender and the receiver use the encryption algorithm. Figure 8.6 shows OFB mode.

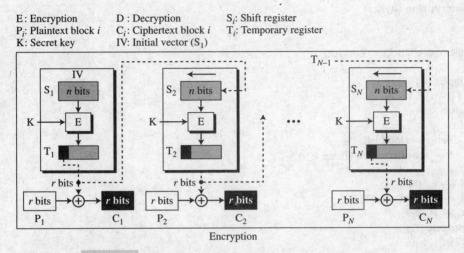

**Fig. 8.6** *Encryption in output feedback (OFB) mode*

### OFB as a Stream Cipher

OFB, like CFB, creates a stream cipher out of the underlying block cipher. The key stream, however, is independent from the plaintext or ciphertext, which means that the stream cipher is synchronous as discussed in Chapter 5. Figure 8.7 shows the encryption and decryption in which the key generator is conspicuous.

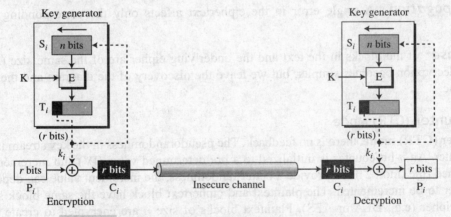

**Fig. 8.7** *Output feedback (OFB) mode as a stream cipher*

### Algorithm

Algorithm 8.4 gives the routine for encryption. The algorithm calls several other routines whose details are left as exercises. Note that we have written the algorithm in such a way to show the stream nature of the mode (real-time situation). The algorithm runs as long as there are plaintext blocks to be encrypted.

---

**Algorithm 8.4**  **Encryption algorithm for OFB**

```
OFB_Encryption (IV, K, r)
{
    i ← 1
    while (more blocks to encrypt)
    {
        input (Pᵢ)
        if (i = 1) S ← IV
        else
        {
            Temp ← shiftLeftᵣ (S)
            S ← concatenate (Temp, kᵢ₋₁)
        }
        T ← E_K (S)
        kᵢ ← selectLeftᵣ (T)
        Cᵢ ← Pᵢ ⊕ kᵢ
        output (Cᵢ)
        i ← i + 1
    }
}
```

---

**Security Issues**   Following are two of the security issues in OFB mode:

1. Just like the CFB mode, patterns at the block level are not preserved.
2. Any change in the ciphertext affects the plaintext encrypted at the receiver side.

**Error Propagation**   A single error in the ciphertext affects only the corresponding bit in the plaintext.

**Special Case**   If the blocks in the text and the underlying cipher are of the same size ($n = r$), the encryption/decryption becomes simpler, but we leave the discovery of the diagram and the algorithm as an exercise.

### 8.1.5   Counter (CTR) Mode

In the **counter (CTR) mode,** there is no feedback. The pseudorandomness in the key stream is achieved using a counter. An $n$-bit counter is initialized to a pre-determined value (IV) and incremented based on a predefined rule (mod $2^n$). To provide a better randomness, the increment value can depend on the block number to be incremented. The plaintext and ciphertext block have the same block size as the underlying cipher (e.g., DEA or AES). Plaintext blocks of size $n$ are encrypted to create ciphertext blocks of size $n$. Figure 8.8 shows the counter mode.

The relation between plaintext and ciphertext blocks is shown below.

**Encryption:** $C_i = P_i \oplus E_{K_i} (\text{Counter})$   **Decryption:** $P_i = C_i \oplus E_{K_i} (\text{Counter})$

CTR uses the encryption function of the underlying block cipher ($E_K$) for both encipherment and decipherment. It is easy to prove that the plaintext block $P_i$ can be recovered from the ciphertext $C_i$. This is left as an exercise.

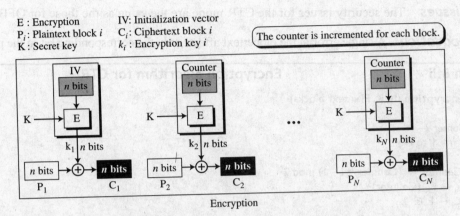

E : Encryption
$P_i$ : Plaintext block $i$
K : Secret key

IV: Initialization vector
$C_i$ : Ciphertext block $i$
$k_i$ : Encryption key $i$

The counter is incremented for each block.

Encryption

**Fig. 8.8** *Encryption in counter (CTR) mode*

We can compare CTR mode to OFB and ECB modes. Like OFB, CTR creates a key stream that is independent from the previous ciphertext block, but CTR does not use feedback. Like ECB, CTR creates $n$-bit ciphertext blocks that are independent from each other; they depend only on the value of the counter. On the negative side, this means that CTR mode, like ECB mode, cannot be used for real-time processing. The encrypting algorithm needs to wait to get a complete $n$-bit block of data before encrypting. On the positive side, CTR mode, like ECB mode can be used to encrypt and decrypt random-access files as long as the value of the counter can be related to the record number in the file.

***CTR as a Stream Cipher***   Like CFB and OFB, CTR is actually a stream cipher (different block are exclusive-ored with different keys). Figure 8.9 shows encryption and decryption of the $i$th data block.

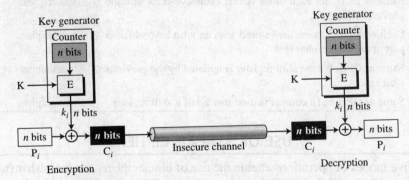

Encryption      Insecure channel      Decryption

**Fig. 8.9** *Counter (CTR) mode as a stream cipher*

***Algorithm***   Algorithm 8.5 gives the routine in pseudocode for encryption; the algorithm for decryption is left as an exercise. In this algorithm, the increment value is dependent on the block number. In other words, the counter values are IV, IV + 1, IV + 3, IV + 6, and so on. It is also assumed that all $N$ plaintext blocks are ready before starting encryption, but the algorithm can be rewritten to avoid this assumption.

***Security Issues*** The security issues for the CTR mode are the same as the those for OFB mode.

***Error Propagation*** A single error in the ciphertext affects only the corresponding bit in the plaintext.

---

**Algorithm 8.5**                   **Encryption algorithm for CTR**

---

```
CTR_Encryption (IV, K, Plaintext blocks)
{
      Counter ← IV
      for (i = 1 to N )
      {
          Counter ← (Counter + i − 1) mod 2^N
          k_i ← E_K (Counter)
          C_i ← P_i ⊕ k_i
      }
      return Ciphertext blocks
}
```

***Comparison of Different Modes*** Table 8.1 briefly compares the five different modes of operation discussed in this chapter.

**Table 8.1** *Summary of operation modes*

| Operation Mode | Description | Type of Result | Data Unit Size |
|---|---|---|---|
| ECB | Each $n$-bit block is encrypted independently with the same cipher key. | Blockcipher | $n$ |
| CBC | Same as ECB, but each block is first exclusive-ored with the previous ciphertext. | Blockcipher | $n$ |
| CFB | Each $r$-bit block is exclusive-ored with an $r$-bit key, which is part of previous cipher text | Streamcipher | $r \leq n$ |
| OFB | Same as CFB, but the shift register is updated by the previous $r$-bit key. | Streamcipher | $r \leq n$ |
| CTR | Same as OFB, but a counter is used instead of a shift register. | Streamcipher | $n$ |

---

## 8.2            USE OF STREAM CIPHERS

Although the five modes of operations enable the use of block ciphers for encipherment of messages or files in large units (ECB, CBC, and CTR) and small units (CFB and OFB), sometimes *pure* stream are needed for enciphering small units of data such as characters or bits. Stream ciphers are more efficient for real-time processing. Several stream ciphers have been used in different protocols during the last few decades. We discuss only two: RC4 and A5/1.

### 8.2.1   RC4

**RC4** is a stream cipher that was designed in 1984 by Ronald Rivest for RSA Data Security. RC4 is used in many data communication and networking protocols, including SSL/TLS (see Chapter 17) and the IEEE802.11 wireless LAN standard.

RC4 is a byte-oriented stream cipher in which a byte (8 bits) of a plaintext is exclusive-ored with a byte of key to produce a byte of a ciphertext. The secret key, from which the one-byte keys in the key stream are generated, can contain anywhere from 1 to 256 bytes.

**State**   RC4 is based on the concept of a state. At each moment, a state of 256 bytes is active, from which one of the bytes is randomly selected to serve as the key for encryption. The idea can be shown as an array of bytes:

$$S[0] \quad S[1] \quad S[2] \ldots S[255]$$

Note that the indices of the elements range between 0 and 255. The contents of each element is also a byte (8 bits) that can be interpreted as an integer between 0 to 255.

**The Idea**   Figure 8.10 shows the whole idea of RC4. The first two boxes are performed only once (initializing); the permutation for creating stream key is repeated as long as there are plaintext bytes to encrypt.

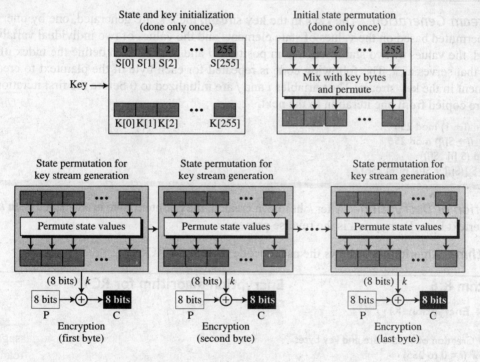

**Fig. 8.10**   *The idea of RC4 stream cipher*

**Initialization**   Initialization is done in two steps:

1.  In the first step, the state is initialized to values 0, 1, …, 255. A key array, K[0], K[1], …, K[255] is also created. If the secret key has exactly 256 bytes, the bytes are copied to the K array; otherwise, the bytes are repeated until the K array is filled.

```
for (i = 0 to 255)
{
    S[i] ← i
    K[i] ← Key [i mod KeyLength]
}
```

2. In the second step, the initialized state goes through a permutation (swapping the elements) based on the value of the bytes in K[$i$]. The key byte is used only in this step to define which elements are to be swapped. After this step, the state bytes are completely shuffled.

```
j ← 0
for (i = 0 to 255)
{
    j ← (j + S[i] + K[i]) mod 256
    swap (S[i] , S[j])
}
```

**Key Stream Generation** The keys in the key stream, the $k$'s, are generated, one by one. First, the state is permuted based on the values of state elements and the values of two individual variables, $i$ and $j$. Second, the values of two state elements in positions $i$ and $j$ are used to define the index of the state element that serves as $k$. The following code is repeated for each byte of the plaintext to create a new key element in the key stream. The variables $i$ and $j$ are initialized to 0 before the first iteration, but the values are copied from one iteration to the next.

```
i ← (i + 1) mod 256
j ← (j + S[i]) mod 256
swap (S [i] , S[j])
k ← S [(S[i] + S[j]) mod 256]
```

**Encryption or Decryption** After $k$ has been created, the plaintext byte is encrypted with $k$ to create the ciphertext byte. Decryption is the reverse process.

**Algorithm** Algorithm 8.6 shows the pseudocode routine for RC4.

---

**Algorithm 8.6**                              **Encryption algorithm for RC4**

---

```
RC4_Encryption (K)
{
    // Creation of initial state and key bytes
    for (i = 0 to 255)
    {
        S[i] ← i
        K[i] ← Key [i mod KeyLength]
    }
    // Permuting state bytes based on values of key bytes
    j ← 0
    for (i = 0 to 255)
    {
        j ← (j + S[i] + K[i]) mod 256
```

```
        swap (S[i] , S[j])
      }
      // Continuously permuting state bytes, generating keys, and encrypting
      i ← 0
      j ← 0
      while (more byte to encrypt)
      {
          i  ← (i + 1) mod 256
          j  ← (j + S[i]) mod 256
          swap (S [i] , S[j])
          k ← S [(S[i] + S[j]) mod 256]
          // Key is ready, encrypt
          input P
          C ← P ⊕ k
          output C
      }
  }
```

**Example 8.5**   To show the randomness of the stream key, we use a secret key with all bytes set to 0. The key stream for 20 values of $k$ is (222, 24, 137, 65, 163, 55, 93, 58, 138, 6, 30, 103, 87, 110, 146, 109, 199, 26, 127, 163).

**Example 8.6**   Repeat Example 8.5, but let the secret key be five bytes of (15, 202, 33, 6, 8). The key stream is (248, 184, 102, 54, 212, 237, 186, 133, 51, 238, 108, 106, 103, 214, 39, 242, 30, 34, 144, 49). Again the randomness in the key stream is obvious.

***Security Issues***   It is believed that the cipher is secure if the key size is at least 128 bits (16 bytes). There are some reported attacks for smaller key sizes (less than 5 bytes), but the protocols that use RC4 today all use key sizes that make RC4 secure. However, like many other ciphers, it is recommended the different keys be used for different sessions. This prevents Eve from using differential cryptanalysis on the cipher.

## 8.2.2  A5/1

In this section we introduce a stream cipher that uses LFSRs (see Chapter 5) to create a bit stream: **A5/1.** A5/1 (a member of the A5 family of ciphers) is used in the **Global System for Mobile Communication (GSM),** a network for mobile telephone communication. Phone communication in GSM is done as a sequence of 228-bit frames in which each frame lasts 4.6 milliseconds. A5/1 creates a bit stream out of a 64-bit key. The bit streams are collected in a 228-bit buffer to be exclusive-ored with a 228-bit frame, as shown in Fig. 8.11.

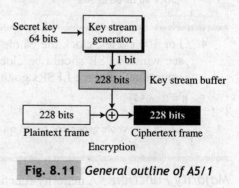

**Fig. 8.11**  *General outline of A5/1*

***Key Generator***   A5/1 uses three LFSRs with 19, 22, and 23 bits. The LFSRs, the characteristic polynomials, and the clocking bits are shown in Fig. 8.12.

Note: The three black boxes are used in the *majority function*

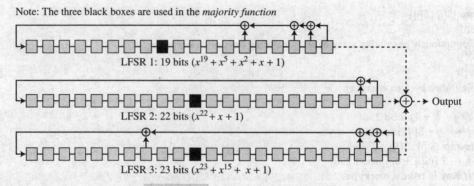

**Fig. 8.12** *Three LFSR's in A5/1*

The one-bit output is fed to the 228-bit buffer to be used for encryption (or decryption).

**Initialization**   Initialization is done for each frame of encryption (or decryption). The initialization uses a 64-bit secret key and 22 bits of the corresponding frame number. Following are the steps:

1.   First, set all bits in three LFSRs to 0.
2.   Second, mix the 64-bit key with the value of register according to the following code. *Clocking* means that each LFSR goes through one shifting process.

```
for (i = 0 to 63)
{
    Exclusive-or K[i] with the leftmost bit in all three registers.
    Clock all three LFSRs
}
```

3.   Then repeat the previous process but use the 22-bit frame number.

```
for (i = 0 to 21)
{
    Exclusive-or FrameNumber [i] with the leftmost bit in all three registers.
    Clock all three LFSRs
}
```

4.   For 100 cycles, clock the whole generator, but use the Majority-function (see next section) to see which LFSR should be clocked. Note that clocking here means that sometimes two and sometimes all three LFSRs go through the shifting process.

```
for (i = 0 to 99)
{
    Clock the whole generator based on the majority function.
}
```

**Majority Function**   A majority function, Majority $(b_1, b_2, b_3)$, is 1 if the majority number of bits is 1; it is 0 if the majority of bits is 0. For example, Majority $(1, 0, 1) = 1$, but Majority $(0, 0, 1) = 0$. The majority function has a value before each click of time; the three input bits are called *clocking bits:* bits LFSR1[10], LFSR2[11], and LFSR3[11] if the rightmost bit is bit zero. Note that the literature calls these bits 8, 10, and 10 counting from the left, but we use 10, 11, and 11 counting from the right. We use this convention to match with the characteristic polynomial.

*Key Stream Bits*    The key generator creates the key stream one bit at each click of time. Before the key is created the majority function is calculated. Then each LFSR is clocked if its clocking bit matches with the result of the majority function; otherwise, it is not clocked.

**Example 8.7**    At a point of time the clocking bits are 1, 0, and 1. Which LFSR is clocked (shifted)?

*Solution*    The result of Majority (1, 0, 1) = 1. LFSR1 and LAFS3 are shifted, but LFSR2 is not.

*Encryption/Decryption*    The bit streams created from the key generator are buffered to form a 228-bit key that is exclusive-ored with the plaintext frame to create the ciphertext frame. Encryption/decryption is done one frame at a time.

*Security Issues*    Although GSM continues to use A5/1, several attacks on GSM have been recorded. Two have been mentioned. In 2000, Alex Biryukov, Adi Shamir, and David Wagner showed a real-time attack that finds the key in minutes from small known plaintexts, but it needs a preprocessing stage with $2^{48}$ steps. In 2003, Ekdahl and Johannson published an attack that broke A5/1 in a few minutes using 2 to 5 minutes of plaintext. With some new attacks on the horizon, GSM may need to replace or fortify A5/1 in the future.

## 8.3                                    OTHER ISSUES

Encipherment using symmetric-key block or stream ciphers requires discussion of other issues.

### 8.3.1    Key Management

Alice and Bob need to share a secret key between themselves to securely communicate using a symmetric-key cipher. If there are $n$ entities in the community, each needs to communicate with $n - 1$ other entities. Therefore, $n(n - 1)$ secret keys are needed. However, in a symmetric-key encipherment a single key can be used in both directions: from Alice to Bob and from Bob to Alice. This means that $n(n - 1)/2$ keys suffice. If $n$ is around a million, then almost half a billion keys must be exchanged. Because this is not feasible, several other solutions have been found. First, each time Alice and Bob want to communicate, they can create a session (temporary) key between themselves. Second, one or more key distribution centers can be established in the community to distribute session keys for entities. All of these issues are part of key management, which will be discussed thoroughly in Chapter 15 after the necessary tools have been discussed.

**Key management is discussed in Chapter 15.**

### 8.3.2    Key Generation

Another issue in symmetric-key encipherment is the generation of a secure key. Different symmetric-key ciphers need keys of different sizes. The selection of the key must be based on a systematic approach to avoid a security leak. If Alice and Bob generate a session key between themselves, they need to choose the key so randomly that Eve cannot guess the next key. If a key distribution center needs to distribute the keys, the keys should be so random that Eve cannot guess the key assigned to Alice and Bob from the key assigned to John and Eve. This implies that there is a need for random (or pseudorandom) number generator. Because the discussion of random number generator involves some topics that have not yet been discussed, the study of *random number generators* is presented in Appendix K.

---

**Random number generators are discussed in Appendix K.**

---

## 8.4                    RECOMMENDED READING

The following books and websites provide more details about subjects discussed in this chapter. The items enclosed in brackets refer to the reference list at the end of the book.

### Books

[Sch99], [Sta06], [PHS03], [Sti06], [MOV97], and [KPS02] discuss modes of operations. [Vau06] and [Sta06] give thorough discussions of stream ciphers.

### WebSites

The following websites give more information about topics discussed in this chapter.
   http://en.wikipedia.org/wiki/Block_cipher_modes_of_operation
   http://www.itl.nist.gov/fipspubs/fip81.htm
   en.wikipedia.org/wiki/A5/1
   en.wikipedia.org/wiki/RC4

## *Key Terms*

| | |
|---|---|
| A5/1 | Global System for Mobile Communication (GSM) |
| cipher block chaining (CBC) mode | initialization vector (IV) |
| cipher feedback (CFB) mode | mode of operation |
| ciphertext stealing (CTS) | output feedback (OFB) mode |
| counter (CTR) mode | RC4 |
| electronic codebook (ECB) mode | |

## *Summary*

*   ★ In real-life applications, the text to be enciphered is of variable size and normally much larger than the block size defined for modern block ciphers. Modes of operation have been devised to encipher text of any size employing modern block ciphers. Five modes of operation were discussed in this chapter.

*   ★ The simplest mode of operation is called the electronic codebook (ECB) mode. The plaintext is divided into $N$ blocks. The block size is $n$ bits. The same key is used to encrypt and decrypt each block.

*   ★ In cipher block chaining (CBC) mode, each plaintext block is exclusive-ored with the previous ciphertext block before being encrypted. When a block is enciphered, the block is sent, but a copy of it is kept in memory to be used in the encryption of the next block. The sender and the receiver agree upon a specific predetermined initialization vector (IV) to be exclusive-ored with the first ciphertext block.

*   ★ To encipher small data units in real-time processing, cipher feedback (CFB) mode was introduced. CFB uses a standard block cipher, such as DES or AES, to encrypt a shift register, but uses the exclusive-or

operation to encrypt or decrypt the actual data units. CFB mode uses block ciphers, but the result is a stream cipher because each data unit is enciphered with a different key.

★ Output feedback (OFB) mode is very similar to CFB mode, with one difference. Each bit in the ciphertext is independent of the previous bit or bits. This avoids error propagation. Instead of using the previous ciphertext block, OFB uses the previous key as feedback.

★ In counter (CTR) mode, there is no feedback. The pseudorandomness in the key stream is achieved using a counter. An *n*-bit counter is initialized to a predetermined value (IV) and incremented based on a predefined rule.

★ To encipher small units of data, such as characters or bits, several stream ciphers have been designed from scratch. These stream ciphers are more efficient for real-time processing. Only two *pure* stream ciphers were discussed in this chapter: RC4 and A5/1.

★ RC4 is a byte-oriented stream cipher in which a byte (8 bits) of a plaintext is exclusive-ored with a byte of a key to produce a byte of a ciphertext. The secret key, from which the one-byte keys in the key stream are generated, can contain anywhere from 1 to 256 bytes. The key stream generator is based on the permutation of a state of 256 bytes.

★ A5/1 is a stream cipher used in mobile telephone communication. A5/1 creates a bit stream out of a 64-bit key using three LFSRs.

# *Practice Set*

## Review Questions

**8.1** Explain why modes of operation are needed if modern block ciphers are to be used for encipherment.

**8.2** List five modes of operation discussed in this chapter.

**8.3** Define ECB and list its advantages and disadvantages.

**8.4** Define CBC and list its advantages and disadvantages.

**8.5** Define CFB and list its advantages and disadvantages.

**8.6** Define OFB and list its advantages and disadvantages.

**8.7** Define CTR and list its advantages and disadvantages.

**8.8** Divide the five modes of operation into two groups: those that use the encryption and decryption functions of the underlying cipher (for example, DES or AES) and those that use only the encryption function.

**8.9** Divide the five modes of operation into two groups: those that need padding and those that do not.

**8.10** Divide the five modes of operation into two groups: those that use the same key for the encipherment of all blocks, and those that use a key stream for encipherment of blocks.

**8.11** Explain the major difference between RC4 and A5/1. Which one uses LFSRs?

**8.12** What is the size of data unit in RC4? What is the size of data unit in A5/1?

**8.13** List the operation modes that can be sped up by parallel processing.

**8.14** List the operation modes that can be used for encipherment of random-access files.

## Exercises

**8.15** Show why CFB mode creates a nonsynchronous stream cipher, but OFB mode creates a synchronous one.

**8.16** In CFB mode, how many blocks are affected by a single-bit error in transmission?

**8.17** In ECB mode, bit 17 in ciphertext block 8 is corrupted during transmission. Find the possible corrupted bits in the plaintext.

**8.18** In CBC mode, bits 17 and 18 in ciphertext block 9 are corrupted during transmission. Find the possible corrupted bits in the plaintext.

**8.19** In CFB mode, bits 3 to 6 in ciphertext block 11 are corrupted ($r = 8$). Find the possible corrupted bits in the plaintext.

**8.20** In CTR mode, blocks 3 and 4 are entirely corrupted. Find the possible corrupted bits in the plaintext.

**8.21** In OFB mode, the entire ciphertext block 11 is corrupted (r = 8), Find the possible corrupted bits in the plaintext.

**8.22** Prove that the plaintext used by Alice is recovered by Bob in CFB mode.

**8.23** Prove that the plaintext used by Alice is recovered by Bob in OFB mode.

**8.24** Prove that the plaintext used by Alice is recovered by Bob in CTR mode.

**8.25** Show the diagram for encryption and decryption in the CFB mode when $r = n$.

**8.26** Show the diagram for encryption and decryption in the OFB mode when $r = n$.

**8.27** Show the processes used for decryption algorithm in ECB mode if ciphertext stealing (CTS) is used.

**8.28** Show the encryption and the decryption diagram for ECB mode (only the last two blocks) when ciphertext stealing (CTS) is used.

**8.29** Show the processes used for decryption algorithm in CBC mode if ciphertext stealing (CTS) is used.

**8.30** Show the encryption and the decryption diagram for CBC mode (only the last two blocks) when ciphertext stealing (CTS) is used.

**8.31** Explain why there is no need for ciphertext stealing in CFB, OFB, and CTR modes.

**8.32** Show the effect of error propagation when ECB uses the CTS technique.

**8.33** Show the effect of error propagation when CBC uses the CTS technique.

**8.34** The *block chaining* (BC) mode is a variation of CBC in which all the previous ciphertext blocks are exclusive-ored with the current plaintext block before encryption. Draw a diagram that shows the encryption and decryption.

**8.35** The *propagating cipher block chaining* (PCBC) mode is a variation of CBC in which both the previous plaintext block and the previous ciphertext block are exclusive-ored with the current plaintext block before encryption. Draw a diagram that shows the encryption and decryption.

**8.36** The *cipher block chaining with checksum* (CBCC) mode is a variation of CBC in which all previous plaintext blocks are exclusive-ored with the current plaintext block before encryption. Draw a diagram to show the encryption and decryption and show the procedure.

**8.37** In RC4, show the first 20 elements of the key stream if the secret key is only 7 bytes with values 1, 2, 3, 4, 5, 6, and 7. You may want to write a small program to do so.

**8.38** In RC4, find a value for the secret key that does not change the state after the first and second initialization steps.

**8.39** Alice and Bob communicate using RC4 for secrecy with a 16-byte secret key. The secret key is changed each time using the recursive definition $K_i = (K_{i-1} + K_{i-2}) \bmod 2^{128}$. Show how many messages they can exchange before the pattern repeats itself.

**8.40**   In A5/1, find the maximum period of each LFSR.

**8.41**   In A5/1, find the value of the following functions. In each case, show how many LFSRs are clocked.
   a.   Majority (1, 0, 0)
   b.   Majority (0, 1, 1)
   c.   Majority (0, 0, 0)
   d.   Majority (1, 1, 1)

**8.42**   In A5/1, find an expression for the Majority function.

**8.43**   Write the decryption algorithm in pseudocode for ECB mode.

**8.44**   Write the decryption algorithm in pseudocode for CBC mode.

**8.45**   Write the decryption algorithm pseudocode for CFB mode.

**8.46**   Write the decryption algorithm in pseudocode for OFB mode.

**8.47**   Write the decryption algorithm in pseudocode for CTR mode.

**8.48**   Write an algorithm for the *shiftLeft* routine used in Algorithm 8.4.

**8.49**   Write an algorithm for the *selectLeft* routine used in Algorithm 8.4.

**8.50**   Write an algorithm for the *concatenate* routine used in Algorithm 8.4.

# PART

# II

# Asymmetric-Key Encipherment

In Chapter 1, we saw that cryptography provides three techniques: symmetric-key ciphers, asymmetric-key ciphers, and hashing. Part Two is devoted to asymmetric-key ciphers. Chapter 9 reviews the mathematical background necessary to understand the rest of the chapters in this part and the rest of the book. Chapter 10 explores the contemporary asymmetric-key ciphers.

### Chapter 9: Mathematics of Asymmetric-Key Cryptography

Chapter 9 reviews some mathematical concepts needed for understanding the next few chapters. It discusses prime numbers and their applications in cryptography. It introduces primality test algorithms and their efficiencies. Other topics include factorization, the Chinese remainder theorem, and quadratic congruence. Modular exponentiation and logarithms are also discussed to pave the way for discussion of public-key cryptosystems in Chapter 10.

### Chapter 10: Asymmetric-Key Cryptography

Chapter 10 discusses asymmetric-key (public-key) ciphers. It introduces several cryptosystems, such as RSA, Rabin, ElGamal, and ECC, mentions most kinds of attacks for each system, and presents recommendations for preventing those attacks.

# 9

# Mathematics of Asymmetric-Key Cryptography

## Prime and Related Congruence Equations

## Objectives

This chapter has several objectives:

☞ To introduce prime numbers and their applications in cryptography.

☞ To discuss some primality test algorithms and their efficiencies.

☞ To discuss factorization algorithms and their applications in cryptography.

☞ To describe the Chinese remainder theorem and its application.

☞ To introduce quadratic congruence.

☞ To introduce modular exponentiation and logarithm.

Asymmetric-key cryptography, which we will discuss in Chapter 10, is based on some topics in number theory, including theories related to primes, factorization of composites into primes, modular exponentiation and logarithm, quadratic residues, and the Chinese remainder theorem. These issues are discussed in this chapter to make Chapter 10 easier to understand.

## 9.1                                     PRIMES

Asymmetric-key cryptography uses primes extensively. The topic of primes is a large part of any book on number theory. This section discusses only a few concepts and facts to pave the way for Chapter 10.

### 9.1.1  Definition

The positive integers can be divided into three groups: the number 1, primes, and composites as shown in Fig. 9.1.

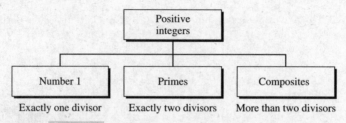

**Fig. 9.1** *Three groups of positive integers*

A positive integer is a **prime** *if and only if* it is exactly divisible by two integers, 1 and itself. A **composite** is a positive integer with more than two divisors.

---

**A prime is divisible only by itself and 1.**

---

**Example 9.1**   What is the smallest prime?

**Solution**   The smallest prime is 2, which is divisible by 2 (itself) and 1. Note that the integer 1 is not a prime according to the definition, because a prime must be divisible by two different integers, no more, no less. The integer 1 is divisible only by itself; it is not a prime.

**Example 9.2**   List the primes smaller than 10.

**Solution**   There are four primes less than 10: 2, 3, 5, and 7. It is interesting to note that the percentage of primes in the range 1 to 10 is 40%. The percentage decreases as the range increases.

**Coprimes**   Two positive integers, $a$ and $b$, are **relatively prime,** or **coprime,** if gcd $(a, b) = 1$. Note that the number 1 is relatively prime with any integer. If $p$ is a prime, then all integers 1 to $p - 1$ are relatively prime to $p$. In Chapter 2, we discussed set $\mathbf{Z}_n{}^*$ whose members are all relatively prime to $n$. Set $\mathbf{Z}_p{}^*$ is the same except that modulus ($p$) is a prime.

### 9.1.2   Cardinality of Primes

After the concept of primes has been defined, two questions naturally arise: Is there a finite number of primes or is the list infinite? Given a number $n$, how many primes are smaller than or equal to $n$?

**Infinite Number of Primes**   The number of primes is infinite. Here is an informal proof: Suppose that the set of primes is finite (limited), with $p$ as the largest prime. Multiply the set of primes and call the result P = $2 \times 3 \times \cdots \times p$. The integer (P + 1) cannot have a factor $q \leq p$. We know that $q$ divides P. If $q$ also divides (P + 1), then $q$ divides (P + 1) – P = 1 The only number that divides 1 is 1, which is not a prime. Therefore, $q$ is larger than $p$.

---

**There is an infinite number of primes.**

---

**Example 9.3**   As a trivial example, assume that the only primes are in the set {2, 3, 5, 7, 11, 13, 17}. Here P = 510510 and P + 1 = 510511. However, 510511 = 19 × 97 × 277; none of these primes were in the original list. Therefore, there are three primes greater than 17.

***Number of Primes*** To answer the second question, a function called $\pi(n)$ is defined that finds the number of primes smaller than or equal to $n$. The following shows the values of this function for different $n$'s.

$$\pi(1) = 0 \quad \pi(2) = 1 \quad \pi(3) = 2 \quad \pi(10) = 4 \quad \pi(20) = 8 \quad \pi(50) = 15 \quad \pi(100) = 25$$

But if $n$ is very large, how can we calculate $\pi(n)$? The answer is that we can only use approximation. It has been shown that

$$[n / (\ln n)] < \pi(n) < [n/(\ln n - 1.08366)]$$

Gauss discovered the upper limit; Lagrange discovered the lower limit.

**Example 9.4**   Find the number of primes less than 1,000,000.

***Solution***   The approximation gives the range 72,383 to 78,543. The actual number of primes is 78,498.

### 9.1.3   Checking for Primeness

The next question that comes to mind is this: Given a number $n$, how can we determine if $n$ is a prime? The answer is that we need to see if the number is divisible by all primes less than $\sqrt{n}$. We know that this method is inefficient, but it is a good start.

**Example 9.5**   Is 97 a prime?

***Solution***   The floor of $\sqrt{97} = 9$. The primes less than 9 are 2, 3, 5, and 7. We need to see if 97 is divisible by any of these numbers. It is not, so 97 is a prime.

**Example 9.6**   Is 301 a prime?

***Solution***   The floor of $\sqrt{301} = 17$. We need to check 2, 3, 5, 7, 11, 13, and 17. The numbers 2, 3, and 5 do not divide 301, but 7 does. Therefore 301 is not a prime.

***Sieve of Eratosthenes***   The Greek mathematician Eratosthenes devised a method to find all primes less than $n$. The method is called the **sieve of Eratosthenes.** Suppose we want to find all prime less than 100. We write down all the numbers between 2 and 100. Because $\sqrt{100} = 10$, we need to see if any number less than 100 is divisible by 2, 3, 5, and 7. Table 9.1 shows the result.

**Table 9.1**   *Sieve of Eratosthenes*

|     | 2  | 3  | 4  | 5  | 6  | 7  | 8  | 9  | 10  |
|-----|----|----|----|----|----|----|----|----|-----|
| 11  | 12 | 13 | 14 | 15 | 16 | 17 | 18 | 19 | 20  |
| 21  | 22 | 23 | 24 | 25 | 26 | 27 | 28 | 29 | 30  |
| 31  | 32 | 33 | 34 | 35 | 36 | 37 | 38 | 39 | 40  |
| 41  | 42 | 43 | 44 | 45 | 46 | 47 | 48 | 49 | 50  |
| 51  | 52 | 53 | 54 | 55 | 56 | 57 | 58 | 59 | 60  |
| 61  | 62 | 63 | 64 | 65 | 66 | 67 | 68 | 69 | 70  |
| 71  | 72 | 73 | 74 | 75 | 76 | 77 | 78 | 79 | 80  |
| 81  | 82 | 83 | 84 | 85 | 86 | 87 | 88 | 89 | 90  |
| 91  | 92 | 93 | 94 | 95 | 96 | 97 | 98 | 99 | 100 |

The following shows the process:
1. Cross out all numbers divisible by 2 (except 2 itself).
2. Cross out all numbers divisible by 3 (except 3 itself).
3. Cross out all numbers divisible by 5 (except 5 itself).
4. Cross out all numbers divisible by 7 (except 7 itself).
5. The numbers left over are primes.

### 9.1.4  Euler's Phi-Function

**Euler's phi-function,** $\phi(n)$, which is sometimes called the **Euler's totient function** plays a very important role in cryptography. The function finds the number of integers that are both smaller than $n$ and relatively prime to $n$. Recall from Chapter 2 that the set $Z_n{}^*$ contains the numbers that are smaller than $n$ and relatively prime to $n$. The function $\phi(n)$ calculates the number of elements in this set. The following helps to find the value of $\phi(n)$.

1. $\phi(1) = 0$.
2. $\phi(p) = p - 1$ if $p$ is a prime.
3. $\phi(m \times n) = \phi(m) \times \phi(n)$ if $m$ and $n$ are relatively prime.
4. $\phi(p^e) = p^e - p^{e-1}$ if $p$ is a prime.

We can combine the above four rules to find the value of $\phi(n)$. For example, if $n$ can be factored as $n = p_1{}^{e1} \times p_2{}^{e2} \times \cdots \times p_k{}^{ek}$, then we combine the third and the fourth rule to find

$$\phi(n) = (p_1{}^{e_1} - p_1{}^{e_1-1}) \times (p_2{}^{e_2} - p_2{}^{e_2-1}) \times \cdots \times (p_k{}^{ek} - p_k{}^{ek-1})$$

It is very important to notice that the value of $\phi(n)$ for large composites can be found only if the number $n$ can be factored into primes. In other words, the difficulty of finding $\phi(n)$ depends on the difficulty of finding the factorization of $n$, which is discussed in the next section.

---

**The difficulty of finding $\phi(n)$ depends on the difficulty of finding the factorization of $n$.**

---

**Example 9.7**  What is the value of $\phi(13)$?

**Solution**  Because 13 is a prime, $\phi(13) = (13 - 1) = 12$.

**Example 9.8**  What is the value of $\phi(10)$?

**Solution**  We can use the third rule: $\phi(10) = \phi(2) \times \phi(5) = 1 \times 4 = 4$, because 2 and 5 are primes.

**Example 9.9**  What is the value of $\phi(240)$?

**Solution**  We can write $240 = 2^4 \times 3^1 \times 5^1$. Then

$$\phi(240) = (2^4 - 2^3) \times (3^1 - 3^0) \times (5^1 - 5^0) = 64$$

**Example 9.10**  Can we say that $\phi(49) = \phi(7) \times \phi(7) = 6 \times 6 = 36$?

**Solution**  No. The third rule applies when $m$ and $n$ are relatively prime. Here $49 = 7^2$. We need to use the fourth rule: $\phi(49) = 7^2 - 7^1 = 42$.

---

**Example 9.11**   What is the number of elements in $Z_{14}^*$?

**Solution**   The answer is $\phi(14) = \phi(7) \times \phi(2) = 6 \times 1 = 6$. The members are 1, 3, 5, 9, 11, and 13.

---

**Interesting point: If $n > 2$, the value of $\phi(n)$ is even.**

---

### 9.1.5  Fermat's Little Theorem

**Fermat's little theorem** plays a very important role in number theory and cryptography. We introduce two versions of the theorem here.

***First Version***   The first version says that if $p$ is a prime and $a$ is an integer such that $p$ does not divide $a$, then $a^{p-1} \equiv 1 \bmod p$.

***Second Version***   The second version removes the condition on $a$. It says that if $p$ is a prime and $a$ is an integer, then $a^p \equiv a \bmod p$.

***Applications***   Although we will see some applications of this theorem later in this chapter, the theorem is very useful for solving some problems.

***Exponentiation***   Fermat's little theorem sometimes is helpful for quickly finding a solution to some exponentiations. The following examples show the idea.

---

**Example 9.12**   Find the result of $6^{10} \bmod 11$.

**Solution**   We have $6^{10} \bmod 11 = 1$. This is the first version of Fermat's little theorem where $p = 11$.

---

**Example 9.13**   Find the result of $3^{12} \bmod 11$.

**Solution**   Here the exponent (12) and the modulus (11) are not the same. With substitution this can be solved using Fermat's little theorem.

$$3^{12} \bmod 11 = (3^{11} \times 3) \bmod 11 = (3^{11} \bmod 11)(3 \bmod 11) = (3 \times 3) \bmod 11 = 9$$

***Multiplicative Inverses***   A very interesting application of Fermat's theorem is in finding some multiplicative inverses quickly if the modulus is a prime. If $p$ is a prime and $a$ is an integer such that $p$ does not divide $a$ ($p \mid a$), then $a^{-1} \bmod p = a^{p-2} \bmod p$.

This can be easily proved if we multiply both sides of the equality by $a$ and use the first version of Fermat's little theorem:

$$a \times a^{-1} \bmod p = a \times a^{p-2} \bmod p = a^{p-1} \bmod p = 1 \bmod p$$

This application eliminates the use of extended Euclidean algorithm for finding some multiplicative inverses.

---

**Example 9.14** The answers to multiplicative inverses modulo a prime can be found without using the extended Euclidean algorithm:

   a.    $8^{-1} \bmod 17 = 8^{17-2} \bmod 17 = 8^{15} \bmod 17 = 15 \bmod 17$
   b.    $5^{-1} \bmod 23 = 5^{23-2} \bmod 23 = 5^{21} \bmod 23 = 14 \bmod 23$
   c.    $60^{-1} \bmod 101 = 60^{101-2} \bmod 101 = 60^{99} \bmod 101 = 32 \bmod 101$
   d.    $22^{-1} \bmod 211 = 22^{211-2} \bmod 211 = 22^{209} \bmod 211 = 48 \bmod 211$

---

### 9.1.6 Euler's Theorem

**Euler's theorem** can be thought of as a generalization of Fermat's little theorem. The modulus in the Fermat theorem is a prime, the modulus in Euler's theorem is an integer. We introduce two versions of this theorem.

*First Version*    The first version of Euler's theorem is similar to the first version of the Fermat's little theorem. If $a$ and $n$ are coprime, then $a^{\phi(n)} \equiv 1 \ (\bmod \ n)$.

*Second Version*    The second version of Euler's theorem (as we call it for the lack of anyname) is similar to the second version of Fermat's little theorem; it removes the condition that $a$ and $n$ should be coprime. If $n = p \times q$, $a < n$, and $k$ an integer, then $a^{k \times \phi(n) + 1} \equiv a \ (\bmod \ n)$.

Let us give an informal proof of the second version based on the first version. Because $a < n$, three cases are possible:

1.    If $a$ is neither a multiple of $p$ nor a multiple of $q$, then $a$ and $n$ are coprimes.

$$a^{k \times \phi(n) + 1} \bmod n = (a^{\phi(n)})^k \times a \bmod n = (1)^k \times a \bmod n = a \bmod n$$

2.    If $a$ is a multiple of $p$ ($a = i \times p$), but not a multiple of $q$,

$$a^{\phi(n)} \bmod q = (a^{\phi(q)} \bmod q)^{\phi(p)} \bmod q = 1 \rightarrow a^{\phi(n)} \bmod q = 1$$
$$a^{k \times \phi(n)} \bmod q = (a^{\phi(n)} \bmod q)^k \bmod q = 1 \rightarrow a^{k \times \phi(n)} \bmod q = 1$$
$$a^{k \times \phi(n)} \bmod q = 1 \rightarrow a^{k \times \phi(n)} = 1 + j \times q \text{ (Interpretation of congruence)}$$
$$a^{k \times \phi(n) + 1} = a \times (1 + j \times q) = a + j \times q \times a = a + (i \times j) \times q \times p = a + (i \times j) \times n$$
$$a^{k \times \phi(n) + 1} = a + (i \times j) \times n \rightarrow a^{k \times \phi(n) + 1} = a \bmod n \text{ (Congruence relation)}$$

3.    If $a$ is a multiple of $q$ ($a = i \times q$), but not a multiple of $p$, the proof is the same as for the second case, but the roles of $p$ and $q$ are changed.

---

**The second version of Euler's theorem is used in the RSA cryptosystem in Chapter 10.**

---

*Applications*    Although we will see some applications of Euler's later in this chapter, the theorem is very useful for solving some problems.

*Exponentiation*    Euler's theorem sometimes is helpful for quickly finding a solution to some exponentiations. The following examples show the idea.

**Example 9.15**   Find the result of $6^{24} \bmod 35$.

***Solution***  We have $6^{24}$ mod 35 = $6^{\phi(35)}$ mod 35 = 1.

**Example 9.16**  Find the result of $20^{62}$ mod 77.

***Solution***  If we let $k = 1$ on the second version, we have $20^{62}$ mod 77 = (20 mod 77) ($20^{\phi(77)+1}$ mod 77) mod 77 = (20)(20) mod 77 = 15.

***Multiplicative Inverses***  Euler's theorem can be used to find multiplicative inverses modulo a prime; Euler's theorem can be used to find multiplicative inverses modulo a composite. If $n$ and $a$ are coprime, then $a^{-1}$ mod $n = a^{\phi(n)-1}$ mod $n$.

This can be easily proved if we multiply both sides of the equality by $a$:

$$a \times a^{-1} \bmod n = a \times a^{\phi(n)-1} \bmod n = a^{\phi(n)} \bmod n = 1 \bmod n$$

**Example 9.17**  The answers to multiplicative inverses modulo a composite can be found without using the extended Euclidean algorithm if we know the factorization of the composite:

a.  $8^{-1}$ mod 77 = $8^{\phi(77)-1}$ mod 77 = $8^{59}$ mod 77 = 29 mod 77
b.  $7^{-1}$ mod 15 = $7^{\phi(15)-1}$ mod 15 = $7^{7}$ mod 15 = 13 mod 15
c.  $60^{-1}$ mod 187 = $60^{\phi(187)-1}$ mod 187 = $60^{159}$ mod 187 = 53 mod 187
d.  $71^{-1}$ mod 100 = $71^{\phi(100)-1}$ mod 100 = $71^{39}$ mod 100 = 31 mod 100

### 9.1.7  Generating Primes

Two mathematicians, Mersenne and Fermat, attempted to develop a formula that could generate primes.

***Mersenne Primes***  Mersenne defined the following formula, called the **Mersenne numbers**, that was supposed to enumerate all primes.

$$M_p = 2^p - 1$$

If $p$ in the above formula is a prime, then $M_p$ was thought to be a prime. Years later, it was proven that not all numbers created by the Mersenne formula are primes. The following lists some Mersenne numbers.

$M_2 = 2^2 - 1 = 3$
$M_3 = 2^3 - 1 = 7$
$M_5 = 2^5 - 1 = 31$
$M_7 = 2^7 - 1 = 127$
$M_{11} = 2^{11} - 1 = 2047$      **Not a prime (2047 = 23 × 89)**
$M_{13} = 2^{13} - 1 = 8191$
$M_{17} = 2^{17} - 1 = 131071$

It turned out that $M_{11}$ is not a prime. However, 41 Mersenne primes have been found; the latest one is $M_{124036583}$, a very large number with 7,253,733 digits. The search continues.

---

> A number in the form $M_p = 2^p - 1$ is called a Mersenne number and may or may not be a prime.

---

***Fermat Primes***   Fermat tried to find a formula to generate primes. The following is the formula for a **Fermat number:**

---

$$F_n = 2^{2^n} + 1$$

---

Fermat tested numbers up to $F_4$, but it turned out that $F_5$ is not a prime. No number greater than $F_4$

$F_1 = 3$
$F_2 = 17$
$F_3 = 257$
$F_4 = 65537$
$F_5 = 4294967297 = 641 \times 6700417$           **Not a prime**

has been proven to be a prime. As a matter of fact many numbers up to $F_{24}$ have been proven to be composite numbers.

## 9.2                 PRIMALITY TESTING

If schemes for generating primes, like Fermat's or Mersenne's, have failed to produce large primes, how can we create large primes for cryptography? We could just choose a large random number and test it to be sure that it is a prime.

Finding an algorithm to correctly and efficiently test a very large integer and output *a prime* or *a composite* has always been a challenge in number theory, and consequently in cryptography. However, recent developments (one of which we discuss in this section) look very promising.

Algorithms that deal with this issue can be divided into two broad categories: **deterministic algorithms** and **probabilistic algorithms.** Some members of both categories are discussed here. A deterministic algorithm always gives a correct answer; a probabilistic algorithm gives an answer that is correct most of the time, but not all of the time. Although a deterministic algorithm is ideal, it is normally less efficient than the corresponding probabilistic one.

### 9.2.1   Deterministic Algorithms

A deterministic primality testing algorithm accepts an integer and always outputs *a prime* or *a composite*. Until recently, all deterministic algorithms were so inefficient at finding larger primes that they were considered infeasible. As we will show shortly, a newer algorithm looks more promising.

***Divisibility Algorithm***   The most elementary deterministic test for primality is the **divisibility test.** We use as divisors all numbers smaller that $\sqrt{n}$. If any of these numbers divides $n$, then $n$ is composite. Algorithm 9.1 shows the divisibility test in its primitive, very inefficient form.

The algorithm can be improved by testing only odd numbers. It can be further improved by using a table of primes between 2 and $\sqrt{n}$. The number of arithmatic operations in Algorithm 9.1 is $\sqrt{n}$. If we assume that each arithmatic operation uses only one bit operation (unrealistic) then the bit-operation complexity of Algorithm 9.1 is $f(n_b) \doteq \sqrt{2^{n_b}} = 2^{n_b/2}$, where $n_b$ is the number of bits in $n$. In Big-O notation, the complexity can be shown as $O(2^{n_b})$: *exponential* (see Appendix L). In other words, the divisibility algorithm is infeasible (intractable) if $n_b$ is large.

---

**The bit-operation complexity of the divisibility test is exponential.**

---

**Example 9.18**   Assume $n$ has 200 bits. What is the number of bit operations needed to run the divisibility-test algorithm?

**Solution**   The bit-operation complexity of this algorithm is $2^{n_b/2}$. This means that the algorithm needs $2^{100}$ bit operations. On a computer capable of doing $2^{30}$ bit operations per second, the algorithm needs $2^{70}$ seconds to do the testing (forever).

---

**Algorithm 9.1**                        **Pseudocode for the divisibility test**

```
Divisibility_Test (n)                    // n is the number to test for primality
{
    r ← 2
    while (r < √n)
    {
    if (r | n) return "a composite"
    r ← r + 1
    }
    return "a prime"
}
```

---

**AKS Algorithm**   In 2002, Agrawal, Kayal, and Saxena announced that they had found an algorithm for primality testing with polynomial bit-operation time complexity of $O((\log_2^{n_b})^{12})$. The algorithm uses the fact that $(x - a)^p \equiv (x^p - a) \bmod p$. It is not surprising to see some future refinements make this algorithm the standard primality test in mathematics and computer science.

---

**Example 9.19**   Assume $n$ has 200 bits. What is the number of bit operations needed to run the AKS algorithm?

**Solution**   The bit-operation complexity of this algorithm is $O((\log_2^{n_b})^{12})$. This means that the algorithm needs only $(\log_2 200)^{12} = 39{,}547{,}615{,}483$ bit operations. On a computer capable of doing 1 billion bit operations per second, the algorithm needs only 40 seconds.

### 9.2.2  Probabilistic Algorithms

*Primality testing* is an extremely important area of study in the field of cryptology. The important question is whether a given number, $n$, is prime. The answer to such questions is either a "yes" or a "no". Such problems which have either a "yes" or a "no" answer are commonly referred to as decisional problems.

The algorithms to solve such problems are either deterministic or randomized. Randomized algorithms, contrary to deterministic algorithms make random choices generated by the toss of an unbiased coin. Deterministic algorithms do not use such random numbers.

There are two types of randomized algorithms: Monte Carlo algorithms and Las Vegas algorithms. A "yes'-biased Monte Carlo algorithm is a randomized algorithm for a decisional problem, for which a "yes" answer is (always) correct, but a "no" answer may be incorrect. When the correct answer to the decision problem is a "yes" and the randomized algorithm returns a "no" answer incorrectly with a probability of at most $\varepsilon$, then the "yes"-biased algorithm is said to have an error probability of $\varepsilon$. The probability is computed over all possible random choices made by the algorithm when it is run with a given input. Similarly, we can define a "no"-biased Monte Carlo algorithms.

A Las Vegas algorithm is a different class of randomized or probabilistic algorithms, for which the algorithm may not give any answer. But if it gives, it will be correct.

Before the AKS algorithm, all efficient methods for primality testing have been probabilistic. These methods may be used for a while until the AKS is formally accepted as the standard. A probabilistic algorithm does not guarantee the correctness of the result. However, we can make the probability of error so small that it is almost certain that the algorithm has returned a correct answer. The bit-operation complexity of the algorithm can become polynomial if we allow a small chance for mistakes. A probabilistic algorithm in this category returns either *a prime* or *a composite* based on the following rules:

a.   If the integer to be tested is actually a prime, the algorithm definitely returns *a prime*.
b.   If the integer to be tested is actually a composite, it returns *a composite* with probability $1- \varepsilon$, but it may return *a prime* with the probability $\varepsilon$.

The probability of mistake can be improved if we run the algorithm more than once with different parameters or using different methods. If we run the algorithm $m$ times, the probability of error may reduce to $\varepsilon^{m}$.

**Fermat Test**   The first probabilistic method we discuss is the **Fermat primality test.** Recall the *Fermat little theorem*

---

**If $n$ is a prime, then $a^{n-1} \equiv 1 \bmod n$.**

---

Note that this means that if $n$ is a prime, the congruence holds. It does not mean that if the congruence holds, $n$ is a prime. The integer can be a prime or composite. We can define the following as the Fermat test

If $n$ is a prime, $a^{n}-1 \equiv 1 \bmod n$

If $n$ is a composite, it is possible that $a^{n}-1 \equiv 1 \bmod n$

A prime passes the Fermat test; a composite may pass the Fermat test with probability $\varepsilon$. The bit-operation complexity of Fermat test is the same as the complexity of an algorithm that calculates exponentiation. Later in this chapter, we introduce an algorithm for fast exponentiation with bit-operation complexity of $O(n_b)$, where $n_b$ is the number of bits in $n$. The probability can be improved by testing with several bases ($a_1, a_2, a_3$, and so on). Each test increases the probability that the number is a prime.

**Example 9.20**   Does the number 561 pass the Fermat test?

**Solution**   Use base 2

$$2^{561-1} = 1 \bmod 561$$

The number passes the Fermat test, but it is not a prime, because $561 = 33 \times 17$.

***Square Root Test*** In modular arithmetic, if $n$ is a prime, the square root of 1 is either $+1$ or $-1$. If $n$ is composite, the square root is $+1$ or $-1$, but there may be other roots. This is known as the **square root primality test.** Note that in modular arithmetic, $-1$ means $n-1$.

> If $n$ is a prime, $\sqrt{1} \bmod n = \pm 1$.
> If $n$ is a composite, $\sqrt{1} \bmod n = \pm 1$ and possibly other values.

**Example 9.21**   What are the square roots of 1 mod $n$ if $n$ is 7 (a prime)?

***Solution***   The only square roots are 1 and $-1$. We can see that

$$1^2 = 1 \bmod 7 \qquad\qquad (-1)^2 = 1 \bmod 7$$
$$2^2 = 4 \bmod 7 \qquad\qquad (-2)^2 = 4 \bmod 7$$
$$3^2 = 2 \bmod 7 \qquad\qquad (-3)^2 = 2 \bmod 7$$

Note that we don't have to test 4, 5 and 6 because $4 = -3 \bmod 7$, $5 = -2 \bmod 7$ and $6 = -1 \bmod 7$.

**Example 9.22**   What are the square roots of 1 mod $n$ if $n$ is 8 (a composite)?

***Solution***   There are four solutions: 1, 3, 5, and 7 (which is $-1$). We can see that

$$1^2 = 1 \bmod 8 \qquad\qquad (-1)^2 = 1 \bmod 8$$
$$3^2 = 1 \bmod 8 \qquad\qquad 5^2 = 1 \bmod 8$$

**Example 9.23**   What are the square roots of 1 mod $n$ if $n$ is 17 (a prime)?

***Solution***   There are only two solutions: 1 and $-1$

$$1^2 = 1 \bmod 17 \qquad\qquad (-1)^2 = 1 \bmod 17$$
$$2^2 = 4 \bmod 17 \qquad\qquad (-2)^2 = 4 \bmod 17$$
$$3^2 = 9 \bmod 17 \qquad\qquad (-3)^2 = 9 \bmod 17$$
$$4^2 = 16 \bmod 17 \qquad\qquad (-4)^2 = 16 \bmod 17$$
$$5^2 = 8 \bmod 17 \qquad\qquad (-5)^2 = 8 \bmod 17$$
$$6^2 = 2 \bmod 17 \qquad\qquad (-6)^2 = 2 \bmod 17$$
$$(7)^2 = 15 \bmod 17 \qquad\qquad (-7)^2 = 15 \bmod 17$$
$$(8)^2 = 13 \bmod 17 \qquad\qquad (-8)^2 = 13 \bmod 17$$

Note that there is no need to check integers larger than 8 because $9 = -8 \bmod 17$, and so on.

**Example 9.24**   What are the square roots of 1 mod $n$ if $n$ is 22 (a composite)?

***Solution***   Surprisingly, there are only two solutions, $+1$ and $-1$, although 22 is a composite.

$$1^2 \quad = 1 \bmod 22$$
$$(-1)^2 = 1 \bmod 22$$

Although this test can tell us if a number is composite, it is difficult to do the testing. Given a number $n$, all numbers less than $n$ (except 1 and $n-1$) must be squared to be sure that none of them is 1. This test can be used for a number (not $+1$ or $-1$) that when squared in modulus $n$ has the value 1. This fact helps in the Miller-Rabin test in the next section.

***Miller-Rabin Test*** We shall discuss the Miller Rabin algorithm for testing whether a given number is prime. In fact, we shall consider the decisional problem, *IsComposite*, to decide whether a given number is composite.

The decisional problem, IsComposite, is stated as below:

**IsComposite**

**Input:** A positive integer $n \geq 2$

**Yes-No Problem**: Is $n$ composite?

There are several probabilistic algorithms proposed for this famous decisional problem: *Solovay Strassen*, *Miller Rabin algorithms* are some notable examples of such algorithms.

---

**Algorithm 9.2**                  **Miller-Rabin(n)**

```
n–1=2^k m, where m is odd (note that n–1 is even)
choose a random integer a, 1 ≤ a ≤ n–1
b=a^m mod n
if b ≡ 1 (mod n)
    then return ("n" is prime)
for i=0 to k–1
{
    if b ≡ –1 (mod n)
    then return("n is prime")
    else b=b^2 mod n
}
Return("n is composite")
```

---

The algorithm Miller-Rabin is a polynomial-time algorithm, with a run time complexity of $O((\log n)^3)$. Next we present a proof of correctness, to show that if the algorithm terminates with a "yes" answer, it is correct, that is the number is surely composite.

Let us assume that the algorithm says that the number $n$ is composite, but the number is a prime number. Since the algorithm returns that the number is composite, it must be that $a^m$ is not congruent to 1 (mod n). Since, in each iteration of the for loop b is squared, then it also must be that $a^m$, $a^{2m}$, ..., $a^{2^{k-1}m} \neq -1 \pmod{n}$.

By the assumption that n is prime, thus we have that $a^{n-1} = 1 \pmod{n}$. Thus we have, $a^{2^k m} \equiv 1 \pmod{n}$.

Thus $a^{2^{k-1}m}$ is a square root of 1 modulo $n$. Because $n$ is prime, there are only two square roots of 1 modulo $n$, $\pm 1$.

But we know that $a^{2^{k-1}m} \neq -1 \pmod{n}$. This implies that $a^{2^{k-1}m} = 1 \pmod{n}$. Thus, $a^{2^{k-2}m}$ must be a square root of 1. By the same argument, $a^{2^{k-1}m}$ must be 1 (mod $n$).

Continuing thus, we have $a^m = 1 \pmod{n}$ which means that the algorithm should have returned that $n$ is prime. But we have assumed that the algorithm returns that $n$ is composite. Thus we have a contradiction, proving that if the number is prime the algorithm can never say "yes" to the ISCOMPOSITE decisional problem.

Thus the algorithm is a "yes" biased Monte-Carlo algorithm. It can be proved that the error probability is at most 1/4 .

**Example 9.25**   Does the number 561 pass the Miller-Rabin test?

**Solution**   Using base 2, let $561 - 1 = 35 \times 2^4$, which means $m = 35$, $k = 4$, and $a = 2$

| | |
|---|---|
| **Initialization:** | $b = 2^{35} \bmod 561 = 263 \bmod 561$ |
| $k = 1$: | $b = 263^2 \bmod 561 = 166 \bmod 561$ |
| $k = 2$: | $b = 166^2 \bmod 561 = 67 \bmod 561$ |
| $k = 3$: | $b = 67^2 \bmod 561 = +1 \bmod 561$ |

Thus all subsequent squares of b is +1, and hence we conclude $b \not\equiv -1 \pmod{n} \rightarrow$ **a composite**

**Example 9.26**   We already know that 27 is not a prime. Let us apply the Miller-Rabin test.

**Solution**   With base 2, let $27 - 1 = 13 \times 2^1$, which means that $m = 13$, $k = 1$, and $a = 2$. In this case, because $k - 1 = 0$, we should do only the initialization step: $b = 2^{13} \bmod 27 = 11 \bmod 27$. However, because the algorithm never enters the loop, it returns *a composite*.

**Example 9.27**   We know that 61 is a prime, let us see if it passes the Miller-Rabin test.

**Solution**   We use base 2.

$61 - 1 = 15 \times 2^2 \rightarrow \quad m = 15 \; k = 2 \; a = 2$

*Initialization:* $b = 2^{15} \bmod 61 = 11 \bmod 61$

$k = 1 \qquad b = 11^2 \bmod 61 = -1 \bmod 61 \qquad \rightarrow$ **a prime**

Note that the last result is 60 mod 61, but we know that $60 = -1$ in mod 61.

## Recommended Primality Test

Today, one of the most popular primality test is a combination of the divisibility test and the Miller-Rabin test. Following are the recommended steps:

1. Choose an odd integer, because all even integers (except 2) are definitely composites.
2. Do some trivial divisibility tests on some known primes such as 3, 5, 7, 11, 13, and so on to be sure that you are not dealing with an obvious composite. If the number passes all of these tests, move to the next step. If the number fails any of these tests, go back to step 1 and choose another odd number.
3. Choose a set of bases for testing. A large set of bases is preferable.
4. Do Miller-Rabin tests on each of the bases. If any of them fails, go back to step 1 and choose another odd number. If the test passes for all bases, declare the number a strong pseudoprime.

**Example 9.28**   The number 4033 is a composite ($37 \times 109$). Does it pass the recommended primality test?

## Solution

1. Perform the divisibility tests first. The numbers 2, 3, 5, 7, 11, 17, and 23 are not divisors of 4033.
2. Perform the Miller-Rabin test with a base of 2, $4033 - 1 = 63 \times 2^6$, which means $m$ is 63 and $k$ is 6.

**Initialization:** $b \equiv 2^{63} \pmod{4033} \equiv 3521 \pmod{4033}$

$k = 1 \qquad b \equiv b^2 \equiv 3521^2 \pmod{4033} \equiv -1 \pmod{4033} \qquad \rightarrow$ **Passes**

3. But we are not satisfied. We continue with another base, 3.

**Initialization:** $b \equiv 3^{63} \pmod{4033} \equiv 3551 \pmod{4033}$

$k = 1 \qquad b \equiv b^2 \equiv 3551^2 \pmod{4033} \equiv 2443 \pmod{4033}$

$k = 2 \qquad b \equiv b^2 \equiv 2443^2 \pmod{4033} \equiv 3442 \pmod{4033}$

$k = 3 \qquad b \equiv b^2 \equiv 3442^2 \pmod{4033} \equiv 2443 \pmod{4033}$

$k = 4 \qquad b \equiv b^2 \equiv 2443^2 \pmod{4033} \equiv 3442 \pmod{4033}$

$k = 5 \qquad b \equiv b^2 \equiv 3442^2 \pmod{4033} \equiv 2443 \pmod{4033} \qquad \rightarrow$ **Failed (composite)**

## 9.3                FACTORIZATION

Factorization has been the subject of continuous research in the past; such research is likely to continue in the future. Factorization plays a very important role in the security of several public-key cryptosystems (see Chapter 10).

### 9.3.1  Fundamental Theorem of Arithmetic

According to the *Fundamental Theorem of Arithmetic,* any positive integer greater than one can be written uniquely in the following prime **factorization** form where $p_1, p_2, \ldots, p_k$ are primes and $e_1, e_2, \ldots, e_k$ are positive integers.

$$n = p_1^{e1} \times p_2^{e2} \times \cdots \times p_k^{ek}$$

There are immediate applications of factorization, such as the calculation of the greatest common divisor and the least common multiplier.

**Greatest Common Divisor**    Chapter 2 discussed the greatest common divisor of two numbers, gcd $(a, b)$. Recall that the Euclidean algorithm gives this value, but this value can also be found if we know the factorization of $a$ and $b$.

$$a = p_1^{a1} \times p_2^{a2} \times \cdots \times p_k^{ak} \qquad\qquad b = p_1^{b1} \times p_2^{b2} \times \cdots \times p_k^{bk}$$
$$\gcd(a, b) = p_1^{\min(a1, b1)} \times p_2^{\min(a2, b2)} \times \cdots \times p_k^{\min(ak, bk)}$$

**Least Common Multiplier**    The *least common multiplier, lcm* $(a, b)$, is the smallest integer that is a multiple of both $a$ and $b$. Using factorization, we also find lcm $(a, b)$.

$$a = p_1^{a1} \times p_2^{a2} \times \cdots \times p_k^{ak} \qquad\qquad b = p_1^{b1} \times p_2^{b2} \times \cdots \times p_k^{bk}$$
$$\text{lcm}(a, b) = p_1^{\max(a1, b1)} \times p_2^{\max(a2, b2)} \times \cdots \times p_k^{\max(ak, bk)}$$

It can be proved that gcd $(a, b)$ and lcm $(a, b)$ are related to each other as shown below:

$$\text{lcm}(a, b) \times \text{gcd}(a, b) = a \times b$$

## 9.3.2 Factorization Methods

There has been a long search for efficient algorithms to factor large composite numbers. Unfortunately, no such perfect algorithm has been found. Although there are several algorithms that can factor a number, none are capable of factoring a very large number in a reasonable amount of time. Later we will see that this is good for cryptography because modern cryptosystems rely on this fact. In this section, we give a few simple algorithms that factor a composite number. The purpose is to make clear that the process of factorization is time consuming.

***Trial Division Method*** By far, the simplest and least efficient algorithm is the **trial division factorization method.** We simply try all the positive integers, starting with 2, to find one that divides $n$. From discussion on the *sieve of Eratosthenes,* we know that if $n$ is composite, then it will have a prime $p \leq \sqrt{n}$. Algorithm 9.3 shows the pseudocode for this method. The algorithm has two loops, one outer and one inner. The outer loop finds unique factors; the inner loop finds duplicates of a factor. For example, $24 = 2^3 \times 3$. The outer loop finds the factors 2 and 3. The inner loop finds that 2 is a multiple factor.

---

**Algorithm 9.3**                                        **Pseudocode for trial-division factorization**

```
Trial_Division_Factorization (n)          // n is the number to be factored
{
    a ← 2
    while (a ≤ √n)
    {
        while (n mod a = 0)
        {
            output a                      // Factors are output one by one
            n = n / a
        }
        a ← a + 1
    }
    if (n > 1) output n                   // n has no more factors
}
```

---

***Complexity*** The trial-division method is normally good if $n < 2^{10}$, but it is very inefficient and infeasible for factoring large integers. The complexity of the algorithm (see Appendix L) is *exponential*.

---

**Example 9.29**   Use the trial division algorithm to find the factors of 1233.

***Solution***   We run a program based on the algorithm and get the following result.

$$1233 = 3^2 \times 137$$

> **Example 9.30** Use the trial division algorithm to find the factors of 1523357784.

**Solution** We run a program based on the algorithm and get the following result.

$$1523357784 = 2^3 \times 3^2 \times 13 \times 37 \times 43987$$

### 9.3.3 Fermat Method

The **Fermat factorization method** (Algorithm 9.4) divides a number $n$ into two positive integers $a$ and $b$ (not necessarily a prime) so that $n = a \times b$.

**Algorithm 9.4**                **Pseudocode for Fermat factorization**

```
Feramat_Factorization (n)           // n is the number to be factored
{
    x ← √n                          // smallest integer greater than √n
    while (x < n)
    {
        w ← x² – n
        if (w is perfect square)  y ← √w;  a ← x + y;  b ← x – y;  return a and b
        x ← x + 1
    }
}
```

The Fermat method is based on the fact that if we can find $x$ and $y$ such that $n = x^2 - y^2$, then we have

$$n = x^2 - y^2 = a \times b \quad \text{with a} = (x + y) \text{ and b} = (x - y)$$

The method tries to find two integers $a$ and $b$ close to each other ($a \approx b$). It starts from the smallest integer greater than $x = \sqrt{n}$ and tries to find another integer $y$ such that the relation $y^2 = x^2 - n$ holds. The whole point is that, in each iteration, we need to see if the result of $x^2 - n$ is a perfect square. If we find such a value for $y$, we calculate $a$ and $b$ and break from the loop. If we do not, we do another iteration.

Note that the method does not necessarily find a prime factorization; the algorithm must be recursively repeated for each value $a$ and $b$ until the prime factors are found.

**Complexity** The complexity of the Fermat method is close to subexponential (see Appendix L).

### 9.3.4 Pollard $p - 1$ Method

In 1974, John M. Pollard developed a method that finds a prime factor $p$ of a number based on the condition that $p - 1$ has no factor larger than a predefined value B, called the bound. Pollard showed that in this case

$$p = \gcd (2^{B!} - 1, n)$$

Algorithm 9.5 shows the pseudocode for **Pollard $p - 1$ factorization method.** Note that when we come out of the loop, $2^{B!}$ is stored in $a$.

## Algorithm 9.5        Pseudocode for Pollard $p - 1$ factorization

```
Pollard_ (p − 1) _Factorization (n, B)        // n is the number to be factored
{
    a ← 2
    e ← 2
    while (e ≤ B)
    {
        a ← aᵉ mod n
        e ← e + 1
    }
    p ← gcd (a −1, n)
    if 1 < p < n return p
    return failure
}
```

*Complexity*    Note that this method needs to do B–1 exponentiation operations ($a = a^e \bmod n$). As we will see later in this chapter, there is a fast exponentiation algorithm that does this in $2\log_2 B$ operations. The method also uses the *gcd* calculation, which needs $\log n^3$ operations. We can say that the complexity is somehow greater than $O(B)$ or $O(2^{n_b})$: exponential, where $n_b$ is the number of bits in B. Another problem is that the algorithm may fail. The probability of success is very small unless B is very close to $\sqrt{n}$.

---

**Example 9.31**    Use the Pollard $p$ - 1 method to find a factor of 57247159 with the bound B = 8.

---

*Solution*    We run a program based on the algorithm and find that $p = 421$. As a matter of fact $57247159 = 421 \times 135979$. Note that 421 is a prime and $p - 1$ has no factor greater than 8 ($421 - 1 = 2^2 \times 3 \times 5 \times 7$).

### 9.3.5   Pollard rho Method

In 1975 John M. Pollard developed a second method for factorization. The **Pollard rho factorization method** is based on the following points:

a. Assume that there are two integers, $x_1$ and $x_2$, such that $p$ divides $x_1 - x_2$, but $n$ does not.

b. It can be proven that $p = \gcd(x_1 - x_2, n)$. Because $p$ divides $x_1 - x_2$, it can be written as $x_1 - x_2 = q \times p$. But because $n$ does not divide $x_1 - x_2$, it is obvious that $q$ does not divide $n$. This means that $\gcd(x_1 - x_2, n)$ is either 1 or a factor of $n$.

The following algorithm repeatedly selects $x_1$ and $x_2$ until it finds an appropriate pair.

1. Choose $x_1$, a small random integer called the seed.

2. Use a function to calculate $x_2$ such that $n$ does not divide $x_1 - x_2$. A function that may be used here is $x_2 = f(x_1) = x_1^2 + a$ ($a$ is normally chosen as 1).

3. Calculate $\gcd(x_1 - x_2, n)$. If it is not 1, the result is a factor of $n$; stop. If it is 1, return to step 1 and repeat the process with $x_2$. Now we are calculating $x_3$. Note that in the next round, we start with $x_3$ and so on. If we list the values of $x$'s using the Pollard rho algorithm, we see that the values are eventually repeated, creating a shape similar to the Greek letter rho ($\rho$), as shown in Fig. 9.2.

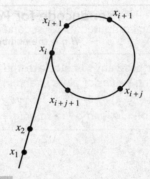

**Fig. 9.2** *Pollard rho successive numbers*

To decrease the number of iterations, the algorithm has been slightly modified. The algorithm starts with the pair $(x_0, x_0)$ and iteratively computes $(x_1, x_2)$, $(x_2, x_4)$, $(x_3, x_6)$, ..., $(x_i, x_{2i})$ using $x_{i+1} = f(x_i)$. In each iteration we use the function (from step 2) once to calculate the first element in the pair and twice to calculate the second element in the pair (see Algorithm 9.6).

---

### Algorithm 9.6              Pseudocode for Pollard rho method

```
Pollard_ rho _Factorization (n, B)          // n is the number to be factored
{
    x ← 2
    y ← 2
    p ← 1
    while (p = 1)
    {
        x ← f(x) mod n
        y ← f(f (y) mod n) mod n
        p ← gcd (x − y, n)
    }
    return p                                 // if p = n, the program has failed
}
```

*Complexity*   The method requires $\sqrt{p}$ arithmetic operations. However, because we expect $p$ to be smaller or equal to $\sqrt{n}$, we expect to do $n^{1/4}$ arithmetic operations. This means that the bit-operation complexity is $O(2^{n_b/4})$, exponential.

---

**Example 9.32**   Assume that there is a computer that can perform $2^{30}$ (almost 1 billion) bit operations per second. What is the approximation time required to factor an integer of size

    a.    60 decimal digits?
    b.    100 decimal digits?

---

**Solution**

    a.    A number of 60 decimal digits has almost 200 bits. The complexity is then $2^{n_b/4}$ or $2^{50}$. With $2^{30}$ operations per second, the algorithm can be computed in $2^{20}$ seconds, or almost 12 days.

b.   A number of 100 decimal digits has almost 300 bits. The complexity is $2^{75}$. With $2^{30}$ operations per second, the algorithm can be computed in $2^{45}$ seconds, many years.

**Example 9.33**   We have written a program to calculate the factors of 434617. The result is 709 (434617 = 709 × 613). Table 9.2 shows the values of pairs (*x* and *y*) and *p* in this run.

**Table 9.2**   *Values of x, y, and p in Example 9.33*

| x | y | p |
|---|---|---|
| 2 | 2 | 1 |
| 5 | 26 | 1 |
| 26 | 23713 | 1 |
| 677 | 142292 | 1 |
| 23713 | 157099 | 1 |
| 346589 | 52128 | 1 |
| 142292 | 41831 | 1 |
| 380320 | 68775 | 1 |
| 157099 | 427553 | 1 |
| 369457 | 2634 | 1 |
| 52128 | 63593 | 1 |
| 102901 | 161353 | 1 |
| 41831 | 64890 | 1 |
| 64520 | 21979 | 1 |
| 68775 | 16309 | 709 |

### 9.3.6   More Efficient Methods

Several factorization methods have been devised during the last few decades. Two of these methods are briefly discussed here.

*Quadratic Sieve*   Pomerance devised a factorization method called the **quadratic sieve method.** The method uses a sieving procedure to find the value of $x^2$ mod *n*. The method was used to factor integers with more than 100 digits. Its complexity is $O(e^C)$, where C ≈ $(\ln n \ \ln\ln n)^{1/2}$. Note that this is subexponential complexity.

*Number Field Sieve*   Hendric Lenstra and Argin Lenstra devised a factorization method called the **number field sieve method.** The method uses a sieving procedure in an algebraic ring structure to find $x^2 \equiv y^2$ mod *n*. It has been shown that this method is faster for factoring numbers with more than 120 digits. Its complexity is $O(e^C)$ where C ≈ 2 $(\ln n)^{1/3} (\ln\ln n)^{2/3}$. Note that this is also subexponential complexity.

**Example 9.34**  Assume that there is a computer that can perform $2^{30}$ (almost 1 billion) bit operations per second. What is the approximate time required for this computer to factor an integer of 100 decimal digits using one of the following methods?

   a.   Quadratic sieve method
   b.   Number field sieve method

**Solution**  A number with 100 decimal digits has almost 300 bits ($n = 2^{300}$). $\ln(2^{300}) = 207$ and $\ln\ln(2^{300}) = 5$.

   a.   For the quadratic sieve method we have $(207)^{1/2} \times (5)^{1/2} = 14 \times 2.23 \approx 32$. This means we need $e^{32}$ bit operation that can be done in $(e^{32})/(2^{30}) \approx 20$ hours.
   b.   For the number field sieve method we have $(207)^{1/3} \times (5)^{2/2} = 6 \times 3 \approx 18$. This means we need $e^{18}$ bit operation that can be done in $(e^{18})/(2^{30}) \approx 6$ seconds.

However, these results are valid only if we have a computer that can perform 1 billion bit operations per second.

**Other Challenges**  Chapter 10 will discuss the application of factorization in breaking public-key cryptosystems. If more efficient factorization methods are devised, public-key cryptosystems need to use larger integers to resist cryptanalysis. The inventors of RSA have created contests for factorization of numbers up to 2048 bits (more than 600 digits).

## 9.4 CHINESE REMAINDER THEOREM

The **Chinese remainder theorem** (CRT) is used to solve a set of congruent equations with one variable but different moduli, which are relatively prime, as shown below:

$$x \equiv a_1 \ (\text{mod } m_1)$$
$$x \equiv a_2 \ (\text{mod } m_2)$$
$$\cdots$$
$$x \equiv a_k \ (\text{mod } m_k)$$

The Chinese remainder theorem states that the above equations have a unique solution if the moduli are relatively prime.

**Example 9.35**  The following is an example of a set of equations with different moduli:

$$x \equiv 2 \ (\text{mod } 3)$$
$$x \equiv 3 \ (\text{mod } 5)$$
$$x \equiv 2 \ (\text{mod } 7)$$

The solution to this set of equations is given in the next section; for the moment, note that the answer to this set of equations is $x = 23$. This value satisfies all equations: $23 \equiv 2 \ (\text{mod } 3)$, $23 \equiv 3 \ (\text{mod } 5)$, and $23 \equiv 2 \ (\text{mod } 7)$.

**Solution**  The solution to the set of equations follows these steps:
   1.   Find $M = m_1 \times m_2 \times \cdots \times m_k$. This is the common modulus.
   2.   Find $M_1 = M/m_1$, $M_2 = M/m_2$, ..., $M_k = M/m_k$.

3. Find the multiplicative inverse of $M_1, M_2, \ldots, M_k$ using the corresponding moduli ($m_1, m_2, \ldots, m_k$). Call the inverses $M_1^{-1}, M_2^{-1}, \ldots, M_k^{-1}$.
4. The solution to the simultaneous equations is

$$x = (a_1 \times M_1 \times M_1^{-1} + a_2 \times M_2 \times M_2^{-1} + \cdots + a_k \times M_k \times M_k^{-1}) \bmod M$$

Note that the set of equations can have a solution even if the moduli are not relatively prime but meet other conditions. However, in cryptography, we are only interested in solving equations with coprime moduli.

**Example 9.36**   Find the solution to the simultaneous equations:

$$x \equiv 2 \bmod 3$$
$$x \equiv 3 \bmod 5$$
$$x \equiv 2 \bmod 7$$

*Solution*   From the previous example, we already know that the answer is $x = 23$. We follow the four steps.
1. $M = 3 \times 5 \times 7 = 105$
2. $M_1 = 105/3 = 35, M_2 = 105/5 = 21, M_3 = 105/7 = 15$
3. The inverses are $M_1^{-1} = 2, M_2^{-1} = 1, M_3^{-1} = 1$
4. $x = (2 \times 35 \times 2 + 3 \times 21 \times 1 + 2 \times 15 \times 1) \bmod 105 = 23 \bmod 105$

**Example 9.37**   Find an integer that has a remainder of 3 when divided by 7 and 13, but is divisible by 12.

*Solution*   This is a CRT problem. We can form three equations and solve them to find the value of x.

$$x = 3 \bmod 7$$
$$x = 3 \bmod 13$$
$$x = 0 \bmod 12$$

If we follow the four steps, we find $x = 276$. We can check that $276 = 3 \bmod 7$, $276 = 3 \bmod 13$ and 276 is divisible by 12 (the quotient is 23 and the remainder is zero).

### Applications
The Chinese remainder theorem has several applications in cryptography. One is to solve quadratic congruence as discussed in the next section. The other is to represent a very large integer in terms of a list of small integers.

**Example 9.38**   Assume we need to calculate $z = x + y$ where $x = 123$ and $y = 334$, but our system accepts only numbers less than 100. These numbers can be represented as follows:

$$x \equiv 24 \ (\bmod\ 99) \qquad y \equiv 37 \ (\bmod\ 99)$$
$$x \equiv 25 \ (\bmod\ 98) \qquad y \equiv 40 \ (\bmod\ 98)$$
$$x \equiv 26 \ (\bmod\ 97) \qquad y \equiv 43 \ (\bmod\ 97)$$

Adding each congruence in $x$ with the corresponding congruence in $y$ gives

$$x + y \equiv 61 \pmod{99} \rightarrow z \equiv 61 \pmod{99}$$
$$x + y \equiv 65 \pmod{98} \rightarrow z \equiv 65 \pmod{98}$$
$$x + y \equiv 69 \pmod{97} \rightarrow z \equiv 69 \pmod{97}$$

Now three equations can be solved using the Chinese remainder theorem to find $z$. One of the acceptable answers is $z = 457$.

## 9.5                                 QUADRATIC CONGRUENCE

Linear congruence was discussed in Chapter 2 and the Chinese remainder theorem was discussed in the previous section. In cryptography, we also need to discuss **quadratic congruence**—that is, equations of the form $a_2 x^2 + a_1 x + a_0 \equiv 0 \pmod{n}$. We limit our discussion to quadratic equations in which $a_2 = 1$ and $a_1 = 0$, that is equations of the form

$$x^2 \equiv a \pmod{n}.$$

### 9.5.1  Quadratic Congruence Modulo a Prime

We first consider the case in which the modulus is a prime. In other words, we want to find the solutions for an equation of the form $x^2 \equiv a \pmod{p}$, in which $p$ is a prime, $a$ is an integer such that $p \nmid a$. It can be proved that this type of equation has either no solution or exactly two incongruent solutions.

**Example 9.39**  The equation $x^2 \equiv 3 \pmod{11}$ has two solutions, $x \equiv 5 \pmod{11}$ and $x \equiv -5 \pmod{11}$. But note that $-5 \equiv 6 \pmod{11}$, so the solutions are actually 5 and 6. Also note that these two solutions are incongruent.

**Example 9.40**  The equation $x^2 \equiv 2 \pmod{11}$ has no solution. No integer $x$ can be found such that its square is 2 mod 11.

**Quadratic Residues and Nonresidue**  In the equation $x^2 \equiv a \pmod{p}$, $a$ is called a **quadratic residue (QR)** if the equation has two solutions; $a$ is called **quadratic nonresidue (QNR)** if the equation has no solutions. It can be proved that in $Z_p^*$, with $p - 1$ elements, exactly $(p - 1)/2$ elements are quadratic residues and $(p - 1)/2$ are quadratic nonresidues.

**Example 9.41**  There are 10 elements in $Z_{11}^*$. Exactly five of them are quadratic residues and five of them are nonresidues. In other words, $Z_{11}^*$ is divided into two separate sets, QR and QNR, as shown in Fig. 9.3.

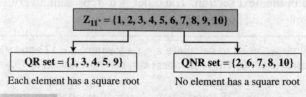

**Fig. 9.3**  *Division of $Z_{11}^*$ elements into QRs and QNRs*

***Euler's Criterion*** How can we check to see if an integer is a QR modulo $p$? Euler's criterion gives a very specific condition:

    a.   If $a^{(p-1)/2} \equiv 1 \pmod{p}$, $a$ is a quadratic residue modulo $p$.

    b.   If $a^{(p-1)/2} \equiv -1 \pmod{p}$, $a$ is a quadratic nonresidue modulo $p$.

---

**Example 9.42**   To find out if 14 or 16 is a QR in $Z_{23}{}^*$, we calculate:

    $14^{(23-1)/2}$ mod 23 $\rightarrow$ $14^{11}$ mod 23 $\rightarrow$ 22 mod 23 $\rightarrow$ -1 mod 23         **nonresidue**

    $15^{(23-1)/2}$ mod 23 $\rightarrow$ $16^{11}$ mod 23 $\rightarrow$ 1 mod 23                **residue**

---

***Solving Quadratic Equation Modulo a Prime*** Although the Euler criterion tells us if an integer $a$ is a QR or QNR in $Z_p{}^*$, it cannot find the solution to $x^2 \equiv a \pmod{p}$. To find the solution to this quadratic equation, we notice that a prime can be either $p = 4k + 1$ or $p = 4k + 3$, in which $k$ is a positive integer. The solution to a quadratic equation is very involved in the first case; it is easier in the second. We will discuss only the second case, which we will use in Chapter 10 when we discuss Rabin cryptosystem.

***Special Case: p = 4k + 3*** If $p$ is in the form $4k + 3$ (that is, $p \equiv 3 \bmod 4$) and $a$ is a QR in $Z_p{}^*$, then

$$x \equiv a^{(p+1)/4} \pmod{p} \quad \text{and} \quad x \equiv -a^{(p+1)/4} \pmod{p}$$

---

**Example 9.43**   Solve the following quadratic equations:

    a.   $x^2 \equiv 3 \pmod{23}$

    b.   $x^2 \equiv 2 \pmod{11}$

    c.   $x^2 \equiv 7 \pmod{19}$

---

***Solutions***

    a.   In the first equation, 3 is a QR in $Z_{23}$. The solution is $x \equiv \pm 16 \pmod{23}$. In other words, $\sqrt{3} \equiv \pm 16 \pmod{23}$.

    b.   In the second equation, 2 is a QNR in $Z_{11}$. There is no solution for $\sqrt{2}$ in $Z_{11}$.

    c.   In the third equation, 7 is a QR in $Z_{19}$. The solution is $x \equiv \pm 11 \pmod{19}$. In other words, $\sqrt{7} \equiv \pm 11 \pmod{19}$.

## 9.5.2 Quadratic Congruence Modulo a Composite

Quadratic congruence modulo a composite can be done by solving a set of congruence modulo a prime. In other words, we can decompose $x^2 \equiv a \pmod{n}$ if we have the factorization of $n$. Now we can solve each decomposed equation (if solvable) and find $k$ pairs of answers for $x$ as shown in Fig. 9.4.

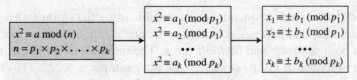

**Fig. 9.4**  *Decomposition of congruence modulo a composite*

From $k$ pairs of answers, we can make $2^k$ set of equations that can be solved using the Chinese remainder theorem to find $2^k$ values for $x$. In cryptography, normally $n$ is made such that $n = p \times q$, which means $k = 2$ and we have only four total answers.

---

**Example 9.44**   Assume that $x^2 \equiv 36 \pmod{77}$. We know that $77 = 7 \times 11$. We can write

$$x^2 \equiv 36 \pmod 7 \equiv 1 \pmod 7 \qquad \text{and} \qquad x^2 \equiv 36 \pmod{11} \equiv 3 \pmod{11}$$

Note that we have chosen 3 and 7 to be of the form $4k + 3$ so that we can solve the equations based on the previous discussion. Both of these equations have quadratic residues in their own sets. The answers are $x \equiv +1 \pmod 7$, $x \equiv -1 \pmod 7$, $x \equiv +5 \pmod{11}$, and $x \equiv -5 \pmod{11}$. Now we can make four sets of equations out of these:

    **Set 1:** $x \equiv +1 \pmod 7$  $x \equiv +5 \pmod{11}$
    **Set 2:** $x \equiv +1 \pmod 7$  $x \equiv -5 \pmod{11}$
    **Set 3:** $x \equiv -1 \pmod 7$  $x \equiv +5 \pmod{11}$
    **Set 4:** $x \equiv -1 \pmod 7$  $x \equiv -5 \pmod{11}$
The answers are $x = \pm 6$ and $\pm 27$.

---

*Complexity*   How hard is it to solve a quadratic congruence modulo a composite? The main task is the factorization of the modulus. In other words, the complexity of solving a quadratic congruence modulo a composite is the same as factorizing a composite integer. As we have seen, if $n$ is very large, factorization is infeasible.

---

**Solving a quadratic congruence modulo a composite is as hard as factorization of the modulus.**

---

## 9.6                       EXPONENTIATION AND LOGARITHM

Exponentiation and logarithm are inverses of each other. The following shows the relationship between them, in which $a$ is called the base of the exponentiation or logarithm.

$$\textbf{Exponentiation: } y = a^x \rightarrow \textbf{Logarithm: } x = \log_a y$$

### 9.6.1   Exponentiation

In cryptography, a common modular operation is **exponentiation.** That is, we often need to calculate

$$y = a^x \bmod n$$

The RSA cryptosystem, which will be discussed in Chapter 10, uses exponentiation for both encryption and decryption with very large exponents. Unfortunately, most computer languages have no operator that can efficiently compute exponentiation, particularly when the exponent is very large. To make this type of calculation more efficient, we need algorithms that are more efficient.

*Fast Exponentiation*   Fast exponentiation is possible using the **square-and-multiply method.** In traditional algorithms only *multiplication* is used to simulate exponentiation, but the fast exponentiation algorithm uses both *squaring* and *multiplication*. The main idea behind this method is to treat the exponent as a binary number of $n_b$ bits ($x_0$ to $x_{n_b - 1}$). For example, $x = 22 = (10110)_2$. In general, $x$ can be written as:

$$x = x_{n_b - 1} \times 2^{k-1} + x_{n_b - 2} \times 2^{k-2} + \cdots + x_2 \times 2^2 + x_1 \times 2^1 + x_0 \times 2^0$$

Now we can write $y = a^x$ as shown in Fig. 9.5.

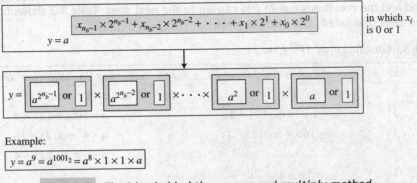

$$y = a^{x_{n_b-1} \times 2^{n_b-1} + x_{n_b-2} \times 2^{n_b-2} + \cdots + x_1 \times 2^1 + x_0 \times 2^0}$$

in which $x_i$ is 0 or 1

$$y = \boxed{a^{2^{n_b-1}} \text{ or } 1} \times \boxed{a^{2^{n_b-2}} \text{ or } 1} \times \cdots \times \boxed{a^2 \text{ or } 1} \times \boxed{a \text{ or } 1}$$

Example:

$$y = a^9 = a^{1001_2} = a^8 \times 1 \times 1 \times a$$

**Fig. 9.5**  *The idea behind the square-and-multiply method*

Note that $y$ is the product of $n_b$ terms. Each term is either 1 (if the corresponding bit is 0) or $a^{2^i}$ (if the corresponding bit is 1). In other words, the term $a^{2^i}$ is included in the multiplication if the bit is 1, it is not included if the bit is 0 (multiplication by 1 has no effect). Figure 9.6 gives the general idea how to write the algorithm. We can continuously square the base, $a$, $a^2$, $a^4$, ..., $a^{2^{n_b}-1}$. If the corresponding bit is 0, the term is not included in the multiplication process; if the bit is 1, it is. Algorithm 9.7 reflects these two observations.

---

**Algorithm 9.7**  **Pseudocode for square-and-multiply algorithm**

```
Square_and_Multiply (a, x, n)
{
    y ← 1
    for (i ← 0 to n_b − 1)                    // n_b is the number of bits in x
    {
        if (x_i = 1) y ← a × y  mod n         // multiply only if the bit is 1
        a ← a² mod n                          // squaring is not needed in the last iteration
    }
    return y
}
```

Algorithm 9.7 uses $n_b$ iterations. In each iteration, it checks the value of the corresponding bit. If the value of the bit is 1, it multiplies the current base with the previous value of the result. It then squares the base for the next iteration. Note that squaring is not needed in the last step (the result is not used).

**Example 9.45**  Figure 9.6 shows the process for calculating $y = a^x$ using the Algorithm 9.7 (for simplicity, the modulus is not shown). In this case, $x = 22 = (10110)_2$ in binary. The exponent has five bits.

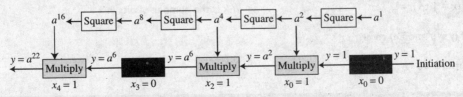

**Fig. 9.6**  *Demonstration of calculation of $a^{22}$ using square-and-multiply method*

Squaring is done in each step except the last. Multiplication is done only if the corresponding bit is 1. Figure 9.7 shows how the values of y are gradually built until $y = a^{22}$. The solid boxes mean that multiplication is ignored and the previous value of y is carried to the next step. Table 9.3 shows how the value for $y = 17^{22} \bmod 21$ is calculated. The result is $y = 4$.

**Table 9.3** *Calculation of $17^{22} \bmod 21$*

| $i$ | $x_i$ | *Multiplication (Initialization: y = 1)* | | *Squaring (Initialization: a = 17)* |
|---|---|---|---|---|
| 0 | 0 | | $\rightarrow$ | $a = 17^2 \bmod 21 = 16$ |
| 1 | 1 | $y = 1 \times 16 \bmod 21 = 16$ | $\rightarrow$ | $a = 16^2 \bmod 21 = 4$ |
| 2 | 1 | $y = 16 \times 4 \bmod 21 = 1$ | $\rightarrow$ | $a = 4^2 \bmod 21 = 16$ |
| 3 | 0 | | $\rightarrow$ | $a = 16^2 \bmod 21 = 4$ |
| 4 | 1 | $y = 1 \times 4 \bmod 21 = 4$ | $\rightarrow$ | |

**Complexity**   Algorithm 9.7 uses a maximum of $2n_b$ arithmetic operations in which $n_b$ is the length of the modulus in bits ($n_b = \log_2 n$), so the bit-operation complexity of the algorithm is $O(n_b)$ or polynomial.

---

**The bit-operation complexity of the fast exponential algorithm is polynomial.**

---

**Alternative Algorithm**   Note that Algorithm 9.7 checks the value of bits in x from the right to the left (least significant to most significant). An algorithm can be written to use the reverse order. We have chosen the above algorithm because the squaring operation is totally independent from the multiplication operation; they can be done in parallel to increase the speed of processing. The alternative algorithm is left as an exercise.

### 9.6.2   Logarithm

In cryptography, we also need to discuss modular logarithm. If we use exponentiation to encrypt or decrypt, the adversary can use logarithm to attack. We need to know how hard it is to reverse the exponentiation.

**Exhaustive Search**   The first solution that might come to mind is to solve $x = \log_a y \pmod n$. We can write an algorithm that continuously calculates $y = a^x \bmod n$ until it finds the value of given y. Algorithm 9.8 shows this approach.

---

**Algorithm 9.8**                           **Exhaustive search for modular logarithm**

```
Modular_Logarithm (a, y, n)
{
    for (x = 1 to n −1)                    // k is the number of bits in x
    {
        if (y ≡ a^x mod n) return x
    }
    return failure
}
```

Algorithm 9.8 is definitely very inefficient. The bit-operation complexity is $O(2^{n_b})$ or exponential.

## Discrete Logarithm

The second approach is to use the concept of **discrete logarithm.** Understanding this concept requires understanding some properties of multiplicative groups.

*Finite Multiplicative Group*   In cryptography, we often use the multiplicative finite group: $\mathbf{G} = <\mathbf{Z}_n^*, \times>$ in which the operation is multiplication. The set $\mathbf{Z}_n^*$ contains those integers from 1 to $n–1$ that are relatively prime to $n$; the identity element is $e = 1$. Note that when the modulus of the group is a prime, we have $\mathbf{G} = <\mathbf{Z}_p^*, \times>$. This group is the special case of the first group, so we concentrate on the first group in this section.

*Order of the Group*   In Chapter 4, we discussed the order of a finite group, $|G|$, to be the number of elements in the group G. In $\mathbf{G} = <\mathbf{Z}_n^*, \times>$, it can be proved that the order of group is $\phi(n)$. We have shown how to calculate $\phi(n)$, when $n$ can be factored into primes.

---

**Example 9.46**   What is the order of group $\mathbf{G} = <\mathbf{Z}_{21}^*, \times>$? $|G| = \phi(21) = \phi(3) \times \phi(7) = 2 \times 6 = 12$. There are 12 elements in this group: 1, 2, 4, 5, 8, 10, 11, 13, 16, 17, 19, and 20. All are relatively prime with 21.

---

*Order of an Element*   In Chapter 4, we also discussed the order of an element, ord($a$). In $\mathbf{G} = <\mathbf{Z}_n^*, \times>$, we continue with the same definition. The order of an element, $a$, is the smallest integer $i$ such that $a^i \equiv e \pmod{n}$. The identity element $e$ is 1 in this case.

---

**Example 9.47**   Find the order of all elements in $\mathbf{G} = <\mathbf{Z}_{10}^*, \times>$.

---

**Solution**   This group has only $\phi(10) = 4$ elements: 1, 3, 7, 9. We can find the order of each element by trial and error. However, recall from Chapter 4 that the order of an element divides the order of the group (Lagrange theorem). The only integers that divide 4 are 1, 2, and 4, which means in each case we need to check only these powers to find the order of the element.

a.   $1^1 \equiv 1 \bmod (10) \rightarrow \text{ord}(1) = 1$.

b.   $3^1 \equiv 3 \bmod (10)$; $3^2 \equiv 9 \bmod (10)$; $3^4 \equiv 1 \bmod (10) \rightarrow \text{ord}(3) = 4$.

c.   $7^1 \equiv 7 \bmod (10)$; $7^2 \equiv 9 \bmod (10)$; $7^4 \equiv 1 \bmod (10) \rightarrow \text{ord}(7) = 4$.

d.   $9^1 \equiv 9 \bmod (10)$; $9^2 \equiv 1 \bmod (10) \rightarrow \text{ord}(9) = 2$.

*Euler's Theorem*   Another related theorem is the Euler's theorem (discussed in this chapter) that says if $a$ is the member of $\mathbf{G} = <\mathbf{Z}_n^*, \times>$, then $a^{\phi(n)} = 1 \bmod n$

This theorem is very helpful because it shows that the relationship $a^i \equiv 1 \pmod{n}$ holds when $i = \phi(n)$, even if it holds when $i < \phi(n)$. In other words, this relation holds at least once.

---

**Example 9.48**   Table 9.4 shows the result of $a^i \equiv x \pmod{8}$ for the group $\mathbf{G} = <\mathbf{Z}_8^*, \times>$. Note that $\phi(8) = 4$. The elements are 1, 3, 5, and 7.

---

**Table 9.4** *Finding the orders of elements in Example 9.48*

|  | i = 1 | i = 2 | i = 3 | i = 4 | i = 5 | i = 6 | i = 7 |
|---|---|---|---|---|---|---|---|
| a = 1 | x: 1 | x: 1 | x: 1 | x: 1 | x: 1 | x: 1 | x: 1 |
| a = 3 | x: 3 | x: 1 | x: 3 | x: 1 | x: 3 | x: 1 | x: 3 |
| a = 5 | x: 5 | x: 1 | x: 5 | x: 1 | x: 5 | x: 1 | x: 5 |
| a = 7 | x: 7 | x: 1 | x: 7 | x: 1 | x: 7 | x: 1 | x: 7 |

Table 9.4 reveals some points. First, the shaded area shows the result of applying Euler's theorem: When $i = \phi(8) = 4$, the result is $x = 1$ for every $a$. Second, the table shows that the value of $x$ can be 1 for many values of $i$. The first time when $x$ is 1, the value of $i$ gives us the order of the element (double-sided boxes). The orders of elements are ord(1) = 1, ord(3) = 2, ord(5) = 2, and ord(7) = 2.

**Primitive Roots** A very interesting concept in multiplicative group is that of **primitive root,** which is used in the ElGamal cryptosystem in Chapter 10. In the group $\mathbf{G} = <Z_n{}^*, \times>$, when the order of an element is the same as $\phi(n)$, that element is called the primitive root of the group.

**Example 9.49** Table 9.4 shows that there are no primitive roots in $\mathbf{G} = <Z_8{}^*, \times>$ because no element has the order equal to $\phi(8) = 4$. The order of elements are all smaller than 4.

**Example 9.50** Table 9.5 shows the result of $a^i \equiv x \pmod 7$ for the group $\mathbf{G} = <Z_7{}^*, \times>$. In this group, $\phi(7) = 6$.

**Table 9.5** *Example 9.50*

|  |  | i = 1 | i = 2 | i = 3 | i = 4 | i = 5 | i = 6 |
|---|---|---|---|---|---|---|---|
|  | a = 1 | x: 1 | x: 1 | x: 1 | x: 1 | x: 1 | x: 1 |
|  | a = 2 | x: 2 | x: 4 | x: 1 | x: 2 | x: 4 | x: 1 |
| Primitive root → | a = 3 | x: 3 | x: 2 | x: 6 | x: 4 | x: 5 | x: 1 |
|  | a = 4 | x: 4 | x: 2 | x: 1 | x: 4 | x: 2 | x: 1 |
| Primitive root → | a = 5 | x: 5 | x: 4 | x: 6 | x: 2 | x: 3 | x: 1 |
|  | a = 6 | x: 6 | x: 1 | x: 6 | x: 1 | x: 6 | x: 1 |

The orders of elements are ord(1) = 1, ord(2) = 3, ord(3) = <u>6</u>, ord(4) = 3, ord(5) = <u>6</u>, and ord(6) = 1. Table 9.5 shows that only two elements, 3 and 5, have the order at $i = \phi(n) = 6$. Therefore, this group has only two primitive roots: 3 and 5.

It has been proved that the group $\mathbf{G} = <Z_n{}^*, \times>$ has a primitive root only if $n = 2, 4, p^t$, or $2p^t$, in which $p$ is an odd prime (not 2) and $t$ is an integer.

---

The group $\mathbf{G} = <Z_n{}^*, \times>$ **has primitive roots only if $n$ is 2, 4, $p^t$, or $2p^t$.**

**Example 9.51** For which value of $n$, does the group $G = <Z_n^*, \times>$ have primitive roots: 17, 20, 38, and 50?

## Solution

a. $G = <Z_{17}^*, \times>$ has primitive roots, because 17 is a prime ($p^t$ where $t$ is 1).
b. $G = <Z_{20}^*, \times>$ has no primitive roots.
c. $G = <Z_{38}^*, \times>$ has primitive roots, because $38 = 2 \times 19$ and 19 is a prime.
d. $G = <Z_{50}^*, \times>$ has primitive roots, because $50 = 2 \times 5^2$ and 5 is a prime.

If a group has a primitive root, then it normally has several of them. The number of primitive roots can be calculated as $\phi(\phi(n))$. For example, the number of primitive roots of $G = <Z_{17}^*, \times>$ is $\phi(\phi(17)) = \phi(16) = 8$. Note that we should first check to see if the group has any primitive root, before we find the number of roots.

---

**If the group $G = <Z_n^*, \times>$ has any primitive root, the number of primitive roots is $\phi(\phi(n))$.**

---

Three questions arise:

1. Given an element $a$ and the group $G = <Z_n^*, \times>$, how can we find out whether $a$ is a primitive root of $G$? This is not an easy task.
   a. We need to find $\phi(n)$, which is as difficult as factorization of $n$.
   b. We need to check whether $\text{ord}(a) = \phi(n)$.
2. Given a group $G = <Z_n^*, \times>$, how can we check all primitive roots of $G$? This is more difficult than the first task because we need to repeat part $b$ for all elements of the group.
3. Given a group $G = <Z_n^*, \times>$, how can we select a primitive root of $G$? In cryptography, we need to find at least one primitive root in the group. However, in this case, the value of $n$ is chosen by the user and the user knows the value of $\phi(n)$. The user tries several elements until he or she finds the first one.

*Cyclic Group* Cyclic groups were discussed in Chapter 4. Note that if the group $G = <Z_n^*, \times>$ has primitive roots, it is cyclic. Each primitive root is a generator and can be used to create the whole set. In other words, if $g$ is a primitive root in the group, we can generate the set $Z_n^*$ as

$$Z_n^* = \{g^1, g^2, g^3, ..., g^{\phi(n)}\}$$

**Example 9.52** The group $G = <Z_{10}^*, \times>$ has two primitive roots because $\phi(10) = 4$ and $\phi(\phi(10)) = 2$. It can be found that the primitive roots are 3 and 7. The following shows how we can create the whole set $Z_{10}^*$ using each primitive root.

| | | | | |
|---|---|---|---|---|
| $g = 3 \rightarrow$ | $g^1 \bmod 10 = 3$ | $g^2 \bmod 10 = 9$ | $g^3 \bmod 10 = 7$ | $g^4 \bmod 10 = 1$ |
| $g = 7 \rightarrow$ | $g^1 \bmod 10 = 7$ | $g^2 \bmod 10 = 9$ | $g^3 \bmod 10 = 3$ | $g^4 \bmod 10 = 1$ |

Note that the group $G = <Z_p^*, \times>$ is always cyclic because $p$ is a prime.

**The group $G = <Z_n^*, \times>$ is a cyclic group if it has primitive roots.**
**The group $G = <Z_p^*, \times>$ is always cyclic.**

*The idea of Discrete Logarithm* The group $G = <Z_p^*, \times>$ has several interesting properties:

1. Its elements include all integers from 1 to $p - 1$.

2.  It always has primitive roots.
3.  It is cyclic. The elements can be created using $g^x$ where $x$ is an integer from 1 to $\phi(n) = p - 1$.
4.  The primitive roots can be thought as the base of logarithm. If the group has $k$ primitive roots, calculations can be done in $k$ different bases. Given $x = \log_g y$ for any element $y$ in the set, there is another element $x$ that is the log of $y$ in base $g$. This type of logarithm is called **discrete logarithm**. A discrete logarithm is designated by several different symbols in the literature, but we will use the notation $L_g$ to show that the base is $g$ (the modulus is understood).

### 9.6.3  Solution to Modular Logarithm Using Discrete Logs

Now let us see how to solve problems of type $y = a^x \pmod{n}$ when $y$ is given and we need to find $x$.

***Tabulation of Discrete Logarithms***   One way to solve the above-mentioned problem is to use a table for each $Z_p^*$ and different bases. This type of table can be precalculated and saved. For example, Table 9.6 shows the tabulation of the discrete logarithm for $Z_7^*$. We know that we have two primitive roots or bases in the set.

**Table 9.6**  *Discrete logarithm for G = <$Z_7^*$, ×>*

| $y$ | 1 | 2 | 3 | 4 | 5 | 6 |
|-----|---|---|---|---|---|---|
| $x = L_3\, y$ | 6 | 2 | 1 | 4 | 5 | 3 |
| $x = L_5\, y$ | 6 | 4 | 5 | 2 | 1 | 3 |

Given the tabulation for other discrete logarithms for every group and all possible bases, we can solve any discrete logarithm problem. This is similar to the past with traditional logarithms. Before the era of calculators and computers, tables were used to calculate logarithms in base 10.

> **Example 9.53**   Find $x$ in each of the following cases:
> a.  $4 \equiv 3^x \pmod 7$.
> b.  $6 \equiv 5^x \pmod 7$.

***Solution***   We can easily use the tabulation of the discrete logarithm in Table 9.6.
a.  $4 \equiv 3^x \bmod 7 \rightarrow x = L_3 4 \bmod 7 = 4 \bmod 7$
b.  $6 \equiv 5^x \bmod 7 \rightarrow x = L_5 6 \bmod 7 = 3 \bmod 7$

***Using Properties of Discrete Logarithms***   To see that discrete logarithms behave just like traditional logarithms, several properties of both types of logarithms are given in Table 9.7. Note that the modulus is $\phi(n)$ instead of $n$.

**Table 9.7**  *Comparison of traditional and discrete logarithms*

| Traditional Logarithm | Discrete Logarithms |
|-----------------------|---------------------|
| $\log_a 1 = 0$ | $L_g 1 \equiv 0 \pmod{\phi(n)}$ |
| $\log_a (x \times y) = \log_a x + \log_a y$ | $L_g(x \times y) \equiv (L_g x + L_g y) \pmod{\phi(n)}$ |
| $\log_a x^k = k \times \log_a x$ | $L_g x^k \equiv k \times L_g x \pmod{\phi(n)}$ |

***Using Algorithms Based on Discrete Logarithms***   Tabulation and the properties of discrete logarithms cannot be used to solve $y \equiv a^x \pmod{n}$ when $n$ is very large. Several algorithms have been devised that use the basic idea of discrete logarithms to solve the problem. Although all of these algorithms are more efficient than the exhaustive-search algorithm that we mentioned at the beginning of this section, none of them have polynomial complexity. Most of these algorithms have the same level of complexity as the factorization problem.

---

**The discrete logarithm problem has the same complexity as the factorization problem.**

---

## 9.7　　　　　　　　　　　　RECOMMENDED READING

For more details about subjects discussed in this chapter, we recommend the following books and websites. The items enclosed in brackets refer to the reference list at the end of the book.

### Books

We recommend [Ros06], [Cou99], and [BW00], and [Bla03] for topics discussed in this chapter.

### WebSites

The following websites give more information about topics discussed in this chapter.

http://en.wikipedia.org/wiki/Prime_number
http://primes.utm.edu/mersenne/
http://en.wikipedia.org/wiki/Primality_test
www.cl.cam.ac.uk/~jeh1004/research/talks/miller-talk.pdf
http://mathworld.wolfram.com/TotientFunction.html
http://en.wikipedia.org/wiki/Proofs_of_Fermat's_little_theorem
faculty.cs.tamu.edu/klappi/629/analytic.pdf

## *Key Terms*

| | |
|---|---|
| Chinese remainder theorem (CRT) | number field sieve method |
| composite | Polard $p$–1 factorization method |
| coprime (relatively prime) | Polard rho factorization method |
| deterministic algorithm | primality test |
| discrete logarithm | prime |
| divisibility test | primitive root |
| Euler's phi-function | probabilistic algorithm |
| Euler's theorem | pseudoprime |
| exponentiation | quadratic congruence |
| factorization | quadratic equation |
| Fermat factorization method | quadratic nonresidue (QNR) |
| Fermat primality test | quadratic residue (QR) |
| Fermat numbers | quadratic sieve method |
| Fermat primes | sieve of Eratosthenes |
| Fermat's little theorem | square-and-multiply method |
| Mersenne numbers | square root primality test method |
| Mersenne primes | strong pseudoprime |
| Miller-Rabin primality test | trial division factorization method |

# Summary

★ The positive integers can be divided into three groups: the number 1, primes, and composites. A positive integer is a prime if and only if it is exactly divisible by two different integers, 1 and itself. A composite is a positive integer with at least two divisors.

★ Euler's phi-function, $\phi(n)$, which is sometimes called Euler's totient function, plays a very important role in cryptography. The function finds the number of integers that are both smaller than $n$ and relatively prime to $n$.

★ Table 9.8 shows Fermat's little theorem and Euler's theorem, as discussed in this chapter.

**Table 9.8** *Fermat's little theorem and Euler's theorem*

| Fermat | **First Version:**<br>If $gcd(a, p) = 1$, then $a^{p-1} \equiv 1 \pmod{p}$ |
| | **Second Version:**<br>$a^p \equiv a \pmod{p}$ |
| Euler | **First Version:**<br>If $gcd(a, n) = 1$, then $a^{\phi(n)} \equiv 1 \pmod{n}$ |
| | **Second Version:**<br>If $n = p \times q$ and $a < n$, then $a^{k \times \phi(n)+1} \equiv a \pmod{n}$ |

★ To create a large prime, we choose a large random number and test it to be sure that it is a prime. The algorithms that deal with this issue can be divided into two broad categories: deterministic algorithms and probabilistic algorithms. Some probabilistic algorithms for primality test are the Fermat test, the square root test, and the Miller-Rabin test. Some deterministic algorithms are the divisibility test and AKS algorithm.

★ According to the *Fundamental Theorem of Arithmetic*, any positive integer greater than 1 can be factored into primes. We mentioned several factorization methods including the trial division, the Fermat, the Pollard $p - 1$, the Pollard rho, the quadratic sieve and the number field sieve.

★ The Chinese remainder theorem (CRT) is used to solve a set of congruent equations with one variable but different moduli that are relatively prime.

★ We discussed solutions to quadratic congruence modulo a prime and quadratic congruence modulo a composite. However, if the modulus is large, solving a quadratic congruence is as hard as factorization of the modulus.

★ In cryptography, a common modular operation is exponentiation. Fast exponentiation is possible using the square-and-multiply method. Cryptography also involves modular logarithms. If exponentiation is used to encrypt or decrypt, the adversary can use logarithms to attack. We need to know how hard it is to reverse the exponentiation. Although exponentiation can be done using fast algorithms, using modular logarithm for a large modulus is as hard has as the factorization problem.

# Practice Set

## Review Questions

9.1 Distinguish between a prime and a composite integer.

9.2 Define the meaning of *relatively prime* (*coprime*).

9.3 Define the following functions and their application:

a.   $\pi(n)$ function

b.   Euler's totient function

**9.4**   Explain the sieve of Eratosthenes and its application.

**9.5**   Define Fermat's little theorem and explain its application.

**9.6**   Define Euler's theorem and explain its application.

**9.7**   What are Mersenne primes? What are Fermat primes?

**9.8**   Distinguish between deterministic and probabilistic algorithms for primality testing.

**9.9**   List some algorithms for factorization of primes.

**9.10**  Define the Chinese remainder theorem and its application.

**9.11**  Define quadratic congruence and the importance of QRs and QNRs in solving quadratic equations.

**9.12**  Define discrete logarithms and explain their importance in solving logarithmic equations.

## Exercises

**9.13**  Using approximation, find

a.   the number of primes between 100,000 and 200,000.

b.   the number of composite integers between 100,000 and 200,000.

c.   the ratio of the primes to composites in the above range and compare it to the same between 1 to 10.

**9.14**  Find the largest prime factor of the following composite integers: 100, 1000, 10,000, 100,000, and 1,000,000. Also find the largest prime -factor of 101, 1001, 10,001, 100,001, and 1,000,001.

**9.15**  Show that every prime is either in the form $4k + 1$ or $4k + 3$, where $k$ is a positive integer.

**9.16**  Find some primes in the form $5k + 1$, $5k + 2$, $5k + 3$, and $5k + 4$, where $k$ is a positive integer.

**9.17**  Find the value of $\phi(29)$, $\phi(32)$, $\phi(80)$, $\phi(100)$, $\phi(101)$.

**9.18**  Show that $2^{24} - 1$ and $2^{16} - 1$ are composites. Hint: Use the expansion of $(a^2 - b^2)$.

**9.19**  There is a conjecture that every integer greater than 2 can be written as the sum of two primes. Check this conjecture for 10, 24, 28, and 100.

**9.20**  There is a conjecture that there are many primes in the form $n^2 + 1$. Find some of them.

**9.21**  Find the results of the following, using Fermat's little theorem:

a.   $5^{15} \bmod 13$

b.   $15^{18} \bmod 17$

c.   $456^{17} \bmod 17$

d.   $145^{102} \bmod 101$

**9.22**  Find the results of the following, using Fermat's little theorem:

a.   $5^{-1} \bmod 13$

b.   $15^{-1} \bmod 17$

c.   $27^{-1} \bmod 41$

d.   $70^{-1} \bmod 101$

Note that all moduli are primes.

**9.23**  Find the results of the following, using Euler's theorem:

a.   $12^{-1} \bmod 77$

b.   $16^{-1} \bmod 323$

    c.   $20^{-1} \bmod 403$

    d.   $44^{-1} \bmod 667$

Note that $77 = 7 \times 11$, $323 = 17 \times 19$, $403 = 31 \times 13$, and $667 = 23 \times 29$.

**9.24** Determine whether the following Mersenne numbers are primes: $M_{23}$, $M_{29}$, and $M_{31}$. Hint: Any divisor of a Mersenne number has the form $2kp + 1$.

**9.25** Write some examples to show that if $2^n - 1$ is a prime, then $n$ is a prime. Can this fact be used for primality testing? Explain.

**9.26** Determine how many of the following integers pass the Fermat primality test: 100, 110, 130, 150, 200, 250, 271, 341, 561. Use base 2.

**9.27** Determine how many of the following integers pass the Miller-Rabin primality test: 100, 109, 201, 271, 341, 349. Use base 2.

**9.28** Use the recommended test to determine whether any of the following integers are primes: 271, 3149, 9673.

**9.29** Use $a = 2$, $x = 3$, and a few primes to show that if $p$ is a prime, the following congruence $(x - a)^p \equiv (x^p - a)$ $(\bmod\ p)$ holds.

**9.30** It is said that the $n$th prime can be approximated as $p_n \approx n\ln n$. Check this with some primes.

**9.31** Find the value of $x$ for the following sets of congruence using the Chinese remainder theorem.

    a.   $x \equiv 2 \bmod 7$, and $x \equiv 3 \bmod 9$

    b.   $x \equiv 4 \bmod 5$, and $x \equiv 10 \bmod 11$

    c.   $x \equiv 7 \bmod 13$, and $x \equiv 11 \bmod 12$

**9.32** Find all QRs and QNRs in $Z_{13}{}^*$, $Z_{17}{}^*$, and $Z_{23}{}^*$.

**9.33** Using quadratic residues, solve the following congruences:

    a.   $x^2 \equiv 4 \bmod 7$

    b.   $x^2 \equiv 5 \bmod 11$

    c.   $x^2 \equiv 7 \bmod 13$

    d.   $x^2 \equiv 12 \bmod 17$

**9.34** Using quadratic residues, solve the following congruences:

    a.   $x^2 \equiv 4 \bmod 14$

    b.   $x^2 \equiv 5 \bmod 10$

    c.   $x^2 \equiv 7 \bmod 33$

    d.   $x^2 \equiv 12 \bmod 34$

**9.35** Find the results of the following using the square-and-multiply method.

    a.   $21^{24} \bmod 8$

    b.   $320^{23} \bmod 461$

    c.   $1736^{41} \bmod 2134$

    d.   $2001^{35} \bmod 2000$

**9.36** For the group $\mathbf{G} = <\mathbf{Z}_{19}{}^*, \times>$:

    a.   Find the order of the group.

    b.   Find the order of each element in the group.

    c.   Find the number of primitive roots in the group.

    d.   Find the primitive roots in the group.

    e.    Show that the group is cyclic.

    f.    Make a table of discrete logarithms.

**9.37**    Using the properties of discrete logarithms, show how to solve the following congruences:

    a.    $x^5 \equiv 11 \bmod 17$

    b.    $2x^{11} \equiv 22 \bmod 19$

    c.    $5x^{12} + 6x \equiv 8 \bmod 23.$

**9.38**    Assume that you have a computer performing 1 million bit operations per second. You want to spend only 1 hour on primality testing. What is the largest number you can test using the following primality testing methods?

    a.    divisibility

    b.    AKS algorithm

    c.    Fermat

    d.    square root

    e.    Miller-Rabin

**9.39**    Assume that you have a computer that performs 1 million bit operations per second. You want to spend only 1 hour on factoring a composite integer. What is the largest number you can factor using the following factorization methods?

    a.    trial division

    b.    Fermat

    c.    Pollard rho

    d.    quadratic sieve

    e.    number field sieve

**9.40**    The square-and-multiply fast exponentiation algorithm allows us to halt the program if the value of the base becomes 1. Modify Algorithm 9.7 to show this.

**9.41**    Rewrite Algorithm 9.7 to test the bits in the exponent in order of the most significant to least significant.

**9.42**    The square-and-multiply fast exponentiation algorithm can also be designed to test whether the exponent is even or odd instead of testing the bit value. Rewrite Algorithm 9.7 to show this.

**9.43**    Write an algorithm in pseudocode for the Fermat primality test.

**9.44**    Write an algorithm in pseudocode for the square root primality test.

**9.45**    Write an algorithm in pseudocode for the Chinese remainder theorem.

**9.46**    Write an algorithm in pseudocode to find QR and QNR for any $\mathbf{Z}_p{}^*$.

**9.47**    Write an algorithm in pseudocode to find a primitive root for the set $\mathbf{Z}_p{}^*$.

**9.48**    Write an algorithm in pseudocode to find all primitive roots for the set $\mathbf{Z}_p{}^*$.

**9.49**    Write an algorithm to find and store the discrete logarithms for the set $\mathbf{Z}_p{}^*$.

# 10

# Asymmetric-Key Cryptography

## Objectives

This chapter has several objectives:

☞ To distinguish between symmetric-key and asymmetric-key cryptosystems
☞ To introduce trapdoor one-way functions and their use in asymmetric-key cryptosystems
☞ To introduce the knapsack cryptosystem as one of the first ideas in asymmetric-key cryptography
☞ To discuss the RSA cryptosystem
☞ To discuss the Rabin cryptosystem
☞ To discuss the ElGamal cryptosystem
☞ To discuss the elliptic curve cryptosystem

This chapter discusses several asymmetric-key cryptosystems: RSA, Rabin, ElGamal, and ECC. Discussion of the Diffie-Hellman cryptosystem is postponed until Chapter 15 because it is mainly a key-exchange algorithm rather than an encryption/decryption algorithm.

**The Diffie-Hellman cryptosystem is discussed in Chapter 15.**

## 10.1                           INTRODUCTION

In Chapters 2 through 8, we emphasized the principles of **symmetric-key cryptography.** In this chapter, we start the discussion of **asymmetric-key cryptography.** Symmetric- and asymmetric-key cryptography will exist in parallel and continue to serve the community. We actually believe that they are complements of each other; the advantages of one can compensate for the disadvantages of the other.

The conceptual differences between the two systems are based on how these systems keep a secret. In symmetric-key cryptography, the secret must be shared between two persons. In asymmetric-key cryptography, the secret is personal (unshared); each person creates and keeps his or her own secret.

In a community of n people, n(n − 1)/2 shared secrets are needed for symmetric-key cryptography; only n personal secrets are needed in asymmetric-key cryptography. For a community with a population of 1 million, symmetric-key cryptography would require half a billion shared secrets; asymmetric-key cryptography would require 1 million personal secrets.

---

**Symmetric-key cryptography is based on sharing secrecy;
asymmetric-key cryptography is based on personal secrecy.**

---

There are some other aspects of security besides encipherment that need asymmetric-key cryptography. These include authentication and digital signatures. Whenever an application is based on a personal secret, we need to use asymmetric-key cryptography.

Whereas symmetric-key cryptography is based on substitution and permutation of symbols (characters or bits), asymmetric-key cryptography is based on applying mathematical functions to numbers. In symmetric-key cryptography, the plaintext and ciphertext are thought of as a combination of symbols. Encryption and decryption permute these symbols or substitute a symbol for another. In asymmetric-key cryptography, the plaintext and ciphertext are numbers; encryption and decryption are mathematical functions that are applied to numbers to create other numbers.

---

**In symmetric-key cryptography, symbols are permuted or substituted; in asymmetric-key cryptography, numbers are manipulated.**

---

### 10.1.1  Keys

Asymmetric key cryptography uses two separate keys: one private and one public. If encryption and decryption are thought of as locking and unlocking padlocks with keys, then the padlock that is locked with a public key can be unlocked only with the corresponding private key. Figure 10.1 shows that if Alice locks the padlock with Bob's public key, then only Bob's private key can unlock it.

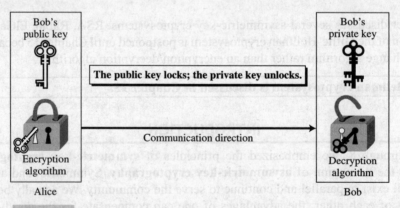

**Fig. 10.1**  *Locking and unlocking in asymmetric-key cryptosystem*

### 10.1.2  General Idea

Figure 10.2 shows the general idea of asymmetric-key cryptography as used for encipherment. We will see other applications of asymmetric-key cryptography in future chapters. The figure shows that, unlike symmetric-key cryptography, there are distinctive keys in asymmetric-key cryptography: a **private key** and a **public key.** Although some books use the term *secret key* instead of *private key,* we use the term *secret key* only for symmetric-key and the terms *private key* and *public key* for asymmetric key cryptography. We even use different symbols to show the three keys. One reason is that we believe the nature of the *secret key* used in symmetric-key cryptography is different from the nature of the *private key* used in asymmetric-key cryptography. The first is normally a string of symbols (bits for example), the second is a number or a set of numbers. In other words, we want to show that a *secret key* is not exchangeable with a *private key;* there are two different types of secrets.

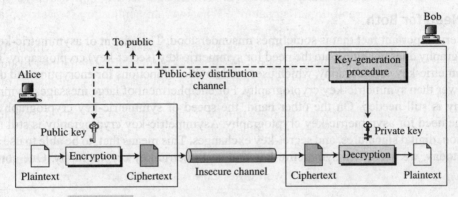

**Fig. 10.2** *General idea of asymmetric-key cryptosystem*

Figure 10.2 shows several important facts. First, it emphasizes the asymmetric nature of the cryptosystem. The burden of providing security is mostly on the shoulders of the receiver (Bob, in this case). Bob needs to create two keys: one private and one public. Bob is responsible for distributing the public key to the community. This can be done through a public-key distribution channel. Although this channel is not required to provide secrecy, it must provide authentication and integrity. Eve should not be able to advertise her public key to the community pretending that it is Bob's public key. Issues regarding public-key distribution are discussed in Chapter 15. For the moment, we assume that such a channel exists.

Second, asymmetric-key cryptography means that Bob and Alice cannot use the same set of keys for two-way communication. Each entity in the community should create its own private and public keys. Figure 10.2 shows how Alice can use Bob's public key to send encrypted messages to Bob. If Bob wants to respond, Alice needs to establish her own private and public keys.

Third, asymmetric-key cryptography means that Bob needs only one private key to receive all correspondence from anyone in the community, but Alice needs *n* public keys to communicate with *n* entities in the community, one public key for each entity. In other words, Alice needs a ring of public keys.

*Plaintext/Ciphertext* Unlike in symmetric-key cryptography, plaintext and ciphertext are treated as integers in asymmetric-key cryptography. The message must be encoded as an integer (or a set of integers) before encryption; the integer (or the set of integers) must be decoded into the message after decryption. Asymmetric-key cryptography is normally used to encrypt or decrypt small pieces of information, such as the cipher key for a symmetric-key cryptography. In other words, asymmetric-key cryptography normally is used for ancillary goals instead of message encipherment. However, these ancillary goals play a very important role in cryptography today.

***Encryption/Decryption*** Encryption and decryption in asymmetric-key cryptography are mathematical functions applied over the numbers representing the plaintext and ciphertext. The ciphertext can be thought of as $C = f(K_{public}, P)$; the plaintext can be thought of as $P = g(K_{private}, C)$. The decryption function $f$ is used only for encryption; the decryption function $g$ is used only for decryption. Next we show that the function $f$ needs to be a *trapdoor one-way function* to allow Bob to decrypt the message but to prevent Eve from doing so.

## 10.1.3  Need for Both

There is a very important fact that is sometimes misunderstood: The advent of asymmetric-key (public-key) cryptography does not eliminate the need for symmetric-key (secret-key) cryptography. The reason is that asymmetric-key cryptography, which uses mathematical functions for encryption and decryption, is much slower than symmetric-key cryptography. For encipherment of large messages, symmetric-key cryptography is still needed. On the other hand, the speed of symmetric-key cryptography does not eliminate the need for asymmetric-key cryptography. Asymmetric-key cryptography is still needed for authentication, digital signatures, and secret-key exchanges. This means that, to be able to use all aspects of security today, we need both symmetric-key and asymmetric-key cryptography. One complements the other.

## 10.1.4  Trapdoor One-Way Function

The main idea behind asymmetric-key cryptography is the concept of the trapdoor one-way function.

### *Functions*

Although the concept of a function is familiar from mathematics, we give an informal definition here. A **function** is a rule that associates (maps) one element in set A, called the domain, to one element in set B, called the range, as shown in Fig. 10.3.

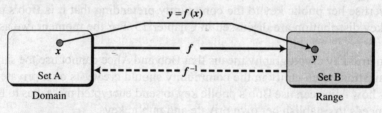

**Fig. 10.3**  *A function as rule mapping a domain to a range*

An **invertible function** is a function that associates each element in the range with exactly one element in the domain.

### *One-Way Function*  A **one-way function (OWF)** is a function that satisfies the following two properties:

1. $f$ is easy to compute. In other words, given $x$, $y = f(x)$ can be easily computed.
2. $f^{-1}$ is difficult to compute. In other words, given $y$, it is computationally infeasible to calculate $x = f^{-1}(y)$.

A **trapdoor one-way function (TOWF)** is a one-way function with a third property:

3.  Given $y$ and a **trapdoor** (secret), $x$ can be computed easily.

---

**Example 10.1**  When $n$ is large, $n = p \times q$ is a one-way function. Note that in this function $x$ is a tuple $(p, q)$ of two primes and $y$ is $n$. Given $p$ and $q$, it is always easy to calculate $n$; given $n$, it is very difficult to compute $p$ and $q$. This is the *factorization problem* that we saw in Chapter 9. There is not a polynomial time solution to the $f^{-1}$ function in this case.

---

**Example 10.2**  When $n$ is large, the function $y = x^k \bmod n$ is a trapdoor one-way function. Given $x$, $k$, and $n$, it is easy to calculate $y$ using the fast exponential algorithm we discussed in Chapter 9. Given $y$, $k$, and $n$, it is very difficult to calculate $x$. This is the *discrete logarithm problem* we discussed in Chapter 9. There is not a polynomial time solution to the $f^{-1}$ function in this case. However, if we know the trapdoor, $k'$ such that $k \times k' = 1 \bmod \phi(n)$, we can use $x = y^{k'} \bmod n$ to find $x$. This is the famous RSA, which will be discussed later in this chapter.

---

## 10.1.5  Knapsack Cryptosystem

The first brilliant idea of public-key cryptography came from Merkle and Hellman, in their **knapsack cryptosystem.** Although this system was found to be insecure with today's standards, the main idea behind this cryptosystem gives an insight into recent public-key cryptosystems discussed later in this chapter.

If we are told which elements, from a predefined set of numbers, are in a knapsack, we can easily calculate the sum of the numbers; if we are told the sum, it is difficult to say which elements are in the knapsack.

***Definition***  Suppose we are given two $k$-tuples, $a = [a_1, a_2, ..., a_k]$ and $x = [x_1, x_2, ..., x_k]$. The first tuple is the predefined set; the second tuple, in which $x_i$ is only 0 or 1, defines which -elements of $a$ are to be dropped in the knapsack. The sum of elements in the knapsack is

$$s = knapsackSum\,(a, x) = x_1 a_1 + x_2 a_2 + \cdots + x_k a_k$$

Given $a$ and $x$, it is easy to calculate $s$. However, given $s$ and $a$ it is difficult to find $x$. In other words, $s = knapsackSum\,(x, a)$ is easy to calculate, but $x = inv\_knapsackSum\,(s, a)$ is difficult. The function *knapsackSum* is a one-way function if $a$ is a general $k$-tuple.

***Superincreasing Tuple***  It is easy to compute *knapsackSum* and *inv_knapsackSum* if the $k$-tuple $a$ is *superincreasing*. In a **superincreasing tuple,** $a_i \geq a_1 + a_2 + \cdots + a_{i-1}$. In other words, each element (except $a_1$) is greater than or equal to the sum of all previous elements. In this case we calculate *knapsackSum* and *inv_knapsackSum* as shown in Algorithm 10.1. The algorithm *inv_knapsackSum* starts from the largest element and proceeds to the smallest one. In each iteration, it checks to see whether an element is in the knapsack.

---

**Algorithm 10.1    knapsacksum and inv_knapsackSum for a superincreasing k-tuple**

```
knapsackSum (x [1 ... k], a [1 ... k])
{
    s ← 0
    for (i = 1 to k)
    {
        s ← s + aᵢ×xᵢ
    }
    return s
}
```

```
inv_knapsackSum (s, a [1 ... k])
{
    for (i = k down to 1)
    {
        if s ≥ aᵢ
        {
            xᵢ ← 1
            s ← s − aᵢ
        }
        else xᵢ ← 0
    }
    return x [1 ... k]
}
```

**Example 10.3**    As a very trivial example, assume that $a = [17, 25, 46, 94, 201, 400]$ and $s = 272$ are given. Table 10.1 shows how the tuple $x$ is found using *inv_knapsackSum* routine in Algorithm 10.1.

**Table 10.1**    *Values of $i$, $a_i$, $s$, and $x_i$ in Example 10.3*

| $i$ | $a_i$ | $s$ | $s \geq a_i$ | $x_i$ | $s \leftarrow s - a_i \times x_i$ |
|---|---|---|---|---|---|
| 6 | 400 | 272 | false | $x_6 = 0$ | 272 |
| 5 | 201 | 272 | true | $x_5 = 1$ | 71 |
| 4 | 94 | 71 | false | $x_4 = 0$ | 71 |
| 3 | 46 | 71 | true | $x_3 = 1$ | 25 |
| 2 | 25 | 25 | true | $x_2 = 1$ | 0 |
| 1 | 17 | 0 | false | $x_1 = 0$ | 0 |

In this case $x = [0, 1, 1, 0, 1, 0]$, which means that 25, 46, and 201 are in the knapsack.

**Secret Communication with Knapsacks**    Let us see how Alice can send a secret message to Bob using a knapsack cryptosystem. The idea is shown in Fig. 10.4.

**Key Generation**
a.    Create a superincreasing $k$-tuple $b = [b_1, b_2, ..., b_k]$
b.    Choose a modulus $n$, such that $n > b_1 + b_2 + \cdots + b_k$
c.    Select a random integer $r$ that is relatively prime with $n$ and $1 \leq r \leq n-1$.
d.    Create a temporary $k$-tuple $t = [t_1, t_2, ..., t_k]$ in which $t_i = r \times b_i \bmod n$.
e.    Select a permutation of $k$ objects and find a new tuple $a = permute(t)$.
f.    The public key is the $k$-tuple $a$. The private key is $n$, $r$, and the $k$-tuple $b$.

**Encryption**    Suppose Alice needs to send a message to Bob.
a.    Alice converts her message to a $k$-tuple $x = [x_1, x_2, ..., x_k]$ in which $x_i$ is either 0 or 1. The tuple $x$ is the plaintext.

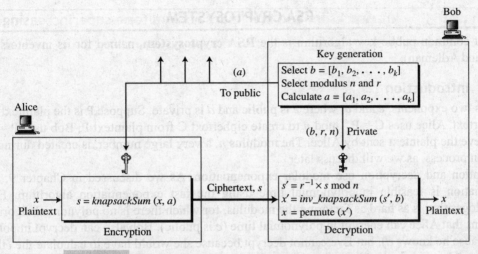

**Fig. 10.4** *Secret communication with knapsack cryptosystem*

b. Alice uses the *knapsackSum* routine to calculate *s*. She then sends the value of *s* as the ciphertext.

***Decryption*** Bob receives the ciphertext *s*.

a. Bob calculates $s' = r^{-1} \times s \bmod n$.

b. Bob uses *inv_knapsackSum* to create $x'$.

c. Bob permutes $x'$ to find *x*. The tuple *x* is the recovered plaintext.

---

**Example 10.4** This is a trivial (very insecure) example just to show the procedure.

1. Key generation:
   a. Bob creates the superincreasing tuple *b* = [7, 11, 19, 39, 79, 157, 313].
   b. Bob chooses the modulus *n* = 900 and *r* = 37, and [4 2 5 3 1 7 6] as permutation table.
   c. Bob now calculates the tuple *t* = [259, 407, 703, 543, 223, 409, 781].
   d. Bob calculates the tuple *a* = permute (*t*) = [543, 407, 223, 703, 259, 781, 409].
   e. Bob publicly announces *a*; he keeps *n*, *r*, and *b* secret.
2. Suppose Alice wants to send a single character "g" to Bob.
   a. She uses the 7-bit ASCII representation of "g", $(1100111)_2$, and creates the tuple *x* = [1, 1, 0, 0, 1, 1, 1]. This is the plaintext.
   b. Alice calculates *s* = knapsackSum (*a*, *x*) = 2165. This is the ciphertext sent to Bob.
3. Bob can decrypt the ciphertext, *s* = 2165.
   a. Bob calculates $s' = s \times r^{-1} \bmod n = 2165 \times 37^{-1} \bmod 900 = 527$.
   b. Bob calculates $x' = Inv\_knapsackSum\ (s', b) = [1, 1, 0, 1, 0, 1, 1]$.
   c. Bob calculates *x* = permute ($x'$) = [1, 1, 0, 0, 1, 1, 1]. He interprets the string $(1100111)_2$ as the character "g".

---

***Trapdoor*** Calculating the sum of items in Alice's knapsack is actually the multiplication of the row matrix *x* by the column matrix *a*. The result is a $1 \times 1$ matrix *s*. Matrix multiplication, $s = x \times a$, in which *x* is a row matrix and *a* is a column matrix, is a one-way function. Given *s* and *x*, Eve cannot find *a* easily. Bob, however, has a trapdoor. Bob uses his $s' = r^{-1} \times s$ and the secret superincreasing column matrix *b* to find a row matrix $x'$ using the *inv_knapsackSum* routine. The permutation allows Bob to find *x* from $x'$.

## 10.2                      RSA CRYPTOSYSTEM

The most common public-key algorithm is the **RSA cryptosystem,** named for its inventors (Rivest, Shamir, and Adleman).

### 10.2.1    Introduction

RSA uses two exponents, $e$ and $d$, where $e$ is public and $d$ is private. Suppose P is the plaintext and C is the ciphertext. Alice uses $C = P^e \bmod n$ to create ciphertext C from plaintext P; Bob uses $P = C^d \bmod n$ to retrieve the plaintext sent by Alice. The modulus $n$, a very large number, is created during the key generation process, as we will discuss later.

Encryption and decryption use modular exponentiation. As we discussed in Chapter 9, modular exponentiation is feasible in polynomial time using the fast exponentiation algorithm. However, modular logarithm is as hard as factoring the modulus, for which there is no polynomial algorithm yet. This means that Alice can encrypt in polynomial time ($e$ is public), Bob also can decrypt in polynomial time (because he knows $d$), but Eve cannot decrypt because she would have to calculate the $e$th root of C using modular arithmetic. Figure 10.5 shows the idea.

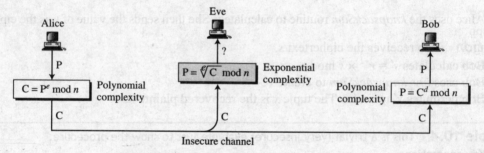

**Fig. 10.5** *Complexity of operations in RSA*

In other words, Alice uses a one-way function (modular exponentiation) with a trapdoor known only to Bob. Eve, who does not know the trapdoor, cannot decrypt the message. If some day, a polynomial algorithm for $e$th root modulo $n$ calculation is found, modular exponentiation is not a one-way function any more.

### 10.2.2    Procedure

Figure 10.6 shows the general idea behind the procedure used in RSA.

---

**RSA uses modular exponentiation for encryption/decryption;
To attack it, Eve needs to calculate $\sqrt[e]{C} \bmod n$.**

---

***Two Algebraic Structures***    RSA uses two algebraic structures: a ring and a group.

***Encryption/Decryption Ring***    Encryption and decryption are done using the commutative ring $\mathbf{R} = <\mathbf{Z}_n, +, \times>$ with two arithmetic operations: addition and multiplication. In RSA, this ring is public because the modulus $n$ is public. Anyone can send a message to Bob using this ring to do encryption.

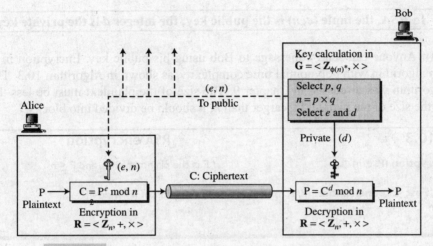

**Fig. 10.6** *Encryption, decryption, and key generation in RSA*

***Key-Generation Group*** RSA uses a multiplicative group $\mathbf{G} = <\mathbf{Z}_{\phi(n)}{}^*, \times>$ for key generation. This group supports only multiplication and division (using multiplicative inverses), which are needed for generating public and private keys. This group is hidden from the public because its modulus, $\phi(n)$, is hidden from the public. We will see shortly that if Eve can find this modulus, she can easily attack the cryptosystem.

**RSA uses two algebraic structures:**
**a public ring $\mathbf{R} = <\mathbf{Z}_n, +, \times>$ and a private group $\mathbf{G} = <\mathbf{Z}_{\phi(n)}{}^*, \times>$.**

***Key Generation*** Bob uses the steps shown in Algorithm 10.2 to create his public and private key. After key generation, Bob announces the tuple $(e, n)$ as his public key; Bob keeps the integer $d$ as his private key. Bob can discard $p$, $q$, and $\phi(n)$; they will not be needed unless Bob needs to change his private key without changing the modulus (which is not recommended, as we will see shortly). To be secure, the recommended size for each prime, $p$ or $q$, is 512 bits (almost 154 decimal digits). This makes the size of $n$, the modulus, 1024 bits (309 digits).

**Algorithm 10.2** **RSA Key Generation**

```
RSA_Key_Generation
{
    Select two large primes p and q such that p ≠ q.
    n ← p × q
    ϕ(n) ← (p − 1) × (q − 1)
    Select e such that 1 < e < ϕ(n) and e is coprime to ϕ(n)
    d ← e⁻¹ mod ϕ(n)              // d is inverse of e modulo ϕ(n)
    Public_key ← (e, n)            // To be announced publicly
    Private_key ← d                // To be kept secret
    return Public_key and Private_key
}
```

---

**In RSA, the tuple $(e, n)$ is the public key; the integer $d$ is the private key.**

---

*Encryption* Anyone can send a message to Bob using his public key. Encryption in RSA can be done using an algorithm with polynomial time complexity, as shown in Algorithm 10.3. The fast exponentiation algorithm was discussed in Chapter 9. The size of the plaintext must be less than $n$, which means that if the size of the plaintext is larger than $n$, it should be divided into blocks.

---

**Algorithm 10.3**                                        **RSA encryption**

---

   **RSA_Encryption** (P, e, n)                // P is the plaintext in $Z_n$ and P < n
   {
        C ← **Fast_Exponentiation** (P, e, n)     // Calculation of ($P^e$ mod n)
        return C
   }

---

*Decryption* Bob can use Algorithm 10.4 to decrypt the ciphertext message he received. Decryption in RSA can be done using an algorithm with polynomial time complexity. The size of the ciphertext is less than $n$.

---

**Algorithm 10.4**                                        **RSA decryption**

---

   **RSA_Decryption** (C, d, n)               //C is the ciphertext in $Z_n$
   {
        P ← **Fast_Exponentiation** (C, d, n)     // Calculation of ($C^d$ mod n)
   return P
   }

---

**In RSA, $p$ and $q$ must be at least 512 bits; $n$ must be at least 1024 bits.**

---

### Proof of RSA

We can prove that encryption and decryption are inverses of each other using the second version of Euler's theorem discussed in Chapter 9:

> If $n = p \times q$, $a < n$, and $k$ is an integer, then $a^{k \times \phi(n)+1} \equiv a \pmod{n}$.

Assume that the plaintext retrieved by Bob is $P_1$ and prove that it is equal to P.

$$P_1 = C^d \bmod n = (P^e \bmod n)^d \bmod n = P^{ed} \bmod n$$
$$ed = k\phi(n) + 1 \qquad\qquad\qquad\qquad \text{// } d \text{ and } e \text{ are inverses modulo } \phi(n)$$
$$P_1 = P^{ed} \bmod n \rightarrow P_1 = P^{k\phi(n)+1} \bmod n$$
$$P_1 = P^{k\phi(n)+1} \bmod n = P \bmod n \qquad\qquad \text{// Euler's theorem (second version)}$$

### 10.2.3 Some Trivial Examples

Following are some trivial (insecure) examples of the RSA procedure. The criteria that make the RSA system secure will be discussed in the later sections.

**Example 10.5** Bob chooses 7 and 11 as $p$ and $q$ and calculates $n = 7 \times 11 = 77$. The value of $\phi(n) =$ $(7 - 1)(11 - 1)$ or 60. Now he chooses two exponents, $e$ and $d$, from $Z_{60}^*$. If he chooses $e$ to be 13, then $d$ is 37. Note that $e \times d \mod 60 = 1$ (they are inverses of each other). Now imagine that Alice wants to send the plaintext 5 to Bob. She uses the public exponent 13 to encrypt 5.

Plaintext: 5     $C = 5^{13} = 26 \mod 77$     Ciphertext: 26

Bob receives the ciphertext 26 and uses the private key 37 to decipher the ciphertext:

Ciphertext: 26     $P = 26^{37} = 5 \mod 77$     Plaintext: 5

The plaintext 5 sent by Alice is received as plaintext 5 by Bob.

**Example 10.6** Now assume that another person, John, wants to send a message to Bob. John can use the same public key announced by Bob (probably on his website), 13; John's plaintext is 63. John calculates the following:

Plaintext: 63     $C = 63^{13} = 28 \mod 77$     Ciphertext: 28

Bob receives the ciphertext 28 and uses his private key 37 to decipher the ciphertext:

Ciphertext: 28     $P = 28^{37} = 63 \mod 77$     Plaintext: 63

**Example 10.7** Jennifer creates a pair of keys for herself. She chooses $p = 397$ and $q = 401$. She calculates $n = 397 \times 401 = 159197$. She then calculates $\phi(n) = 396 \times 400 = 158400$. She then chooses $e = 343$ and $d = 12007$. Show how Ted can send a message to Jennifer if he knows $e$ and $n$.

***Solution*** Suppose Ted wants to send the message "NO" to Jennifer. He changes each character to a number (from 00 to 25), with each character coded as two digits. He then concatenates the two coded characters and gets a four-digit number. The plaintext is 1314. Ted then uses $e$ and $n$ to encrypt the message. The ciphertext is $1314^{343} = 33677 \mod 159197$. Jennifer receives the message 33677 and uses the decryption key $d$ to decipher it as $33677^{12007} = 1314 \mod 159197$. Jennifer then decodes 1314 as the message "NO". Figure 10.7 shows the process.

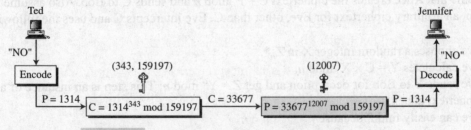

**Fig. 10.7** *Encryption and decryption in Example 10.7*

## 10.2.4 Attacks on RSA

No devastating attacks on RSA have been yet discovered. Several attacks have been predicted based on the weak plaintext, weak parameter selection, or inappropriate implementation. Figure 10.8 shows the categories of potential attacks.

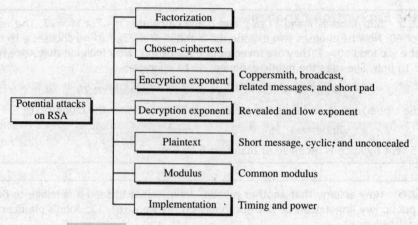

**Fig. 10.8**   *Taxonomy of potential attacks on RSA*

***Factorization Attack***   The security of RSA is based on the idea that the modulus is so large that it is infeasible to factor it in a reasonable time. Bob selects $p$ and $q$ and calculates $n = p \times q$. Although $n$ is public, $p$ and $q$ are secret. If Eve can factor $n$ and obtain $p$ and $q$, she can calculate $\phi(n) = (p-1)(q-1)$. Eve then can calculate $d = e^{-1} \bmod \phi(n)$ because $e$ is public. The private exponent $d$ is the trapdoor that Eve can use to decrypt any encrypted message.

As we learned in Chapter 9, there are many factorization algorithms, but none of them can factor a large integer with polynomial time complexity. To be secure, RSA presently requires that $n$ should be more than 300 decimal digits, which means that the modulus must be at least 1024 bits. Even using the largest and fastest computer available today, factoring an integer of this size would take an infeasibly long period of time. This means that RSA is secure as long as an efficient algorithm for factorization has not been found.

***Chosen-Ciphertext Attack***   A potential attack on RSA is based on the multiplicative property of RSA. Assume that Alice creates the ciphertext $C = P^e \bmod n$ and sends C to Bob. Also assume that Bob will decrypt an arbitrary ciphertext for Eve, other than C. Eve intercepts C and uses the following steps to find P:

    a.   Eve chooses a random integer X in $Z_n{}^*$.
    b.   Eve calculates $Y = C \times X^e \bmod n$.
    c.   Eve sends Y to Bob for decryption and get $Z = Y^d \bmod n$; This step is an instance of a chosen-ciphertext attack.
    d.   Eve can easily find P because

$$Z = Y^d \bmod n = (C \times X^e)^d \bmod n = (C^d \times X^{ed}) \bmod n = (C^d \times X) \bmod n = (P \times X) \bmod n$$
$$Z = (P \times X) \bmod n \rightarrow P = Z \times X^{-1} \bmod n$$

Eve uses the extended Euclidean algorithm to find the multiplicative inverse of X and eventually the value of P.

## Attacks on the Encryption Exponent

To reduce the encryption time, it is tempting to use a small encryption exponent $e$. The common value for $e$ is $e = 3$ (the second prime). However, there are some potential attacks on low encryption exponent that we briefly discuss here. These attacks do not generally result in a breakdown of the system, but they still need to be prevented. To thwart these kinds of attacks, the recommendation is to use $e = 2^{16} + 1 = 65537$ (or a prime close to this value).

*Coppersmith Theorem Attack*    The major low encryption exponent attack is referred to as the **Coppersmith theorem attack.** This theorem states that in a modulo-$n$ polynomial $f(x)$ of degree $e$, one can use an algorithm of the complexity log $n$ to find the roots if one of the roots is smaller than $n^{1/e}$. This theorem can be applied to the RSA cryptosystem with $C = f(P) = P^e$ mod $n$. If $e = 3$ and only two thirds of the bits in the plaintext P are known, the algorithm can find all bits in the plaintext.

*Broadcast Attack*    The **broadcast attack** can be launched if one entity sends the same message to a group of recipients with the same low encryption exponent. For example, assume the following scenario: Alice wants to send the same message to three recipients with the same public exponent $e = 3$ and the moduli $n_1$, $n_2$, and $n_3$.

$$C_1 = P^3 \text{ mod } n_1 \qquad C_2 = P^3 \text{ mod } n_2 \qquad C_3 = P^3 \text{ mod } n_3$$

Applying the Chinese remainder theorem to these three equations, Eve can find an equation of the form $C' = P^3$ mod $n_1 n_2 n_3$. This means that $P^3 < n_1 n_2 n_3$. This means $C' = P^3$ is in regular arithmetic (not modular arithmetic). Eve can find the value of $C' = P^{1/3}$.

*Related Message Attack*    The **related message attack,** discovered by Franklin Reiter, can be briefly described as follows. Alice encrypts two plaintexts, $P_1$ and $P_2$, and encrypts them with $e = 3$ and sends $C_1$ and $C_2$ to Bob. If $P_1$ is related to $P_2$ by a linear function, then Eve can recover $P_1$ and $P_2$ in a feasible computation time.

*Short Pad Attack*    The **short pad attack,** discovered by Coppersmith, can be briefly described as follows. Alice has a message M to send to Bob. She pads the message with $r_1$, encrypts the result to get $C_1$, and sends $C_1$ to Bob. Eve intercepts $C_1$ and drops it. Bob informs Alice that he has not received the message, so Alice pads the message again with $r_2$, encrypts it, and sends it to Bob. Eve also intercepts this message. Eve now has $C_1$ and $C_2$, and she knows that they both are ciphertexts belonging to the same plaintext. Coppersmith proved that if $r_1$ and $r_2$ are short, Eve may be able to recover the original message M.

## Attacks on the Decryption Exponent

Two forms of attacks can be launched on the decryption exponent: **revealed decryption exponent attack** and **low decryption exponent attack.** They are discussed briefly.

### Revealed Decryption Exponent Attack

It is obvious that if Eve can find the decryption exponent, $d$, she can decrypt the current encrypted message. However, the attack does not stop here. If Eve knows the value of $d$, she can use a probabilistic algorithm (not discussed here) to factor $n$ and find the value of $p$ and $q$. Consequently, if Bob changes only the compromised decryption exponent but keeps the same modulus, $n$, Eve will be able to decrypt future messages because she has the factorization of $n$. This means that if Bob finds out that the decryption exponent is compromised, he needs to choose new value for $p$ and $q$, calculate $n$, and create totally new private and public keys.

---

**In RSA, if $d$ is comprised, then $p$, $q$, $n$, $e$, and $d$ must be regenerated.**

---

*Low Decryption Exponent Attack*  Bob may think that using a small private-key $d$, would make the decryption process faster for him. Wiener showed that if $d < 1/3 \, n^{1/4}$, a special type of attack based on *continuous fraction,* a topic discussed in number theory, can jeopardize the security of RSA. For this to happen, it must be the case that $q < p < 2q$. If these two conditions exist, Eve can factor $n$ in polynomial time.

---

**In RSA, the recommendation is to have $d \geq 1/3 \, n^{1/4}$ to prevent low decryption exponent attack.**

---

## Plaintext Attacks

Plaintext and ciphertext in RSA are permutations of each other because they are integers in the same interval (0 to $n-1$). In other words, Eve already knows something about the plaintext. This characteristic may allow some attacks on the plaintext. Three attacks have been mentioned in the literature: short message attack, cycling attack, and unconcealed attack.

*Short Message Attack*  In the **short message attack,** if Eve knows the set of possible plaintexts, she then knows one more piece of information in addition to the fact that the ciphertext is the permutation of plaintext. Eve can encrypt all of the possible messages until the result is the same as the ciphertext intercepted. For example, if it is known that Alice is sending a four-digit number to Bob, Eve can easily try plaintext numbers from 0000 to 9999 to find the plaintext. For this reason, short messages must be padded with random bits at the front and the end to thwart this type of attack. It is strongly recommended that messages be padded with random bits before encryption using a method called OAEP, which is discussed later in this chapter.

*Cycling Attack*  The **cycling attack** is based on the fact that if the ciphertext is a permutation of the plaintext, the continuous encryption of the ciphertext will eventually result in the plaintext. In other words, if Eve continuously encrypts the intercepted ciphertext C, she will eventually get the plaintext. However, Eve does not know what the plaintext is, so she does not know when to stop. She needs to go one step further. When she gets the ciphertext C again, she goes back one step to find the plaintext.

Intercepted ciphertext: C
$C_1 = C^e \bmod n$
$C_2 = C_1{}^e \bmod n$
...
$C_k = C_{k-1}{}^e \bmod n \rightarrow$ If $C_k = C$, stop: the plaintext is  $P = C_{k-1}$

Is this a serious attack on RSA? It has been shown that the complexity of the algorithm is equivalent to the complexity of factoring $n$. In other words, there is no efficient algorithm that can launch this attack in polynomial time if $n$ is large.

*Unconcealed Message Attack*  Another attack that is based on the permutation relationship between plaintext and ciphertext is the **unconcealed message attack.** An unconcealed message is a message that encrypts to itself (cannot be concealed). It has been proven that there are always some messages that are encrypted to themselves. Because the encryption exponent normally is odd, there are some plaintexts that are encrypted to themselves such as P = 0 and P = 1. Although there are more, if the encrypting exponent is selected carefully, the number of these message is negligible. The encrypting program can always check if the calculated ciphertext is the same as the plaintext and reject the plaintext before submitting the ciphertext.

## Attacks on the Modulus

The main attack on RSA, as discussed previously, is the factorization attack. The factorization attack can be considered an attack on the low modulus. However, because we have already discussed this attack, we will concentrate on another attack on the modulus: the common modulus attack.

*Common Modulus Attack* The **common modulus attack** can be launched if a community uses a common modulus, $n$. For example, people in a community might let a trusted party select $p$ and $q$, calculate $n$ and $\phi(n)$, and create a pair of exponents $(e_i, d_i)$ for each entity. Now assume Alice needs to send a message to Bob. The ciphertext to Bob is $C = P^{e_B} \bmod n$. Bob uses his private exponent, $d_B$, to decrypt his message, $P = C^{d_B} \bmod n$. The problem is that Eve can also decrypt the message if she is a member of the community and has been assigned a pair of exponents $(e_E$ and $d_E)$, as we learned in the section "Low Decryption Exponent Attack". Using her own exponents $(e_E$ and $d_E)$, Eve can launch a probabilistic attack to factor $n$ and find Bob's $d_B$. To thwart this type of attack, the modulus must not be shared. Each entity needs to calculate her or his own modulus.

## Attacks on Implementation

Previous attacks were based on the underlying structure of RSA. As Dan Boneh has shown, there are several attacks on the implementation of RSA. We mention two of these attacks: the timing attack and the power attack.

*Timing Attack* Paul Kocher elegantly demonstrated a ciphertext-only attack, called the **timing attack.** The attack is based on the fast-exponential algorithm discussed in Chapter 9. The algorithm uses only squaring if the corresponding bit in the private exponent $d$ is 0; it uses both squaring and multiplication if the corresponding bit is 1. In other words, the timing required to do each iteration is longer if the corresponding bit is 1. This timing difference allows Eve to find the value of bits in $d$, one by one.

Assume that Eve has intercepted a large number of ciphertexts, $C_1$ to $C_m$. Also assume that Eve has observed how long it takes for Bob to decrypt each ciphertext, $T_1$ to $T_m$. Eve, who knows how long it takes for the underlying hardware to calculate a multiplication operation, calculated $t_1$ to $t_m$, where $t_i$ is the time required to calculate the multiplication operation Result = Result $\times C_i \bmod n$.

Eve can use Algorithm 10.5, which is a simplified version of the algorithm used in practice, to calculate all bits in $d$ ($d_0$ to $d_{k-1}$).

The algorithm sets $d_0 = 1$ (because $d$ should be odd) and calculates new values for $T_i$'s (decryption time related to $d_1$ to $d_{k-1}$). The algorithm then assumes the next bit is 1 and finds some new values $D_1$ to $D_m$ based on this assumption. If the assumption is -correct, each $D_i$ is probably smaller than the corresponding $T_i$. However, the algorithm uses the variance (or other correlation criteria) to consider all variations of $D_i$ and $T_i$. If the difference in variance is positive, the algorithm assumes that the next bit is 1; otherwise, it assumes that the next bit is 0. The algorithm then calculates the new $T_i$'s to be used for remaining bits.

---

**Algorithm 10.5**                                   **Timing attack on RSA**

---

```
RSA_Timing_Attack ([T₁ ... Tₘ])
{
    d₀ ← 1                                        // Because d is odd
    Calculate [t₁ ... tₘ]
    [T₁ ... Tₘ] ← [T₁ ... Tₘ] – [t₁ ... tₘ]      // Update Tᵢ for the next bit
    for ( j from 1 to k – 1)
    {
        Recalculate [t₁ ... tₘ]                   // Recalculate tᵢ assuming the next bit is 1
        [D₁ ... Dₘ] ← [T₁ ... Tₘ] – [t₁ ... tₘ]
        var ← variance ([D₁ ... Dₘ]) – variance ([T₁ ... Tₘ])
        if (var > 0) dⱼ ← 1        else   dⱼ ← 0
        [T₁ ... Tₘ] ← [T₁ ... Tₘ] – dⱼ × [t₁ ... tₘ]    // Update Tᵢ for the next bit
    }
}
```

There are two methods to thwart timing attack:

1.  Add random delays to the exponentiations to make each exponentiation take the same amount of time.

2.  Rivest recommended **blinding.** The idea is to multiply the ciphertext by a random number before decryption. The procedure is as follows:
    a.  Select a secret random number $r$ between 1 and $(n-1)$.
    b.  Calculate $C_1 = C \times r^e \bmod n$.
    c.  Calculate $P_1 = C_1^d \bmod n$.
    d.  Calculate $P = P_1 \times r^{-1} \bmod n$.

***Power Attack***   The **Power attack** is similar to the timing attack. Kocher showed that if Eve can precisely measure the power consumed during decryption, she can launch a power attack based on the principle discussed for timing attack. An iteration involving multiplication and squaring consumes more power than an iteration that uses only squaring. The same kind of techniques used to prevent timing attacks can be used to thwart power attacks.

## 10.2.5  Recommendations

The following recommendations are based on theoretical and experimental results.

1.  The number of bits for $n$ should be at least 1024. This means that $n$ should be around $2^{1024}$, or 309 decimal digits.

2.  The two primes $p$ and $q$ must each be at least 512 bits. This means that $p$ and $q$ should be around $2^{512}$ or 154 decimal digits.

3.  The values of $p$ and $q$ should not be very close to each other.

4.  Both $p-1$ and $q-1$ should have at least one large prime factor.

5.  The ratio $p/q$ should not be close to a rational number with a small numerator or denominator.

6.  The modulus $n$ must not be shared.

7.  The value of $e$ should be $2^{16} + 1$ or an integer close to this value.

8.  If the private key $d$ is leaked, Bob must immediately change $n$ as well as both $e$ and $d$. It has been proven that knowledge of $n$ and one pair $(e, d)$ can lead to the discovery of other pairs of the same modulus.

9. Messages must be padded using OAEP, discussed later.

## 10.2.6 Optimal Asymmetric Encryption Padding (OAEP)

As we mentioned earlier, a short message in RSA makes the ciphertext vulnerable to *short message attacks*. It has been shown that simply adding bogus data (padding) to the message might make Eve's job harder, but with additional efforts she can still attack the ciphertext. The solution proposed by the RSA group and some vendors is to apply a procedure called **optimal asymmetric encryption padding (OAEP)**. Figure 10.9 shows a simple version of this procedure; the implementation may use a more sophisticated version.

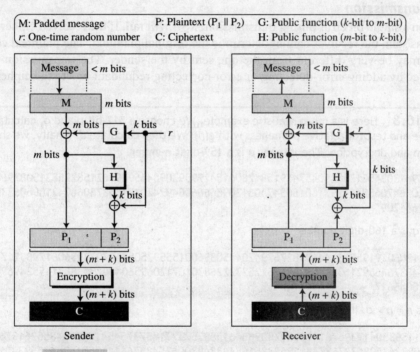

**Fig. 10.9** *Optimal asymmetric encryption padding (OAEP)*

The whole idea in Fig. 10.9 is that $P = P_1 \| P_2$, where $P_1$ is the masked version of the padded message, M; $P_2$ is sent to allow Bob to find the mask.

***Encryption*** The following shows the encryption process:

1. Alice pads the message to make an $m$-bit message, which we call M.
2. Alice chooses a random number $r$ of $k$ bits. Note that $r$ is used only once and is then destroyed.
3. Alice uses a public one-way function, G, that takes an $r$-bit integer and creates an $m$-bit integer ($m$ is the size of M, and $r < m$). This is the mask.
4. Alice applies the mask $G(r)$ to create the first part of the plaintext $P_1 = M \oplus G(r)$. $P_1$ is the masked message.
5. Alice creates the second part of the plaintext as $P_2 = H(P_1) \oplus r$. The function H is another public function that takes an $m$-bit input and creates an $k$-bit output. This function can be a

*cryptographic hash function* (see Chapter 12). $P_2$ is used to allow Bob to recreate the mask after decryption.

6.  Alice creates $C = P^e = (P_1 \| P_2)^e$ and sends C to Bob.

**Decryption**   The following shows the decryption process:

1.  Bob creates $P = C^d = (P_1 \| P_2)$.
2.  Bob first recreates the value of r using $H(P_1) \oplus P_2 = H(P_1) \oplus H(P_1) \oplus r = r$.
3.  Bob uses $G(r) \oplus P = G(r) \oplus G(r) \oplus M = M$ to recreate the value of the padded message.
4.  After removing the padding from M, Bob finds the original message.

## Error in Transmission

If there is even a single bit error during transmission, RSA will fail. If the received ciphertext is different from what was sent, the receiver cannot determine the original plaintext. The plaintext calculated at the receiver site may be very different from the one sent by the sender. The transmission media must be made error-free by adding error-detecting or error-correcting redundant bits to the ciphertext.

---

**Example 10.8**   Here is a more realistic example. We choose a 512-bit p and q, calculate n and $\phi(n)$, then choose e and test for relative primeness with $\phi(n)$. We then calculate d. Finally, we show the results of encryption and decryption. The integer p is a 159-digit number.

| $p =$ | 961303453135835045741915812806154279093098455949962158225831508796479404550564706384912571601803475031209866660649242019180878066742109606335421992666 1209 |
|---|---|

The integer q is a 160-digit number.

| $q =$ | 120601919572314469182767942044508960015559250546370339360617983217314821484837646592153894532091752252732268301071206956046025138871455249690003596600 45617 |
|---|---|

The modulus $n = p \times q$. It has 309 digits.

| $n =$ | 115935041739676149688925098646158875237714573754541447754855261376147885408326350817276878815968325168468849300625485764111250162414552339182927162507656772727460097082714127730434960500556347274566628060099924037102991424472292215772279853172703383938133469268413732762200096667667183183108837342082344437095 3 |
|---|---|

$\phi(n) = (p - 1)(q - 1)$ has 309 digits.

| $\phi(n) =$ | 115935041739676149688925098646158875237714573754541447754855261376147788540832635081727687881596832516846884930062548576411125016241455233918292716250765675105423360849291675203448262798811755478765701392344440571698958172819609822636107546721186461217135910735864061400888517026537727726446734106624385766412 8 |
|---|---|

Bob chooses e = 35535 (the ideal is 65537) and tests it to make sure it is relatively prime with $\phi(n)$. He then finds the inverse of e modulo $\phi(n)$ and calls it d.

| e = | 35535 |
|---|---|
| d = | 5800830286003776393609366128967791759466906208965096218042286611138059385282235873170628691003002171085904433840217072986908760061153062025249598844480475682409662470814858171304632406440777048331340108509473852956450719367740611973265574242372176176746207763716420760033708533328853214470885955136670294831 |

Alice wants to send the message "THIS IS A TEST", which can be changed to a numeric value using the 00-26 encoding scheme (26 is the *space* character).

| P = | 19070818260818260026190418819 |
|---|---|

The ciphertext calculated by Alice is C = P $^e$, which is

| C = | 4753091236462268272063655506105451809423717960704917165232392430544529606131993285666178434183591141511974112520056829797945717360361012782188478927415660904800235071907152771859149751884658886321011483541033616578984679683867637337657774656250792805211481418440481418443081277305900469287424855916646210865 6 |
|---|---|

Bob can recover the plaintext from the ciphertext using P = C$^d$, which is

| P = | 19070818260818260026190418819 |
|---|---|

The recovered plaintext is "THIS IS A TEST" after decoding.

## Applications

Although RSA can be used to encrypt and decrypt actual messages, it is very slow if the message is long. RSA, therefore, is useful for short messages. In particular, we will see that RSA is used in digital signatures and other cryptosystems that often need to encrypt a small message without having access to a symmetric key. RSA is also used for authentication, as we will see in later chapters.

## 10.3                              RABIN CRYPTOSYSTEM

The **Rabin cryptosystem,** devised by M. Rabin, is a variation of the RSA cryptosystem. RSA is based on the exponentiation congruence; Rabin is based on quadratic congruence. The Rabin cryptosystem can be thought of as an RSA cryptosystem in which the value of $e$ and $d$ are fixed; $e = 2$ and $d = 1/2$. In other words, the encryption is $C \equiv P^2 \pmod{n}$ and the decryption is $P \equiv C^{1/2} \pmod{n}$.

The public key in the Rabin cryptosystem is $n$; the private key is the tuple $(p, q)$. Everyone can encrypt a message using $n$; only Bob can decrypt the message using $p$ and $q$. Decryption of the message is infeasible for Eve because she does not know the values of $p$ and $q$. Figure 10.10 shows the encryption and decryption.

We need to emphasize a point here. If Bob is using RSA, he can keep $d$ and $n$ and discard $p$, $q$, and $\phi(n)$ after key generation. If Bob is using Rabin cryptosystem, he needs to keep $p$ and $q$.

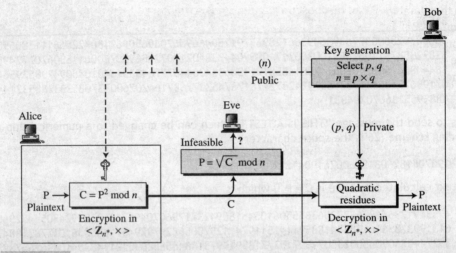

**Fig. 10.10** *Encryption, decryption, and key generation in the Rabin cryptosystem*

## 10.3.1 Procedure

Key generation, encryption, and decryption are described below.

***Key Generation*** Bob uses the steps shown in Algorithm 10.6 to create his public key and private key.

---

**Algorithm 10.6** **Key generation for Rabin cryptosystem**

```
Rabin_Key_Generation
{
    Choose two large primes p and q in the form 4k + 3 and p ≠ q.
    n ← p × q
    Public_key ← n                    // To be announced publicly
    Private_key ← (q, n)              // To be kept secret
    return Public_key and Private_key
}
```

---

Although the two primes, $p$ and $q$, can be in the form $4k + 1$ or $4k + 3$, the decryption process becomes more difficult if the first form is used. It is recommended to use the second form, $4k + 3$, to make the decryption for Alice much easier.

***Encryption*** Anyone can send a message to Bob using his public key. The encrypting process is shown in Algorithm 10.7.

---

**Algorithm 10.7** **Encryption in Rabin cryptosystem**

```
Rabin_Encryption (n, P)              // n is the public key; P is the ciphertext from Zₙ*
{
    C ← P² mod n                     // C is the ciphertext
    return C
}
```

Although the plaintext P can be chosen from the set $Z_n$, we have defined the set to be in $Z_n{}^*$ to make the decryption easier.

Encryption in the Rabin cryptosystem is very simple. The operation needs only one multiplication, which can be done quickly. This is beneficial when resources are limited. For example, smart cards have limited memory and need to use short CPU time.

***Decryption*** Bob can use Algorithm 10.8 to decrypt the received ciphertext.

| Algorithm 10.8 | Decryption in Rabin cryptosystem |
| --- | --- |

```
Rabin_Decryption (p, q, C)          // C is the ciphertext; p and q are private keys
{
    a₁ ← +(C^((p+1)/4)) mod p
    a₂ ← −(C^((p+1)/4)) mod p
    b₁ ← +(C^((q+1)/4)) mod q
    b₂ ← −(C^((q+1)/4)) mod q
    // The algorithm for the Chinese remainder algorithm is called four times.
    P₁ ← Chinese_Remainder (a₁, b₁, p, q)
    P₂ ← Chinese_Remainder (a₁, b₂, p, q)
    P₃ ← Chinese_Remainder (a₂, b₁, p, q)
    P₄ ← Chinese_Remainder (a₂, b₂, p, q)
    return P₁, P₂, P₃, and P₄
}
```

Several points should be emphasized here. The decryption is based on the solution of quadratic congruence, discussed in Chapter 9. Because the received ciphertext is the square of the plaintext, it is guaranteed that C has roots (quadratic residues) in $Z_n{}^*$. The Chinese remainder algorithm is used to find the four square roots.

The most important point about the Rabin system is that it is not deterministic. The decryption has four answers. It is up to the receiver of the message to choose one of the four as the final answer. However, in many situations, the receiver can easily pick up the right answer.

---

**The Rabin cryptosystem is not deterministic: Decryption creates four equally probable plaintexts.**

---

**Example 10.9** Here is a very trivial example to show the idea.
1. Bob selects $p = 23$ and $q = 7$. Note that both are congruent to 3 mod 4.
2. Bob calculates $n = p \times q = 161$.
3. Bob announces $n$ publicly; he keeps $p$ and $q$ private.
4. Alice wants to send the plaintext P = 24. Note that 161 and 24 are relatively prime; 24 is in $Z_{161}{}^*$. She calculates $C = 24^2 = 93 \bmod 161$, and sends the ciphertext 93 to Bob.
5. Bob receives 93 and calculates four values:
   a. $a_1 = +(93^{(23+1)/4}) \bmod 23 = 1 \bmod 23$
   b. $a_2 = -(93^{(23+1)/4}) \bmod 23 = 22 \bmod 23$
   c. $b_1 = +(93^{(7+1)/4}) \bmod 7 = 4 \bmod 7$
   d. $b_2 = -(93^{(7+1)/4}) \bmod 7 = 3 \bmod 7$

6. Bob takes four possible answers, $(a_1, b_1)$, $(a_1, b_2)$, $(a_2, b_1)$, and $(a_2, b_2)$, and uses the Chinese remainder theorem to find four possible plaintexts: 116, **24**, 137, and 45 (all of them relatively prime to 161). Note that only the second answer is Alice's plaintext. Bob needs to make a decision based on the situation. Note also that all four of these answers, when squared modulo $n$, give the ciphertext 93 sent by Alice.

$$116^2 = 93 \bmod 161 \quad 24^2 = 93 \bmod 161 \quad 137^2 = 93 \bmod 161 \quad 45^2 = 93 \bmod 161$$

### 10.3.2 Security of the Rabin System

The Rabin system is secure as long as $p$ and $q$ are large numbers. The complexity of the Rabin system is at the same level as factoring a large number $n$ into its two prime factors $p$ and $q$. In other words, the Rabin system is as secure as RSA.

## 10.4                  ELGAMAL CRYPTOSYSTEM

Besides RSA and Rabin, another public-key cryptosystem is **ElGamal,** named after its inventor, Taher ElGamal. ElGamal is based on the discrete logarithm problem discussed in Chapter 9.

### 10.4.1 ElGamal Cryptosystem

Recall from Chapter 9 that if $p$ is a very large prime, $e_1$ is a primitive root in the group $\mathbf{G} = \langle \mathbf{Z}_p^*, \times \rangle$ and $r$ is an integer, then $e_2 = e_1^r \bmod p$ is easy to compute using the fast exponential algorithm (square-and-multiply method), but given $e_2$, $e_1$, and $p$, it is infeasible to calculate $r = \log e_1 e_2 \bmod p$ (discrete logarithm problem).

### 10.4.2 Procedure

Figure 10.11 shows key generation, encryption, and decryption in ElGamal.

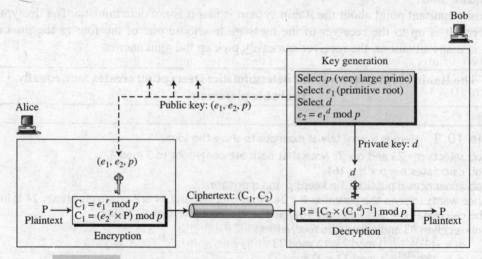

**Fig. 10.11** *Key generation, encryption, and decryption in ElGamal*

### 10.4.3   Key Generation

Bob uses the steps shown in Algorithm 10.9 to create his public and private keys.

**Algorithm 10.9**                        **ElGamal key generation**

```
ElGamal_Key_Generation
{
        Select a large prime p
        Select d to be a member of the group G = < Z_p*, × > such that 1 ≤ d ≤ p − 2
        Select e₁ to be a primitive root in the group G = < Z_p*, × >
        e₂ ← e₁^d mod p
        Public_key ← (e₁, e₂, p)                    // To be announced publicly
        Private_key ← d                             // To be kept secret
        return Public_key and Private_key
}
```

*Encryption*     Anyone can send a message to Bob using his public key. The encryption process is shown in Algorithm 10.10. If the fast exponential algorithm (see Chapter 9) is used, encryption in the ElGamal cryptosystem can also be done in polynomial time complexity.

**Algorithm 10.10**                      **ElGamal encryption**

```
ElGamal_Encryption (e₁, e₂, p, P)                   // P is the plaintext
{
        Select a random integer r in the group G = < Z_p*, × >
        C₁ ← e₁^r mod p
        C₂ ← (P × e₂^r) mod p                        // C₁ and C₂ are the ciphertexts
        return C₁ and C₂
}
```

*Decryption*     Bob can use Algorithm 10.11 to decrypt the ciphertext message received.

**Algorithm 10.11**                      **ElGamal decryption**

```
ElGamal_Decryption (d, p, C₁, C₂)                   // C₁ and C₂ are the ciphertexts
{
        P ← [C₂ (C₁^d)^−1] mod p                     // P is the plaintext
        return P
}
```

---

**The bit-operation complexity of encryption or decryption in ElGamal cryptosystem is polynomial.**

**Proof** The ElGamal decryption expression $C_2 \times (C_1^d)^{-1}$ can be verified to be P through substitution:

$$[C_2 \times (C_1^d)^{-1}] \bmod p = [(e_2^r \times P) \times (e_1^{rd})^{-1}] \bmod p = (e_1^{dr}) \times P \times (e_1^{rd})^{-1} = P$$

---

**Example 10.10** Here is a trivial example. Bob chooses 11 as $p$. He then chooses $e_1 = 2$. Note that 2 is a primitive root in $Z_{11}^*$ (see Appendix J). Bob then chooses $d = 3$ and calculates $e_2 = e_1^d = 8$. So the public keys are (2, 8, 11) and the private key is 3. Alice chooses $r = 4$ and calculates $C_1$ and $C_2$ for the plaintext 7.

Plaintext: 7
$C_1 = e_1^r \bmod 11 = 16 \bmod 11 = 5 \bmod 11$
$C_2 = (P \times e_2^r) \bmod 11 = (7 \times 4096) \bmod 11 = 6 \bmod 11$
Ciphertext: (5, 6)

Bob receives the ciphertexts (5 and 6) and calculates the plaintext.

Ciphertext: $[C_2 \times (C_1^d)^{-1}] \bmod 11 = 6 \times (5^3)^{-1} \bmod 11 = 6 \times 3 \bmod 11 = 7 \bmod 11$
Plaintext: 7

---

**Example 10.11** Instead of using $P = [C_2 \times (C_1^d)^{-1}] \bmod p$ for decryption, we can avoid the calculation of multiplicative inverse and use $P = [C_2 \times C_1^{p-1-d}] \bmod p$ (see Fermat's little theorem in Chapter 9). In Example 10.10, we can calculate $P = [6 \times 5^{11-1-3}] \bmod 11 = 7 \bmod 11$.

---

**Analysis** A very interesting point about the ElGamal cryptosystem is that Alice creates $r$ and keeps it secret; Bob creates $d$ and keeps it secret. The puzzle of this cryptosystem can be solved as follows:

a. Alice sends $C_2 = [e_2^r \times P] \bmod p = [(e_1^{rd}) \times P] \bmod p$. The expression $(e_1^{rd})$ acts as a mask that hides the value of P. To find the value of P, Bob must remove this mask.

b. Because modular arithmetic is being used, Bob needs to create a replica of the mask and invert it (multiplicative inverse) to cancel the effect of the mask.

c. Alice also sends $C_1 = e_1^r$ to Bob, which is a part of the mask. Bob needs to calculate $C_1^d$ to make a replica of the mask because $C_1^d = (e_1^r)^d = (e_1^{rd})$. In other words, after obtaining the mask replica, Bob inverts it and multiplies the result with $C_2$ to remove the mask.

d. It might be said that Bob helps Alice make the mask $(e_1^{rd})$ without revealing the value of $d$ ($d$ is already included in $e_2 = e_1^d$); Alice helps Bob make the mask $(e_1^{rd})$ without revealing the value of $r$ ($r$ is already included in $C_1 = e_1^r$).

## 10.4.4 Security of ElGamal

Two attacks have been mentioned for the ElGamal cryptosystem in the literature: attacks based on low modulus and known-plaintext attacks.

**Low-Modulus Attacks** If the value of $p$ is not large enough, Eve can use some efficient algorithms (see Chapter 9) to solve the discrete logarithm problem to find $d$ or $r$. If $p$ is small, Eve can easily find $d = \log_{e_1} e_2 \bmod p$ and store it to decrypt any message sent to Bob. This can be done once and used as long as Bob uses the same keys. Eve can also use the value of $C_1$ to find random number $r$ used by Alice in each transmission $r = \log_{e_1} C_1 \bmod p$. Both of these cases emphasize that security of the ElGamal cryptosystem depends on the infeasibility of solving a discrete logarithm problem with a very large modulus. It is recommended that $p$ be at least 1024 bits (300 decimal digits).

**Known-Plaintext Attack**    If Alice uses the same random exponent r, to encrypt two plaintexts P and P', Eve -discovers P' if she knows P. Assume that $C_2 = P \times (e_2') \bmod p$ and $C'_2 = P' \times (e_2') \bmod p$. Eve finds P' using the following steps:

1. $(e_2') = C_2 \times P^{-1} \bmod p$
2. $P' = C'_2 \times (e_2')^{-1} \bmod p$

It is recommended that Alice use a fresh value of $r$ to thwart the known-plaintext attacks.

---

**For the ElGamal cryptosystem to be secure, $p$ must be at least 300 digits and $r$ must be new for each encipherment.**

---

**Example 10.12**    Here is a more realistic example. Bob uses a random integer of 512 bits (the ideal is 1024 bits). The integer $p$ is a 155-digit number (the ideal is 300 digits). Bob then chooses $e_1$, $d$, and calculates $e_2$, as shown below: Bob announces ($e_1$, $e_2$, $p$) as his public key and keeps $d$ as his private key.

| | |
|---|---|
| $p =$ | 11534899272561676244925313717014331740490094532609834959814346921905689869 86226459321297547378718951443688917652647309361592999372806116596434735344 0008577 |
| $e_1 =$ | 2 |
| $d =$ | 1007 |
| $e_2 =$ | 97886413043009189508766856938097739043880062887337687610022062233255450707 41561892123183177046101416733601508841329408572485377031582066010072558707 455 |

Alice has the plaintext P = 3200 to send to Bob. She chooses $r$ = 545131, calculates $C_1$ and $C_2$, and sends them to Bob.

| | |
|---|---|
| $P =$ | 3200 |
| $r =$ | 545131 |
| $C_1 =$ | 88729706938352847102257047149227566312026006725656212501818835142941722359 97126811141053636617051730515815333189165400973736355080295736788569060619 152881 |
| $C_2 =$ | 70845433304892994457701601238079499956743602183619244696177450692124469615 51658007794555930803458896144024085995259195792097216288796813505827795664 302950 |

Bob calculates the plaintext P = $C_2 \times ((C_1)^d)^{-1} \bmod p$ = 3200 mod $p$.

| | |
|---|---|
| $P =$ | 3200 |

---

**Application**    ElGamal can be used whenever RSA can be used. It is used for key exchange, authentication, and encryption and decryption of small messages.

## 10.5      ELLIPTIC CURVE CRYPTOSYSTEMS

Although RSA and ElGamal are secure asymmetric-key cryptosystems, their security comes with a price, their large keys. Researchers have looked for alternatives that give the same level of security with smaller key sizes. One of these promising alternatives is the **elliptic curve cryptosystem (ECC)**. The system is based on the theory of **elliptic curves**. Although the deep involvement of this theory is beyond the scope of this book, this section first gives a very simple introduction to three types of elliptic curves and then suggests a flavor of a cryptosystem that uses some of these curves.

### 10.5.1    Elliptic Curves over Real Numbers

Elliptic curves, which are not directly related to ellipses, are cubic equations in two variables that are similar to the equations used to calculate the length of a curve in the circumference of an ellipse. The general equation for an elliptic curve is

$$y^2 + b_1 xy + b_2 y = x^3 + a_1 x^2 + a_2 x + a_3$$

Elliptic curves over real numbers use a special class of elliptic curves of the form

$$y^2 = x^3 + ax + b$$

In the above equation, if $4a^3 + 27b^2 \neq 0$, the equation represents a **nonsingular elliptic curve;** otherwise, the equation represented a **singular elliptic curve**. In a nonsingular elliptic curve, the equation $x^3 + ax + b = 0$ has three distinct roots (real or complex); in a singular elliptic curve the equation $x^3 + ax + b = 0$ does not have three distinct roots.

Looking at the equation, we can see that the left-hand side has a degree of 2 while the right-hand side has a degree of 3. This means that a horizontal line can intersects the curve in three points if all roots are real. However, a vertical line can intersects the curve at most in two points.

---

**Example 10.13**    Figure 10.12 shows two elliptic curves with equations $y^2 = x^3 - 4x$ and $y^2 = x^3 - 1$. Both are nonsingular. However, the first has three real roots ($x = -2$, $x = 0$, and $x = 2$), but the second has only one real root ($x = 1$) and two imaginary ones.

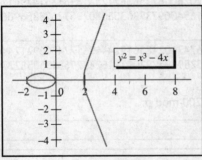

a. Three real roots

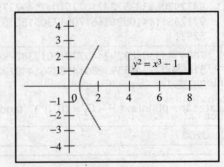

b. One real and two imaginary roots

**Fig. 10.12**    *Two elliptic curves over a real field*

## An Abelian Group

Let us define an abelian (commutative) group (see Chapter 4) using points on an elliptic curve. A tuple $P = (x_1, y_1)$ represents a point on the curve if $x_1$ and $y_1$ are the coordinates of a point on the curve that satisfy the equation of the curve. For example, the points $P = (2.0, 0.0)$, $Q = (0.0, 0.0)$, $R = (-2.0, 0.0)$, $S = (10.0, 30.98)$, and $T = (10.0, -30.98)$ are all points on the curve $y^2 = x^3 - 4x$. Note that each point is represented by two real numbers. Recall from Chapter 4 that to create an abelian group we need a set, an operation on the set, and five properties that are satisfied by the operation. The group in this case is $G = <E, +>$.

**Set**  We define the set as the points on the curve, where each point is a pair of real numbers. For example, the set E for the elliptic curve $y^2 = x^3 - 4x$ is shown as

$$E = \{(2.0, 0.0), (0.0, 0.0), (-2.0, 0.0), (10.0, 30.98), (10.0, -30.98), \ldots\}$$

**Operation**  The specific properties of a nonsingular elliptic curve allows us to define an *addition* operation on the points of the curve. However, we need to remember that the *addition* operation here is different from the operation that has been defined for integers. The operation is the addition of two points on the curve to get another point on the curve

$$R = P + Q, \text{ where } P = (x_1, y_1), Q = (x_2, y_2), \text{ and } R = (x_3, y_3)$$

To find R on the curve, consider three cases as shown in Fig. 10.13.

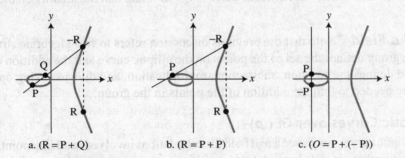

**Fig. 10.13**  *Three adding cases in an elliptic curve*

1. In the first case, the two points $P = (x_1, y_1)$ and $Q = (x_2, y_2)$ have different x-coordinates and y-coordinates ($x_1 \neq y_1$ and $x_2 \neq y_2$), as shown in Fig. 10.13a. The line connecting P and Q intercepts the curve at a point called $-R$. R is the reflection of $-R$ with respect to the x-axis. The coordinates of the point R, $x_3$ and $y_3$, can be found by first finding the slope of the line, $\lambda$, and then calculating the values of $x_3$ and $y_3$, as shown below:

$$\lambda = (y_2 - y_1) / (x_2 - x_1)$$
$$x_3 = \lambda^2 - x_1 - x_2 \qquad y_3 = \lambda (x_1 - x_3) - y_1$$

2. In the second case, the two points overlap ($R = P + P$), as shown in Fig. 10.13b. In this case, the slope of the line and the coordinates of the point R can be found as shown below:

$$\lambda = (3x_1^2 + a)/(2y_1)$$

$$x_3 = \lambda^2 - x_1 - x_2 \qquad y_3 = \lambda (x_1 - x_3) - y_1$$

3. In the third case, the two points are additive inverses of each other as shown in Fig. 10.13c. If the first point is $P = (x_1, y_1)$, the second point is $Q = (x_1, -y_1)$. The line connecting the two points does not intercept the curve at a third point. Mathematicians say that the intercepting point is at infinity; they define a point $O$ as the *point at infinity* or *zero point*, which is the *additive identity* of the group.

**Properties of the Operation**   The following are brief definitions of the properties of the operation as discussed in Chapter 4:

1. *Closure:* It can be proven that adding two points, using the addition operation defined in the previous section, creates another point on the curve.
2. *Associativity:* It can be proven that $(P + Q) + R = P + (Q + R)$.
3. *Commutativity:* The group made from the points on a non-singular elliptic curve is an abelian group; it can be proven that $P + Q = Q + P$.
4. *Existence of identity:* The additive identity in this case is the *zero point, O*. In other words $P = P + O = O + P$.
5. *Existence of inverse*: Each point on the curve has an inverse. The inverse of a point is its reflection with respect to the x-axis. In other words, the point $P = (x_1, y_1)$ and $Q = (x_1, -y_1)$ are inverses of each other, which means that $P + Q = O$. Note that the identity element is the inverse of itself.

**A Group and a Field**   Note that the previous discussion refers to two algebraic structures: a group and a field. The group defines the set of the points on the elliptic curve and the addition operation on the points. The field defines the addition, subtraction, multiplication, and division using operations on real numbers that are needed to find the addition of the points in the group.

## 10.5.2   Elliptic Curves over GF( p)

Our previous elliptic curve group used a real field for calculations involved in adding points. Cryptography requires modular arithmetic. We have defined an elliptic curve group with an addition operation, but the operation on the coordinates of the point are over the **GF**(p) field with $p > 3$. In modular arithmetic, the points on the curve do not make nice graphs as seen in the previous figures, but the concept is the same. We use the same addition operation with the calculation done in modulo $p$. We call the resulting elliptic curve $E_p(a, b)$, where $p$ defines the modulus and $a$ and $b$ are the coefficient of the equation $y^2 = x^3 + ax + b$. Note that although the value of $x$ in this case ranges from 0 to $p$, normally not all points are on the curve.

**Finding an Inverse**   The inverse of a point $(x, y)$ is $(x, -y)$, where $-y$ is the additive inverse of $y$. For example, if $p = 13$, the inverse of (4, 2) is (4, 11).

**Finding Points on the Curve**

Algorithm 10.12 shows the pseudocode for finding the points on the curve $E_p(a, b)$.

## Algorithm 10.12         Pseudocode for finding points on an elliptic curve

```
ellipticCurve_points (p, a, b)                          // p is the modulus
{
    x ← 0
    while (x < p)
    {
        w ← (x³ + ax + b) mod p                          // w is y²
        if (w is a perfect square in Zₚ) output (x, √w) (x, − √w)
        x ← x + 1
    {
}
```

**Example 10.14**    Define an elliptic curve $E_{13}(1, 1)$. The equation is $y^2 = x^3 + x + 1$ and the calculation is done modulo 13. Points on the curve can be found as shown in Fig. 10.14.

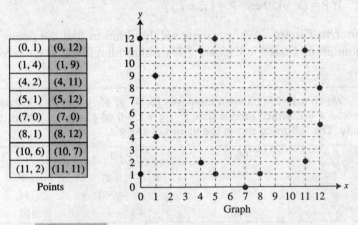

| | |
|---|---|
| (0, 1) | (0, 12) |
| (1, 4) | (1, 9) |
| (4, 2) | (4, 11) |
| (5, 1) | (5, 12) |
| (7, 0) | (7, 0) |
| (8, 1) | (8, 12) |
| (10, 6) | (10, 7) |
| (11, 2) | (11, 11) |

Points                             Graph

**Fig. 10.14**   *Points on an elliptic curve over GF(p)*

Note the following:
a. Some values of $y^2$ do not have a square root in modulo 13 arithmetic. These are not points on this elliptic curve. For example, the points with $x = 2$, $x = 3$, $x = 6$, and $x = 9$ are not on the curve.
b. Each point defined for the curve has an inverse. The inverses are listed as pairs. Note that (7, 0) is the inverse of itself.
c. Note that for a pair of inverse points, the y values are additive inverses of each other in $Z_p$. For example, 4 and 9 are additive inverses in $Z_{13}$. So we can say that if 4 is y, then 9 is -y.
d. The inverses are on the same vertical lines.

***Adding Two Points***    We use the elliptic curve group defined earlier, but calculations are done in **GF(p)**. Instead of subtraction and division, we use additive and multiplicative inverses.

**Example 10.15**    Let us add two points in Example 10.14, R = P + Q, where P = (4, 2) and Q = (10, 6).
a. $\lambda = (6 - 2) \times (10 - 4)^{-1} \bmod 13 = 4 \times 6^{-1} \bmod 13 = 5 \bmod 13$.
b. $x = (5^2 - 4 - 10) \bmod 13 = 11 \bmod 13$.
c. $y = [5 (4 - 11) - 2] \bmod 13 = 2 \bmod 13$.
d. R = (11, 2), which is a point on the curve in Example 10.14.

***Multiplying a Point by a Constant*** In arithmetic, multiplying a number by a constant $k$ means adding the number to itself $k$ times. The situation here is the same. Multiplying a point P on an elliptic curve by a constant $k$ means adding the point P to itself $k$ times. For example, in $E_{13}$ (1, 1), if the point (1, 4) is multiplied by 4, the result is the point (5, 1). If the point (8, 1) is multiplied by 3, the result is the point (10, 7).

### 10.5.3 Elliptic Curves over GF($2^n$)

Calculation in the elliptic curve group can be defined over the GF($2^n$) field. Recall from Chapter 4 that elements of the set in this field are $n$-bit words that can be interpreted as polynomials with coefficient in **GF**(2). Addition and multiplication on the elements are the same as addition and multiplication on polynomials. To define an elliptic curve over **GF**($2^n$), one needs to change the cubic equation. The common equation is

$$y^2 + xy = x^3 + ax^2 + b$$

where $b \neq 0$. Note that the value of $x$, $y$, $a$, and $b$ are polynomials representing $n$-bit words.

***Finding Inverses*** If P = $(x, y)$, then $-$P = $(x, x + y)$.

***Finding Points on the Curve*** We can write an algorithm to find the points on the curve using generators for polynomials discussed in Chapter 7. This algorithm is left as an exercise. Following is a very trivial example.

---

**Example 10.16** We choose **GF**($2^3$) with elements {0, 1, $g$, $g^2$, $g^3$, $g^4$, $g^5$, $g^6$} using the irreducible polynomial of $f(x) = x^3 + x + 1$, which means that $g^3 + g + 1 = 0$ or $g^3 = g + 1$. Other powers of $g$ can be calculated accordingly. The following shows the values of the $g$'s.

| 0 | 000 | $g^3 = g + 1$ | 011 |
|---|-----|---------------|-----|
| 1 | 001 | $g^4 = g^2 + g$ | 110 |
| $g$ | 010 | $g^5 = g^2 + g + 1$ | 111 |
| $g^2$ | 100 | $g^6 = g^2 + 1$ | 101 |

Using the elliptic curve $y^2 + xy = x^3 + g^3x^2 + 1$, with $a = g^3$ and $b = 1$, we can find the points on this curve, as shown in Fig. 10.15.

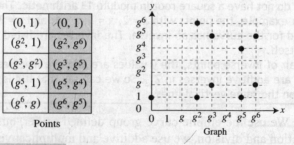

| (0, 1) | (0, 1) |
|--------|--------|
| $(g^2, 1)$ | $(g^2, g^6)$ |
| $(g^3, g^2)$ | $(g^3, g^5)$ |
| $(g^5, 1)$ | $(g^5, g^4)$ |
| $(g^6, g)$ | $(g^6, g^5)$ |

Points                          Graph

**Fig. 10.15** *Points on an elliptic curve over GF($2^n$)*

---

***Adding Two Points*** The rules for adding points in **GF**($2^n$) is slightly different from the rules for **GF**($p$).

1. If $P = (x_1, y_1)$, $Q = (x_2, y_2)$, $Q \neq -P$, and $Q \neq P$, then $R = (x_3, y_3) = P + Q$ can be found as

$$\lambda = (y_2 + y_1) / (x_2 + x_1)$$
$$x_3 = \lambda^2 + \lambda + x_1 + x_2 + a \qquad y_3 = \lambda (x_1 + x_3) + x_3 + y_1$$

2. If $Q = P$, then $R = P + P$ (or $R = 2P$) can be found as

$$\lambda = x_1 + y_1 / x_1$$
$$x_3 = \lambda^2 + \lambda + a \qquad y_3 = x_1^2 + (\lambda + 1) x_3$$

---

**Example 10.17**   Let us find $R = P + Q$, where $P = (0, 1)$ and $Q = (g^2, 1)$. We have $\lambda = 0$ and $R = (g^5, g^4)$.

---

**Example 10.18**   Let us find $R = 2P$, where $P = (g^2, 1)$. We have $\lambda = g^2 + 1/g^2 = g^2 + g^5 = g + 1$ and $R = (g^6, g^5)$.

---

*Multiplying a Point by a Constant*   To multiply a point by a constant, the points must be added continuously with attention to the rule for $R = 2P$.

## 10.5.4   Elliptic Curve Cryptography Simulating ElGamal

Several methods have been used to encrypt and decrypt using elliptic curves. The common one is to simulate the ElGamal cryptosystem using an elliptic curve over $\mathbf{GF}(p)$ or $\mathbf{GF}(2^n)$, as shown in Fig. 10.16.

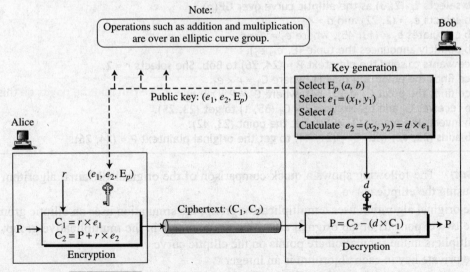

**Fig. 10.16**  *ElGamal cryptosystem using the elliptic curve*

*Generating Public and Private Keys*

1. Bob chooses $E(a, b)$ with an elliptic curve over $\mathbf{GF}(p)$ or $\mathbf{GF}(2^n)$.
2. Bob chooses a point on the curve, $e_1(x_1, y_1)$.

3. Bob chooses an integer $d$.
4. Bob calculates $e_2(x_2, y_2) = d \times e_1(x_1, y_1)$. Note that multiplication here means multiple addition of points as defined before.
5. Bob announces $E(a, b)$, $e_1(x_1, y_1)$, and $e_2(x_2, y_2)$ as his public key; he keeps $d$ as his private key.

**Encryption** Alice selects P, a point on the curve, as her plaintext, P. She then calculates a pair of points on the text as ciphertexts:

$$C_1 = r \times e_1 \qquad\qquad C_2 = P + r \times e_2$$

The reader may wonder how an arbitrary plaintext can be a point on the elliptic curve. This is one of the challenging issues in the use of the elliptic curve for simulation. Alice needs to use an algorithm to find a one-to-one correspondence between symbols (or a block of text) and the points on the curve.

**Decryption** Bob, after receiving $C_1$ and $C_2$, calculates P, the plaintext using the following formula.

$$P = C_2 - (d \times C_1) \qquad \text{The minus sign here means adding with the inverse.}$$

We can prove that the P calculated by Bob is the same as that intended by Alice, as shown below:

$$P + r \times e_2 - (d \times r \times e_1) = P + (r \times d \times e_1) - (r \times d \times e_1) = P + O = P$$

P, $C_1$, $C_2$, $e_1$, and $e_2$ are all points on the curve. Note that the result of adding two inverse points on the curve is the *zero point*.

---

**Example 10.19** Here is a very trivial example of encipherment using an elliptic curve over **GF**($p$).

1. Bob selects $E_{67}(2, 3)$ as the elliptic curve over **GF**($p$).
2. Bob selects $e_1 = (2, 22)$ and $d = 4$.
3. Bob calculates $e_2 = (13, 45)$, where $e_2 = d \times e_1$.
4. Bob publicly announces the tuple $(E, e_1, e_2)$.
5. Alice wants to send the plaintext P = (24, 26) to Bob. She selects $r = 2$.
6. Alice finds the point $C_1 = (35, 1)$, where $C_1 = r \times e_1$.
7. Alice finds the point $C_2 = (21, 44)$, where $C_2 = P + r \times e_2$.
8. Bob receives $C_1$ and $C_2$. He uses $2 \times C_1$ (35, 1) to get (23, 25).
9. Bob inverts the point (23, 25) to get the point (23, 42).
10. Bob adds (23, 42) with $C_2 = (21, 44)$ to get the original plaintext P = (24, 26).

---

**Comparison** The following shows a quick comparison of the original ElGamal algorithm with its simulation using the elliptic curve.

a. The original algorithm uses a multiplicative group; the simulation uses an elliptic group.
b. The two exponents in the original algorithm are numbers in the multiplicative group; the two multipliers in the simulation are points on the elliptic curve.
c. The private key in each algorithm is an integer.
d. The secret numbers chosen by Alice in each algorithm are integers.
e. The exponentiation in the original algorithm is replaced by the multiplication of a point by a constant.
f. The multiplication in the original algorithm is replaced by addition of points.

g. The inverse in the original algorithm is the multiplicative inverse in the multiplicative group; the inverse in the simulation is the additive inverse of a point on the curve.

h. Calculation is usually easier in the elliptic curve because multiplication is simpler than exponentiation, addition is simpler than multiplication, and finding the inverse is much simpler in the elliptic curve group than in a multiplicative group.

**Security of ECC**   To decrypt the message, Eve needs to find the value of $r$ or $d$.

a. If Eve knows $r$, she can use $P = C_2 - (r \times e_2)$ to find the point P related to the plaintext. But to find $r$, Eve needs to solve the equation $C_1 = r \times e_1$. This means, given two points on the curve, $C_1$ and $e_1$, Eve must find the multiplier that creates $C_1$ starting from $e_1$. This is referred to as the **elliptic curve logarithm problem,** and the only method available to solve it is the Polard rho algorithm, which is infeasible if $r$ is large, and $p$ in GF($p$) or $n$ in GF($2^n$) is large.

b. If Eve knows $d$, she can use $P = C_2 - (d \times C_1)$ to find the point P related to the plaintext. Because $e_2 = d \times e_1$, this is the same type of problem. Eve knows the value of $e_1$ and $e_2$; she needs to find the multiplier $d$.

---

**The security of ECC depends on the difficulty of solving the elliptic curve logarithm problem.**

---

**Modulus Size**   For the same level of security (computational effort), the modulus, $n$, can be smaller in ECC than in RSA. For example, ECC over the **GF($2^n$)** with $n$ of 160 bits can provide the same level of security as RSA with $n$ of 1024 bits.

## 10.6   RECOMMENDED READING

The following books and websites provide more details about subjects discussed in this chapter. The items enclosed in brackets refer to the reference list at the end of the book.

### Books

The RSA cryptosystem is discussed in [Sti06], [Sta06], [PHS03], [Vau06], [TW06], and [Mao04]. The Rabin and ElGamal cryptosystems are discussed in [Sti06] and [Mao04]. Elliptic curve cryptography is discussed in [Sti06], [Eng99], and [Bla99].

### WebSites

The following websites give more information about topics discussed in this chapter.

http://www1.ics.uci.edu/~mingl/knapsack.html
www.dtc.umn.edu/~odlyzko/doc/arch/**knapsack**.survey.pdf
http://en.wikipedia.org/wiki/RSA
citeseer.ist.psu.edu/boneh99twenty.html
www.mat.uniroma3.it/users/pappa/SLIDES/**RSA**-HRI_05.pdf
http://en.wikipedia.org/wiki/Rabin_cryptosystem
http://en.wikipedia.org/wiki/ElGamal_encryption
ww.cs.purdue.edu/homes/wspeirs/**elgamal**.pdf
http://en.wikipedia.org/wiki/Elliptic_curve_cryptography
www.cs.utsa.edu/~rakbani/publications/Akbani-ECC-IEEESMC03.pdf

# Key Terms

| | |
|---|---|
| asymmetric-key cryptography | power attack |
| blinding | private key |
| broadcast attack | public key |
| common modulus attack | Rabin cryptosystem |
| Coppersmith theorem attack | random fault attack |
| cycling attack | related message attack |
| ElGamal cryptosystem | revealed decryption exponent attack |
| elliptic curve | RSA (Rivest, Shamir, Adleman) cryptosystem |
| elliptic curve cryptosystem (ECC) | short message attack |
| elliptic curve logarithm problem | short pad attack |
| function | singular elliptic curve |
| invertible function | superincreasing tuple |
| knapsack cryptosystem | symmetric-key cryptography |
| low decryption exponent attack | timing attack |
| low encryption exponent attack | trapdoor |
| nonsingular elliptic curve | trapdoor one-way function (TOWF) |
| one-way function (OWF) | unconcealed message attack |
| optimal asymmetric encryption padding (OAEP) | |

# Summary

★ There are two ways to achieve secrecy: symmetric-key cryptography and asymmetric-key cryptography. These two will exist in parallel and complement each other; the advantages of one can compensate for the disadvantages of the other.

★ The conceptual differences between the two systems are based on how they keep a secret. In symmetric-key cryptography, the secret needs to be shared between two entities; in asymmetric-key cryptography, the secret is personal (unshared).

★ Symmetric-key cryptography is based on substitution and permutation of symbols; asymmetric-key cryptography is based on applying mathematical functions to numbers.

★ Asymmetric-key cryptography uses two separate keys: one private and one public. Encryption and decryption can be thought of as locking and unlocking padlocks with keys. The padlock that is locked with a public key can be unlocked only with the corresponding private key.

★ In asymmetric-key cryptography, the burden of providing security is mostly on the shoulder of the receiver (Bob), who needs to create two keys: one private and one public. Bob is responsible for distributing the private key to the community. This can be done through a public-key distribution channel.

★ Unlike in symmetric-key cryptography, in asymmetric-key cryptography plaintexts and ciphertexts are treated as integers. The message must be encoded as an integer (or a set of integers) before encryption; the integer (or the set of integers) must be decoded into the message after decryption. Asymmetric-key cryptography is normally used to encrypt or decrypt small messages, such as a cipher key for symmetric-key cryptography.

★ The main idea behind asymmetric-key cryptography is the concept of the trapdoor one-way function (TOWF), which is a function such that $f$ is easy to compute, but $f^{-1}$ is computationally infeasible unless a trapdoor is used.

★ A brilliant idea of public-key cryptography came from Merkle and Hellman in their knapsack cryptosystem. If we are told which elements, from a predefined set of numbers, are in a knapsack, we can easily calculate the sum of the numbers; if we are told the sum, it is difficult to say which elements are in the knapsack unless the knapsack is filled with elements from a superincreasing set.

★ The most common public-key algorithm is the RSA cryptosystem. RSA uses two exponents, $e$ and $d$, where $e$ is public and $d$ is private. Alice uses $C = P^e \bmod n$ to create ciphertext C from plaintext P; Bob uses $P = C^d \bmod n$ to retrieve the plaintext sent by Alice.

★ RSA uses two algebraic structures: a ring and a group. Encryption and decryption are done using the commutative ring $\mathbf{R} = <\mathbf{Z}_n, +, \times >$ with two arithmetic operations: addition and multiplication. RSA uses a multiplicative group $\mathbf{G} = <\mathbf{Z}_n^*, \times >$ for key generation.

★ No devastating attacks have yet been discovered on RSA. Several attacks have been predicted based on factorization, chosen-ciphertext, decryption exponent, encryption exponent, plaintext, modulus, and implementation.

★ The Rabin cryptosystem is a variation of the RSA cryptosystem. RSA is based on the exponentiation congruence; Rabin is based on quadratic congruence. We can think of Rabin as the RSA in which the value of $e = 2$ and $d = 1/2$. The Rabin cryptosystem is secure as long as $p$ and $q$ are large numbers. The complexity of the Rabin cryptosystem is at the same level as factoring a large number $n$ into its two prime factors $p$ and $q$.

★ The ElGamal cryptosystem is based on the discrete logarithm problem. ElGamal uses the idea of primitive roots in $\mathbf{Z}_p^*$. Encryption and decryption in ElGamal use the group $\mathbf{G} = <\mathbf{Z}_p^*, \times >$. The public key is two exponents $e_1$ and $e_2$; the private key is an integer $d$. The security of ElGamal is based on the infeasibility of solving -discrete logarithm problems. However, an attack based on low modulus and a known-plaintext attack have been mentioned in the literature.

★ Another cryptosystem discussed in this chapter is based on elliptic curves. Elliptic curves are cubic equations in two variables. Elliptic curves over real numbers use a special class of elliptic curves $y^2 = x^3 + ax + b$ where $4a^3 + 27b^2 \neq 0$. An abelian group has been defined over the elliptic curve with an addition operation that shows how two points on the curve can be added to get another point on the curve.

★ Elliptic curve cryptography (ECC) uses two algebraic structures, an abelian group and a field. The field can be the nonfinite field of real numbers, $\mathbf{GF}(p)$ and $\mathbf{GF}(2^n)$. We have been shown how the ElGamal cryptosystem can be simulated using elliptic curves over finite fields. The security of the ECC depends on the *elliptic curve logarithm problem,* a solution which is infeasible if the modulus is large.

# Practice Set

## Review Questions

**10.1** Distinguish between symmetric-key and asymmetric-key cryptosystems.

**10.2** Distinguish between public and private keys in an asymmetric-key cryptosystem. Compare and contrast the keys in symmetric-key and asymmetric-key cryptosystems.

**10.3** Define a trapdoor one-way function and explain its use in asymmetric-key cryptography.

**10.4** Briefly explain the idea behind the knapsack cryptosystem.

    a.   What is the one-way function in this system?

    b.   What is the trapdoor in this system?

    c.   Define the public and private keys in this system.

    d.   Describe the security of this system.

**10.5**   Briefly explain the idea behind the RSA cryptosystem.
   a.   What is the one-way function in this system?
   b.   What is the trapdoor in this system?
   c.   Define the public and private keys in this system.
   d.   Describe the security of this system.

**10.6**   Briefly explain the idea behind the Rabin cryptosystem.
   a.   What is the one-way function in this system?
   b.   What is the trapdoor in this system?
   c.   Define the public and private keys in this system.
   d.   Describe the security of this system.

**10.7**   Briefly explain the idea behind the ElGamal cryptosystem.
   a.   What is the one-way function in this system?
   b.   What is the trapdoor in this system?
   c.   Define the public and private keys in this system.
   d.   Describe the security of this system.

**10.8**   Briefly explain the idea behind ECC.
   a.   What is the one-way function in this system?
   b.   What is the trapdoor in this system?
   c.   Define the public and private keys in this system.
   d.   Describe the security of this system.

**10.9**   Define elliptic curves and explain their applications in cryptography.

**10.10**   Define the operation used in the abelian group made of points on an elliptic curve.

## Exercises

**10.11**   Given the superincreasing tuple $b$ = [7, 11, 23, 43, 87, 173, 357], $r$ = 41, and modulus $n$ = 1001, encrypt and decrypt the letter "a" using the knapsack cryptosystem. Use [7 6 5 1 2 3 4] as the permutation table.

**10.12**   In RSA:
   a.   Given $n$ = 221 and $e$ = 5, find $d$.
   b.   Given $n$ =3937 and $e$ =17, find $d$.
   c.   Given $p$ = 19, $q$ = 23, and $e$ = 3, find $n$, $\phi(n)$, and $d$.

**10.13**   To understand the security of the RSA algorithm, find $d$ if you know that $e$ = 17 and $n$ = 187.

**10.14**   In RSA, given $n$ and $\phi(n)$, calculate $p$ and $q$.

**10.15**   In RSA, given $e$ = 13 and $n$ = 100
   a.   encrypt the message "HOW ARE YOU" using 00 to 25 for letters A to Z and 26 for the space. Use different blocks to make P < $n$.

**10.16**   In RSA, given $n$ = 12091 and $e$ = 13, Encrypt the message "THIS IS TOUGH" using the 00 to 26 encoding scheme. Decrypt the ciphertext to find the original message.

**10.17**   In RSA:
   a.   Why can't Bob choose 1 as the public key $e$?
   b.   What is the problem in choosing 2 as the public key $e$?

**10.18**   Alice uses Bob's RSA public key ($e$ = 17, $n$ = 19519) to send a four-character message to Bob using the (A $\leftrightarrow$ 0, B $\leftrightarrow$ 1, ... Z $\leftrightarrow$ 25) encoding scheme and encrypting each character separately. Eve intercepts the ciphertext (6625 0 2968 17863) and decrypts the message without factoring the modulus. Find the plaintext and explain why Eve could easily break the ciphertext.

**10.19** Alice uses Bob's RSA public key ($e = 7$, $n = 143$) to send the plaintext P = 8 encrypted as ciphertext C = 57. Show how Eve can use the chosen-ciphertext attack if she has access to Bob's computer to find the plaintext.

**10.20** Alice uses Bob's RSA public key ($e = 3$, $n = 35$) and sends the ciphertext 22 to Bob. Show how Eve can find the plaintext using the *cycling attack*.

**10.21** Suggest how Alice can prevent a *related message attack* on RSA.

**10.22** Using the Rabin cryptosystem with $p = 47$ and $q = 11$:
  a. Encrypt P = 17 to find the ciphertext.
  b. Use the Chinese remainder theorem to find four possible plaintexts.

**10.23** In ElGamal, given the prime $p = 31$:
  a. Choose an appropriate $e_1$ and $d$, then calculate $e_2$.
  b. Encrypt the message "HELLO"; use 00 to 25 for encoding. Use different blocks to make P < $p$.
  c. Decrypt the ciphertext to obtain the plaintext.

**10.24** In ElGamal, what happens if $C_1$ and $C_2$ are swapped during the transition?

**10.25** Assume that Alice uses Bob's ElGamal public key ($e_1 = 2$ and $e_2 = 8$) to send two messages P = 17 and P' = 37 using the same random integer $r = 9$. Eve intercepts the ciphertext and somehow she finds the value of P = 17. Show how Eve can use a known-plaintext attack to find the value of P'.

**10.26** In the elliptic curve E(1, 2) over the **GF(11)** field:
  a. Find the equation of the curve.
  b. Find all points on the curve and make a figure similar to Fig. 10.14.
  c. Generate public and private keys for Bob.
  d. Choose a point on the curve as a plaintext for Alice.
  e. Create ciphertext corresponding to the plaintext in part d for Alice.
  f. Decrypt the ciphertext for Bob to find the plaintext sent by Alice.

**10.27** In the elliptic curve E($g^4$, 1) over the **GF($2^4$)** field:
  a. Find the equation of the curve.
  b. Find all points on the curve and make a figure similar to Fig. 10.15.
  c. Generate public and private keys for Bob.
  d. Choose a point on the curve as a plaintext for Alice.
  e. Create ciphertext corresponding to the plaintext in part d for Alice.
  f. Decrypt the ciphertext for Bob to find the plaintext sent by Alice.

**10.28** Using the knapsack cryptosystem:
  a. Write an algorithm for encryption.
  b. Write an algorithm for decryption.

**10.29** In RSA:
  a. Write an algorithm for encryption using OAEP.
  b. Write an algorithm for decryption using OAEP.

**10.30** Write an algorithm for a *cycling attack* on RSA.

**10.31** Write an algorithm to add two points on an elliptic curve over **GF($p$)**.

**10.32** Write an algorithm to add two points on an elliptic curve over **GF($2^n$)**.

# PART
# III

# *Integrity, Authentication, and Key Management*

In Chapter 1, we saw that cryptography provides three techniques: symmetric-key ciphers, asymmetric-key ciphers, and hashing. Part Three discusses cryptographic hash functions and their applications. This part also explores other issues related to topics discussed in Parts One and Two, such as key management. Chapter 11 discusses the general idea behind message integrity and message authentication. Chapter 12 explores several cryptographic hash functions. Chapter 13 discusses digital signatures. Chapter 14 shows the ideas and methods of entity authentication. Finally, Chapter 15 discusses key management used for symmetric-key and asymmetric-key cryptography.

## Chapter 11: Message Integrity and Message Authentication
Chapter 11 discusses general ideas related to cryptographic hash functions that are used to create a message digest from a message. Message digests guarantee the integrity of the message. The chapter then shows how simple message digests can be modified to authenticate the message.

## Chapter 12: Cryptographic Hash Functions
Chapter 12 investigates several standard cryptographic hash function belonging to two broad categories: those with a compression function made from scratch and those with a block cipher as the compression function. The chapter then describes one hash function from each category, SHA-512 and Whirlpool.

## Chapter 13: Digital Signature
Chapter 13 discusses digital signature. The chapter introduces several digital signature schemes, including RSA, ElGamal, Schnorr, DSS, and elliptic curve. The chapter also investigates some attacks on the above schemes and how they can be prevented.

## Chapter 14: Entity Authentication
Chapter 14 first distinguishes between message authentication and entity authentication. The chapter then discusses some methods of entity authentication, including the use of a password, challenge-response methods, and zero-knowledge protocols. The chapter also includes some discussion on biometrics.

## Chapter 15: Key Management

Chapter 15 first explains different approaches to key managements including the use of a key-distribution center (KDC), certification authorities (CAs), and public-key infrastructure (PKI). This chapter shows how symmetric-key and asymmetric-key cryptography can complement each other to solve some problems such as key management.

# 11

# Message Integrity
# and Message Authentication

## Objectives

This chapter has several objectives:

- ☞ To define message integrity
- ☞ To define message authentication
- ☞ To define criteria for a cryptographic hash function
- ☞ To define the Random Oracle Model and its role in evaluating the security of cryptographic hash functions
- ☞ To distinguish between an MDC and a MAC
- ☞ To discuss some common MACs

This is the first of three chapters devoted to message integrity, message authentication, and entity authentication. This chapter discusses general ideas related to cryptographic hash functions that are used to create a message digest from a message. Message digests guarantee the integrity of the message. We then discuss how simple message digests can be modified to authenticate the message. The standard cryptography cryptographic hash functions are developed in Chapter 12.

## 11.1　　　　　　　　　　MESSAGE INTEGRITY

The cryptography systems that we have studied so far provide *secrecy*, or *confidentiality*, but not *integrity*. However, there are occasions where we may not even need secrecy but instead must have integrity. For example, Alice may write a will to distribute her estate upon her death. The will does not need to be encrypted. After her death, anyone can examine the will. The integrity of the will, however, needs to be preserved. Alice does not want the contents of the will to be changed.

### 11.1.1　Document and Fingerprint

One way to preserve the integrity of a document is through the use of a *fingerprint*. If Alice needs to be sure that the contents of her document will not be changed, she can put her fingerprint at the bottom of the document. Eve cannot modify the contents of this document or create a false document because she cannot forge Alice's fingerprint. To ensure that the document has not been changed, Alice's fingerprint on the document can be compared to Alice's fingerprint on file. If they are not the same, the document is not from Alice.

### 11.1.2 Message and Message Digest

The electronic equivalent of the document and fingerprint pair is the *message* and *digest* pair. To preserve the integrity of a message, the message is passed through an algorithm called a **cryptographic hash function.** The function creates a compressed image of the message that can be used like a fingerprint. Figure 11.1 shows the message, cryptographic hash function, and **message digest**.

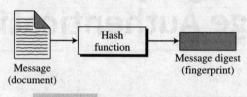

**Fig. 11.1** *Message and digest*

### 11.1.3 Difference

The two pairs (document/fingerprint) and (message/message digest) are similar, with some differences. The document and fingerprint are physically linked together. The message and message digest can be unlinked (or sent) separately, and, most importantly, the message digest needs to be safe from change.

---

**The message digest needs to be safe from change.**

---

### 11.1.4 Checking Integrity

To check the integrity of a message, or document, we run the cryptographic hash function again and compare the new message digest with the previous one. If both are the same, we are sure that the original message has not been changed. Figure 11.2 shows the idea.

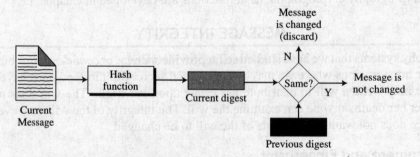

**Fig. 11.2** *Checking integrity*

### 11.1.5 Cryptographic Hash Function Criteria

Cryptographic hash functions need to satisfy certain properties, which are essential for the hash functions to be useful for various applications. The properties are three-fold, namely:

1. Preimage resistance
2. Second Preimage resistance
3. Collision resistance

We define these criteria one by one, and also try to develop their inter relations. Figure 11.3 shows this criteria.

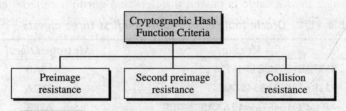

**Fig. 11.3** *Criteria of a cryptographics hash function*

***Preimage Resistance*** This property of the hash function implies given a hashed value it should be difficult for an adversary to compute the preimage of the hashed value. Thus mathematically, a hash function $h$ is said to be preimage resistant, if given the value of $y = h(x)$, for some $x$ it is difficult to compute the value of any $x'$ such that $h(x') = y$.

It may be noted that the definition of preimage resistance does not exclude the condition that $x = x'$.

***Second Preimage Resistance*** In this criterion, an adversary is provided with the value of $x$ and is asked to compute the value of $x' \neq x$, such that $h(x) = h(x')$. If it is difficult for the adversary to perform this computation we claim that the hash function is second preimage resistant. We call the pair $(x', h(x'))$ a valid pair.

***Collision Resistance*** Collision of a hash function is the event when two values $x$ and $x'$, such that $x \neq x'$ hash to the same value, i.e., $h(x) = h(x')$. A given hash function is said to have the property of collision resistance when it is difficult for the adversary to find the collisions. It may be noted that since the domain of a hash function is much larger compared to the range, collisions are bound to occur for any hash function. What the criterion of collision resistance guarantees is that these collisions are hard to compute or find out.

## 11.2                      RANDOM ORACLE MODEL

The **Random Oracle Model,** which was introduced in 1993 by Bellare and Rogaway, is an ideal mathematical model for a hash function. A function based on this model behaves as follows:

1. When a new message of any length is given, the oracle creates and gives a fixed-length message digest that is a random string of 0s and 1s. The oracle records the message and the message digest.
2. When a message is given for which a digest exists, the oracle simply gives the digest in the record.
3. The digest for a new message needs to be chosen independently from all previous digests.

**Example 11.1** Assume an oracle with a table and a fair coin. The table has two columns. The left column shows the messages whose digests have been issued by the oracle. The second column lists the digests created for those messages. We assume that the digest is always 16 bits regardless of the size of the message. Table 11.1 shows an example of this table in which the message and the message digest are listed in hexadecimal. The oracle has already created three digests.

**Table 11.1** *Oracle table after issuing the first three digests*

| Message | Message Digest |
|---|---|
| 4523AB1352CDEF45126 | 13AB |
| 723BAE38F2AB3457AC | 02CA |
| AB45CD1048765412AAAB6662BE | A38B |

Now assume that two events occur:

a. The message AB1234CD8765BDAD is given for digest calculation. The oracle checks its table. This message is not in the table, so the oracle flips its coin 16 times. Assume that result is HHTHHHTTHTHHTTTH, in which the letter H represents *heads* and the letter T represents *tails*. The oracle interprets H as a 1-bit and T as a 0-bit and gives 1101110010110001 in binary, or DCB1 in hexadecimal, as the message digest for this message and adds the note of the message and the digest in the table (Table 11.2).

**Table 11.2** *Oracle table after issuing the fourth digest*

| Message | Message Digest |
|---|---|
| 4523AB1352CDEF45126 | 13AB |
| 723BAE38F2AB3457AC | 02CA |
| AB1234CD8765BDAD | DCB1 |
| AB45CD1048765412AAAB6662BE | A38B |

b. The message 4523AB1352CDEF45126 is given for digest calculation. The oracle checks its table and finds that there is a digest for this message in the table (first row). The oracle simply gives the corresponding digest (13AB).

**Example 11.2** The oracle in Example 11.1 cannot be achieved using an arbitrary formula or algorithm. For example, the oracle cannot use linear equations of the type $h(M) = M \bmod n$.

The reason is that it violates the condition 3, required of a random oracle. This can be understood from the fact that the hash value of two messages, $m_1$ and $m_2$, which are different can be used to compute the hash of a third message $m = m_1 + m_2$, since $h(m) = m \bmod n = (m_1 + m_2) \bmod n = h(m_1) + h(m_2)$.

This violates the requirement that the hash of a new message should be independent of the previous hash computations.

## 11.2.1 Pigeonhole Principle

The first thing we need to be familiar with to understand the analysis of the Random Oracle Model is the **pigeonhole principle:** if $n$ pigeonholes are occupied by $n + 1$ pigeons, then at least one pigeonhole is occupied by two pigeons. The generalized version of the pigeonhole principle is that if $n$ pigeonholes are occupied by $kn + 1$ pigeons, then at least one pigeonhole is occupied by $k + 1$ pigeons.

Because the whole idea of hashing dictates that the digest should be shorter than the message, according to the pigeonhole principle there can be collisions. In other words, there are some digests that correspond to more than one message; the relationship between the possible messages and possible digests is many-to-one.

> **Example 11.3** Assume that the messages in a hash function are 6 bits long and the digests are only 4 bits long. Then the possible number of digests (pigeonholes) is $2^4 = 16$, and the possible number of messages (pigeons) is $2^6 = 64$. This means $n = 16$ and $kn + 1 = 64$, so $k$ is larger than 3. The conclusion is that at least one digest corresponds to four ($k + 1$) messages.

### 11.2.2 Birthday Problems

The second thing we need to know before analyzing the Random Oracle Model is the famous **birthday problems.** Four different birthday problems are usually encountered in the probability courses. The third problem, sometimes referred to as *birthday paradox,* is the most common one in the literature. Figure 11.4 shows the idea of each problem.

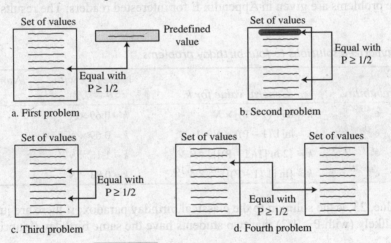

**Fig. 11.4** *Four birthday problems*

### Description of Problems

Below the birthday problems are described in terms that can be applied to the security of hash functions. Note that the term *likely* in all cases means with the probability $P \geq 1/2$.

- ❑ *Problem 1:* What is the minimum number, $k$, of students in a classroom such that it is *likely* that at least one student has a predefined birthday? This problem can be generalized as follows. We have a uniformly distributed random variable with $N$ possible values (between 0 and $N - 1$). What is the minimum number of instances, $k$, such that it is *likely* that at least one instance is equal to a predefined value?

❑ *Problem 2:* What is the minimum number, $k$, of students in a classroom such that it is *likely* that at least one student has the same birthday as the student selected by the professor? This problem can be generalized as follows. We have a uniformly distributed random variable with $N$ possible values (between 0 and $N - 1$). What is the minimum number of instances, $k$, such that it is *likely* that at least one instance is equal to the selected one?

❑ *Problem 3:* What is the minimum number, $k$, of students in a classroom such that it is *likely* that at least two students have the same birthday? This problem can be generalized as follows. We have a uniformly distributed random variable with $N$ possible values (between 0 and $N - 1$). What is the minimum number of instances, $k$, such that it is *likely* that at least two instances are equal?

❑ *Problem 4:* We have two classes, each with $k$ students. What is the minimum value of $k$ so that it is *likely* that at least one student from the first classroom has the same birthday as a student from the second classroom? This problem can be generalized as follows. We have a uniformly distributed random variable with $N$ possible values (between 0 and $N - 1$). We generate two sets of random values each with $k$ instances. What is the minimum number of, $k$, such that it is *likely* that at least one instance from the first set is equal to one instance in the second set?

## Summary of Solutions

Solutions to these problems are given in Appendix E for interested readers; The results are summarized in Table 11.3.

**Table 11.3** *Summarized solutions to four birthday problems*

| Problem | Probability | General value for k | Value of k with $P = 1/2$ | Number of students $(N = 365)$ |
|---------|-------------|---------------------|---------------------------|-------------------------------|
| 1 | $P \approx 1 - e^{-k/N}$ | $k \approx \ln[1/(1 - P)] \times N$ | $k \approx 0.69 \times N$ | 253 |
| 2 | $P \approx 1 - e^{-(k-1)/N}$ | $k \approx \ln[1/(1 - P)] \times N + 1$ | $k \approx 0.69 \times N + 1$ | 254 |
| 3 | $P \approx 1 - e^{k(k-1)/2N}$ | $k \approx \{2 \ln [1/(1 - P)]\}^{1/2} \times N^{1/2}$ | $k \approx 1.18 \times N^{1/2}$ | 23 |
| 4 | $P \approx 1 - e^{-k^2/2N}$ | $k \approx \{\ln [1/(1 - P)]\}^{1/2} \times N^{1/2}$ | $k \approx 0.83 \times N^{1/2}$ | 16 |

The shaded value, 23, is the solution to the classical birthday paradox; if there are just 23 students in a classroom, it is likely (with $P \geq 1/2$) that two students have the same birthday (ignoring the year they have been born).

## Comparison

The value of $k$ in problems 1 or 2 is proportional to $N$; the value of $k$ in problems 3 or 4 is proportional to $N^{1/2}$. As we will see shortly, the first two problems are related to preimage and second preimage attacks; the third and the fourth problems are related to the collision attack. The comparison shows it is much more difficult to launch a preimage or second preimage attack than to launch a collision attack. Figure 11.5 gives the graph of P versus $k$. For the first and second problem only one graph is shown (probabilities are very close). The graphs for the second and the third problems are more distinct.

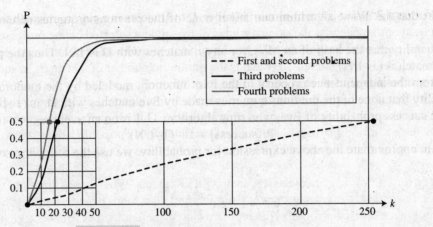

**Fig. 11.5** *Graph of four birthday problems*

## 11.2.3  Attacks on Random Oracle Model

To better understand the complexities of the three problems or criteria defined for hash functions, we analyze the algorithms in the random oracle model. The hash function can be thought to be an instance of the random oracle. Thus the hash function produces a random output of say $n$ bits when queried on a new input. However, if the hash function is queried on the same input as before, then the old value if returned. Thus the total number of possible hash outputs is $N = 2^n$.

We state some randomized algorithms to solve the three problems of preimage, second preimage and collision. The algorithms are of a class called Las Vegas algorithm. These algorithms may fail to give an answer, but if it terminates give a correct answer. The algorithms make q number of queries to either provide answer or say that is has failed. The average case success probability is often denoted by $\varepsilon$, where $0 \leq \varepsilon \leq 1$. The performance of an algorithm is quantified by the tuple, $(\varepsilon, q)$.

### Preimage Attack

Let Eve intercept a digest $D = h(M)$, of a message M. The objective of Eve is to compute any preimage of D. Eve adopts a randomized algorithm, as stated in Algorithm 11.1. She makes q queries to the hash function, modeled as a random oracle. Let the domain of the hash function be denoted by X and the q queries made by Eve form a subset of X, denoted by $X_0$. Let each message belonging to the subset $X_0$ be denoted by $M[i]$, $0 \leq i < q$.

## Algorithm 11.1

```
Input: h, D
Choose, any X₀ ⊆ X,|X₀|=q
For any message M[i] ∈ X₀
if(h(M[i]=D)
    return(M[i])
else
    return(Fail)
```

It is clear that the above algorithm can fail if none of the previous q queries resulted in the same digest as D.

The probability that the hash of an M[$i$], for any $i$, matches with D is 1/N. Thus the probability that it does not match is (1–1/N).

Hence from the independence property of the hash function, modeled by the random oracle model, the probability that none of the previous q queries made by Eve matches with D, is $(1-1/N)^q$.

Thus the success probability of Eve, who runs algorithm 11.1 is on an average

$$Pr[success] = 1 - (1-1/N)^q.$$

In order to approximate the above expression for probability, we use the following series expansion of $e^{-x}$,

$$e^{-x} = 1 - x + \frac{x^2}{2!} - \frac{x^3}{3!} + \cdots$$

Thus, if $x$ is small we can replace $1-x$ by $e^{-x}$. If N is large, thus we can write $1 - 1/N = e^{-(1/N)}$. Thus, we have $Pr[success] = 1 - e^{-q/N}$.

If we equate the probability to 0.5, like we did for the Birthday problems, $q = \ln(0.5)N = 0.69 \times 2^n$.

---

**Example 11.4**   An ideal cryptographic hash function uses a digest of 64 bits. How many minimum digests does Eve need to compute to find a preimage of the digest with a probability more than 0.5?

---

**Solution**   Thus if Eve uses algorithm 11.1 to compute the preimage of the ideal hash function, the number of queries needed is given by $0.69 \times 2^{64}$. This is a very large number and the hash function can be said to be preimage resistant if the digest is of 64 bits.

## Second Preimage Attack

The problem of computing the second preimage of a message, M is to compute another message M' $\neq$ M, such that h(M) = h(M'). Thus if D is the digest of M, then Eve needs to compute another preimage of D. In order to do this, Eve now engages another algorithm 11.2, similar to 11.1 but with a subtle change. The choice of the queries has to exclude M. Thus Eve chooses $X_0$, which is a subset of X\{M}, that is X except M. Like the preimage attack, Eve makes q queries out of which one query is for computing D. Thus the cardinality of $X_0$ is q–1.

---

## Algorithm 11.2

```
Input: h, M
Compute, D = h(M)
Choose, any  X₀ ⊆ X\{M},|X₀| = q–1
For any message  M[i] ∈ X₀
if( h(M[i] = D)
    return(M[i])
else
    return(Fail)
```

The success probability of Eve can thus be computed similar to that for a preimage attack. Since there are q–1 queries been made and the attack will fail when none of the q–1 queries hash to the same digest D,

$$\Pr[\text{success}] \approx 1 - e^{-(q-1)/N}$$

If the probability be equated to 0.5, thus we have $q = \ln(0.5) \times N + 1 \approx 0.69 \times 2^n + 1$.

Thus we see that using algorithms 11.1 and 11.2 the complexities of a preimage attack and a second preimage attack for an ideal hash function is proportional to $2^n$. However as we shall see next, that an attack against the collision property for an ideal hash function is proportional to $2^{n/2}$. This is due to the Birthday Paradox, and an extremely important result for the analysis of hash functions in particular, and cryptanalysis in general.

## Collision Attack

In this attack Eve tries to compute two distinct messages M and M' which hash to the same value. Like the previous two attacks, Eve maintains a list of q queries of messages and their digest values. If Eve finds that the digests match, then she returns the corresponding message values as the colliding messages and the attack is successful. Otherwise the algorithm returns failure. Algorithm 11.3 details the procedure of the attack.

---

## Algorithm 11.3

```
Input: h
Choose, any  X₀ ⊆ X,|X₀|=q
For any message pair,  M[i], M[i'] ∈ X₀, i ≠ i'
     if(h(M[i])=h(M[i']))
           return (M[i],M[i'])
     else
           return(Fail)
```

Next we compute the average case success probability of the above algorithm. Let the $q$ messages in the set $X_0$ be indexed by the variable, $0 \le i < q$. Let us first address the question, what is the probability that the hash of the first two messages, M[0] and M[1] does not collide? It is clearly $1 - 1/N$, based on the assumption that the hash outputs a random value, that is all possible digests are equally likely. This is guaranteed by the Random Oracle Model as described earlier.

Now include a third message, M[2] and consider its hash value. The probability that the hash value of M[2] does not collide with the hash values of M[0] and M[1] is $(1-1/M)(1-2/M)$.

Similarly, the probability that the q hash values of all the messages chosen from $X_0$ does not collide is: $(1-1/M)(1-2/M)\ldots(1-(q-1)/M)$. Thus,

$$\Pr[No \text{ collision}] = \prod_{i=1}^{q-1}\left(1 - \frac{i}{N}\right) \approx \prod_{i=1}^{q-1} e^{-i/N} \approx e^{-\frac{q^2}{N}}$$

Thus, $\Pr[\text{collision}] = 1 - e^{-\frac{q^2}{N}}$. Equating this probability to 0.5, thus we have $q = \sqrt{\ln(0.5)N} \approx 1.17\sqrt{N}$. Thus in order to be successful Eve with a probability of more than 0.5, Eve needs to compute a list of digest values proportional to $N^{1/2} = 2^{n/2}$.

This complexity analysis shows that although a 64 bit ideal hash function can prevent preimage and second preimage attacks, the complexity against collision attacks is of the order of only $2^{32}$, which is within practical limits. Thus to prevent collision attacks, it is advised to keep the size of the digest larger than 160 bits.

## 11.2.4 Comparision of the Three Security Criteria

Although the previous analysis for ideal hash functions show that the collision problem is an easier problem compared to the other two problems, it is intriguing to know their interrelations for arbitrary hash functions. We use the following reduction based arguments to understand the following inter-relations:

### 1. Collision Resistance Implies Second Preimage Resistance

Assume that the second preimage problem can be solved by an algorithm $2^{nd}$ Preimage. We show in Algorithm 11.4, this implies that then the collision problem can also be solved. Thus the easiness of $2^{nd}$ preimage implies that the collision problem is easy. The equivalent statement is the hardness of collision resistance implies the hardness of the $2^{nd}$ preimage problem.

### Algorithm 11.4

Choose x at random from X, the domain of the hash function h.
if($2^{nd}$Preimage(h,x)=x')
    return(x,x')
else
    return(fail)

It may be noted that since the $2^{nd}$ Preimage algorithm is a Las Vegas algorithm, it always gives the correct answer. That is x and x' are distinct and they have the same digest. Thus $(x, x')$ is indeed a correct colliding pair.

### 2. Does Collision Resistance Imply Preimage Problem?

The inter-relation between the preimage problem and the collision problem is however not so straight forward. We have to make a further assumption, which is quite realistic. We assume that the hash function, has domain X and range Y, such that $|X| \geq 2|Y|$. Suppose that Preimage is a Las Vegas algorithm to solve the preimage problem with q queries and a probability of 1. Algorithm 11.5 shows how the algorithm Preimage can be used to compute a colliding pair for the hash function.

### Algorithm 11.5

Choose x at random from X, the domain of the hash function h.
Compute y=h(x)
if((Preimage(y)=x') and (x'≠x))
    return(x, x')
else
    return(fail)

It may be noted that the algorithm Preimage may return x itself as the preimage. Thus we check that the returned preimage is indeed different from the value of x.

The entire domain X can be divided into $|Y|$ partitions. Each partition signifies one digest value and the preimages of Y form the elements of a particular partition. In algorithm 11.5, a value of x is chosen randomly from one of these partitions.

The number of preimages of the hash of x which are not equal to x are thus $|[x]|-1$, where $[x]$ denotes the partition containing the chosen x, and $|[x]|$ denotes the number of elements in the partition.

Hence for a chosen $x$, the probability that the collision is successfully obtained is $(|[x]|-1)/|[x]|$. Thus the average probability of success of the adversary in obtaining a collision is:

$$\Pr[success] = \frac{1}{|X|} \sum_{x \in X} \frac{|[x]|-1}{|[x]|}$$

$$= \frac{1}{|X|} \sum_{c \in C} \sum_{x \in c} \frac{|c|-1}{|c|} \quad \text{(C denotes the set of partitions and c denotes a particular partition)}$$

$$= \frac{1}{|X|} \sum_{c \in C} (|c|-1)$$

$$= \frac{1}{|X|} (\sum_{c \in C} (|c|) - \sum_{c \in C} (1))$$

$$= \frac{1}{|X|} (|X|-|Y|) \geq \frac{1}{|X|} (|X|-|X|/2) = \frac{1}{2}.$$

This shows that existence of a Las Vegas algorithm for computing the preimage with q queries and probability 1, implies that there exists a Las Vegas algorithm for determining the collision for a hash function, with q+1 queries and a probability of ½.

***Summary of Attacks*** Table 11.4 shows the level of difficulty for each attack if the digest is $n$ bits.

**Table 11.4** *Levels of difficulties for each type of attack*

| Attack | Value of k with P=1/2 | Order |
|---|---|---|
| Preimage | $k \approx 0.69 \times 2^n$ | $2^n$ |
| Second preimage | $k \approx 0.69 \times 2^n + 1$ | $2^n$ |
| Collision | $k \approx 1.18 \times 2^{n/2}$ | $2^{n/2}$ |
| Alternate collision | $k \approx 0.83 \times 2^{n/2}$ | $2^{n/2}$ |

Table 11.4 shows that the order, or the difficulty rate of the attack, is much less for collision attack than for preimage or second preimage attacks. If a hash algorithm is resistant to collision, we should not worry about preimage and second preimage attacks.

**Example 11.5** Originally hash functions with a 64-bit digest were believed to be immune to collision attacks. But with the increase in the processing speed, today everyone agrees that these hash functions are no longer secure. Eve needs only $2^{64/2} = 2^{32}$ tests to launch an attack with probability 1/2 or more. Assume she can perform $2^{20}$ (one million) tests per second. She can launch an attack in $2^{32}/2^{20} = 2^{12}$ seconds (almost an hour).

**Example 11.6** MD5 (see Chapter 12), which was one of the standard hash functions for a long time, creates digests of 128 bits. To launch a collision attack, the adversary needs to test $2^{64}$ ($2^{128/2}$) tests in the collision algorithm. Even if the adversary can perform $2^{30}$ (more than one billion) tests in a second, it takes $2^{34}$ seconds (more than 500 years) to launch an attack. This type of attack is based on the Random Oracle Model. It has been proved that MD5 can be attacked on less than $2^{64}$ tests because of the structure of the algorithm.

---

**Example 11.7** SHA-1 (see Chapter 12), a standard hash function developed by NIST, creates digests of 160 bits. The function is attacks. To launch a collision attack, the adversary needs to test $2^{160/2} = 2^{80}$ tests in the collision algorithm. Even if the adversary can perform $2^{30}$ (more than one billion) tests in a second, it takes $2^{50}$ seconds (more than ten thousand years) to launch an attack. However, researchers have discovered some features of the function that allow it to be attacked in less time than calculated above.

---

**Example 11.8** The new hash function, that is likely to become NIST standard, is SHA-512 (see Chapter 12), which has a 512-bit digest. This function is definitely resistant to collision attacks based on the Random Oracle Model. It needs $2^{512/2} = 2^{256}$ tests to find a collision with the probability of 1/2.

---

### 11.2.5 Attacks on the Structure

All discussions related to the attacks on hash functions have been based on an ideal cryptographic hash function that acts like an oracle; they were based on the Random Oracle Model. Although this type of analysis provides systematic evaluation of the algorithms, practical hash functions can have some internal structures that can make them much weaker. It is not possible to make a hash function that creates digests that are completely random. The adversary may have other tools to attack hash function. One of these tools, for example, is the *meet-in-the-middle* attack that we discussed in Chapter 6 for double DES. We will see in the next chapters that some hash algorithms are subject to this type of attack. These types of hash function are far from the ideal model and should be avoided.

## 11.3 MESSAGE AUTHENTICATION

A message digest guarantees the integrity of a message. It guarantees that the message has not been changed. A message digest, however, does not authenticate the sender of the message. When Alice sends a message to Bob, Bob needs to know if the message is coming from Alice. To provide message authentication, Alice needs to provide proof that it is Alice sending the message and not an impostor. A message digest per se cannot provide such a proof. The digest created by a cryptographic hash function is normally called a modification detection code (MDC). The code can detect any modification in the message. What we need for message authentication (data origin authentication) is a message authentication code (MAC).

### 11.3.1 Modification Detection Code

**A modification detection code (MDC)** is a message digest that can prove the integrity of the message: that message has not been changed. If Alice needs to send a message to Bob and be sure that the message will not change during transmission, Alice can create a message digest, MDC, and send both the message and the MDC to Bob. Bob can create a new MDC from the message and compare the received MDC and the new MDC. If they are the same, the message has not been changed. Figure 11.6 shows the idea.

Figure 11.6 shows that the message can be transferred through an insecure channel. Eve can read or even modify the message. The MDC, however, needs to be transferred through a safe channel. The term *safe* here means immune to change. If both the message and the MDC are sent through the insecure channel, Eve can intercept the message, change it, create a new MDC from the message, and send both to Bob. Bob never knows that the message has come from Eve. Note that the term *safe* can mean a trusted party; the term *channel* can mean the passage of time. For example, if Alice makes an MDC from her will and deposits it with her attorney, who keeps it locked away until her death, she has used a safe channel.

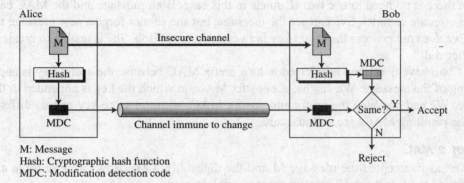

M: Message
Hash: Cryptographic hash function
MDC: Modification detection code

**Fig. 11.6** *Modification detection code (MDC)*

Alice writes her will and announces it publicly (insecure channel). Alice makes an MDC from the message and deposits it with her attorney, which is kept until her death (a secure channel). Although Eve may change the contents of the will, the attorney can create an MDC from the will and prove that Eve's version is a forgery. If the cryptography hash function used to create the MDC has the three properties described at the beginning of this chapter, Eve will lose.

## 11.3.2 Message Authentication Code (MAC)

To ensure the integrity of the message and the data origin authentication—that Alice is the originator of the message, not somebody else—we need to change a modification detection code (MDC) to a **message authentication code (MAC).** The difference between a MDC and a MAC is that the second includes a secret between Alice and Bob—for example, a secret key that Eve does not possess. Figure 11.7 shows the idea.

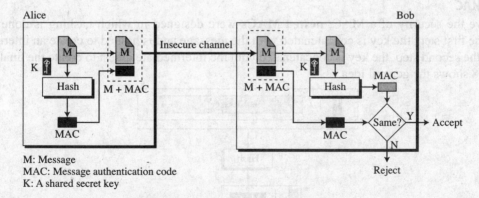

M: Message
MAC: Message authentication code
K: A shared secret key

**Fig. 11.7** *Message authentication code*

Alice uses a hash function to create a MAC from the concatenation of the key and the message, h (K|M). She sends the message and the MAC to Bob over the insecure channel. Bob separates the message from the MAC. He then makes a new MAC from the concatenation of the message and the secret key. Bob then compares the newly created MAC with the one received. If the two MACs match, the message is authentic and has not been modified by an adversary.

Note that there is no need to use two channels in this case. Both message and the MAC can be sent on the same insecure channel. Eve can see the message, but she cannot forge a new message to replace it because Eve does not possess the secret key between Alice and Bob. She is unable to create the same MAC as Alice did.

The MAC we have described is referred to as a prefix MAC because the secret key is appended to the beginning of the message. We can have a postfix MAC, in which the key is appended to the end of the message. We can combine the prefix and postfix MAC, with the same key or two different keys. However, the resulting MACs are still insecure.

## Security of a MAC

Suppose Eve has intercepted the message M and the digest h(K | M). How can Eve forge a message without knowing the secret key? There are three possible cases:

1. If the size of the key allows exhaustive search, Eve may prepend all possible keys at the beginning of the message and make a digest of the (K | M) to find the digest equal to the one intercepted. She then knows the key and can successfully replace the message with a forged message of her choosing.

2. The size of the key is normally very large in a MAC, but Eve can use another tool: the preimage attack discussed in Algorithm 11.1. She uses the algorithm until she finds X such that h(X) is equal to the MAC she has intercepted. She now can find the key and successfully replace the message with a forged one. Because the size of the key is normally very large for exhaustive search, Eve can only attack the MAC using the preimage algorithm.

3. Given some pairs of messages and their MACs, Eve can manipulate them to come up with a new message and its MAC.

---

**The security of a MAC depends on the security of the underlying hash algorithm.**

---

## Nested MAC

To improve the security of a MAC, **nested MACs** were designed in which hashing is done in two steps. In the first step, the key is concatenated with the message and is hashed to create an intermediate digest. In the second step, the key is concatenated with the intermediate digest to create the final digest. Figure 11.8 shows the general idea.

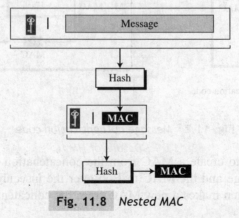

**Fig. 11.8** *Nested MAC*

**HMAC** NIST has issued a standard (FIPS 198) for a nested MAC that is often referred to as **HMAC** (hashed MAC, to distinguish it from CMAC, discussed in the next section). The implementation of HMAC is much more complex than the simplified nested MAC shown in Fig. 11.8. There are additional features, such as padding. Figure 11.9 shows the details. We go through the steps:

1. The message is divided into $N$ blocks, each of $b$ bits.
2. The secret key is left-padded with 0's to create a $b$-bit key. Note that it is recommended that the secret key (before padding) be longer than $n$ bits, where n is the size of the HMAC.
3. The result of step 2 is exclusive-ored with a constant called **ipad** (**input pad**) to create a $b$-bit block. The value of ipad is the $b/8$ repetition of the sequence 00110110 (36 in hexadecimal).
4. The resulting block is prepended to the $N$-block message. The result is $N + 1$ blocks.
5. The result of step 4 is hashed to create an $n$-bit digest. We call the digest the intermediate HMAC.
6. The intermediate $n$-bit HMAC is left padded with 0s to make a $b$-bit block.
7. Steps 2 and 3 are repeated by a different constant opad (**output pad**). The value of opad is the $b/8$ repetition of the sequence 01011100 (5C in hexadecimal).
8. The result of step 7 is prepended to the block of step 6.
9. The result of step 8 is hashed with the same hashing algorithm to create the final $n$-bit HMAC.

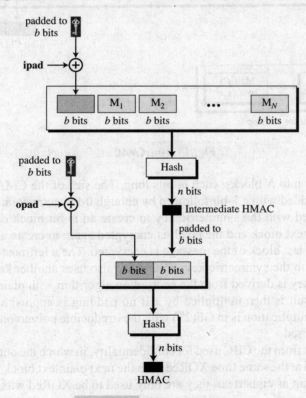

**Fig. 11.9** *Details of HMAC*

**CMAC**  NIST has also defined a standard (FIPS 113) called Data Authentication Algorithm, or **CMAC**, or **CBCMAC.** The method is similar to the cipher block chaining (CBC) mode discussed in Chapter 8 for symmetric-key encipherment. However, the idea here is not to create $N$ blocks of ciphertext from $N$ blocks of plaintext. The idea is to create one block of MAC from $N$ blocks of plaintext using a symmetric-key cipher $N$ times. Figure 11.10 shows the idea.

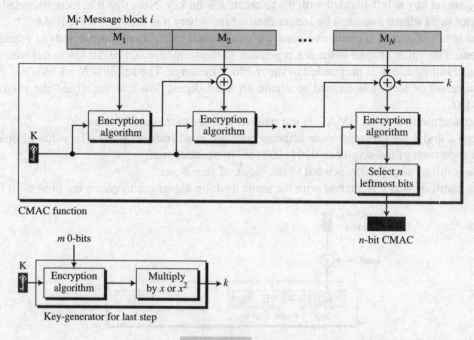

**Fig. 11.10**  *CMAC*

The message is divided into $N$ blocks, each $m$ bits long. The size of the CMAC is $n$ bits. If the last block is not $m$ bits, it is padded with a 1-bit followed by enough 0-bits to make it $m$ bits. The first block of the message is encrypted with the symmetric key to create an $m$-bit block of encrypted data. This block is XORed with the next block and the result is encrypted again to create a new $m$-bit block. The process continues until the last block of the message is encrypted. The $n$ leftmost bit from the last block is the CMAC. In addition to the symmetric key, K, CMAC also uses another key, $k$, which is applied only at the last step. This key is derived from the encryption algorithm with plaintext of m 0-bits using the cipher key, K. The result is then multiplied by $x$ if no padding is applied and multiplied by $x^2$ if padding is applied. The multiplication is in $GF(2^m)$ with the irreducible polynomial of degree $m$ selected by the particular protocol used.

Note that this is different from the CBC used for confidentiality, in which the output of each encryption is sent as the ciphertext and at the same time XORed with the next plaintext block. Here the intermediate encrypted blocks are not sent as ciphertext; they are only used to be XORed with the next block.

# 11.4                    RECOMMENDED READING

The following books and websites give more details about subjects discussed in this chapter. The items enclosed in brackets refer to the reference list at the end of the book.

## Books

Several books that give a good coverage of cryptographic hash functions include [Sti06], [Sta06], [Sch99], [Mao04], [KPS02], [PHS03], and [MOV96].

## WebSites

The following websites give more information about topics discussed in this chapter.

http://en.wikipedia.org/wiki/Preimage_attack
http://en.wikipedia.org/wiki/Collision_attack#In_cryptography
http://en.wikipedia.org/wiki/Pigeonhole_principle
csrc.nist.gov/ispab/2005-12/B_Burr-Dec2005-ISPAB.pdf
http://en.wikipedia.org/wiki/Message_authentication_code
http://en.wikipedia.org/wiki/HMAC
csrc.nist.gov/publications/fips/fips198/fips-198a.pdf
http://www.faqs.org/rfcs/rfc2104.html
http://en.wikipedia.org/wiki/Birthday_paradox

# *Key Terms*

birthday problems
CBCMAC
CMAC
collision resistance
cryptographic hash function
hashed message authentication code (HMAC)
input pad (ipad)
message authentication code (MAC)
message digest

message digest domain
modification detection code (MDC)
nested MAC
output pad (opad)
pigeonhole principle
preimage resistance
Random Oracle Model
second preimage resistance

# *Summary*

★ A fingerprint or a message digest can be used to ensure the integrity of a document or a message. To ensure the integrity of a document, both the document and the fingerprint are needed; to ensure the integrity of a message, both the message and the message digest are needed. The message digest needs to be kept safe from change.

★ A cryptographic hash function creates a message digest out of a message. The function must meet three criteria: preimage resistance, second preimage resistance, and collision resistance.

★ The first criterion, preimage resistance, means that it must be extremely hard for Eve to create any message from the digest. The second criterion, second preimage resistance, ensures that if Eve has a message and the corresponding digest, she should not be able to create a second message whose digest is the same as the first. The third criterion, collision resistance, ensures that Eve cannot find two messages that hash to the same digest.

★   The Random Oracle Model, which was introduced in 1993 by Bellare and Rogaway, is an ideal mathematical model for a hash function.

★   The pigeonhole principle states that if *n* pigeonholes are occupied by *n* + 1 pigeons, then at least one pigeonhole is occupied by two pigeons. The generalized version of pigeonhole principle is that if *n* pigeonholes are occupied by *kn* + 1 pigeons, then at least one pigeonhole is occupied by *k* + 1 pigeons.

★   The four birthday problems are used to analyze the Random Oracle Model. The first problem is used to analyze the preimage attack, the second problem is used to analyze the second preimage attack, and the third and the fourth problems are used to analyze the collision attack.

★   A modification detection code (MDC) is a message digest that can prove the integrity of the message: that the message has not been changed. To prove the integrity of the message and the data origin authentication, we need to change a modification detection code (MDC) to a message authentication code (MAC). The difference between an MDC and a MAC is that the second includes a secret between the sender and the receiver.

★   NIST has issued a standard (FIPS 198) for a nested MAC that is often referred to as HMAC (hashed MAC). NIST has also defined another standard (FIPS 113) called CMAC, or CBCMAC.

## *Practice Set*

### Review Questions

11.1   Distinguish between message integrity and message authentication.

11.2   Define the first criterion for a cryptographic hash function.

11.3   Define the second criterion for a cryptographic hash function.

11.4   Define the third criterion for a cryptographic hash function.

11.5   Define the Random Oracle Model and describe its application in analyzing attacks on hash functions.

11.6   State the pigeonhole principle and describe its application in analyzing hash functions.

11.7   Define the four birthday problems discussed in this chapter.

11.8   Associate each birthday problem with one of the attacks on a hash function.

11.9   Distinguish between an MDC and a MAC.

11.10   Distinguish between HMAC and CMAC.

### Exercises

11.11   In the Random Oracle Model, why does the oracle need to make a note of the digest created for a message and give the same digest for the same message?

11.12   Explain why private-public keys cannot be used in creating a MAC.

11.13   Ignoring the birth month, how many attempts, on average, are needed to find a person with the same birth date as yours? Assume that all months have 30 days.

11.14   Ignoring the birth month, how many attempts, on average, are needed to find two persons with the same birth date? Assume that all months have 30 days.

11.15   How many attempts, on average, are needed to find a person the same age as you, given a group of people born after 1950?

**11.16** How many attempts, on average, are needed to find two people of the same age if we look for people born after 1950?

**11.17** Answer the following questions about a family of six people, assuming that the birthdays are uniformly distributed through the days of a week, through the days of a month, through each month of a year, and through the 365 days of the year. Also assume that a year is exactly 365 days and each month is exactly 30 days.

    a.    What is the probability that two of the family members have the same birthday? What is the probability that none of them have the same birthday?

    b.    What is the probability that two of the family members are born in the same month? What is the probability that none of them were born in the same month?

    c.    What is the probability that one of the family members is born on the first day of a month?

    d.    What is the probability that three of the family members are born on the same day of the week?

**11.18** What is the probability of birthday collision in two classes, one with $k$ students and the other with $l$ students?

**11.19** In a class of 100 students, what is the probability that two or more students have Social Security Numbers with the same last four digits?

**11.20** There are 100 students in a class and the professor assigns five grades (A, B, C, D, E) to a test. Show that at least 20 students have one of the grades.

**11.21** Does the pigeonhole principle require the random distribution of pigeons to the pigeonholes?

**11.22** Assume that Eve is determined to find a preimage in Algorithm 11.1 What is the average number of times Eve needs to repeat the algorithm?

**11.23** Assume Eve is determined to find a collision in Algorithm 11.3 What is the average number of times Eve needs to repeat the algorithm?

**11.24** Assume we have a very simple message digest. Our unrealistic message digest is just one number between 0 and 25. The digest is initially set to 0. The cryptographic hash function adds the current value of the digest to the value of the current character (between 0 and 25). Addition is in modulo 26. Figure 11.11 shows the idea. What is the value of the digest if the message is "HELLO"? Why is this digest not secure?

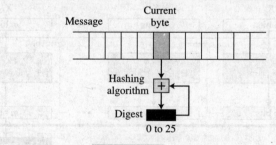

**Fig. 11.11** *Exercise 24*

**11.25** Let us increase the complexity of the previous exercise. We take the value of the current character, substitute it with another number, and then add it to the previous value of the digest in modulo 100 arithmetic. The digest is initially set to 0. Figure 11.12 shows the idea. What is the value of the digest if the message is "HELLO"? Why is this digest not secure?

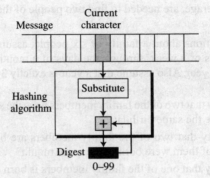

**Fig. 11.12** *Exercise 25*

**11.26** Use modular arithmetic to find the digest of a message. Figure 11.13 shows the procedure. The steps are as follows:

a. Let the length of the message digest be $n$ bits.

b. Choose a prime number, $p$, of $n$ bits as the modulus.

c. Represent the message as a binary number and pad the message with extra 0's to make it multiple of $m$ bits.

d. Divide the padded message into $N$ blocks, each of $m$ bits. Call the $i$th block $X_i$.

e. Choose an initial digest of $N$ bits, $H_0$.

f. Repeat the following N times:

$$H_i = (H_{i-1} + X_i)^2 \bmod p$$

g. The digest is $H_N$.

What is the value of the digest if the message is "HELLO"? Why is this digest not secure?

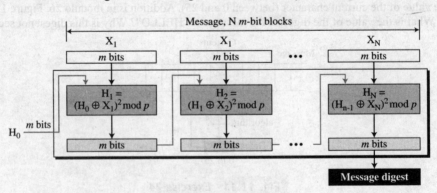

**Fig. 11.13** *Exercise 26*

**11.27** A hash function, called Modular Arithmetic Secure Hash (**MASH**), is described below. Write an algorithm to calculate the digest, given the message. Find the digest of a message of your own.

a. Let the length of the message digest be $N$ bits.

b. Choose two prime numbers, $p$ and $q$. Calculate $M = pq$.

c. Represent the message as a binary number and pad the message with extra 0s to make it a multiple of $N/2$ bits. N is chosen as a multiple of 16, less than the number of bits in M.

d. Divide the padded message into $m$ blocks, each of N/2 bits. Call each block $X_i$.

e. Add the length of the message modulo N/2 as a binary number to the message. This makes the message $m + 1$ blocks of N/2 bits.

f. Expand the message to obtain $m + 1$ blocks, each of N bits as shown below:

Divide blocks $X_1$ to $X_m$ into 4-bit groups. Insert 1111 before each group.

Divide block $X_{m+1}$ into 4-bit groups. Insert 1010 before each group.

Call the expanded blocks $Y_1, Y_2, ..., Y_{m+1}$

g. Choose an initial digest of N bits, $H_0$.

h. Choose a constant K of N bits.

i. Repeat the following $m + 1$ times ($T_i$ and $G_i$ are intermediate values). The "$\|$" symbol means to concatenate.

$$T_i = ((H_{i-1} + Y_i) \| K)^{257} \bmod M \quad G_i = H_i \bmod 2^N \quad H_i = H_{i-1} + G_i$$

j. The digest is $H_{m+1}$.

**11.28** Write an algorithm in pseudocode to solve the first birthday problem (in general form).

**11.29** Write an algorithm in pseudocode to solve the second birthday problem (in general form).

**11.30** Write an algorithm in pseudocode to solve the third birthday problem (in general form).

**11.31** Write an algorithm in pseudocode to solve the fourth birthday problem (in general form).

**11.32** Write an algorithm in pseudocode for HMAC.

**11.33** Write an algorithm in pseudocode for CMAC.

# 12

# Cryptographic Hash Functions

## Objectives

This chapter has several objectives:

- ☞ To introduce general ideas behind cryptographic hash functions
- ☞ To discuss the Merkle-Damgard scheme as the basis for iterated hash functions
- ☞ To distinguish between two categories of hash functions: those with a compression function made from scratch and those with a block cipher as the compression function
- ☞ To discuss the structure of SHA-512 as an example of a cryptographic hash function with a compression function made from scratch
- ☞ To discuss the structure of Whirlpool as an example of a cryptographic hash function with a block cipher as the compression function

## 12.1                      INTRODUCTION

As discussed in Chapter 11, a cryptographic hash function takes a message of arbitrary length and creates a message digest of fixed length. The ultimate goal of this chapter is to discuss the details of the two most promising cryptographic hash algorithms—*SHA-512* and *Whirlpool*. However, we first need to discuss some general ideas that may be applied to any cryptographic hash function.

### 12.1.1   Iterated Hash Function

All cryptographic hash functions need to create a fixed-size digest out of a variable-size message. Creating such a function is best accomplished using iteration. Instead of using a hash function with variable-size input, a function with fixed-size input is created and is used a necessary number of times. The fixed-size input function is referred to as a **compression function.** It compresses an $n$-bit string to create an $m$-bit string where $n$ is normally greater than $m$. The scheme is referred to as an **iterated cryptographic hash function.**

### Merkle-Damgard Scheme

The **Merkle-Damgard scheme** is an iterated hash function that is collision resistant if the compression function is collision resistant. This can be proved, but the proof is left as an exercise. The scheme is shown in Fig. 12.1.

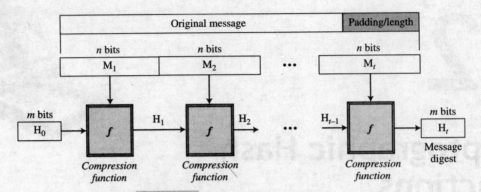

**Fig. 12.1** *Merkle-Damgard scheme*

The scheme uses the following steps:

1. The message length and padding are appended to the message to create an augmented message that can be evenly divided into blocks of $n$ bits, where $n$ is the size of the block to be processed by the compression function.
2. The message is then considered as $t$ blocks, each of $n$ bits. We call each block $M_1, M_2, \ldots, M_t$. We call the digest created at $t$ iterations $H_1, H_2, \ldots, H_t$.
3. Before starting the iteration, the digest $H_0$ is set to a fixed value, normally called IV (initial value or initial vector).
4. The compression function at each iteration operates on $H_{i-1}$ and $M_i$ to create a new $H_i$. In other words, we have $H_i = f(H_{i-1}, M_i)$, where $f$ is the compression function.
5. $H_t$ is the cryptographic hash function of the original message, that is, h(M).

---

**If the compression function in the Merkle-Damgard scheme is collision resistant, the hash function is also collision resistant.**

---

## 12.1.2 Two Groups of Compression Functions

The Merkle-Damgard scheme is the basis for many cryptographic hash functions today. The only thing we need to do is design a compression function that is collision resistant and insert it in the Merkle-Damgard scheme. There is a tendency to use two different approaches in designing a hash function. In the first approach, the compression function is made from scratch: it is particularly designed for this purpose. In the second approach, a symmetric-key block cipher serves as a compression function.

### Hash Functions Made from Scratch

A set of cryptographic hash functions uses compression functions that are made from scratch. These compression functions are specifically designed for the purposes they serve.

***Message Digest (MD)***   Several hash algorithms were designed by Ron Rivest. These are referred to as **MD2, MD4,** and **MD5,** where MD stands for Message Digest. The last version, MD5, is a strengthened version of MD4 that divides the message into blocks of 512 bits and creates a 128-bit digest. It turned out that a message digest of size 128 bits is too small to resist collision attack.

### Secure Hash Algorithm (SHA)

The **Secure Hash Algorithm (SHA)** is a standard that was developed by the National Institute of Standards and Technology (NIST) and published as a Federal Information Processing standard (FIP

180). It is sometimes referred to as **Secure Hash Standard (SHS).** The standard is mostly based on MD5. The standard was revised in 1995 under FIP 180-1, which includes **SHA-1**. It was revised later under FIP 180-2, which defines four new versions: **SHA-224, SHA-256, SHA-384,** and **SHA-512.** Table 12.1 lists some of the characteristics of these versions.

**Table 12.1** *Characteristics of Secure Hash Algorithms (SHAs)*

| Characteristics | SHA-1 | SHA-224 | SHA-256 | SHA-384 | SHA-512 |
|---|---|---|---|---|---|
| Maximum Message size | $2^{64} - 1$ | $2^{64} - 1$ | $2^{64} - 1$ | $2^{128} - 1$ | $2^{128} - 1$ |
| Block size | 512 | 512 | 512 | 1024 | 1024 |
| Message digest size | 160 | 224 | 256 | 384 | 512 |
| Number of rounds | 80 | 64 | 64 | 80 | 80 |
| Word size | 32 | 32 | 32 | 64 | 64 |

All of these versions have the same structure. SHA-512 is discussed in detail later in this chapter.

*Other Algorithms* **RACE Integrity Primitives Evaluation Message Digest (RIPMED)** has several versions. **RIPEMD-160** is a hash algorithm with a 160-bit message digest. RIPEMD-160 uses the same structure as MD5 but uses two parallel lines of execution. **HAVAL** is a variable-length hashing algorithm with a message digest of size 128, 160, 192, 224, and 256. The block size is 1024 bits.

## Hash Functions Based on Block Ciphers

An iterated cryptographic hash function can use a symmetric-key block cipher as a compression function. The whole idea is that there are several secure symmetric-key block ciphers, such as triple DES or AES, that can be used to make a one-way function instead of creating a new compression function. The block cipher in this case only performs encryption. Several schemes have been proposed. We later describe one of the most promising, *Whirlpool.*

*Rabin Scheme* The iterated hash function proposed by Rabin is very simple. The **Rabin scheme** is based on the Merkle-Damgard scheme. The compression function is replaced by any encrypting cipher. The message block is used as the key; the previously created digest is used as the plaintext. The ciphertext is the new message digest. Note that the size of the digest is the size of data block cipher in the underlying cryptosystem. For example, if DES is used as the block cipher, the size of the digest is only 64 bits. Although the scheme is very simple, it is subject to a meet-in-the-middle attack discussed in Chapter 6, because the adversary can use the decryption algorithm of the cryptosystem. Figure 12.2 shows the Rabin scheme.

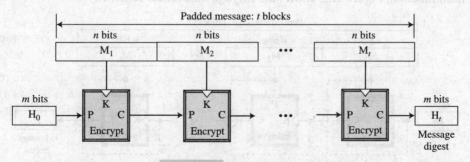

**Fig. 12.2** *Rabin scheme*

***Davies-Meyer Scheme***   The **Davies-Meyer scheme** is basically the same as the Rabin scheme except that it uses forward feed to protect against meet-in-the-middle attack. Figure 12.3 shows the Davies-Meyer scheme.

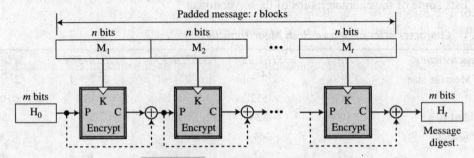

**Fig. 12.3**  *Davies-Meyer scheme*

***Matyas-Meyer-Oseas Scheme***   The **Matyas-Meyer-Oseas scheme** is a dual version of the Davies-Meyer scheme: the message block is used as the key to the cryptosystem. The scheme can be used if the data block and the cipher key are the same size. For example, AES is a good candidate for this purpose. Figure 12.4 shows the Matyas-Meyer-Oseas scheme.

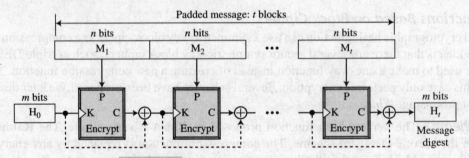

**Fig. 12.4**  *Matyas-Meyer-Oseas scheme*

***Miyaguchi-Preneel Scheme***   The **Miyaguchi-Preneel scheme** is an extended version of Matyas-Meyer-Oseas. To make the algorithm stronger against attack, the plaintext, the cipher key, and the ciphertext are all exclusive-ored together to create the new digest. This is the scheme used by the Whirlpool hash function. Figure 12.5 shows the Miyaguchi-Preneel scheme.

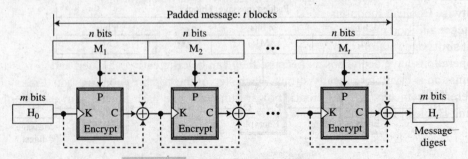

**Fig. 12.5**  *Miyaguchi-Preneel scheme*

## 12.2       DESCRIPTION OF MD HASH FAMILY

Hash functions of the MD-family are iterated hash functions and follow the MD-design principle. Further, these hash functions share a common structure of the compression function, which is shown in Fig. 12.6. The compression function consists of two major parts which are the message expansion and the consecutive evaluation of a number of similar operations, called steps. These steps are usually grouped together into 3-5 rounds. After the last step of the compression function, the input chaining variables are added to the output, which complicates the inversion of the compression function.

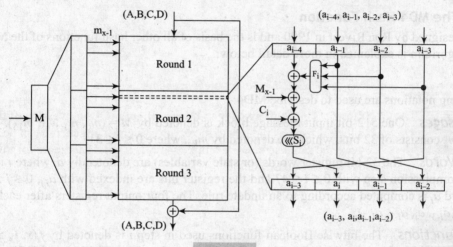

**Fig. 12.6**

The Message Expansion ensures, that each message block is used more than once during one iteration of the compression function. There are two different types of message expansions: the roundwise permutation and the recursive message expansion. In roundwise permutation the message words are not changed, but rather used in a different order in each round. The recursive message expansion was designed to increase the diffusion of the message words. Nearly all inputs of each step depend on all message words. Thus, a small change in one message word immediately effects many steps. See \ cite{Dau05} for more details on the message expansions.

In each Step of the compression function, a number of registers (4-8, depending on the algorithm) are updated by compressing one word of the expanded message. The operations of one step are very similar in every specific hash function and consist of the following basic operations:

1. Bitwise Boolean functions
2. Integer addition modulo $2^w$
3. Bit shifts and rotations

These operations have been chosen, because they can be efficiently evaluated and it is assumed that their combination is cryptographically strong. Each step of the compression function differs only in the use of different parameters or a different Boolean function. The hash functions of the MD-family use the following Boolean functions in their step:

## Bitwise Boolean Functions

$$XOR(x, y, z) = x \oplus y \oplus z$$
$$MAJ(x, y, z) = xy \oplus xz \oplus yz$$
$$IF(x, y, z) = xy \oplus xz \oplus z$$

These functions are considered to have strong cryptographic properties. See [Pre93] and [Dau05] for a detailed analysis of these Boolean functions.

### 12.2.1   The MD4 Hash Function

MD4 was designed by Ron Rivest in 1990 and is the basis of all other hash functions of the MD-family. The hash algorithm is explained in more detail below:

### Notation

The following notations are used to describe MD4:

**Input Messages**   One 512-bit input message block is denoted by $M = (m_0, m_1, \ldots, m_{15})$. Each message word $m_k$ consists of 32 bits, which are denoted by $m_{k,j}$, where $0 \leq j \leq 31$.

**Register Words**   The 32-bit register words (or state variables) are denoted by $a_i$ where $i$ is the number of the compression step with $0 \leq i \leq 47$ and the register bits are indexed with $a_{i,j}$, $0 \leq j \leq 31$. Each register word $a_i$ is computed according to an update rule. The four output registers after each step $i$ are grouped to $(a_{i-3}, a_i, a_{i-1}, a_{i-2})$.

**Boolean Functions**   The bitwise Boolean functions used in step $i$ is denoted by $f_i(x, y, z)$ (or short $f\_i$). The variables $x, y, z$ are 32-bit words and the Boolean functions IF, MAJ and XOR are applied bitwise to these words.

**Description**   The MD4 algorithm compresses an input with a maximum length of $2^{64}$ to a 128-bit hash value. The size of one message block in MD4 is 512 bit. The input message is padded to fit this message block size. First, the padding scheme always appends a single 1 bit to the end of the message. Then, 0 bits are appended until the message length is congruent to 448 modulo 512. Finally, the 64-bit representation of the message length before the padding was applied is appended.

Each 512-bit message block of the padded message is compressed by the compression function which consists of three rounds having 16 steps each. In each round a different Boolean function $f_i$ is used. The IF function is used for the first, the MAJ function for the second and the XOR function for the third round, as shown in the following table. Each message word $m_k$ with $0 \leq k \leq 15$ of a message block M is added exactly once in each round.

**Table 12.2**   *Boolean Function $f_i$ and constant $c_i$ in MD4*

| $i$ | $f_i$ | $c_i$ |
|---|---|---|
| 0...15 | IF $(x, y, z)$ | 0x00000000 |
| 16...31 | MAJ$(x, y, z)$ | 0x5a827999 |
| 21...47 | XOR$(x, y, z)$ | 0x6ed9eba1 |

In every step of MD4, a 32-bit register value (or often called state variable) $a_i$ is computed according to the following recursive update rule:

$$a_i = (a_{i-4} + f_i (a_{i-1}, a_{i-2}, a_{i-3}) + m_{wi} + c_i) << s_i, \ 0 \leq i \leq 47.$$

The operator + denotes the addition modulo $2^{32}$ and the term $s_i$ denotes a circular left shift (rotation) by $s_i$ positions. The variable $m_{wi}$ specifies the message word to compress. The variable $c_i$ defines a round constant, which is the same for each step in one round (See Table 12.2). The permutation of the message words is determined by the index $w_i$ which are described in Table 12.3.

**Table 12.3** *The permutation of the message block words in MD4*

| $i$ | $w_i$ |
|---|---|
| 0 ... 15 | 0, 1, 2, 3, 4, 5, 6, 7, 8, 9, 10, 11, 12, 13, 14, 15 |
| 16 ... 31 | 0, 4, 8, 12, 1, 5, 9, 13, 2, 6, 10, 14, 3, 7, 11, 15 |

The number of bit positions $s_i$ in a rotation is changed for each step but repeated four times in every round. For each message block, the update rule of the compression function is initialized by the chaining variables $(A, B, C, D) = (a_{-1}, a_{-4}, a_{-3}, a_{-2})$. The initial values for MD4 are:

$$(A, B, C, D) = (0x67452301, 0xefcdab89, 0x98badcfe, 0x10325476)$$

**Table 12.4** *The size of the rotation $s_i$ in each step of MD4*

| $i$ | $s_i$ |
|---|---|
| 0 ... 15 | 3, 7, 11, 19, 3, 7, 11, 19, 3, 7, 11, 19, 3, 7, 11, 19 |
| 16 ... 31 | 3, 5, 9, 13, 3, 5, 9, 13, 3, 5, 9, 13, 3, 5, 9, 13 |
| 21 ... 47 | 3, 9, 11, 15, 3, 9, 11, 15, 3, 9, 11, 15, 3, 9, 11, 15 |

After the processing of all 48 steps, the last four register values are added to the chaining variables: (A, B, C, D) = (A, B, C, D) + ($a_{47}$, $a_{44}$, $a_{45}$, $a_{46}$). If no message block is processed anymore, the resulting hash value is the concatenation of the four chaining variables (A, B, C, D).

Because of the initial cryptanalysis done on MD4 by Ralph Merkle (who attacked the first two rounds) and Eli Biham (who launched a differential attack on the first two rounds), MD4 was improved to MD5 by Rivest.

The structure of MD4 is quite similar, but there are some important differences. There are four non-linear functions, one used in each encryption (a different one for each round).

$$F(x, y, z) = \text{IF}(x, y, z)$$
$$G(x, y, z) = (x \wedge y) \vee (y \wedge (\neg z))$$
$$H(x, y, z) = XOR(x, y, z)$$
$$I(x, y, z) = y \oplus (x \vee (\neg z))$$

The symbols $\oplus$ stands for XOR, $\wedge$ stands for AND, $\vee$ stands for OR, stands for complement.

MD5 starts with four initial values stored in 4, 32-bit registers, $A$, $B$, $C$ and $D$. These are called the chaining variables. The four initial values are copied into 4 temporary registers of size 32 bits each: A is stored in a, $B$ in $b$, $C$ in $c$ and $D$ in $d$.

MD5 has 4 rounds, one round more than its ancestor MD4. Each round uses 16 operations. The rounds of the hash function operates on 512 bits, and the message is divided into 16, 32-bits denoted by $M_0,...,M_{15}$.

Each operation of MD5 is defined as follows: If $M_j$ represents the $j^{th}$ sub-block of the message from 0-15, and $<< s$ represents a left circular shift by s-bits, then an operation of MD5 is:

$$MD5-operation(a,b,c,d,M_j,s,t_i):$$

$$a = b + ((a + NL(b,c,d) + M_j + t_i) << s)$$

Here NL stands for one of the four non-linear functions mentioned above (F, G, H or I).

The constant $t_i$ was chosen as: in step i, $t_i$ is the integer part of $2^{32}$(absolute(sin(i))), where i is in radians.

As described before each round performs 16 operations. In round 1, the 16 operations are on $M_0$, $M_1$, ...,$M_{15}$ respectively. Each of the operation also acts on 4, 32-bit registers as defined in the above function as $a$, $b$, $c$ and $d$. However for successive operations they are given a circular shift; like the first operation acts on $a$, $b$, $c$ and $d$. The next operation acts on $d$, $a$, $b$, $c$, the next operates on $c$, $d$, $a$, $b$, while the next one operates on $b$, $c$, $d$, $a$. The next operation thus gain acts on $a$, $b$, $c$ and $d$. The non-linear function used in the 16 operations in round 1 is $F$. Similarly, the other rounds are constructed.

In round 2, the non-linear function is G, in round 3, it is H and in round 4 it is I. However the 16 operations in round 2 acts on the message blocks in a different order, $M_1$, $M_6$, $M_{11}$,...,$M_{12}$. In round 2, the message blocks are $M_5$, $M_8$,...,$M_2$, while in round 3, the message blocks are $M_0$, $M_7$, $M_{14}$,..., $M_9$.

The improvements of MD5 over MD4 are outlined below:
1. A fourth step has been added.
2. Each step has a unique additive constant.
3. The function G in round 2 was changed to a less symmetric form.
4. The hash function has a faster diffusion and a stronger avalanche effect.
5. The order in which the message blocks are transformed by the operations are changed.
6. The left circular shift amounts have been optimized to obtain a faster diffusion. The four shifts used in each round are different from the shifts used in other rounds.

However there have been significant improvements in collision attacks on the hash functions, like MD4 and MD5. The basic design principle of MD5 has thus been challenged. Hence we are at a crucial juncture where new hash function paradigms are being developed and standards for hash functions are being searched.

NIST has opened a public competition to develop a new cryptographic hash algorithm, which converts a variable length message into a short "message digest" that can be used for digital signatures, message authentication and other applications. The competition is NIST's response to recent advances in the cryptanalysis of hash functions. The new hash algorithm will be called "SHA-3" and will augment the hash algorithms currently specified in FIPS 180-2 (refer http://csrc.nist.gov/groups/ST/hash/sha-3/index.html)

## 12.3                 WHIRLPOOL

**Whirlpool** is designed by Vincent Rijmen and Paulo S. L. M. Barreto. It is endorsed by the **New European Schemes for Signatures, Integrity, and Encryption (NESSIE).** Whirlpool is an iterated cryptographic hash function, based on the Miyaguchi-Preneel scheme, that uses a symmetric-key block cipher in place of the compression function. The block cipher is a modified AES cipher that has been tailored for this purpose. Figure 12.7 shows the Whirlpool hash function.

***Preparation***    Before starting the hash algorithm, the message needs to be prepared for processing. Whirlpool requires that the length of the original message be less than $2^{256}$ bits. A message needs to be padded before being processed. The padding is a single 1-bit followed by the necessary numbers of 0-bits to make the length of the padding an odd multiple of 256 bits. After padding, a block of 256 bits is added to define the length of the original message. This block is treated as an unsigned number.

After padding and adding the length field, the augmented message size is an even multiple of 256 bits or a multiple of 512 bits. Whirlpool creates a digest of 512 bits from a multiple 512-bit block message. The 512-bit digest, $H_0$, is initialized to all 0's. This value becomes the cipher key for encrypting the first block. The ciphertext resulting from encrypting each block becomes the cipher key for the next block after being exclusive-ored with the previous cipher key and the plaintext block. The message digest is the final 512-bit ciphertext after the last exclusive-or operation.

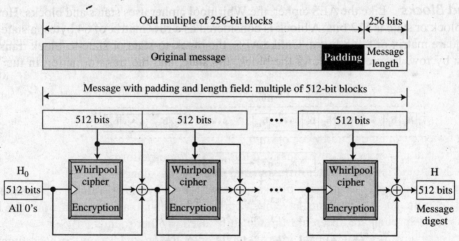

**Fig. 12.7**   *Whirlpool hash function*

### 12.3.1   Whirlpool Cipher

The **Whirlpool cipher** is a non-Feistel cipher like AES that was mainly designed as a block cipher to be used in a hash algorithm. Instead of giving the whole description of this cipher, we just assume that the reader is familiar with AES from Chapter 7. Here the Whirlpool cipher is compared with the AES cipher and their differences are mentioned.

***Rounds***    Whirlpool is a round cipher that uses 10 rounds. The block size and key size are 512 bits. The cipher uses 11 round keys, $K_0$ to $K_{10}$, each of 512 bits. Figure 12.8 shows the general design of the Whirlpool cipher.

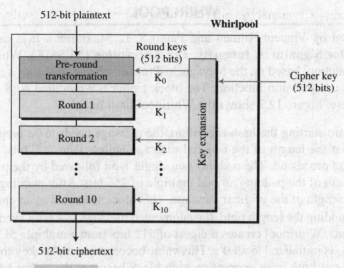

**Fig. 12.8** *General idea of the Whirlpool cipher*

**States and Blocks** Like the AES cipher, the Whirlpool cipher uses states and blocks. However, the size of the block or state is 512 bits. A block is considered as a row matrix of 64 bytes; a state is considered as a square matrix of 8 × 8 bytes. Unlike AES, the block-to-state or state-to-block transformation is done row by row. Figure 12.9 shows the block, the state, and the transformation in the Whirlpool cipher.

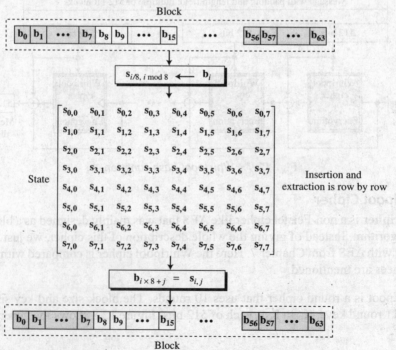

**Fig. 12.9** *Block and state in the Whirlpool cipher*

***Structure of Each Round***   Figure 12.10 shows the structure of each round. Each round uses four transformations.

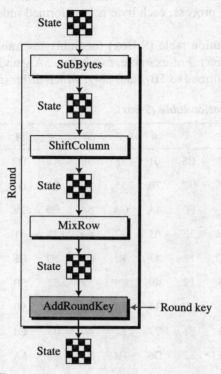

**Fig. 12.10**   *Structure of each round in the Whirlpool cipher*

***SubBytes***   Like in AES, **SubBytes** provide a nonlinear transformation. A byte is represented as two hexadecimal digits. The left digit defines the row and the right digit defines the column of the substitution table. The two hexadecimal digits at the junction of the row and the column are the new byte. Figure 12.11 shows the idea.

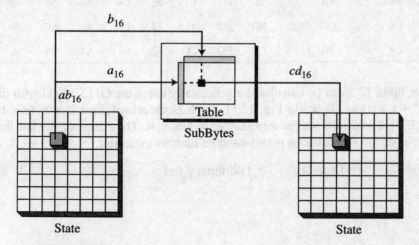

**Fig. 12.11**   *SubBytes transformations in the Whirlpool cipher*

In the SubBytes transformation, the state is treated as an $8 \times 8$ matrix of bytes. Transformation is done one byte at a time. The contents of each byte are changed, but the arrangement of the bytes in the matrix remains the same. In the process, each byte is transformed independently; we have 64 distinct byte-to-byte transformations.

Table 12.5 shows the substitution table (S-Box) for SubBytes transformation. The transformation definitely provides confusion effect. For example, two bytes, $5A_{16}$ and $5B_{16}$, which differ only in one bit (the rightmost bit), are transformed to $5B_{16}$ and $88_{16}$, which differ in five bits.

**Table 12.5** *SubBytes transformation table (S-Box)*

|   | 0 | 1 | 2 | 3 | 4 | 5 | 6 | 7 | 8 | 9 | A | B | C | D | E | F |
|---|---|---|---|---|---|---|---|---|---|---|---|---|---|---|---|---|
| 0 | 18 | 23 | C6 | E8 | 87 | B8 | 01 | 4F | 36 | A6 | D2 | F5 | 79 | 6F | 91 | 52 |
| 1 | 16 | BC | 9B | 8E | A3 | 0C | 7B | 35 | 1D | E0 | D7 | C2 | 2E | 4B | FE | 57 |
| 2 | 15 | 77 | 37 | E5 | 9F | F0 | 4A | CA | 58 | C9 | 29 | 0A | B1 | A0 | 6B | 85 |
| 3 | BD | 5D | 10 | F4 | CB | 3E | 05 | 67 | E4 | 27 | 41 | 8B | A7 | 7D | 95 | C8 |
| 4 | FB | EF | 7C | 66 | DD | 17 | 47 | 9E | CA | 2D | BF | 07 | AD | 5A | 83 | 33 |
| 5 | 63 | 02 | AA | 71 | C8 | 19 | 49 | C9 | F2 | E3 | 5B | 88 | 9A | 26 | 32 | B0 |
| 6 | E9 | 0F | D5 | 80 | BE | CD | 34 | 48 | FF | 7A | 90 | 5F | 20 | 68 | 1A | AE |
| 7 | B4 | 54 | 93 | 22 | 64 | F1 | 73 | 12 | 40 | 08 | C3 | EC | DB | A1 | 8D | 3D |
| 8 | 97 | 00 | CF | 2B | 76 | 82 | D6 | 1B | B5 | AF | 6A | 50 | 45 | F3 | 30 | EF |
| 9 | 3F | 55 | A2 | EA | 65 | BA | 2F | C0 | DE | 1C | FD | 4D | 92 | 75 | 06 | 8A |
| A | B2 | E6 | 0E | 1F | 62 | D4 | A8 | 96 | F9 | C5 | 25 | 59 | 84 | 72 | 39 | 4C |
| B | 5E | 78 | 38 | 8C | C1 | A5 | E2 | 61 | B3 | 21 | 9C | 1E | 43 | C7 | FC | 04 |
| C | 51 | 99 | 6D | 0D | FA | DF | 7E | 24 | 3B | AB | CE | 11 | 8F | 4E | B7 | EB |
| D | 3C | 81 | 94 | F7 | 9B | 13 | 2C | D3 | E7 | 6E | C4 | 03 | 56 | 44 | 7E | A9 |
| E | 2A | BB | C1 | 53 | DC | 0B | 9D | 6C | 31 | 74 | F6 | 46 | AC | 89 | 14 | E1 |
| F | 16 | 3A | 69 | 09 | 70 | B6 | C0 | ED | CC | 42 | 98 | A4 | 28 | 5C | F8 | 86 |

The entries in Table 12.5 can be calculated algebraically using the $GF(2^4)$ field with the irreducible polynomials $(x^4 + x + 1)$ as shown in Fig. 12.11. Each hexadecimal digit in a byte is the input to a minibox ($E$ and $E^{-1}$). The results are fed into another minibox, $R$. The $E$ boxes calculate the exponential of input hexadecimal; the $R$ box uses a pseudorandom number generator.

$E(\text{input}) = (x^3 + x + 1)^{\text{input}} \bmod (x^4 + x + 1) \text{ if input} \neq 0xF$

$E(0xF) = 0$

The $E^{-1}$ box is just the inverse of the E box where the roles of input and output are changed. The input/output values for boxes are also tabulated in Fig. 12.12.

**ShiftColumns** To provide permutation, Whirlpool uses the **ShiftColumns** transformation, which is similar to the *ShiftRows* transformation in AES, except that the columns instead of rows are shifted. Shifting depends on the position of the column. Column 0 goes through 0-byte shifting (no shifting), while column 7 goes through 7-byte shifting. Figure 12.13 shows the shifting transformation.

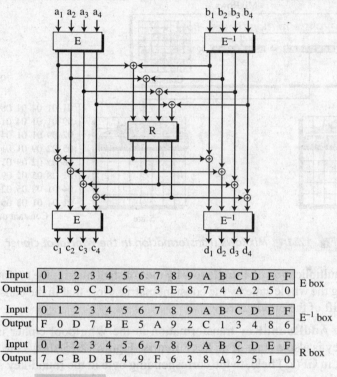

| Input | 0 | 1 | 2 | 3 | 4 | 5 | 6 | 7 | 8 | 9 | A | B | C | D | E | F | |
|---|---|---|---|---|---|---|---|---|---|---|---|---|---|---|---|---|---|
| Output | 1 | B | 9 | C | D | 6 | F | 3 | E | 8 | 7 | 4 | A | 2 | 5 | 0 | E box |

| Input | 0 | 1 | 2 | 3 | 4 | 5 | 6 | 7 | 8 | 9 | A | B | C | D | E | F | |
|---|---|---|---|---|---|---|---|---|---|---|---|---|---|---|---|---|---|
| Output | F | 0 | D | 7 | B | E | 5 | A | 9 | 2 | C | 1 | 3 | 4 | 8 | 6 | $E^{-1}$ box |

| Input | 0 | 1 | 2 | 3 | 4 | 5 | 6 | 7 | 8 | 9 | A | B | C | D | E | F | |
|---|---|---|---|---|---|---|---|---|---|---|---|---|---|---|---|---|---|
| Output | 7 | C | B | D | E | 4 | 9 | F | 6 | 3 | 8 | A | 2 | 5 | 1 | 0 | R box |

**Fig. 12.12** *SubBytes in the Whirlpool cipher*

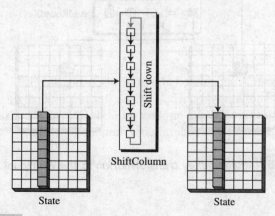

**Fig. 12.13** *ShiftColumns transformation in the Whirlpool cipher*

*MixRows*   The **MixRows** transformation has the same effect as the MixColumns transformation in AES: it diffuses the bits. The MixRows transformation is a matrix transformation where bytes are interpreted as 8-bit words (or polynomials) with coefficients in GF(2). Multiplication of bytes is done in $GF(2^8)$, but the modulus is different from the one used in AES. The Whirlpool cipher uses (0x11D) or $(x^8 + x^4 + x^3 + x^2 + 1)$ as the modulus. Addition is the same as XORing of 8-bit words. Figure 12.14 shows the MixRows transformation.

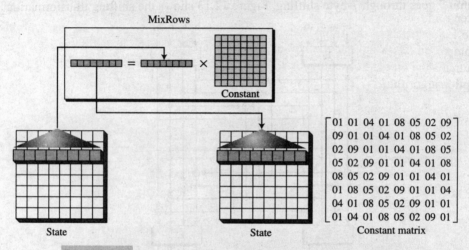

**Fig. 12.14**   *MixRows transformation in the Whirlpool cipher*

The figure shows multiplication of a single row by the constant matrix; the multiplication can actually be done by multiplying the whole state by the constant matrix. Note that in the constant matrix, each row is the circular right shift of the previous row.

*AddRoundKey*   The **AddRoundKey** transformation in the Whirlpool cipher is done byte by byte, because each round key is also a state of an $8 \times 8$ matrix. Figure 12.15 shows the process. A byte from the data state is added, in $GF(2^8)$ field, to the corresponding byte in the round-key state. The result is the new byte in the new state.

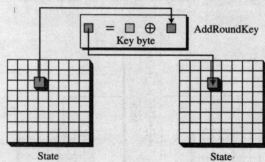

**Fig. 12.15**   *AddRoundKey transformation in the Whirlpool cipher*

## Key Expansion

As Fig. 12.16 shows, the key-expansion algorithm in Whirlpool is totally different from the algorithm in AES. Instead of using a new algorithm for creating round keys, Whirlpool uses a copy of the encryption algorithm (without the pre-round) to create the round keys. The output of each round in the encryption algorithm is the round key for that round. At first glance, this looks like a circular definition; where do the round keys for the key expansion algorithm come from? Whirlpool has elegantly solved this problem by using ten round constants (RCs) as the virtual round keys for the key-expansion algorithm. In other words, the key-expansion algorithm uses constants as the round keys and the encryption algorithm uses the output of each round of the key-expansion algorithm as the round keys. The key-generation algorithm treats the cipher key as the *plaintext* and encrypts it. Note that the cipher key is also $K_0$ for the encryption algorithm.

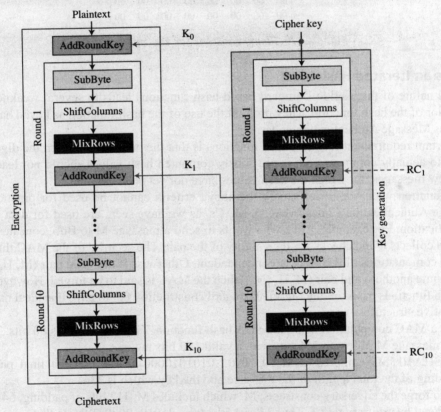

**Fig. 12.16** *Key expansion in the Whirlpool cipher*

**Round Constants** Each round constant, $RC_r$, is an $8 \times 8$ matrix where only the first row has non-zero values. The rest of the entries are all 0's. The values for the first row in each constant matrix can be calculated using the SubBytes transformation (Table 12.5).

$$RC_{round}[row, column] = SubBytes\ (8(round - 1) + column) \qquad \text{if row} = 0$$

$$RC_{round}[row, column] = 0 \quad \text{if row} \neq 0$$

In other words, $RC_1$ uses the first eight entries in the SubBytes transformation table [Table 12.5]; $RC_2$ uses the second eight entries, and so on. For example, Fig. 12.17 shows $RC_3$, where the first row is the third eight entries in the SubBytes table.

$$RC_3 = \begin{bmatrix} 1D & E0 & D7 & C2 & 2E & 4B & FE & 57 \\ 00 & 00 & 00 & 00 & 00 & 00 & 00 & 00 \\ 00 & 00 & 00 & 00 & 00 & 00 & 00 & 00 \\ 00 & 00 & 00 & 00 & 00 & 00 & 00 & 00 \\ 00 & 00 & 00 & 00 & 00 & 00 & 00 & 00 \\ 00 & 00 & 00 & 00 & 00 & 00 & 00 & 00 \\ 00 & 00 & 00 & 00 & 00 & 00 & 00 & 00 \\ 00 & 00 & 00 & 00 & 00 & 00 & 00 & 00 \end{bmatrix}$$

**Fig. 12.17** *Round constant for the third round*

## 12.3.2 Is an Iterated Hash Ideal?

The iterated nature of the Merkle Damgard based hash functions leads to several weaknesses or non-ideal behavior of the hash function. They prohibit the use of the hash function as keyed hash functions, to be used as Message Authentication codes.

An important requirement for ideal hash functions is that the only way to learn the digest for a new message is to actually compute. That is previously computed hash values should not lead to the hash values of new messages, for which the hash values have not yet been obtained.

A hash function which does not satisfy the above criteria cannot be used for practical purposes, like Message Authentication Codes (MACs). MACs, as we have seen, are used for data integrity and data authentication. For example, Alice who wants to send a message M to Bob, concatenates M with $H_K(M)$. Bob collects it and checks for the validity of the pair. The security of the MAC thus lies on the fact that the computations of the MAC are independent. Otherwise if the valid pair $(M, H_K(M))$ can be used to compute another valid pair $(M', H_K(M'))$ then the MAC is said to be forged. However as we shall discuss, hash functions based on the Merkle Damgard construction fail to have this ideal nature because of their iterative structure.

Consider a MAC computation using the SHA hash function. The key length is 80 bits. The aversary intercepts a message M of length 256 bits with a valid 160 bits tag, t.

Thus, $t = SHA1(k\|M) = compress(k\|M\|10\ldots0\|0\ldots0101010000)$. Note that the final padding is the binary encoding of the total length of the message and the key which is 336.

In order to forge the adversary constructs, M' which includes M, 112 bits of padding, 64 bit encoding of 336, followed by arbitrary text T. Thus $M' = k\| 10\ldots00\ldots0101010000\|T$. Note that

$SHA(k\|M') = compress(compress(k\|M\| 10\ldots00\ldots0101010000)$, $T\|padding + length) = compress$ $(t, T\|padding + length)$. In other words, the adversary may compute a valid tag on M', by applying the compression function to t, T and some padding all of which are known! Thus the naive MAC construction based on iterative hash function can be easily forged.

This is the reason MACs are not realized by the iterated hash function with one of the inputs as the key. But rather they are implemented as NMACs or HMACs as described previously. It may be observed that NMAC which uses two keyed hash function, prevents the above mentioned extension attack by the outer hash function application. It prevents the exposure of the inner iterative function. Thus the above forgery does not work.

### Security Criteria for NMAC

Let us study the security criteria of a given NMAC, defined by the keyed hash functions $h_L$ and $g_K$. The composition as defined previously is $z=NMAC(x)=h_L(g_K(x))$. Now let us assume that the NMAC can be forged after q queries. That is after q queries the adversary is able to create a valid pair, $(x,z)$. This means that the adversary is able to create $(x,z)$ from q valid pairs $(x_1,z_1),...(x_q,z_q)$.

Now the adversary can obtain the elements $y_1=g_K(x_1),...,y_q=g_K(x_q)$, $y=g_K(x)$. Now there can be two mutually exclusive cases:

**Case 1:** $y$ matches with at least one of $y_1,...,y_q$, say $y_i$. Then $(x,x_i)$ are two colliding messages for the hash function $g_K$, without knowing the key.

**Case 2:** $y$ does not match with any one of $y_1,...,y_q$. Then the pair $(y,z)$ is a valid pair for the outer hash function, $h_L$.

Thus if there exists a forgery against the big NMAC with q queries, then there either exists a collision attack against the inner MAC with q+1 queries or there exists a forgery against the outer MAC with q queries. In other words, if there does not exist a collision attack against the inner MAC and their does not exist a forgery against the outer MAC, then there does not exist a forgery against the NMAC.

### Joux's Multi-collision attacks on Iterated Hash Functions

Next we study another attack on iterated hash functions because they are not ideal. A generic collision-finding algorithm takes $2^{n/2}$ order, where n is the block length of the digest. Suppose we have two functions, $G,H:\{0,1\}^* \rightarrow \{0,1\}^n$, each having an ideal security $2^{n/2}$

We shall address the question, can we construct a collision-resistant hash with ideal security $2^n$? We define $F(M)=G(M)\|H(M)$. This indeed works if both the hashes are ideal. We claim that it fails if one of the hash functions is iterative.

Define a multi-collisions as a collection of several messages which hash to the same output. Assume that one of the functions, say G is based on Merkle Damgard construction. Let C be its compression function. A collision is thus found on C in time order $2^{n/2}$. Let the messages be: $M_1^{(0)}$ and $M_1^{(1)}$. Continuing this for $k$ times, in time $O(k2^{n/2})$ we have: $C(h_i, M_{i+1}^{(0)}) = C(h_i, M_{i+1}^{(1)}) = h_{i+1}$, where $1 \leq i \leq k$.

We thus now have a treasure of collisions. Any message that has the form:

$M_1^{(b_1)}\| M_2^{(b_2)} \| L \| M_k^{(b_k)}$, where $b_1, ..., b_k \in \{0,1\}$ collides. There are thus $2^k$ such messages, many times more than what one would have found in time $k2^{n/2}$, had G been ideal!

By Birthday Paradox, even if H is ideal there is a high probability that there is a collision in these $2^k = 2^{n/2}$ messages (set $k = n/2$). Thus we have a collision of the hash F in time $O(n2^{n/2})$. This is lesser than $O(2^n)$, thus proving we do not get the security of a hash of $2n$ bits.

### 12.3.3 A Practical Attack on a Hash Function

We have argued that if the message can be modified to a different value, so that the hash digest does not change, then the hash function cannot function. However if a meaningful message be modified then there is a large probability that the altered message which collides will be meaningless. Hence such a collision will not be of any practical significance. Does that imply that the collision attacks do not have practical significance?

Consider a message $M=M_1\|M_2\|...\|M_k$. Create, $C(h_j,N)=C(h_j,N')$, which is a collision of the compression function. Create two messages that differ in the $j^{th}$ block:

- $M=M_1\|M_2\|...M_{j-1}\|N\|M_{j+1}\|...\|M_k$
- $M'=M_1\|M_2\|...M_{j-1}\|N'\|M_{j+1}\|...\|M_k$

The messages M and M' are thus bound to collide although N and N' may be completely gibberish.

They are now part of a longer text which may be carefully doctored. A common example where two documents can lead to the same hash value was shown for two post-script (ps) documents. Post-script files are programs with a syntax like (R1)(R2){message1}{message2}. This indicates that if the values of R1 and R2, are equal then message 1 is displayed, else message 2 is displayed. Thus if the above messages M and M' are cleverly placed in the values of R1 and R2, they shall not be noticed in the viewer. One can create two documents, one with both R1 and R2 same as that in M and the other in which say R2 has the value of M'. Thus when the user opens the first document he sees message 1, while the second document shows message 2. The hash values of both the documents are however the same. This can lead to catastrophic disaster! The principle we learn is that one should not hash a program, but rather should do for *ascii text*.

*y* be complete gibberish, they are now part of a longer text, which may be carefully constructed to accommodate them!

Theoreticians used to believe that the collisions on the hash functions were of no practical use.

## Conclusion

Table 12.6 summarizes some characteristics of the Whirlpool cipher.

**Table 12.6** *Main characteristics of the Whirlpool cipher*

| |
|---|
| Block size: 512 bits |
| Cipher key size: 512 bits |
| Number of rounds: 10 |
| Key expansion: using the cipher itself with round constants as round keys |
| Substitution: SubBytes transformation |
| Permutation: ShiftColumns transformation |
| Mixing: MixRows transformation |
| Round Constant: cubic roots of the first eighty prime numbers |

## Analysis

Although Whirlpool has not been extensively studied or tested, it is based on a robust scheme (Miyaguchi-Preneel), and for a compression function uses a cipher that is based on AES, a cryptosystem that has been proved very resistant to attacks. In addition, the size of the message digest is the same as for SHA-512. Therefore it is expected to be a very strong cryptographic hash function. However, more testing and researches are needed to confirm this. The only concern is that Whirlpool, which is based on a cipher as the compression function, may not be as efficient as SHA-512, particularly when it is implemented in hardware.

## 12.4         SHA-512

SHA-512 is the version of SHA with a 512-bit message digest. This version, like the others in the SHA family of algorithms, is based on the Merkle-Damgard scheme. We have chosen this particular version for discussion because it is the latest version, it has a more complex structure than the others, and its message digest is the longest. Once the structure of this version is understood, it should not be difficult to understand the structures of the other versions. For characteristics of SHA-512 see Table 12.1.

### 12.4.1   Introduction

SHA-512 creates a digest of 512 bits from a multiple-block message. Each block is 1024 bits in length, as shown in Fig. 12.18.

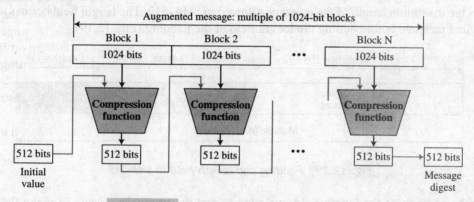

**Fig. 12.18** *Message digest creation SHA-512*

The digest is initialized to a predetermined value of 512 bits. The algorithm mixes this initial value with the first block of the message to create the first intermediate message digest of 512 bits. This digest is then mixed with the second block to create the second intermediate digest. Finally, the $(N-1)$th digest is mixed with the $N$th block to create the $N$th digest. When the last block is processed, the resulting digest is the message digest for the entire message.

### Message Preparation

SHA-512 insists that the length of the original message be less than $2^{128}$ bits. This means that if the length of a message is equal to or greater than $2^{128}$, it will not be processed by SHA-512. This is not usually a problem because $2^{128}$ bits is probably larger than the total storage capacity of any system.

---

**SHA-512 creates a 512-bit message digest out of a message less than $2^{128}$.**

---

**Example 12.1**   This example shows that the message length limitation of SHA-512 is not a serious problem. Suppose we need to send a message that is $2^{128}$ bits in length. How long does it take for a communications network with a data rate of $2^{64}$ bits per second to send this message?

**Solution**   A communications network that can send $2^{64}$ bits per second is not yet available. Even if it were, it would take many years to send this message. This tells us that we do not need to worry about the SHA-512 message length restriction.

**Example 12.2** This example also concerns the message length in SHA-512. How many pages are occupied by a message of $2^{128}$ bits?

***Solution*** Suppose that a character is 32, or $2^6$, bits. Each page is less than 2048, or approximately $2^{12}$, characters. So $2^{128}$ bits need at least $2^{128} / 2^{18}$, or $2^{110}$, pages. This again shows that we need not worry about the message length restriction.

### Length Field and Padding

Before the message digest can be created, SHA-512 requires the addition of a 128-bit unsigned-integer length field to the message that defines the length of the message in bits. This is the length of the original message before padding. An unsigned integer field of 128 bits can define a number between 0 and $2^{128} - 1$, which is the maximum length of the message allowed in SHA-512. The length field defines the length of the original message before adding the length field or the padding (Fig. 12.19).

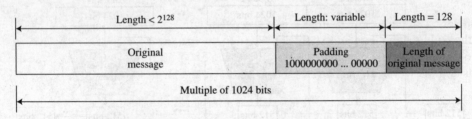

**Fig. 12.19** *Padding and length field in SHA-512*

Before the addition of the length field, we need to pad the original message to make the length a multiple of 1024. We reserve 128 bits for the length field, as shown in Fig. 12.19. The length of the padding field can be calculated as follows. Let |M| be the length of the original message and |P| be the length of the padding field.

$$(|M| + |P| + 128) = 0 \bmod 1024 \rightarrow |P| = (-|M| - 128) \bmod 1024$$

The format of the padding is one 1 followed by the necessary number of 0s.

**Example 12.3** What is the number of padding bits if the length of the original message is 2590 bits?

***Solution*** We can calculate the number of padding bits as follows:

$$|P| = (-2590 - 128) \bmod 1024 = -2718 \bmod 1024 = 354$$

The padding consists of one 1 followed by 353 0's.

**Example 12.4** Do we need padding if the length of the original message is already a multiple of 1024 bits?

***Solution*** Yes we do, because we need to add the length field. So padding is needed to make the new block a multiple of 1024 bits.

**Example 12.5** What is the minimum and maximum number of padding bits that can be added to a message?

**Solution**

a. The minimum length of padding is 0 and it happens when $(-M - 128)$ mod 1024 is 0. This means that $|M| = -128$ mod $1024 = 896$ mod 1024 bits. In other words, the last block in the original message is 896 bits. We add a 128-bit length field to make the block complete.

b. The maximum length of padding is 1023 and it happens when $(-|M| -128) = 1023$ mod 1024. This means that the length of the original message is $|M| = (-128 -1023)$ mod 1024 or the length is $|M| = 897$ mod 1024. In this case, we cannot just add the length field because the length of the last block exceeds one bit more than 1024. So we need to add 897 bits to complete this block and create a second block of 896 bits. Now the length can be added to make this block complete.

**Words** SHA-512 operates on words; it is **word oriented**. A word is defined as 64 bits. This means that, after the padding and the length field are added to the message, each block of the message consists of sixteen 64-bit words. The message digest is also made of 64-bit words, but the message digest is only eight words and the words are named A, B, C, D, E, F, G, and H, as shown in Fig. 12.20.

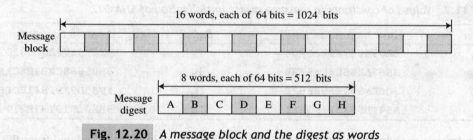

**Fig. 12.20** *A message block and the digest as words*

**SHA-252 is word-oriented. Each block is 16 words; the digest is only 8 words.**

**Word Expansion** Before processing, each message block must be expanded. A block is made of 1024 bits, or sixteen 64-bit words. As we will see later, we need 80 words in the processing phase. So the 16-word block needs to be expanded to 80 words, from $W_0$ to $W_{79}$. Figure 12.21 shows the **word-expansion** process. The 1024-bit block becomes the first 16 words; the rest of the words come from already-made words according to the operation shown in the figure.

**Example 12.6** Show how $W_{60}$ is made.

**Solution** Each word in the range $W_{16}$ to $W_{79}$ is made from four previously-made words. $W_{60}$ is made as

$$W_{60} = W_{44} \oplus \text{RotShift}_{1\text{-}8\text{-}7} (W_{45}) \oplus W_{53} \oplus \text{RotShift}_{19\text{-}61\text{-}6} (W_{58})$$

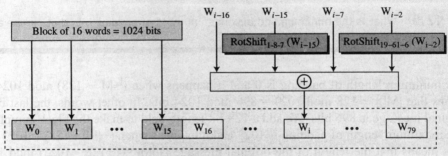

RotShift$_{1\text{-}m\text{-}n}$ ($x$): $RotR_l(x) \oplus RotR_m(x) \oplus ShL_n(x)$

$RotR_i(x)$: Right-rotation of the argument $x$ by $i$ bits
$ShL_i(x)$: Shift-left of the argument $x$ by $i$ bits and padding the left by 0's.

**Fig. 12.21** *Word expansion in SHA-512*

**Message Digest Initialization** The algorithm uses eight constants for message digest initialization. We call these constants $A_0$ to $H_0$ to match with the word naming used for the digest. Table 12.7 shows the value of these constants.

**Table 12.7** *Values of constants in message digest initialization of SHA-512*

| Buffer | Value (in hexadecimal) | Buffer | Value (in hexadecimal) |
|--------|------------------------|--------|------------------------|
| $A_0$ | 6A09E667F3BCC908 | $E_0$ | 510E527FADE682D1 |
| $B_0$ | BB67AE8584CAA73B | $F_0$ | 9B05688C2B3E6C1F |
| $C_0$ | 3C6EF372EF94F828 | $G_0$ | 1F83D9ABFB41BD6B |
| $D_0$ | A54FE53A5F1D36F1 | $H_0$ | 5BE0CD19137E2179 |

The reader may wonder where these values come from. The values are calculated from the first eight prime numbers (2, 3, 5, 7, 11, 13, 17, and 19). Each value is the fraction part of the square root of the corresponding prime number after converting to binary and keeping only the first 64 bits. For example, the eighth prime is 19, with the square root $(19)^{1/2} = 4.35889894354$. Converting the number to binary with only 64 bits in the fraction part, we get

$$(100.0101\ 1011\ 1110 \ldots 1001)_2 \rightarrow (4.5BE0CD19137E2179)_{16}$$

SHA-512 keeps the fraction part, $(5BE0CD19137E2179)_{16}$, as an unsigned integer.

### 12.4.2 Compression Function

SHA-512 creates a 512-bit (eight 64-bit words) message digest from a multiple-block message where each block is 1024 bits. The processing of each block of data in SHA-512 involves 80 rounds. Figure 12.22 shows the general outline for the compression function. In each round, the contents of eight previous buffers, one word from the expanded block ($W_i$), and one 64-bit constant ($K_i$) are mixed together and then operated on to create a new set of eight buffers. At the beginning of processing, the values of the eight buffers are saved into eight temporary variables. At the end of the processing (after step 79), these values are added to the values created from step 79. We call this last operation the *final adding,* as shown in Fig. 12.22.

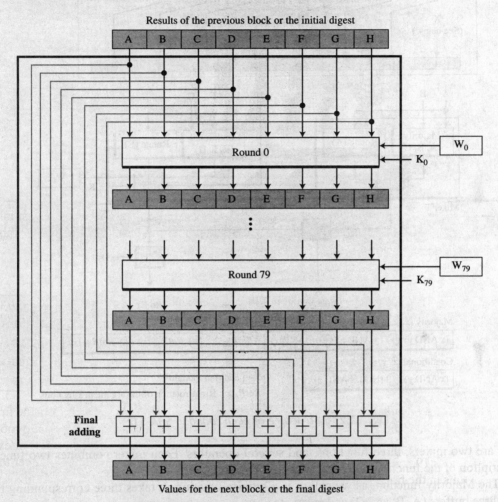

**Fig. 12.22** *Compression function in SHA-512*

## Structure of Each Round

In each round, eight new values for the 64-bit buffers are created from the values of the buffers in the previous round. As Fig. 12.23 shows, six buffers are the exact copies of one of the buffers in the previous round as shown below:

$$A \rightarrow B \quad B \rightarrow C \quad C \rightarrow D \quad E \rightarrow F \quad F \rightarrow G \quad G \rightarrow H$$

Two of the new buffers, A and E, receive their inputs from some complex functions that involve some of the previous buffers, the corresponding word for this round ($W_i$), and the corresponding constant for this round ($K_i$). Figure 12.23 shows the structure of each round.

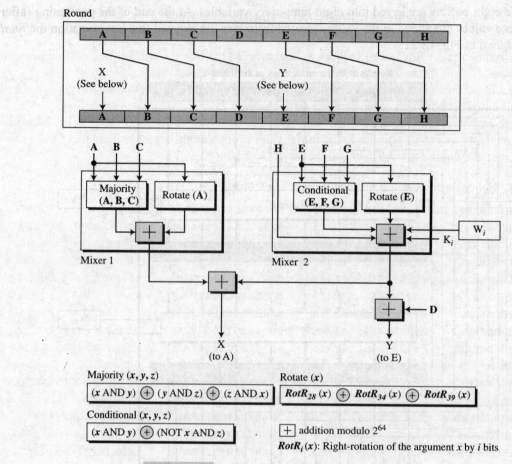

Majority $(x, y, z)$

$(x \text{ AND } y) \oplus (y \text{ AND } z) \oplus (z \text{ AND } x)$

Rotate $(x)$

$RotR_{28} (x) \oplus RotR_{34} (x) \oplus RotR_{39} (x)$

Conditional $(x, y, z)$

$(x \text{ AND } y) \oplus (\text{NOT } x \text{ AND } z)$

$\boxed{+}$ addition modulo $2^{64}$

$RotR_i (x)$: Right-rotation of the argument $x$ by $i$ bits

**Fig. 12.23** *Structure of each round in SHA-512*

There are two mixers, three functions, and several operators. Each mixer combines two functions. The description of the functions and operators follows:

1. The Majority function, as we call it, is a bitwise function. It takes three corresponding bits in three buffers (A, B, and C) and calculates

$$(A_j \text{ AND } B_j) \oplus (B_j \text{ AND } C_j) \oplus (C_j \text{ AND } A_j)$$

The resulting bit is the majority of three bits. If two or three bits are 1's, the resulting bit is 1; otherwise it is 0.

2. The Conditional function, as we call it, is also a bitwise function. It takes three corresponding bits in three buffers (E, F, and G) and calculates

$$(E_j \text{ AND } F_j) \oplus (\text{NOT } E_j \text{ AND } G_j)$$

The resulting bit is the logic "If $E_j$ then $F_j$; else $G_j$."

3. The Rotate function, as we call it, right-rotates the three instances of the same buffer (A or E) and applies the exclusive-or operation on the results.

$$\textbf{Rotate (A): } \textbf{RotR}_{28}(A) \oplus \textbf{RotR}_{34}(A) \oplus \textbf{RotR}_{29}(A)$$
$$\textbf{Rotate (E): } \textbf{RotR}_{28}(E) \oplus \textbf{RotR}_{34}(E) \oplus \textbf{RotR}_{29}(E)$$

4. The right-rotation function, $RotR_i(x)$, is the same as the one we used in the word-expansion process. It right-rotates its argument $i$ bits; it is actually a circular shift- right operation.

5. The addition operator used in the process is addition modulo $2^{64}$. This means that the result of adding two or more buffers is always a 64-bit word.

6. There are 80 constants, $K_0$ to $K_{79}$, each of 64 bits as shown in Table 12.8 in hexadecimal format (four in a row). Similar to the initial values for the eight digest buffers, these values are calculated from the first 80 prime numbers (2, 3,..., 409).

**Table 12.8**  *Eighty constants used for eighty rounds in SHA-512*

| | | | |
|---|---|---|---|
| 428A2F98D728AE22 | 7137449123EF65CD | B5C0FBCFEC4D3B2F | E9B5DBA58189DBBC |
| 3956C25BF348B538 | 59F111F1B605D019 | 923F82A4AF194F9B | AB1C5ED5DA6D8118 |
| D807AA98A3030242 | 12835B0145706FBE | 243185BE4EE4B28C | 550C7DC3D5FFB4E2 |
| 72BE5D74F27B896F | 80DEB1FE3B1696B1 | 9BDC06A725C71235 | C19BF174CF692694 |
| E49B69C19EF14AD2 | EFBE4786384F25E3 | 0FC19DC68B8CD5B5 | 240CA1CC77AC9C65 |
| 2DE92C6F592B0275 | 4A7484AA6EA6E483 | 5CB0A9DCBD41FBD4 | 76F988DA831153B5 |
| 983E5152EE66DFAB | A831C66D2DB43210 | B00327C898FB213F | BF597FC7BEEF0EE4 |
| C6E00BF33DA88FC2 | D5A79147930AA725 | 06CA6351E003826F | 142929670A0E6E70 |
| 27B70A8546D22FFC | 2E1B21385C26C926 | 4D2C6DFC5AC42AED | 53380D139D95B3DF |
| 650A73548BAF63DE | 766A0ABB3C77B2A8 | 81C2C92E47EDAEE6 | 92722C851482353B |
| A2BFE8A14CF10364 | A81A664BBC423001 | C24B8B70D0F89791 | C76C51A30654BE30 |
| D192E819D6EF5218 | D69906245565A910 | F40E35855771202A | 106AA07032BBD1B8 |
| 19A4C116B8D2D0C8 | 1E376C085141AB53 | 2748774CDF8EEB99 | 34B0BCB5E19B48A8 |
| 391C0CB3C5C95A63 | 4ED8AA4AE3418ACB | 5B9CCA4F7763E373 | 682E6FF3D6B2B8A3 |
| 748F82EE5DEFB2FC | 78A5636F43172F60 | 84C87814A1F0AB72 | 8CC702081A6439EC |
| 90BEFFFA23631E28 | A4506CEBDE82BDE9 | BEF9A3F7B2C67915 | C67178F2E372532B |
| CA273ECEEA26619C | D186B8C721C0C207 | EADA7DD6CDE0EB1E | F57D4F7FEE6ED178 |
| 06F067AA72176FBA | 0A637DC5A2C898A6 | 113F9804BEF90DAE | 1B710B35131C471B |
| 28DB77F523047D84 | 32CAAB7B40C72493 | 3C9EBE0A15C9BEBC | 431D67C49C100D4C |
| 4CC5D4BECB3E42B6 | 4597F299CFC657E2 | 5FCB6FAB3AD6FAEC | 6C44198C4A475817 |

Each value is the fraction part of the cubic root of the corresponding prime number after converting it to binary and keeping only the first 64 bits. For example, the 80th prime is 409, with the cubic root $(409)^{1/3} = 7.42291412044$. Converting this number to binary with only 64 bits in the fraction part, we get

$$(111.0110\ 1100\ 0100\ 0100\ \ldots\ 0111)_2 \rightarrow (7.6C44198C4A475817)_{16}$$

SHA-512 keeps the fraction part, $(6C44198C4A475817)_{16}$, as an unsigned integer.

**Example 12.7**  We apply the Majority function on buffers A, B, and C. If the leftmost hexadecimal digits of these buffers are 0x7, 0xA, and 0xE, respectively, what is the leftmost digit of the result?

**Solution**   The digits in binary are 0111, 1010, and 1110.

a.   The first bits are 0, 1, and 1. The majority is 1. We can also prove it using the definition of the Majority function:

$$(0 \text{ AND } 1) \oplus (1 \text{ AND } 1) \oplus (1 \text{ AND } 0) = 0 \oplus 1 \oplus 0 = 1$$

b.   The second bits are 1, 0, and 1. The majority is 1.

c.   The third bits are 1, 1, and 1. The majority is 1.

d.   The fourth bits are 1, 0, and 0. The majority is 0.

The result is 1110, or 0xE in hexadecimal.

**Example 12.8**   We apply the Conditional function on E, F, and G buffers. If the leftmost hexadecimal digits of these buffers are 0x9, 0xA, and 0xF respectively, what is the leftmost digit of the result?

**Solution**   The digits in binary are 1001, 1010, and 1111.

a.   The first bits are 1, 1, and 1. Since $E_1 = 1$, the result is $F_1$, which is 1. We can also use the definition of the Condition function to prove the result:

$$(1 \text{ AND } 1) \oplus (\text{NOT } 1 \text{ AND } 1) = 1 \oplus 0 = 1$$

b.   The second bits are 0, 0, and 1. Since $E_2$ is 0, the result is $G_2$, which is 1.

c.   The third bits are 0, 1, and 1. Since $E_3$ is 0, the result is $G_3$, which is 1.

d.   The fourth bits are 1, 0, and 1. Since $E_4$ is 1, the result is $F_4$, which is 0.

The result is 1110, or 0xE in hexadecimal.

**Analysis**   With a message digest of 512 bits, SHA-512 expected to be resistant to all attacks, including collision attacks. It has been claimed that this version's improved design makes it more efficient and more secure than the previous versions. However, more research and testing are needed to confirm this claim.

## 12.4   RECOMMENDED READING

For more details about subjects discussed in this chapter, we recommend the following books and websites. The items enclosed in brackets refer to the reference list at the end of the book.

### Books

Several books give a good coverage of cryptographic hash functions, including [Sti06], [Sta06], [Sch99], [Mao04], [KPS02], [PHS03], and [MOV97].

### References

1.   Applied Cryptography, Bruice Schneier, Second Edition, Wiley Publishers.

2.   Joan Daemen and Rene Govaerts and Joos Vandewalle and Joos V, Weak Keys for IDEA, Advances in Cryptology, CRYPTO 93 Proceedings, 1993, 224–231, Springer-Verlag

3.   Bart Preneel, "Analysis and Design of Cryptographic Hash Functions". PhD Thesis, Katholieke Universiteit Leuven. 1993.

4. Magnus Daum, "Cryptanalysis of hash functions of the MD4-family. PhD Thesis", Ruhr University, Bochum. .

5. Xiaoyun Wang and Dengguo Feng and Xuejia Lai and Hongbo Yu, "Collisions for Hash Functions MD4, MD5, HAVAL-128 and RIPEMD", Cryptology ePrint Archive, Report 2004/199, 2004, http://eprint.iacr.org/

## WebSites

The following websites give more information about topics discussed in this chapter.

http://www.unixwiz.net/techtips/iguide-crypto-hashes.html

http://www.faqs.org/rfcs/rfc4231.html

http://www.itl.nist.gov/fipspubs/fip180-1.htm

http://www.ietf.org/rfc/rfc3174.txt

http://paginas.terra.com.br/informatica/paulobarreto/WhirlpoolPage.html

## Key Terms

| | |
|---|---|
| AddRoundKey | RACE Integrity Primitives Evaluation |
| compression function | Message Digest (RIPMED) |
| Davies-Meyer scheme | RIPEMD-160 |
| HAVAL | Secure Hash Algorithm (SHA) |
| iterated cryptographic hash function | Secure Hash Standard (SHS) |
| Matyas-Meyer-Oseas scheme | SHA-1 |
| MD2 | SHA-224 |
| MD4 | SHA-256 |
| MD5 | SHA-384 |
| Merkle-Damgard scheme | SHA-512 |
| Message Digest (MD) | ShiftColumns |
| MixRows | SubBytes |
| Miyaguchi-Preneel scheme | Whirlpool cipher |
| New European Schemes for Signatures, | Whirlpool cryptographic hash function |
| Integrity, and Encryption (NESSIE) | word expansion |
| Rabin scheme | |

## Summary

★ All cryptographic hash functions must create a fixed-size digest out of a variable-size message. Creating such a function is best accomplished using iteration. A compression function is repeatedly used to create the digest. The scheme is referred to as an iterated hash function.

★ The Merkle-Damgard scheme is an iterated cryptographic hash function that is collision resistant if the compression function is collision resistant. The Merkle-Damgard scheme is the basis for many cryptographic hash functions today.

★ There is a tendency to use two different approaches in designing the compression function. In the first approach, the compression function is made from scratch: it is particularly designed for this purpose. In the second approach, a symmetric-key block cipher serves instead of a compression function.

★ A set of cryptographic hash functions uses compression functions that are made from scratch. These compression functions are specifically designed for the purpose they serve. Some examples are the Message Digest (MD) group, the Secure Hash Algorithm (SHA) group, RIPEMD, and HAVAL.

★ An iterated cryptographic hash function can use a symmetric-key block cipher instead of a compression function. Several schemes for this approach have been proposed, including the Rabin scheme, Davies-Meyer scheme, Matyas-Meyer-Oseas scheme, and Miyaguchi-Preneel scheme.

★ One of the promising cryptographic hash functions is SHA-512 with a 512-bit -message digest based on the Merkle-Damgard scheme. It is made from scratch for this purpose.

★ Another promising cryptographic hash function is Whirlpool, which is endorsed by NESSIE. Whirlpool is an iterated cryptographic hash function, based on the Miyaguchi-Preneel scheme, that uses a symmetric-key block cipher in place of the compression function. The block cipher is a modified AES cipher tailored for this purpose.

## Practice Set

### Review Questions

**12.1** Define a cryptographic hash function.

**12.2** Define an iterated cryptographic hash function.

**12.3** Describe the idea of the Merkle-Damgard scheme and why this idea is so important for the design of a cryptographic hash function.

**12.4** List some family of hash functions that do not use a cipher as the compression function.

**12.5** List some schemes that have been designed to use a block cipher as the compression function.

**12.6** List the main features of the SHA-512 cryptographic hash function. What kind of compression function is used in SHA-512?

**12.7** List some features of the Whirlpool cryptographic hash function. What kind of compression function is used in Whirlpool?

**12.8** Compare and contrast features of SHA-512 and Whirlpool cryptographic hash functions.

### Exercises

**12.9** In SHA-512, show the value of the length field in hexadecimal for the following message lengths:
    a. 1000 bits
    b. 10,000 bits
    c. 1000,000 bits

**12.10** In Whirlpool, show the value of the length field in hexadecimal for the following message lengths:
    a. 1000 bits
    b. 10,000 bits
    c. 1000,000 bits

**12.11** What is the padding for SHA-512 if the length of the message is:
    a. 5120 bits

    b.   5121 bits

    c.   6143 bits

**12.12**  What is the padding for Whirlpool if the length of the message is:

    a.   5120 bits

    b.   5121 bits

    c.   6143 bits

**12.13**  In each of the following cases, show that if two messages are the same, their last blocks are also the same (after padding and adding the length field):

    a.   The hash function is SHA-512.

    b.   The hash function is Whirlpool.

**12.14**  Calculate $G_0$ in Table 12.2 using the seventh prime (17).

**12.15**  Compare the compression function of SHA-512 without the last operation (final adding) with a Feistel cipher of 80 rounds. Show the similarities and differences.

**12.16**  The compression function used in SHA-512 (Fig. 12.10) can be thought of as an encrypting cipher with 80 rounds. If the words, $W_0$ to $W_{79}$, are thought of as round keys, which one of the schemes described in this chapter (Rabin, Davies-Meyer, Matyas-Meyer Oseas, or Miyaguchi-Preneel) does it resemble? Hint: Think about the effect of the *final adding* operation.

**12.17**  Show that SHA-512 is subject to meet-in-the middle attack if the *final adding* operation is removed from the compression function.

**12.18**  Make a table similar to Table 12.5 to compare AES and Whirlpool.

**12.19**  Show that the third operation does not need to be removed from the tenth round in Whirlpool cipher, but it must be removed in the AES cipher.

**12.20**  Find the result of $RotR_{12}(x)$ if

        $x = 1234\ 5678\ ABCD\ 2345\ 34564\ 5678\ ABCD\ 2468$

**12.21**  Find the result of $ShL_{12}(x)$ if

        $x = 1234\ 5678\ ABCD\ 2345\ 34564\ 5678\ ABCD\ 2468$

**12.22**  Find the result of $Rotate(x)$ if

        $x = 1234\ 5678\ ABCD\ 2345\ 34564\ 5678\ ABCD\ 2468$

**12.23**  Find the result of Conditional $(x, y, z)$ if

        $x = 1234\ 5678\ ABCD\ 2345\ 34564\ 5678\ ABCD\ 2468$

        $y = 2234\ 5678\ ABCD\ 2345\ 34564\ 5678\ ABCD\ 2468$

        $x = 3234\ 5678\ ABCD\ 2345\ 34564\ 5678\ ABCD\ 2468$

**12.24**  Find the result of Majority $(x, y, z)$ if

        $x = 1234\ 5678\ ABCD\ 2345\ 34564\ 5678\ ABCD\ 2468$

        $y = 2234\ 5678\ ABCD\ 2345\ 34564\ 5678\ ABCD\ 2468$

        $x = 3234\ 5678\ ABCD\ 2345\ 34564\ 5678\ ABCD\ 2468$

**12.25**  Write a routine (in pseudocode) to calculate $RotR_i(x)$ in SHA-512 (Fig. 12.9).

**12.26**  Write a routine (in pseudocode) to calculate $ShL_i(x)$ in SHA-512 (Fig. 12.9).

**12.27**  Write a routine (in pseudocode) for the Conditional function in SHA-512 (Fig. 12.11).

**12.28**  Write a routine (in pseudocode) for the Majority function in SHA-512 (Fig. 12.11).

**12.29**   Write a routine (in pseudocode) for the Rotate function in SHA-512 (Fig. 12.11).

**12.30**   Write a routine (in pseudocode) to calculate the initial digest (values of $A_0$ to $H_0$) in SHA-512 (Table 12.2).

**12.31**   Write a routine (in pseudocode) to calculate the eighty constants in SHA-512 (Table 12.3).

**12.32**   Write a routine (in pseudocode) for word-expansion algorithm in SHA-512 as shown in Fig. 12.9. Consider two cases:

    a.    Using an array of 80 elements to hold all words

    b.    Using an array of 16 elements to hold only 16 words at a time

**12.33**   Write a routine (in pseudocode) for the compression function in SHA-512.

**12.34**   Write a routine (in pseudocode) to change a block of 512 bits to an $8 \times 8$ state matrix (Fig. 12.4).

**12.35**   Write a routine (in pseudocode) to change an $8 \times 8$ state matrix to a block of 512 bits (Fig. 12.4).

**12.36**   Write a routine (in pseudocode) for the SubBytes transformation in the Whirlpool cipher (Fig. 12.16).

**12.37**   Write a routine (in pseudocode) for the ShiftColumns transformation in the Whirlpool cipher (Fig. 12.18).

**12.38**   Write a routine (in pseudocode) for the MixRows transformation in the Whirlpool cipher (Fig. 12.19).

**12.39**   Write a routine (in pseudocode) for the AddRoundKey transformation in the Whirlpool cipher (Fig. 12.20).

**12.40**   Write a routine (in pseudocode) for key expansion in Whirlpool cipher (Fig. 12.21).

**12.41**   Write a routine (in pseudocode) to create the round constants in the Whirlpool cipher (Fig. 12.20).

**12.42**   Write a routine (in pseudocode) for the Whirlpool cipher.

**12.43**   Write a routine (in pseudocode) for the Whirlpool cryptographic hash function.

**12.44**   Use the Internet (or other available resources) to find information about SHA-1. Then compare the compression function in SHA-1 with that in SHA-512. What are the similarities? What are the differences?

**12.45**   Use the Internet (or other available resources) to find information about the following compression functions, and compare them with SHA-512.

    a.    SHA-224

    b.    SHA-256

    c.    SHA-384

**12.46**   Use the Internet (or other available resources) to find information about RIPEMD, and compare it with SHA-512.

**12.47**   Use the Internet (or other available resources) to find information about HAVAL, and compare it with SHA-512

# 13

# Digital Signature

## Objectives

This chapter has several objectives:

☞ To define a digital signature
☞ To define security services provided by a digital signature
☞ To define attacks on digital signatures
☞ To discuss some digital signature schemes, including RSA, ElGamal, Schnorr, DSS, and elliptic curve
☞ To describe some applications of digital signatures

We are all familiar with the concept of a signature. A person signs a document to show that it originated from her or was approved by her. The signature is proof to the recipient that the document comes from the correct entity. When a customer signs a check, the bank needs to be sure that the check is issued by that customer and nobody else. In other words, a signature on a document, when verified, is a sign of authentication—the document is authentic. Consider a painting signed by an artist. The signature on the art, if authentic, means that the painting is probably authentic.

When Alice sends a message to Bob, Bob needs to check the authenticity of the sender; he needs to be sure that the message comes from Alice and not Eve. Bob can ask Alice to sign the message electronically. In other words, an electronic signature can prove the authenticity of Alice as the sender of the message. We refer to this type of signature as a **digital signature.**

In this chapter, we first introduce some issues related to digital signatures and then we walk through different digital signature schemes.

## 13.1                  COMPARISON

Let us begin by looking at the differences between conventional signatures and digital signatures.

### 13.1.1   Inclusion

A conventional signature is included in the document; it is part of the document. When we write a check, the signature is on the check; it is not a separate document. But when we sign a document digitally, we send the signature as a separate document. The sender sends two documents: the message and the signature. The recipient receives both documents and verifies that the signature belongs to the supposed sender. If this is proven, the message is kept; otherwise, it is rejected.

### 13.1.2 Verification Method

The second difference between the two types of signatures is the method of verifying the signature. For a conventional signature, when the recipient receives a document, she compares the signature on the document with the signature on file. If they are the same, the document is authentic. The recipient needs to have a copy of this signature on file for comparison. For a digital signature, the recipient receives the message and the signature. A copy of the signature is not stored anywhere. The recipient needs to apply a verification technique to the combination of the message and the signature to verify the authenticity.

### 13.1.3 Relationship

For a conventional signature, there is normally a one-to-many relationship between a signature and documents. A person uses the same signature to sign many documents. For a digital signature, there is a one-to-one relationship between a signature and a message. Each message has its own signature. The signature of one message cannot be used in another message. If Bob receives two messages, one after another, from Alice, he cannot use the signature of the first message to verify the second. Each message needs a new signature.

### 13.1.4 Duplicity

Another difference between the two types of signatures is a quality called *duplicity*. In conventional signature, a copy of the signed document can be distinguished from the original one on file. In digital signature, there is no such distinction unless there is a factor of time (such as a timestamp) on the document. For example, suppose Alice sends a document instructing Bob to pay Eve. If Eve intercepts the document and the signature, she can replay it later to get money again from Bob.

## 13.2 PROCESS

Figure 13.1 shows the digital signature process. The sender uses a **signing algorithm** to sign the message. The message and the signature are sent to the receiver. The receiver receives the message and the signature and applies the **verifying algorithm** to the combination. If the result is true, the message is accepted; otherwise, it is rejected.

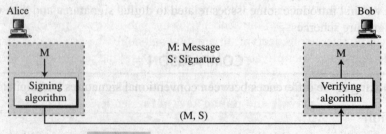

**Fig. 13.1** *Digital signature process*

## 13.2.1 Need for Keys

A conventional signature is like a private "key" belonging to the signer of the document. The signer uses it to sign documents; no one else has this signature. The copy of the signature is on file like a public key; anyone can use it to verify a document, to compare it to the original signature.

In a digital signature, the signer uses her private key, applied to a signing algorithm, to sign the document. The verifier, on the other hand, uses the public key of the signer, applied to the verifying algorithm, to verify the document.

We can add the private and public keys to Fig. 13.1 to give a more complete concept of digital signature (see Fig. 13.2). Note that when a document is signed, anyone, including Bob, can verify it because everyone has access to Alice's public key. Alice must not use her public key to sign the document because then anyone could forge her signature.

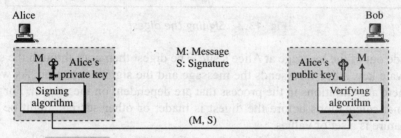

**Fig. 13.2** *Adding key to the digital signature process*

Can we use a secret (symmetric) key to both sign and verify a signature? The answer is negative for several reasons. First, a secret key is known by only two entities (Alice and Bob, for example). So if Alice needs to sign another document and send it to Ted, she needs to use another secret key. Second, as we will see, creating a secret key for a session involves authentication, which uses a digital signature. We have a vicious cycle. Third, Bob could use the secret key between himself and Alice, sign a document, send it to Ted, and pretend that it came from Alice.

---

**A digital signature needs a public-key system. The signer signs with her private key; the verifier verifies with the signer's public key.**

---

We should make a distinction between private and public keys as used in digital signatures and public and private keys as used in a cryptosystem for confidentiality. In the latter, the private and public keys of the receiver are used in the process. The sender uses the public key of the receiver to encrypt; the receiver uses his own private key to decrypt. In a digital signature, the private and public keys of the sender are used. The sender uses her private key; the receiver uses the sender's public key.

---

**A cryptosystem uses the private and public keys of the receiver: a digital signature uses the private and public keys of the sender.**

---

## 13.2.2 Signing the Digest

In Chapter 10, we learned that the asymmetric-key cryptosystems are very inefficient when dealing with long messages. In a digital signature system, the messages are normally long, but we have to use asymmetric-key schemes. The solution is to sign a digest of the message, which is much shorter than the message. As we learned in Chapter 11, a carefully selected message digest has a one-to-one relationship with the message. The sender can sign the message digest and the receiver can verify the message digest. The effect is the same. Figure 13.3 shows signing a digest in a digital signature system.

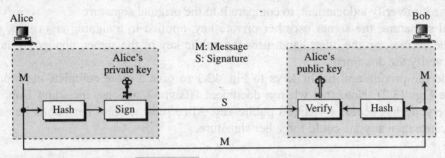

**Fig. 13.3** *Signing the digest*

A digest is made out of the message at Alice's site. The digest then goes through the signing process using Alice's private key. Alice then sends the message and the signature to Bob. As we will see later in this chapter, there are variations in the process that are dependent on the system. For example, there might be additional calculations before the digest is made, or other secrets might be used. In some systems, the signature is a set of values.

At Bob's site, using the same public hash function, a digest is first created out of the received message. Calculations are done on the signature and the digest. The verifying process also applies criteria on the result of the calculation to determine the authenticity of the signature. If authentic, the message is accepted; otherwise, it is rejected.

## 13.3                                    SERVICES

We discussed several security services in Chapter 1 including *message confidentiality, message authentication, message integrity,* and *nonrepudiation.* A digital signature can directly provide the last three; for message confidentiality we still need encryption/decryption.

### 13.3.1  Message Authentication

A secure digital signature scheme, like a secure conventional signature (one that cannot be easily copied) can provide message authentication (also referred to as data-origin authentication). Bob can verify that the message is sent by Alice because Alice's public key is used in verification. Alice's public key cannot verify the signature signed by Eve's private key.

---

**A digital signature provides message authentication.**

---

### 13.3.2  Message Integrity

The integrity of the message is preserved even if we sign the whole message because we cannot get the same signature if the message is changed. The digital signature schemes today use a hash function in the signing and verifying algorithms that preserve the integrity of the message.

---

**A digital signature provides message integrity.**

---

### 13.3.3 Nonrepudiation

If Alice signs a message and then denies it, can Bob later prove that Alice actually signed it? For example, if Alice sends a message to a bank (Bob) and asks to transfer $10,000 from her account to Ted's account, can Alice later deny that she sent this message? With the scheme we have presented so far, Bob might have a problem. Bob must keep the signature on file and later use Alice's public key to create the original message to prove the message in the file and the newly created message are the same. This is not feasible because Alice may have changed her private or public key during this time; she may also claim that the file containing the signature is not authentic.

One solution is a trusted third party. People can create an established trusted party among themselves. In future chapters, we will see that a trusted party can solve many other problems concerning security services and key exchange. Figure 13.4 shows how a trusted party can prevent Alice from denying that she sent the message.

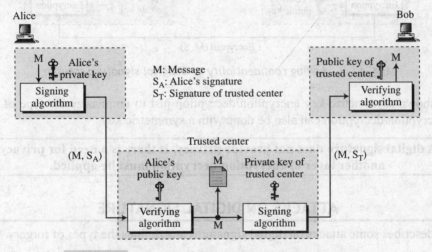

**Fig. 13.4** *Using a trusted center for nonrepudiation*

Alice creates a signature from her message ($S_A$) and sends the message, her identity, Bob's identity, and the signature to the center. The center, after checking that Alice's public key is valid, verifies through Alice's public key that the message came from Alice. The center then saves a copy of the message with the sender identity, recipient identity, and a timestamp in its archive. The center uses its private key to create another signature ($S_T$) from the message. The center then sends the message, the new signature, Alice's identity, and Bob's identity to Bob. Bob verifies the message using the public key of the trusted center.

If in the future Alice denies that she sent the message, the center can show a copy of the saved message. If Bob's message is a duplicate of the message saved at the center, Alice will lose the dispute. To make everything confidential, a level of encryption/decryption can be added to the scheme, as discussed in the next section.

---

**Nonrepudiation can be provided using a trusted party.**

---

### 13.3.4 Confidentiality

A digital signature does not provide confidential communication. If confidentiality is required, the message and the signature must be encrypted using either a secret-key or public-key cryptosystem. Figure 13.5 shows how this extra level can be added to a simple digital signature scheme.

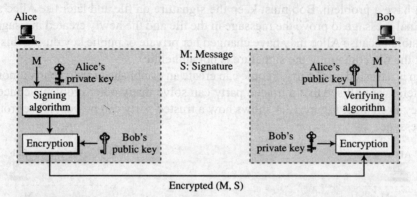

**Fig. 13.5** *Adding confidentiality to a digital signature scheme*

We have shown asymmetric-key encryption/decryption just to emphasize the type of keys used at each end. Encryption/decryption can also be done with a symmetric key.

---

**A digital signature does not provide privacy. If there is a need for privacy, another layer of encryption/decryption must be applied.**

---

## 13.4        ATTACKS ON DIGITAL SIGNATURE

This section describes some attacks on digital signatures and defines the types of forgery.

### 13.4.1  Attack Types

We will look on three kinds of attacks on digital signatures: key-only, known-message, and chosen-message.

**Key-Only Attack**    In the **key-only attack,** Eve has access only to the public information released by Alice. To forge a message, Eve needs to create Alice's signature to convince Bob that the message is coming from Alice. This is the same as the ciphertext-only attack we discussed for encipherment.

**Known-Message Attack**    In the **known-message attack,** Eve has access to one or more message-signature pairs. In other words, she has access to some documents previously signed by Alice. Eve tries to create another message and forge Alice's signature on it. This is similar to the known-plaintext attack we discussed for encipherment.

**Chosen-Message Attack**    In the **chosen-message attack,** Eve somehow makes Alice sign one or more messages for her. Eve now has a chosen-message/signature pair. Eve later creates another message, with the content she wants, and forges Alice's signature on it. This is similar to the chosen-plaintext attack we discussed for encipherment.

### 13.4.2 Forgery Types

If the attack is successful, the result is a forgery. We can have two types of forgery: existential and selective.

***Existential Forgery*** In an **existential forgery,** Eve may be able to create a valid message-signature pair, but not one that she can really use. In other words, a document has been forged, but the content is randomly calculated. This type of forgery is probable, but fortunately Eve cannot benefit from it very much. Her message could be syntactically or semantically unintelligible.

***Selective Forgery*** In **selective forgery,** Eve may be able to forge Alice's signature on a message with the content selectively chosen by Eve. Although this is beneficial to Eve, and may be very detrimental to Alice, the probability of such forgery is low, but not negligible.

## 13.5 DIGITAL SIGNATURE SCHEMES

Several **digital signature schemes** have evolved during the last few decades. Some of them have been implemented. In this section, we discuss these schemes. In the following section we discuss one that will probably become the standard.

### 13.5.1 RSA Digital Signature Scheme

In Chapter 10 we discussed how to use RSA cryptosystem to provide privacy. The RSA idea can also be used for signing and verifying a message. In this case, it is called the **RSA digital signature scheme.** The digital signature scheme changes the roles of the private and public keys. First, the private and public keys of the sender, not the receiver, are used. Second, the sender uses her own private key to sign the document; the receiver uses the sender's public key to verify it. If we compare the scheme with the conventional way of signing, we see that the private key plays the role of the sender's own signature, the sender's public key plays the role of the copy of the signature that is available to the public. Obviously Alice cannot use Bob's public key to sign the message because then any other person could do the same. Figure 13.6 gives the general idea behind the RSA digital signature scheme.

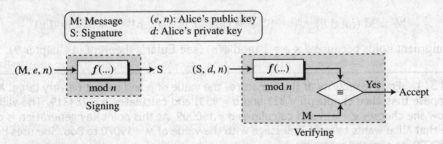

**Fig. 13.6** *General idea behind the RSA digital signature scheme*

The signing and verifying sites use the same function, but with different parameters. The verifier compares the message and the output of the function for congruence. If the result is true, the message is accepted.

**Key Generation**   Key generation in the RSA digital signature scheme is exactly the same as key generation in the RSA cryptosystem (see Chapter 10). Alice chooses two primes $p$ and $q$ and calculates $n = p \times q$. Alice calculates $\phi(n) = (p-1)(q-1)$. She then chooses $e$, the public exponent, and calculates $d$, the private exponent such that $e \times d = 1 \bmod \phi(n)$. Alice keeps $d$; she publicly announces $n$ and $e$.

---

**In the RSA digital signature scheme, $d$ is private; $e$ and $n$ are public.**

---

## Signing and Verifying

Figure 13.7 shows the RSA digital signature scheme.

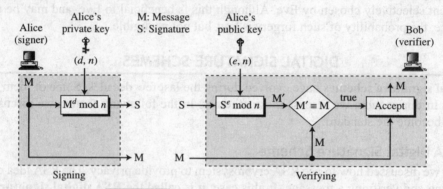

**Fig. 13.7**   *RSA digital signature scheme*

**Signing**   Alice creates a signature out of the message using her private exponent, $S = M^d \bmod n$ and sends the message and the signature to Bob.

**Verifying**   Bob receives M and S. Bob applies Alice's public exponent to the signature to create a copy of the message $M' = S^e \bmod n$. Bob compares the value of M' with the value of M. If the two values are congruent, Bob accepts the message. To prove this, we start with the verification criteria:

$$M' \equiv M \pmod{n} \quad \rightarrow \quad S^e \equiv M \pmod{n} \quad \rightarrow \quad M^{d \times e} \equiv M \pmod{n}$$

The last congruent holds because $d \times e = 1 \bmod \phi(n)$ (see Euler's theorem in Chapter 9).

---

**Example 13.1**   For the security of the signature, the value of $p$ and $q$ must be very large. As a trivial example, suppose that Alice chooses $p = 823$ and $q = 953$, and calculates $n = 784319$. The value of $\phi(n)$ is 782544. Now she chooses $e = 313$ and calculates $d = 160009$. At this point key generation is complete. Now imagine that Alice wants to send a message with the value of M = 19070 to Bob. She uses her private exponent, 160009, to sign the message:

$$\text{M: } 19070 \quad \rightarrow \quad S = (19070^{160009}) \bmod 784319 = 210625 \bmod 784319$$

Alice sends the message and the signature to Bob. Bob receives the message and the signature. He calculates

$$M' = 210625^{313} \bmod 784319 = 19070 \bmod 784319 \rightarrow M \equiv M' \bmod n$$

Bob accepts the message because he has verified Alice's signature.

## 13.5.2 Attacks on RSA Signature

There are some attacks that Eve can apply to the RSA digital signature scheme to forge Alice's signature.

***Key-Only Attack***   Eve has access only to Alice's public key. Eve intercepts the pair (M, S) and tries to create another message M' such that $M' \equiv S^e \pmod{n}$. This problem is as difficult to solve as the discrete logarithm problem we saw in Chapter 9. Besides, this is an existential forgery and normally is useless to Eve.

***Known-Message Attack***   Here Eve uses the *multiplicative property* of RSA. Assume that Eve has intercepted two message-signature pairs $(M_1, S_1)$ and $(M_2, S_2)$ that have been created using the same private key. If $M = (M_1 \times M_2) \bmod n$, then $S = (S_1 \times S_2) \bmod n$. This is simple to prove because we have

$$S = (S_1 \times S_2) \bmod n = (M_1^d \times M_2^d) \bmod n = (M_1 \times M_2)^d \bmod n = M^d \bmod n$$

Eve can create $M = (M_1 \times M_2) \bmod n$, and she can create $S = (S_1 \times S_2) \bmod n$, and fool Bob into believing that S is Alice's signature on the message M. This attack, which is sometimes referred to as *multiplicative attack,* is easy to launch. However, this is an existential forgery as the message M is a multiplication of two previous messages created by Alice, not Eve; M is normally useless.

***Chosen-Message Attack***   This attack also uses the multiplicative property of RSA. Eve can some-how ask Alice to sign two legitimate messages, $M_1$ and $M_2$, for her and later creates a new message $M = M_1 \times M_2$. Eve can later claim that Alice has signed M. The attack is also referred to as *multiplicative attack*. This is a very serious attack on the RSA digital signature scheme because it is a selective forgery (Eve can manipulate $M_1$ and $M_2$ to get a useful M).

***RSA Signature on the Message Digest***   As we discussed before, signing a message digest using a strong hash algorithm has several advantages. In the case of RSA, it can make the signing and verifying processes much faster because the RSA digital signature scheme is nothing other than encryption with the private key and decryption with the public key. The use of a strong cryptographic hashing function also makes the attack on the signature much more difficult as we will explain shortly. Figure 13.8 shows the scheme.

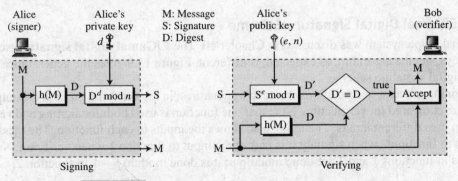

**Fig. 13.8**   *The RSA signature on the message digest*

Alice, the signer, first uses an agreed-upon hash function to create a digest from the message, $D = h(M)$. She then signs the digest, $S = D^d \bmod n$. The message and the signature are sent to Bob. Bob, the verifier, receives the message and the signature. He first uses Alice's public exponent to retrieve the digest, $D' = S^e \bmod n$. He then applies the hash algorithm to the message received to obtain $D = h(M)$. Bob now compares the two digests, $D$ and $D'$. If they are congruent to modulo $n$, he accepts the message.

## Attacks on RSA Signed Digests

How susceptible to attack is the RSA digital signature scheme when the digest is signed?

**Key-Only Attack**   We can have three cases of this attack:

a.   Eve intercepts the pair (S, M) and tries to find another message M′ that creates the same digest, $h(M) = h(M')$. As we learned in Chapter 11, if the hash algorithm is *second preimage resistant,* this attack is very difficult.

b.   Eve finds two messages M and M′ such that $h(M) = h(M')$. She lures Alice to sign $h(M)$ to find S. Now Eve has a pair (M′, S) which passes the verifying test, but it is the forgery. We learned in Chapter 11 that if the hash algorithm is *collision resistant,* this attack is very difficult.

c.   Eve may randomly find message digest D, which may match with a random signature S. She then finds a message M such that $D = h(M)$. As we learned in Chapter 11, if the hash function is *preimage resistant,* this attack is very difficult to launch.

**Known-Message Attack**   Let us assume Eve has two message-signature pairs $(M_1, S_1)$ and $(M_2, S_2)$ which have been created using the same private key. Eve calculates $S \equiv S_1 \times S_2$. If she can find a message M such that $h(M) \equiv h(M_1) \times h(M_2)$, she has forged a new message. However, finding M given $h(M)$ is very difficult if the hash algorithm is *preimage resistant.*

**Chosen-Message Attack**   Eve can ask Alice to sign two legitimate messages $M_1$ and $M_2$ for her. Eve then creates a new signature $S \equiv S_1 \times S_2$. Since Eve can calculate $h(M) \equiv h(M_1) \times h(M_2)$, if she can find a message M given $h(M)$, the new message is a forgery. However, finding M given $h(M)$ is very difficult if the hash algorithm is *preimage resistant.*

---

**When the digest is signed instead of the message itself, the susceptibility of the RSA digital signature scheme depends on the strength of the hash algorithm.**

---

## 13.5.3   ElGamal Digital Signature Scheme

The ElGamal cryptosystem was discussed in Chapter 10. The **ElGamal digital signature scheme** uses the same keys, but the algorithm, as expected, is different. Figure 13.9 gives the general idea behind the ElGamal digital signature scheme.

In the signing process, two functions create two signatures; in the verifying process the outputs of two functions are compared for verification. Note that one function is used both for signing and verifying but the function uses different inputs. The figure also shows the inputs to each function. The message is part of the input to function 2 when signing; it is part of the input to function 1 when verifying. Note that the calculations in functions 1 and 3 are done modulo $p$; it is done modulo $p - 1$ in function 2.

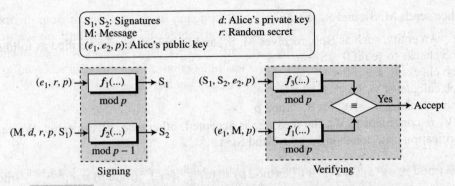

**Fig. 13.9** *General idea behind the ElGamal digital signature scheme*

## Key Generation

The key generation procedure here is exactly the same as the one used in the cryptosystem. Let $p$ be a prime number large enough that the discrete log problem is intractable in $\mathbf{Z}_p{}^*$. Let $e_1$ be a primitive element in $\mathbf{Z}_p{}^*$. Alice selects her private key $d$ to be less than $p - 1$. She calculates $e_2 = e_1{}^d$. Alice's public key is the tuple $(e_1, e_2, p)$; Alice's private key is $d$.

> **In ElGamal digital signature scheme, $(e_1, e_2, p)$ is Alice's public key; $d$ is her private key.**

## Verifying and Signing

Figure 13.10 shows the ElGamal digital signature scheme.

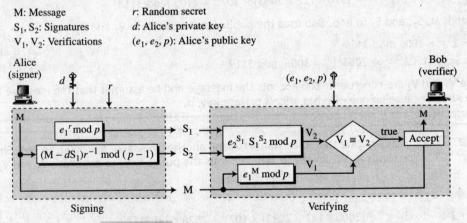

**Fig. 13.10** *ElGamal digital signature scheme*

**Signing**  Alice can sign the digest of a message to any entity, including Bob:

1. Alice chooses a secret random number $r$. Note that although public and private keys can be used repeatedly, Alice needs a new $r$ each time she signs a new message.
2. Alice calculates the first signature $S_1 = e_1{}^r \bmod p$.
3. Alice calculates the second signature $S_2 = (M - d \times S_1) \times r^{-1} \bmod (p - 1)$, where $r^{-1}$ is the multiplicative inverse of $r$ modulo $p$.

4. Alice sends M, $S_1$, and $S_2$ to Bob.

**Verifying**  An entity, such as Bob, receives M, $S_1$, and $S_2$, which can be verified as follows:
1. Bob checks to see if $0 < S_1 < p$
2. Bob checks to see if $0 < S_2 < p - 1$
3. Bob calculates $V_1 = e_1{}^M \bmod p$
4. Bob calculates $V_2 = e_2{}^{S_1} \times S_1{}^{S_2} \bmod p$
5. If $V_1$ is congruent to $V_2$, the message is accepted; otherwise, it is rejected. We can prove the verification criterion using $e_2 = e_1{}^d$ and $S_1 = e_1{}^r$.

$$V_1 \equiv V_2 \, (\bmod \, p) \rightarrow e_1{}^M \equiv e_2{}^{S_1} \times S_1{}^{S_2} \, (\bmod \, p) \equiv (e_1{}^d)^{S_1} (e_1{}^r)^{S_2} \, (\bmod \, p) \equiv e_1{}^{d\,S_1 + r\,S_2} \, (\bmod \, p)$$

We get: $e_1{}^M \equiv e_1{}^{d\,S_1 + r\,S_2} \, (\bmod \, p)$

Because $e_1$ is a primitive root, it can be proved that the above congruence holds if and only if M $\equiv [d\,S_1 + r\,S_2] \bmod (p - 1)$ or $S_2 \equiv [(M - d \times S_1) \times r^{-1}] \bmod (p - 1)$, which is the same $S_2$ we started in the signing process.

---

**Example 13.2**  Here is a trivial example. Alice chooses $p = 3119$, $e_1 = 2$, $d = 127$ and calculates $e_2$ $= 2^{127} \bmod 3119 = 1702$. She also chooses $r$ to be 307. She announces $e_1$, $e_2$, and $p$ publicly; she keeps $d$ secret. The following shows how Alice can sign a message.

M = 320

$\qquad S_1 = e_1{}^r = 2^{307} = 2083 \bmod 3119$

$\qquad S_2 = (M - d \times S_1) \times r^{-1} = (320 - 127 \times 2083) \times 307^{-1} = 2105 \bmod 3118$

Alice sends M, $S_1$, and $S_2$ to Bob. Bob uses the public key to calculate $V_1$ and $V_2$.

$V_1 = e_1{}^M = 2^{320} = 3006 \bmod 3119$

$V_2 = d^{S_1} \times S_1{}^{S_2} = 1702^{2083} \times 2083^{2105} = 3006 \bmod 3119$

Because $V_1$ and $V_2$ are congruent, Bob accepts the message and he assumes that the message has been signed by Alice because no one else has Alice's private key, d.

---

**Example 13.3**  Now imagine that Alice wants to send another message, M = 3000, to Ted. She chooses a new $r$, 107. Alice sends M, $S_1$, and $S_2$ to Ted. Ted uses the public keys to calculate $V_1$ and $V_2$.

M = 3000

$\qquad S_1 = e_1{}^r = 2^{107} = 2732 \bmod 3119$

$\qquad S_2 = (M - d \times S_1) \, r^{-1} = (3000 - 127 \times 2083) \times 107^{-1} = 2526 \bmod 3118$

$V_1 = e_1{}^M = 2^{3000} = 704 \bmod 3119$

$V_2 = d^{S_1} \times S_1{}^{S} = 1702^{2732} \times 2083^{2526} = 704 \bmod 3119$

Because $V_1$ and $V_2$ are congruent, Ted accepts the message; he assumes that the message has been signed by Alice because no one else has Alice's private key, $d$. Note that any person can receive the message. The goal is not to hide the message, but to prove that it is sent by Alice.

### Forgery in the ElGamal Digital Signature Scheme

The ElGamal scheme is vulnerable to existential forgery, but it is very hard to do a selective forgery on this scheme.

*Key-Only Forgery*   In this type of forgery, Eve has access only to the public key. Two kinds of forgery are possible:

1.  Eve has a predefined message M. She needs to forge Alice's signature on it. Eve must find two valid signatures $S_1$ and $S_2$ for this message. This is a selective forgery.

    a.  Eve can choose $S_1$ and calculate $S_2$. She needs to have $d^{S_1} S_1^{S_2} \equiv e_1^M \pmod p$. In other words, $S_1^{S_1} \equiv e_1^M d^{-S_2} \pmod p$ or $S_2 \equiv \log_{S_1} (e_1^M d^{-S_1}) \pmod p$. This means computing the discrete logarithm, which is very difficult.

    b.  Eve can choose $S_2$ and calculate $S_1$. This is much harder than part *a*.

2.  Eve may be able to find three random values, M, $S_1$, and $S_2$ such that the last two are the signature of the first one. If Eve can find two new parameters $x$ and $y$ such that M = $xS_2$ mod $(p-1)$ and $S_1 = -yS_2$ mod $(p-1)$, she can forge the message, but it might not be very useful for her. This is an existential forgery.

*Known-Message Forgery*   If Eve has intercepted a message M and its two signatures $S_1$ and $S_2$, she can find another message M', with the same pair of signatures $S_1$ and $S_2$. However, note that this is also an existential forgery that does not help Eve very much.

## 13.5.4   Schnorr Digital Signature Scheme

The problem with the ElGamal digital signature scheme is that $p$ needs to be very large to guarantee that the discrete log problem is intractable in $\mathbf{Z}_p^*$. The recommendation is a $p$ of at least 1024 bits. This could make the signature as large as 2048 bits. To reduce the size of the signature, Schnorr proposed a new scheme based on ElGamal, but with a reduced signature size. Figure 13.11 gives the general idea behind the **Schnorr digital signature scheme.**

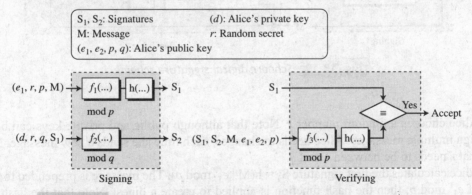

**Fig. 13.11**   *General idea behind the Schnorr digital signature scheme*

In the signing process, two functions create two signatures; in the verifying process, the output of one function is compared to the first signature for verification. Figure 13.11 also shows the inputs to each function. The important point is that the scheme uses two moduli: $p$ and $q$. Functions 1 and 3 use $p$; function 2 uses $q$. The details of inputs and the functions will be discussed shortly.

### *Key Generation*

Before signing a message, Alice needs to generate keys and announce the public ones to the public.

1. Alice selects a prime $p$, which is usually 1024 bits in length.
2. Alice selects another prime $q$, which is the same size as the digest created by the cryptographic hash function (currently 160 bits, but it many change in the future). The prime $q$ needs to divide $(p - 1)$. In other words, $(p - 1) = 0 \bmod q$.
3. Alice chooses $e_1$ to be the $q$th root of 1 modulo $p$. To do so, Alice chooses a primitive element in $\mathbf{Z}_p$, $e_0$ (see Appendix J), and calculates $e_1 = e_0^{(p-1)/q} \bmod p$.
4. Alice chooses an integer, $d$, as her private key.
5. Alice calculates $e_2 = e_1^{d} \bmod p$.
6. Alice's public key is $(e_1, e_2, p, q)$; her private key is $(d)$;

**In the Schnorr digital signature scheme, Alice's public key is $(e_1, e_2, p, q)$; her private key $(d)$.**

### *Signing and Verifying*

Figure 13.12 shows the Schnorr digital signature scheme.

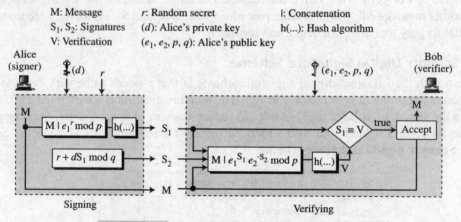

**Fig. 13.12** *Schnorr digital signature scheme*

### *Signing*

1. Alice chooses a random number $r$. Note that although public and private keys can be used to sign multiple messages, Alice needs to change $r$ each time she sends a new message. Note also that $r$ needs to be between 1 and $q$.
2. Alice calculates the first signature $S_1 = h(M \mid e_1^{r} \bmod p)$. The message is prepended to the value of $e_1^{r} \bmod p$; then the hash function is applied to create a digest. Note that the hash function is not directly applied to the message, but instead is applied to the concatenation of M and $e_1^{r} \bmod p$.
3. Alice calculates the second signature $S_2 = r + d \times S_1 \bmod q$. Note that part of the calculation of $S_2$ is done in modulo $q$ arithmetic.
4. Alice sends M, $S_1$, and $S_2$.

***Verifying Message*** The receiver, Bob, for example, receives M, $S_1$, and $S_2$.

1. Bob calculates $V = h (M | e_1^{S_2} e_2^{-S_1} \bmod p)$.
2. If $S_1$ is congruent to V modulo $p$, the message is accepted; otherwise, it is rejected.

---

**Example 13.4** Here is a trivial example. Suppose we choose $q = 103$ and $p = 2267$. Note that $p = 22 \times q + 1$. We choose $e_0 = 2$, which is a primitive in $Z_{2267}^*$. Then $(p -1) / q = 22$, so we have $e_1 = 2^{22} \bmod 2267 = 354$. We choose $d = 30$, so $e_2 = 354^{30} \bmod 2267 = 1206$. Alice's private key is now ($d$); her public key is ($e_1, e_2, p, q$).

Alice wants to send a message M. She chooses $r = 11$ and calculates $e_2^r = 354^{11} = 630 \bmod 2267$. Assume that the message is 1000 and concatenation means 1000630. Also assume that the hash of this value gives the digest h(1000630) = 200. This means $S_1 = 200$. Alice calculates $S_2 = r + d \times S_1 \bmod q = 11 + 1026 \times 200 \bmod 103 = 11 + 24 = 35$. Alice sends the message M =1000, $S_1 = 200$, and $S_2 = 35$. The verification is left as an exercise.

---

***Forgery on Schnorr Signature Scheme*** It looks like all attacks on ElGamal scheme can be applied on Schnorr scheme. However, Schnorr is in a better position because $S_1 = h(M | e_1^r \bmod p)$, which means that the hash function is applied to the combination of the message and $e_1^r$, in which $r$ is a secret.

### 13.5.5 Digital Signature Standard (DSS)

The **Digital Signature Standard (DSS)** was adopted by the National Institute of Standards and Technology (NIST) in 1994. NIST published DSS as FIPS 186. DSS uses a **digital signature algorithm (DSA)** based on the ElGamal scheme with some ideas from the Schnorr scheme. DSS has been criticized from the time it was published. The main complaint regards the secrecy of DSS design. The second complaint regards the size of the prime, 512 bits. Later NIST made the size variable to respond to this complaint. Figure 13.13 gives the general idea behind the DSS scheme.

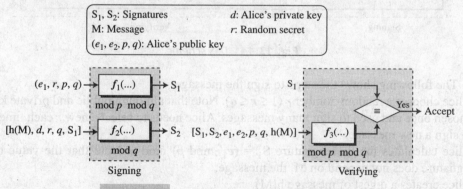

**Fig. 13.13** *General idea behind DSS scheme*

In the signing process, two functions create two signatures; in the verifying process, the output of one function is compared to the first signature for verification. This is similar to Schnorr, but the inputs are different. Another difference is that this scheme uses the message digest (not the message) as part of inputs to functions 1 and 3. The interesting point is that the scheme uses two public moduli: $p$ and $q$. Functions 1 and 3 use both $p$ and $q$; function 2 uses only $q$. The details of inputs and the functions will be discussed shortly.

## Key Generation

Before signing a message to any entity, Alice needs to generate keys and announce the public ones to the public.

1. Alice chooses a prime $p$, between 512 and 1024 bits in length. The number of bits in $p$ must be a multiple of 64.
2. Alice chooses a 160-bit prime $q$ in such a way that $q$ divides $(p-1)$.
3. Alice uses two multiplication groups $<\mathbf{Z}_p{}^*, \times>$ and $<\mathbf{Z}_q{}^*, \times>$; the second is a subgroup of the first.
4. Alice creates $e_1$ to be the $q$th root of 1 modulo $p$ ($e_1{}^p = 1 \bmod p$). To do so, Alice chooses a primitive element in $\mathbf{Z}_p$, $e_0$, and calculates $e_1 = e_0{}^{(p-1)/q} \bmod p$.
5. Alice chooses $d$ as the private key and calculates $e_2 = e_1{}^d$.
6. Alice's public key is $(e_1, e_2, p, q)$; her private key is $(d)$.

## Verifying and Signing

Figure 13.14 shows the DSS scheme.

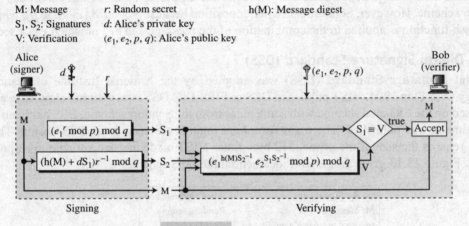

M: Message     $r$: Random secret     h(M): Message digest
$S_1, S_2$: Signatures     $d$: Alice's private key
V: Verification     $(e_1, e_2, p, q)$: Alice's public key

**Fig. 13.14** *DSS scheme*

## Signing

The following shows the steps to sign the message:

1. Alice chooses a random number $r$ ($1 \le r \le q$). Note that although public and private keys can be chosen once and used to sign many messages, Alice needs to select a new $r$ each time she needs to sign a new message.
2. Alice calculates the first signature $S_1 = (e_1{}^r \bmod p) \bmod q$. Note that the value of the first signature does not depend on M, the message.
3. Alice creates a digest of message h(M).
4. Alice calculates the second signature $S_2 = (h(M) + d\,S_1)r^{-1} \bmod q$. Note that the calculation of $S_2$ is done in modulo $q$ arithmetic.
5. Alice sends M, $S_1$, and $S_2$ to Bob.

## Verifying

Following are the steps used to verify the message when M, $S_1$, and $S_2$ are received:

1. Bob checks to see if $0 < S_1 < q$.
2. Bob checks to see if $0 < S_2 < q$.
3. Bob calculates a digest of M using the same hash algorithm used by Alice.

4. Bob calculates $V = [(e_1^{h(M)S_2^{-1}} e_2^{S_1 S_2^{-1}}) \bmod p] \bmod q$.
5. If $S_1$ is congruent to V, the message is accepted; otherwise, it is rejected.

---

**Example 13.5** Alice chooses $q = 101$ and $p = 8081$. Alice selects $e_0 = 3$ and calculates $e_1 = e_0^{(p-1)/q} \bmod p = 6968$. Alice chooses $d = 61$ as the private key and calculates $e_2 = e_1^d \bmod p = 2038$. Now Alice can send a message to Bob. Assume that $h(M) = 5000$ and Alice chooses $r = 61$:

$h(M) = 5000 \quad r = 61$
$S_1 = (e_1^r \bmod p) \bmod q = 54$
$S_2 = ((h(M) + d\,S_1)\,r^{-1}) \bmod q = 40$

Alice sends M, $S_1$, and $S_2$ to Bob. Bob uses the public keys to calculate V.

$S_2^{-1} = 48 \bmod 101$
$V = [(6968^{5000 \times 48} \times 2038^{54 \times 48}) \bmod 8081] \bmod 101 = 54$

Because $S_1$ and V are congruent, Bob accepts the message.

---

**DSS Versus RSA** Computation of DSS signatures is faster than computation of RSA signatures when using the same $p$.

**DSS Versus ElGamal** DSS signatures are smaller than ElGamal signatures because $q$ is smaller than $p$.

### 13.5.6 Elliptic Curve Digital Signature Scheme

Our last scheme is the **elliptic curve digital signature scheme,** which is DSA based on elliptic curves, as we discussed in Chapter 10. The scheme sometimes is referred to as ECDSA (elliptic curve DSA). Figure 13.15 gives the general idea behind ECDSS.

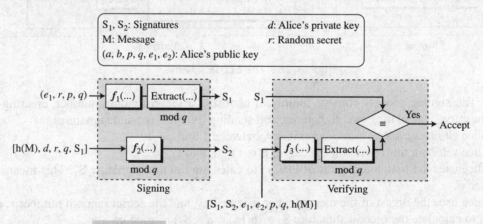

**Fig. 13.15** *General idea behind the ECDSS scheme*

In the signing process, two functions and an extractor create two signatures; in the verifying process the output of one function (after passing through the extractor) is compared to the first signature for verification. Functions $f_1$ and $f_3$ actually create points on the curve. The first creates a new point from the signer's private key (which is a point); the second creates a new point from the signer's two public keys (which are the points). Each extractor extracts the first coordinates of the corresponding point in modular arithmetic. The details of inputs and the functions will be discussed shortly.

**Key Generation**   Key generation follows these steps:

1. Alice chooses an elliptic curve $E_p(a, b)$ with $p$ a prime number.
2. Alice chooses another prime number $q$ to be used in the calculation.
3. Alice chooses the private key $d$, an integer.
4. Alice chooses $e_1(\ldots, \ldots)$, a point on the curve.
5. Alice calculates $e_2(\ldots, \ldots) = d \times e_1(\ldots, \ldots)$, another point on the curve.
6. Alice's public key is $(a, b, p, q, e_1, e_2)$; her private key is $d$.

## Signing and Verifying

Figure 13.16 shows the elliptic curve digital signature scheme.

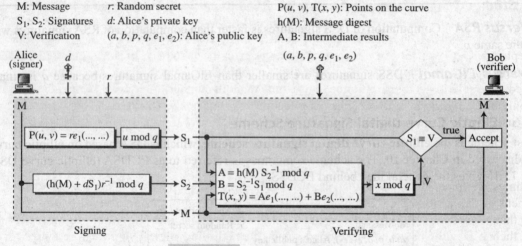

**Fig. 13.16**   *The ECDSS scheme*

**Signing**   The signing process consists mainly of choosing a secret random number, creating a third point on the curve, calculating two signatures, and sending the message and signatures.

1. Alice chooses a secret random number $r$, between 1 and $q - 1$.
2. Alice selects a third point on the curve, $P(u, v) = r \times e_1 (\ldots, \ldots)$.
3. Alice uses the first coordinates of $P(u, v)$ to calculate the first signature $S_1$. This means $S_1 = u \bmod q$.
4. Alice uses the digest of the message, her private key, and the secret random number $r$, and the $S_1$ to calculate the second signature $S_2 = (h(M) + d \times S_1) \, r^{-1} \bmod q$.
5. Alice sends M, $S_1$, and $S_2$.

**Verifying**   The verification process consists mainly of reconstructing the third point and verifying that the first coordinate is equivalent to $S_1$ in modulo $q$. Note that the third point was created by the signer using the secret random number $r$. The verifier does not have this value. He needs to make the third point from the message digest, $S_1$ and $S_2$:

1. Bob uses M, $S_1$, and $S_2$ to create two intermediate results, A and B:

$$A = h(M) \, S_2^{-1} \bmod q \qquad \text{and} \qquad B = S_2^{-1} \, S_1 \bmod q$$

Bob then reconstructs the third point $T(x, y) = A \times e_1 \, (\ldots, \ldots) + B \times e_2(\ldots, \ldots)$.

2. Bob uses the first coordinate of $T(x, y)$ to verify the message. If $x = S_1 \bmod q$, the signature is verified; otherwise, it is rejected.

## 13.6                         VARIATIONS AND APPLICATIONS

This section briefly discusses variations and applications for digital signatures.

### 13.6.1   Variations

Following are brief discussions of several variations and additions to the main concept of digital signatures. For more insight, the reader can consult the specialized literature.

**Time Stamped Signatures**    Sometimes a signed document needs to be timestamped to prevent it from being replayed by an adversary. This is called **timestamped digital signature scheme.** For example, if Alice signs a request to her bank, Bob, to transfer some money to Eve, the document can be intercepted and replayed by Eve if there is no timestamp on the document. Including the actual date and time on the documents may create a problem if the clocks are not synchronized and a universal time is not used. One solution is to use a **nonce** (a one-time random number). A nonce is a number that can be used only once. When the receiver receives a document with a nonce, he makes a note that the number is now used by the sender and cannot be used again. In other words, a new nonce defines the "present time"; a used nonce defines "past time".

**Blind Signatures**

Sometimes we have a document that we want to get signed without revealing the contents of the document to the signer. For example, a scientist, say Bob, might have discovered a very important theory that needs to be signed by a notary public, say Alice, without allowing Alice to know the contents of the theory. David Chaum has developed some patented **blind digital signature schemes** for this purpose. The main idea is as follows:

    a.   Bob creates a message and blinds it. Bob sends the blinded message to Alice.
    b.   Alice signs the blinded message and returns the signature on the blinded message.
    c.   Bob unblinds the signature to obtain a signature on the original message.

**Blind Signature Based on the RSA Scheme**    Let us briefly describe a blind digital signature scheme developed by David Chaum. Blinding can be done using a variation of the RSA scheme. Bob selects a random number, $b$, and calculates the blinded message $B = M \times b^e \bmod n$, in which $e$ is Alice's public key and $n$ is the modulus defined in the RSA digital signature scheme. Note that $b$ is sometimes called the blinding factor. Bob sends B to Alice.

Alice signs the blinded message using the signing algorithm defined in the RSA digital signature $S_{\text{blind}} = B^d \bmod n$, in which $d$ is Alice's private key. Note that $S_b$ is the signature on the blind version of the message.

Bob simply uses the multiplicative inverse of his random number $b$ to remove the blind from the signature. The signature is $S = S_b \, b^{-1} \bmod n$. We can prove that S is the signature on the original message as defined in the RSA digital signature scheme:

$$S \equiv S_b \, b^{-1} \equiv B^d \, b^{-1} \equiv (M \times b^e)^d \, b^{-1} \equiv M^d \, b^{ed} \, b^{-1} \equiv M^d \, b \, b^{-1} \equiv M^d$$

S is the signature if Bob has sent the original message to be signed by Alice.

*Preventing Fraud*   It appears that Bob can get Alice to sign a blind message that may later hurt her. For example, Bob's message could be a document, claiming to be Alice's will, that will give everything to Bob after her death. There are at least three ways to prevent such damage:

a.   The authorities can pass a law that Alice is not responsible for signing any blind message that is against her interest.

b.   Alice can request a document from Bob that the message she will sign does not hurt Alice.

c.   Alice could require that Bob proves his honesty before she signs the blind message.

## Undeniable Digital Signatures

**Undeniable digital signature schemes** are elegant inventions of Chaum and van Antwerpen. An undeniable digital signature scheme has three components: a signing algorithm, a verification protocol, and a disavowal protocol. The signing algorithm allows Alice to sign a message. The verification protocol uses the challenge-response mechanism (discussed in Chapter 14) to involve Alice for verifying the signature. This prevents the duplication and distribution of the signed message without Alice's approval. The disavowal protocol helps Alice deny a forged signature. To prove that the signature is a forgery, Alice needs to take part in the disavowal protocol.

### 13.6.2   Applications

Later chapters discuss several applications of cryptography in network security. Most of these applications directly or indirectly require the use of public keys. To use a public key, a person should prove that she actually owns the public key. For this reason, the idea of certificates and certificate authorities (CAs) has been developed (See Chapter 14 and Chapter 15). The certificates must be signed by the CA to be valid. Digital signatures are used to provide such a proof. When Alice needs to use Bob's public key, she uses the certificates issued by a CA. The CA signs the certificate with its private key and Alice verifies the signature using the public key of the CA. The certificate itself contains Bob's public key.

Today's protocols that use the services of CA include IPSec (Chapter 18), SSL/TLS (Chapter 17), and S/MIME (Chapter 16). Protocol PGP uses certificates, but they can be issued by people in the community.

## 13.7                                      RECOMMENDED READING

The following books and websites give more details about subjects discussed in this chapter. The items enclosed in brackets refer to the reference list at the end of the book.

### Books

[Sti06], [TW06], and [PHS03] discuss digital signatures in detail.

### WebSites

The following websites give more information about topics discussed in this chapter.
   http://www.itl.nist.gov/fipspubs/fip186.htm
   csrc.nist.gov/publications/fips/fips186-2/fips186-2-change1

http://en.wikipedia.org/wiki/ElGamal_signature_scheme
csrc.nist.gov/cryptval/dss/ECDSAVS.pdf
http://en.wikipedia.org/wiki/ElGamal_signature_scheme
http://en.wikipedia.org/wiki/Digital_signature

## Key Terms

blind digital signature scheme
chosen-message attack
digital signature
digital signature algorithm (DSA)
digital signature scheme
digital signature standard (DSS)
ElGamal digital signature scheme
elliptic curve digital signature scheme
existential forgery
key-only attack

known-message attack
nonce
RSA digital signature scheme
Schnorr digital signature scheme
selective forgery
signing algorithm
timestamped digital signature
undeniable digital signatures
verifying algorithm

## Summary

★ A digital signature scheme can provide the same services provided by a conventional signature. A conventional signature is included in the document; a digital signature is a separate entity. To verify a conventional signature, the recipient compares the signature with the signature on file; to verify a digital signature, the recipient applies a verifying process to the document and signature. There is a one-to-many relationship between a document and the conventional signature; there is a one-to-one relationship between a document and a digital signature.

★ Digital signatures provide message authentication. Digital signatures provide message integrity if the digest of the message is signed instead of the message itself. Digital signatures provide nonrepudiation if a trusted third party is used.

★ Digital signatures cannot provide confidentiality for the message. If confidentiality is needed, a cryptosystem must be applied over the digital signature scheme.

★ A digital signature needs an asymmetric-key system. In a cryptosystem, we use the private and public keys of the receiver; for digital signatures, we use the private and public keys of the sender.

★ The RSA digital signature scheme uses the RSA cryptosystem, but the roles of the private and public keys are swapped. The ElGamal digital signature scheme uses the ElGamal cryptosystem (with some minor changes), but the roles of the private and public keys are swapped. The Schnorr digital signature scheme is a modification of the ElGamal scheme in which the size of the signature can be smaller. The Digital Signature Standard (DSS) uses the digital signature algorithm (DSA), which is based on the ElGamal scheme with some ideas from the Schnorr scheme.

★ Timestamped digital signature schemes are designed to prevent the replaying of signatures. Blind digital signature schemes allow Bob to let Alice sign a document without revealing the contents of the document to Alice. The undeniable digital signature scheme needs the signer to be involved in verifying the signature to prevent the duplication and distribution of the signed message without the signer's approval.

★ The main application of digital signatures is in signing the certificates issued by a certificate authority (CA).

# Practice Set

## Review Questions

**13.1** Compare and contrast a conventional signature and a digital signature.

**13.2** List the security services provided by a digital signature.

**13.3** Compare and contrast attacks on digital signatures with attacks on cryptosystems.

**13.4** Compare and contrast existential and selective forgery.

**13.5** Define the RSA digital signature scheme and compare it to the RSA cryptosystem.

**13.6** Define the ElGamal scheme and compare it to the RSA scheme.

**13.7** Define the Schnorr scheme and compare it to the ElGamal scheme.

**13.8** Define the DSS scheme and compare it with the ElGamal and the Schnorr schemes.

**13.9** Define the elliptic curve digital signature scheme and compare it to the elliptic curve cryptosystem.

**13.10** Mention three variations of digital signatures discussed in this chapter and briefly state the purpose of each.

## Exercises

**13.11** Using the RSA scheme, let $p = 809$, $q = 751$, and $d = 23$. Calculate the public key e. Then
   a. Sign and verify a message with $M_1 = 100$. Call the signature $S_1$.
   b. Sign and verify a message with $M_2 = 50$. Call the signature $S_2$.
   c. Show that if $M = M_1 \times M_2 = 5000$, then $S = S_1 \times S_2$.

**13.12** Using the ElGamal scheme, let $p = 881$ and $d = 700$. Find values for $e_1$ and $e_2$. Choose $r = 17$. Find the value of $S_1$ and $S_2$ if $M = 400$.

**13.13** Using the Schnorr scheme, let $q = 83$, $p = 997$, and $d = 23$. Find values for $e_1$ and $e_2$. Choose $r = 11$. If $M = 400$ and $h(400) = 100$, find the value of $S_1$, $S_2$, and V. Is $S_1 \equiv V(\mod p)$?

**13.14** Using the DSS scheme, let $q = 59$, $p = 709$, and $d = 14$. Find values for $e_1$ and $e_2$. Choose $r = 13$. Find the value of $S_1$ and $S_2$ if $h(M) = 100$. Verify the signature.

**13.15** Do the following:
   a. In the RSA scheme, find the relationship between the size of S and the size of n.
   b. In the ElGamal scheme, find the size of $S_1$ and $S_2$ in relation to the size of p.
   c. In the Schnorr scheme, find the size of $S_1$ and $S_2$ in relation to the size of p and q.
   d. In the DSS scheme, find the size of $S_1$ and $S_2$ in relation to the size of p and q.

**13.16** The NIST specification insists that, in DSS, if the value of $S_2 = 0$, the two signatures must be recalculated using a new r. What is the reason?

**13.17** In ElGamal, Schnorr, or DSS, what happens if Eve can find the value of r used by the signer? Explain your answer for each protocol separately.

**13.18** In ElGamal, Schnorr, or DSS, what happens if Alice uses the same value of r to sign two messages? Explain your answer for each protocol separately.

**13.19** Show an example of the vulnerability of RSA to selective forgery when the values of p and q are small. Use $p = 19$ and $q = 3$.

**13.20** Show an example of the vulnerability of ElGamal to selective forgery when the value of p is small. Use $p = 19$.

**13.21** Show an example of the vulnerability of Schnorr to selective forgery when the values of $p$ and $q$ are small. Use $p = 29$ and $q = 7$.

**13.22** Show an example of the vulnerability of DSS to selective forgery when the values of $p$ and $q$ are small. Use $p = 29$ and $q = 7$.

**13.23** In the ElGamal scheme, if Eve can find the value of $r$, can she forge a message? Explain.

**13.24** In the Schnorr scheme, if Eve can find the value of $r$, can she forge a message? Explain.

**13.25** In the DSS scheme, if Eve can find the value of $r$, can she forge a message? Explain.

**13.26** Suppose that the values of $p$, $q$, $e_1$, and $r$ in the Schnorr scheme are the same as the corresponding values in the DSS scheme. Compare the values of $S_1$ and $S_2$ in the Schnorr scheme with the corresponding values in the DSS scheme.

**13.27** In the ElGamal scheme, explain why the calculation of $S_1$ is done in modulo $p$, but the calculation of $S_2$ is done in modulo $p - 1$.

**13.28** In the Schnorr scheme, explain why the calculation of $S_1$ is done in modulo $p$, but the calculation of $S_2$ is done in modulo $q$.

**13.29** In the DSS scheme, explain why the calculation of $S_1$ is done in modulo $p$ modulo $q$, but the calculation of $S_2$ is done only in modulo $q$.

**13.30** In the Schnorr scheme, prove the correctness of the verifying process.

**13.31** In the DSS scheme, prove the correctness of the verifying process.

**13.32** In the elliptic curve digital signature scheme, prove the correctness of the verifying process.

**13.33** Write two algorithms for the RSA scheme: one for the signing process and one for the verifying process.

**13.34** Write two algorithms for the ElGamal scheme: one for the signing process and one for the verifying process.

**13.35** Write two algorithms for the Schnorr scheme: one for the signing process and one for the verifying process.

**13.36** Write two algorithms for the DSS scheme: one for the signing process and one for the verifying process.

**13.37** Write two algorithms for the elliptic curve scheme: one for the signing process and one for the verifying process.

# 14

# Entity Authentication

## Objectives

This chapter has several objectives:
- ☞ To distinguish between message authentication and entity authentication
- ☞ To define witnesses used for identification
- ☞ To discuss some methods of entity authentication using a password
- ☞ To introduce some challenge-response protocols for entity authentication
- ☞ To introduce some zero-knowledge protocols for entity authentication
- ☞ To define biometrics and distinguish between physiological and behavioral techniques

## 14.1 INTRODUCTION

**Entity authentication** is a technique designed to let one party prove the identity of another party. An *entity* can be a person, a process, a client, or a server. The entity whose identity needs to be proved is called the *claimant;* the party that tries to prove the identity of the claimant is called the *verifier*. When Bob tries to prove the identity of Alice, Alice is the claimant, and Bob is the verifier.

### 14.1.1 Data-Origin Versus Entity Authentication

There are two differences between *message authentication (data-origin authentication),* discussed in Chapter 13, and *entity authentication,* discussed in this chapter.
1. Message authentication (or data-origin authentication) might not happen in real time; entity authentication does. In the former, Alice sends a message to Bob. When Bob authenticates the message, Alice may or may not be present in the communication process. On the other hand, when Alice requests entity authentication, there is no real message communication involved until Alice is authenticated by Bob. Alice needs to be online and to take part in the process. Only after she is authenticated can messages be communicated between Alice and Bob. Data-origin authentication is required when an email is sent from Alice to Bob. Entity authentication is required when Alice gets cash from an automatic teller machine.
2. Second, message authentication simply authenticates one message; the process needs to be repeated for each new message. Entity authentication authenticates the claimant for the entire duration of a session.

### 14.1.2 Verification Categories

In entity authentication, the claimant must identify herself to the verifier. This can be done with one of three kinds of witnesses: *something known, something possessed,* or *something inherent.*

❑ **Something known.** This is a secret known only by the claimant that can be checked by the verifier. Examples are a password, a PIN, a secret key, and a private key.

❑ **Something possessed**. This is something that can prove the claimant's identity. Examples are a passport, a driver's license, an identification card, a credit card, and a smart card.

❑ **Something inherent**. This is an inherent characteristic of the claimant. Examples are conventional signatures, fingerprints, voice, facial characteristics, retinal pattern, and handwriting.

### 14.1.3 Entity Authentication and Key Management

This chapter discusses entity authentication. The next chapter discusses key managment. These two topics are very closely related; most key management protocols use entity authentication protocols. This is why these two topics are discussed together in most books. In this book they are treated separately for clarity.

## 14.2                                          PASSWORDS

The simplest and oldest method of entity authentication is the **password-based authentication,** where the password is something that the **claimant** *knows.* A password is used when a user needs to access a system to use the system's resources (login). Each user has a user identification that is public, and a password that is private. We can divide these authentication schemes into two groups: the **fixed password** and the **one-time password.**

### 14.2.1 Fixed Password

A fixed password is a password that is used over and over again for every access. Several schemes have been built, one upon the other.

#### First Approach

In the very rudimentary approach, the system keeps a table (a file) that is sorted by user identification. To access the system resources, the user sends her user identification and password, in plaintext, to the system. The system uses the identification to find the password in the table. If the password sent by the user matches the password in the table, access is granted; otherwise, it is denied. Figure 14.1 shows this approach.

#### Attacks on the First Approach   This approach is subject to several kinds of attack.

❑ **Eavesdropping.** Eve can watch Alice when she types her password. Most systems, as a security measure, do not show the characters a user types. Eavesdropping can take a more sophisticated form. Eve can listen to the line and intercept the message, thereby capturing the password for her own use.

❑ **Stealing a password.** The second type of attack occurs when Eve tries to physically steal Alice's password. This can be prevented if Alice does not write down the password and instead she just commits it to memory. For this reason the password should be very simple or else related to something familiar to Alice. But this makes the password vulnerable to other types of attacks.

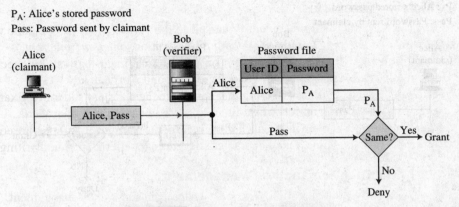

P$_A$: Alice's stored password
Pass: Password sent by claimant

**Fig. 14.1** *User ID and password file*

❑ **Accessing a password file.** Eve can hack into the system and get access to the ID/password file. Eve can read the file and find Alice's password or even change it. To prevent this type of attack, the file can be read/write protected. However, most systems need this type of file to be readable by the public. We will see how the second approach can protect the file from this type of attack.

❑ **Guessing.** Using a guessing attack, Eve can log into the system and try to guess Alice's password by trying different combinations of characters. The password is particularly vulnerable if the user is allowed to choose a short password (a few characters). It is also vulnerable if Alice has chosen something trivial, such as her birthday, her child's name, or the name of her favorite actor. To prevent guessing, a long random password is recommended, something that is not very obvious. However, the use of such a random password may also create a problem. Because she could easily forget such a password, Alice might store a copy of it somewhere, which makes the password subject to stealing.

### Second Approach

A more secure approach is to store the hash of the password (instead of the plaintext password) in the password file. Any user can read the contents of the file, but, because the hash function is a one-way function, it is almost impossible to guess the value of the password. Figure 14.2 shows the situation. When the password is created, the system hashes it and stores the hash in the password file.

When the user sends the ID and the password, the system creates a hash of the password and then compares the hash value with the one stored in the file. If there is a match, the user is granted access; otherwise, access is denied. In this case, the file does not need to be read protected.

*Dictionary Attack*   The hash function prevents Eve from gaining access to the system even though she has the password file. However, there is still the possibility of **dictionary attack**. In this attack, Eve is interested in finding one password, regardless of the user ID. For example, if the password is 6 digits, Eve can create a list of 6-digit numbers (000000 to 999999), and then apply the hash function to every number; the result is a list of one million hashes. She can then get the password file and search the second-column entries to find a match. This could be programmed and run offline on Eve's private computer. After a match is found, Eve can go online and use the password to access the system. The third approach shows how to make this attack more difficult.

P_A: Alice's stored password
Pass: Password sent by claimant

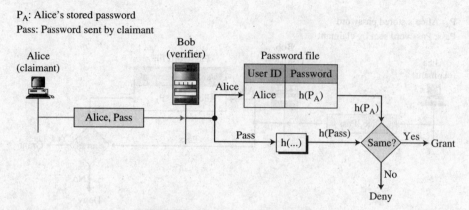

**Fig. 14.2** *Hashing the password*

**Third Approach**   The third approach is called **salting** the password. When the password string is created, a random string, called the salt, is concatenated to the password. The salted password is then hashed. The ID, the salt, and the hash are then stored in the file. Now, when a user asks for access, the system extracts the salt, concatenates it with the received password, makes a hash out of the result, and compares it with the hash stored in the file. If there is a match, access is granted; otherwise, it is denied (see Fig. 14.3).

P_A: Alice's password
S_A: Alice's salt
Pass: Password sent by claimant

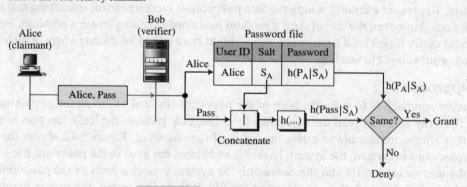

**Fig. 14.3** *Salting the password*

Salting makes the dictionary attack more difficult. If the original password is 6 digits and the salt is 4 digits, then hashing is done over a 10-digit value. This means that Eve now needs to make a list of 10 million items and create a hash for each of them. The list of hashes has 10 million entries, and the comparison takes much longer. Salting is very effective if the salt is a very long random number. The UNIX operating system uses a variation of this method.

**Fourth Approach**   In the fourth approach, two identification techniques are combined. A good example of this type of authentication is the use of an ATM card with a PIN (personal identification number). The card belongs to the category "*something possessed*" and the PIN belongs to the category "*something known*". The PIN is a password that enhances the security of the card. If the card is stolen, it cannot be used unless the PIN is known. The PIN number, however, is traditionally very short so it is easily remembered by the owner. This makes it vulnerable to the guessing type of attack.

## 14.2.2  One-Time Password

A **one-time password** is a password that is used only once. This kind of password makes eavesdropping and salting useless. Three approaches are discussed here.

***First Approach***  In the first approach, the user and the system agree upon a *list of passwords*. Each password on the list can be used only once. There are some drawbacks to this approach. First, the system and the user must keep a long list of passwords. Second, if the user does not use the passwords in sequence, the system needs to perform a long search to find the match. This scheme makes eavesdropping and reuse of the password useless. The password is valid only once and cannot be used again.

***Second Approach***  In the second approach, the user and the system agree to *sequentially update the password*. The user and the system agree on an original password, $P_1$, which is valid only for the first access. During the first access, the user generates a new password, $P_2$, and encrypts this password with $P_1$ as the key. $P_2$ is the password for the second access. During the second access, the user generates a new password, $P_3$, and encrypts it with $P_2$; $P_3$ is used for the third access. In other words, $P_i$ is used to create $P_{i+1}$. Of course, if Eve can guess the first password ($P_1$), she can find all of the subsequent ones.

***Third Approach***  In the third approach, the user and the system create a sequentially updated password using a hash function In this approach, elegantly devised by Leslie Lamport, the user and the system agree upon an original password, $P_0$, and a counter, $n$. The system calculates $h^n(P_0)$, where $h^n$ means applying a hash function $n$ times. In other words,

$$h^n(x) = h(h^{n-1}(x)) \; h^{n-1}(x) = h(h^{n-2}(x)) \; \dots \; h^2(x) = h(h(x)) \; h^1(x) = h(x)$$

The system stores the identity of Alice, the value of $n$, and the value of $h^n(P_0)$. Figure 14.4 shows how the user accesses the system the first time.

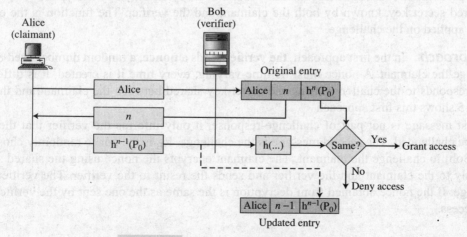

**Fig. 14.4**  *Lamport one-time password*

When the system receives the response of the user in the third message, it applies the hash function to the value received to see if it matches the value stored in the entry. If there is a match, access is granted; otherwise, it is denied. The system then decrements the value of $n$ in the entry and replaces the old value of the password $h^n(P_0)$ with the new value $h^{n-1}(P_0)$.

When the user tries to access the system for the second time, the value of the counter it receives is $n - 1$. The third message from the user is now $h^{n-2}(P_0)$. When the system receives this message, it applies the hash function to get $h^{n-1}(P_0)$, which can be compared with the updated entry.

The value of $n$ in the entry is decremented each time there is an access. When the value becomes 0, the user can no longer access the system; everything must be set up again. For this reason, the value of $n$ is normally chosen as a large number such as 1000.

## 14.3                  CHALLENGE-RESPONSE

In password authentication, the claimant proves her identity by demonstrating that she knows a secret, the password. However, because the claimant reveals this secret, it is susceptible to interception by the adversary. In **challenge-response authentication,** the claimant proves that she *knows* a secret without sending it. In other words, the claimant does not send the secret to the verifier; the verifier either has it or finds it.

---

**In challenge-response authentication, the claimant proves that she knows a secret without sending it to the verifier.**

---

The *challenge* is a time-varying value such as a random number or a timestamp that is sent by the verifier. The claimant applies a function to the challenge and sends the result, called a *response,* to the verifier. The response shows that the claimant knows the secret.

---

**The challenge is a time-varying value sent by the verifier; the response is the result of a function applied on the challenge.**

---

### 14.3.1   Using a Symmetric-Key Cipher

Several approaches to challenge-response authentication use symmetric-key encryption. The secret here is the shared secret key, known by both the claimant and the verifier. The function is the encrypting algorithm applied on the challenge.

***First Approach***    In the first approach, the verifier sends a **nonce,** a random number used only once, to challenge the claimant. A nonce must be time-varying; every time it is created, it is different. The claimant responds to the challenge using the secret key shared between the claimant and the verifier. Figure 14.5 shows this first approach.

The first message is not part of challenge-response, it only informs the verifier that the claimant wants to be challenged. The second message is the challenge. $R_B$ is the nonce randomly chosen by the verifier (Bob) to challenge the claimant. The claimant encrypts the nonce using the shared secret key known only to the claimant and the verifier and sends the result to the verifier. The verifier decrypts the message. If the nonce obtained from decryption is the same as the one sent by the verifier, Alice is granted access.

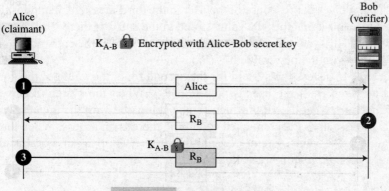

**Fig. 14.5** *Nonce challenge*

Note that in this process, the claimant and the verifier need to keep the symmetric key used in the process secret. The verifier must also keep the value of the nonce for claimant identification until the response is returned.

The reader may have noticed that use of a nonce prevents a replay of the third message by Eve. Eve cannot replay the third message and pretend that it is a new request for authentication by Alice, because once Bob receives the response, the value of $R_B$ is not valid any more. The next time a new value is used.

***Second Approach*** In the second approach, the time-varying value is a timestamp, which obviously changes with time. In this approach the challenge message is the current time sent from the verifier to the claimant. However, this supposes that the client and the server clocks are synchronized; the claimant knows the current time. This means that there is no need for the challenge message. The first and third messages can be combined. The result is that authentication can be done using one message, the response to an implicit challenge, the current time. Figure 14.6 shows the approach.

**Fig. 14.6** *Timestamp challenge*

***Third Approach*** The first and second approaches are for unidirectional authentication. Alice is authenticated to Bob, but not the other way around. If Alice also needs to be sure about Bob's identity, we need bidirectional authentication. Figure 14.7 shows a scheme.

The second message $R_B$ is the challenge from Bob to Alice. In the third message, Alice responds to Bob's challenge and at the same time, sends her challenge $R_A$ to Bob. The third message is Bob's response. Note that in the fourth message the order of $R_A$ and $R_B$ are switched to prevent a replay attack of the third message by an adversary.

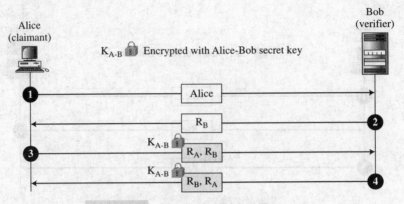

**Fig. 14.7** *Bidirectional authentication*

## 14.3.2 Using Keyed-Hash Functions

Instead of using encryption/decryption for entity authentication, we can also use a keyed-hash function (MAC). One advantage to the scheme is that it preserves the integrity of challenge and response messages and at the same time uses a secret, the key.

Figure 14.8 shows how we can use a keyed-hash function to create a challenge response with a timestamp.

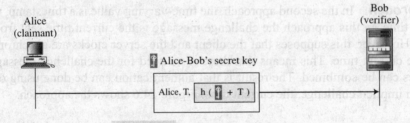

**Fig. 14.8** *Keyed-hash function*

Note that in this case, the timestamp is sent both as plaintext and as text scrambled by the keyed-hash function. When Bob receives the message, he takes the plaintext T, applies the keyed-hash function, and then compares his calculation with what he received to determine the authenticity of Alice.

## 14.3.3 Using an Asymmetric-Key Cipher

Instead of a symmetric-key cipher, we can use an asymmetric-key cipher for entity authentication. Here the secret must be the private key of the claimant. The claimant must show that she owns the private key related to the public key that is available to everyone. This means that the verifier must encrypt the challenge using the public key of the claimant; the claimant then decrypts the message using her private key. The response to the challenge is the decrypted challenge. Following are two approaches: one for unidirectional authentication and one for bidirectional authentication.

***First Approach*** In the first approach, Bob encrypts the challenge using Alice's public key. Alice decrypts the message with her private key and sends the nonce to Bob. Figure 14.9 shows this approach.

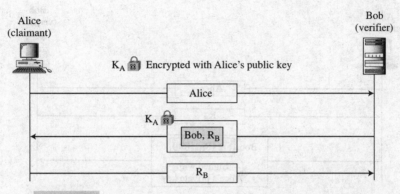

**Fig. 14.9** *Unidirectional, asymmetric-key authentication*

**Second Approach** In the second approach, two public keys are used, one in each direction. Alice sends her identity and nonce encrypted with Bob's public key. Bob responds with his nonce encrypted with Alice's public key. Finally, Alice, responds with Bob's decrypted nonce. Figure 14.10 shows this approach.

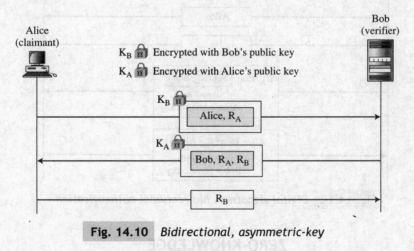

**Fig. 14.10** *Bidirectional, asymmetric-key*

### 14.3.4 Using Digital Signature

Entity authentication can also be achieved using a digital signature. When a digital signature is used for entity authentication, the claimant uses her private key for signing. Two approaches are shown here, the others are left as exercises.

**First Approach** In the first approach, shown in Fig. 14.11, Bob uses a plaintext challenge and Alice signs the response.

**Second Approach** In the second approach, shown in Fig. 14.12, Alice and Bob authenticate each other.

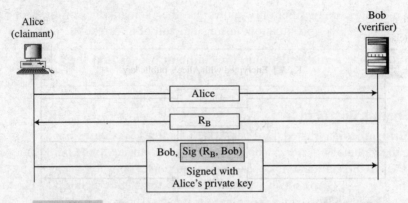

**Fig. 14.11** *Digital signature, unidirectional authentication*

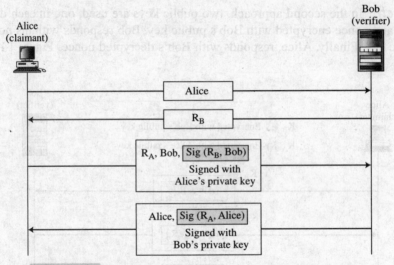

**Fig. 14.12** *Digital signature, bidirectional authentication*

## 14.4 ZERO-KNOWLEDGE

In password authentication, the claimant needs to send her secret (the password) to the verifier; this is subject to eavesdropping by Eve. In addition, a dishonest verifier could reveal the password to others or use it to impersonate the claimant.

In challenge-response entity authentication, the claimant's secret is not sent to the verifier. The claimant applies a function on the challenge sent by the verifier that includes her secret. In some challenge-response methods, the verifier actually knows the claimant's secret, which could be misused by a dishonest verifier. In other methods, the verifier can extract some information about the secret from the claimant by choosing a preplanned set of challenges.

In **zero-knowledge authentication,** the claimant does not reveal anything that might endanger the confidentiality of the secret. The claimant proves to the verifier that she knows a secret, without revealing it. The interactions are so designed that they cannot lead to revealing or guessing the secret.

After exchanging messages, the verifier only knows that the claimant does or does not have the secret, nothing more. The result is a yes/no situation, just a single bit of information.

---

**In zero-knowledge authentication, the claimant proves that she knows a secret without revealing it.**

---

### 14.4.1 Fiat-Shamir Protocol

In the **Fiat-Shamir protocol,** a trusted third party (see Chapter 15) chooses two large prime numbers $p$ and $q$ to calculate the value of $n = p \times q$. The value of $n$ is announced to the public; the values of $p$ and $q$ are kept secret. Alice, the claimant, chooses a secret number $s$ between 1 and $n - 1$ (exclusive). She calculates $v = s^2 \bmod n$. She keeps $s$ as her private key and registers $v$ as her public key with the third party. Verification of Alice by Bob can be done in four steps as shown in Fig. 14.13.

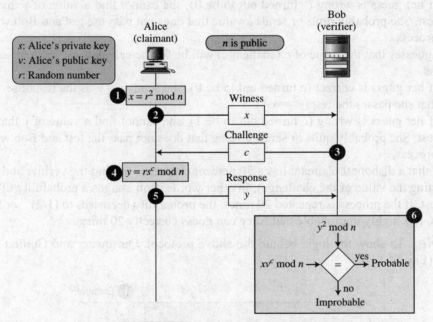

**Fig. 14.13** *Fiat-Shamir protocol*

1. Alice, the claimant, chooses a random number $r$ between 0 and $n - 1$ ($r$ is called the commitment). She then calculates the value of $x = r^2 \bmod n$; $x$ is called the witness.
2. Alice sends $x$ to Bob as the witness.
3. Bob, the verifier, sends the challenge $c$ to Alice. The value of $c$ is either 0 or 1.
4. Alice calculates the response $y = rs^c$. Note that $r$ is the random number selected by Alice in the first step, $s$ is her private key, and $c$ is the challenge (0 or 1).
5. Alice sends the response to Bob to show that she knows the value of her private key, $s$. She claims to be Alice.
6. Bob calculates $y^2$ and $xv^c$. If these two values are congruent, then Alice either knows the value of $s$ (she is honest) or she has calculated the value of $y$ in some other ways (dishonest) because we can easily prove that $y^2$ is the same as $xv^c$ in modulo $n$ arithmetic as shown below:

$$y^2 = (rs^c)^2 = r^2 s^{2c} = r^2(s^2)^c = xv^c$$

The six steps constitute a round; the verification is repeated several times with the value of $c$ equal to 0 or 1 (chosen randomly). The claimant must pass the test in each round to be verified. If she fails one single round, the process is aborted and she is not authenticated.

Let us elaborate on this interesting protocol. Alice can be honest (knows the value of $s$) or dishonest (does not know the value of $s$). If she is honest, she passes each round. If she is not, she still can pass a round by predicting the value of challenge correctly. Two situations can happen:

1.  Alice guesses that the value of $c$ (the challenge) will be 1 (a prediction). She calculates $x = r^2/v$ and sends $x$ as the witness.
    a.  If her guess is correct ($c$ turned out to be 1), she sends $y = r$ as the response. We can see that she passes the test ($y^2 = xv^c$).
    b.  If her guess is wrong ($c$ turned out to be 0), she cannot find a value of $y$ that passes the test. She probably quits or sends a value that does not pass the test and Bob will abort the process.
2.  Alice guesses that the value of $c$ (challenge) will be 0. She calculates $x = r^2$ and sends $x$ as the witness.
    c.  If her guess is correct ($c$ turned out to be 0), she sends $y = r$ as the response. We can see that she passes the test ($y^2 = xv^c$).
    d.  If her guess is wrong ($c$ turned out to be 1), she cannot find a value of $y$ that passes the rest. She probably quits or sends a value that does not pass the test and Bob will abort the process.

We can see that a dishonest claimant has a 50 percent chance of fooling the verifier and passing the test (by predicting the value of the challenge). In other words, Bob assigns a probability of 1/2 to each round of the test. If the process is repeated 20 times, the probability decreases to $(1/2)^{20}$ or $9.54 \times 10^{-7}$. In other words, it is highly improbable that Alice can guess correctly 20 times.

*Cave Example*  To show the logic behind the above protocol, Quisquater and Guillou devised the cave example (Fig. 14.14).

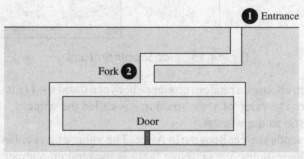

**Fig. 14.14**  *Cave example*

Suppose there is an underground cave with a door at the end of the cave that can only be opened with a magic word. Alice claims that she knows the word and that she can open the door. At the beginning, Alice and Bob are standing at the entrance (point 1). Alice enters the cave and reaches the fork (point 2). Bob cannot see Alice from the entrance. Now the game starts.

1. Alice chooses to go either right or left. This corresponds to the sending of the witness ($x$).
2. After Alice disappears into the cave, Bob comes to the fork (point 2) and asks Alice to come up from either the right or left. This corresponds to sending the challenge ($c$).
3. If Alice knows the magic word (her private key), she can come up from the requested side. She may have to use the magic word (if she is on the wrong side) or she can just come up without using the magic word (if she is at the right side). However, if Alice does not know the magic word, she may come up from the correct side if she has guessed Bob's challenge. With a probability of 1/2, Alice can fool Bob and make him believe that she knows the magic word. This corresponds to the response ($y$).
4. The game is repeated many times. Alice will win if she passes the test all of the time. The probability that she wins the game is very low if she does not know the magic word. In other words, $P = (1/2)^N$ where P is the probability of winning without knowing the magic word and N is the number of times the test is run.

## 14.4.2 Feige-Fiat-Shamir Protocol

The **Feige-Fiat-Shamir protocol** is similar to the first approach except that it uses a vector of private keys $[s_1, s_2, ..., s_k]$, a vector of public keys $[v_1, v_2, ..., v_k]$, and a vector of challenges $(c_1, c_2, ..., c_k)$. The private keys are chosen randomly, but they must be relatively prime to $n$. The public keys are chosen such that $v_i = (s_i^2)^{-1} \mod n$. The three steps in the process are shown in Fig. 14.15.

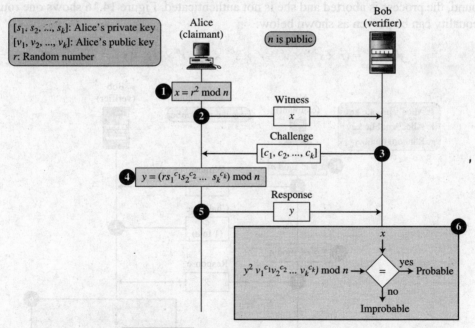

**Fig. 14.15** *Feige-Fiat-Shamir protocol*

We can prove that $y^2 v_1^{c1} v_2^{c2} \dots v_k^{ck}$ is the same as $x$:

$$y^2 v_1^{c1} v_2^{c2} \dots v_k^{ck} = r^2 (s_1^{c1})^2 (s_2^{c2})^2 \dots (s_k^{ck})^2 v_1^{c1} v_2^{c2} \dots v_k^{ck}$$

$$= x (s_1^2)^{c1} (v_1^{c1}) (s_2^2)^{c2} (v_2^{c2}) \dots (s_2^2)^{c2} (v_2^{ck})$$

$$= x (s_1^2 v_1)^{c1} (s_2^2 v_2)^{c2} \dots (s_k^2 v_k)^{ck} = x (1)^{c1} (1)^{c2} \dots (1)^{ck} = x$$

The three exchanges constitute a round; verification is repeated several times with the value of $c$'s equal to 0 or 1 (chosen randomly). The claimant must pass the test in each round to be verified. If she fails a single round, the process is aborted and she is not authenticated.

### 14.4.3 Guillou-Quisquater Protocol

The **Guillou-Quisquater protocol** is an extension of the Fiat-Shamir protocol in which fewer number of rounds can be used to prove the identity of the claimant. A trusted third party (see Chapter 15) chooses two large prime numbers $p$ and $q$ to calculate the value of $n = p \times q$. The trusted party also chooses an exponent, $e$, which is coprime with $\phi$, where $\phi = (p-1)(q-1)$. The values of $n$ and $e$ are announced to the public; the values of $p$ and $q$ are kept secret. The trusted party chooses two numbers for each entity, $v$ which is public and $s$ which is secret. However, in this case, the relationship between $v$ and $s$ is different: $s^e \times v = 1 \bmod n$.

The three exchanges constitute a round; verification is repeated several times with a random value of $c$ (challenge) between 1 and $e$. The claimant must pass the test in each round to be verified. If she fails a single round, the process is aborted and she is not authenticated. Figure 14.16 shows one round.

The equality can be proven as shown below:

$$y^e \times v^c = (r \times s^c)^e \times v^c = r^e \times s^{ce} \times v^c = r^e \times (s^e \times v)^c = x \times 1^c = x$$

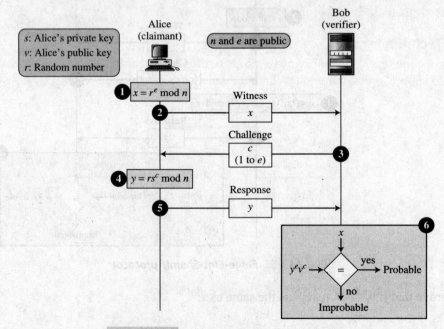

**Fig. 14.16** *Guillou-Quisquater protocol*

## 14.5                                 BIOMETRICS

**Biometrics** is the measurement of physiological or behavioral features that identify a person (authentication by something inherent). Biometrics measures features that cannot be guessed, stolen, or shared.

### 14.5.1   Components

Several components are needed for biometrics, including capturing devices, processors, and storage devices. Capturing devices such as readers (or sensors) measure biometrics features. Processors change the measured features to the type of data appropriate for saving. Storage devices save the result of processing for authentication.

### 14.5.2   Enrollment

Before using any biometric techniques for authentication, the corresponding feature of each person in the community should be available in the database. This is referred to as enrollment.

### 14.5.3   Authentication

Authentication is done by verification or identification.

*Verification*   In **verification,** a person's feature is matched against a single record in the database (one-to-one matching) to find if she is who she is claiming to be. This is useful, for example, when a bank needs to verify a customer's signature on a check.

*Identification*   In **identification,** a person's feature is matched against all records in the database (one-to-many matching) to find if she has a record in the database. This is useful, for example, when a company needs to allow access to the building only to employees.

### 14.5.4   Techniques

Biometrics techniques can be divided into two broad categories: physiological and behavioral. Figure 14.17 shows several common techniques under each category.

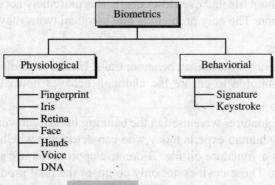

**Fig. 14.17** *Biometrics*

## Physiological Techniques

Physiological techniques measure the physical traits of the human body for verification and identification. To be effective, the trait should be unique among all or most of the population. In addition, the feature should be changeable due to aging, surgery, illness, disease, and so on. There are several physiological techniques.

*Fingerprint* Although there are several methods for measuring characteristics associated with fingerprints, the two most common are *minutiae-based* and *image-based*. In the minutiae-based technique, the system creates a graph based on where individual ridges start/stop or branch. In the image-based technique, the system creates an image of the fingertip and finds similarities to the image in the database. Fingerprints have been used for a long time. They show a high level of accuracy and support verification and identification. However, fingerprints can be altered by aging, injury, or diseases.

*Iris* This technique measures the pattern within the iris that is unique for each person. It normally requires a laser beam (infrared). They are very accurate and stable over a person's life. They also support verification and identification. However, some eye diseases, such as cataracts, can alter the iris pattern.

*Retina* The devices for this purpose examine the blood vessels in the back of the eyes. However, these devices are expensive and not common yet.

*Face* This technique analyzes the geometry of the face based on the distance between facial features such as the nose, mouth, and eyes. Some technologies combine geometric features with skin texture. Standard video cameras and this technique support both verification and identification. However, accuracy can be affected by eyeglasses, growing facial hair, and aging.

*Hands* This technique measures the dimension of hands, including the shape and length of the fingers. This technique can be used indoors and outdoors. However, it is better suited to verification rather than identification.

*Voice* Voice recognition measures pitch, cadence, and tone in the voice. It can be used locally (microphone) or remotely (audio channel). This method is mostly used for verification. However, accuracy can be diminished by background noise, illness, or age.

*DNA* DNA is the chemical found in the nucleus of all cells of humans and most other organsims. The pattern is persistent throughout life and even after death. It is extremely accurate. It can be used for both verification and identification. The only problem is that identical twins may share the same DNA.

## Behavioral Techniques

Behavioral techniques measure some human behavior traits. Unlike physiological techniques, behavioral techniques need to be monitored to ensure the claimant behaves normally and does not attempt to impersonate someone else.

*Signature* In the past, signatures were used in the banking industry to verify the identity of the check writer. There are still many human experts today who can determine whether a signature on a check or a document is the same as a signature on file. Biometric approaches use signature tablets and special pens to identify the person. These devices not only compare the final product, the signature, they also measure some other behavioral traits, such as the timing needed to write the signature. Signatures are mostly used for verification.

***Keystroke*** The keystrokes (typing rhythm) technique measures the behavior of a person related to working with a keyboard. It can measure the duration of key depression, the time between keystrokes, number and frequency of errors, the pressure on the keys, and so on. It is inexpensive because it does not require new equipment. However, it is not very accurate because the trait can change with time (people become faster or slower typists). It is also text dependent.

### 14.5.5 Accuracy

Accuracy of biometric techniques is measured using two parameters: **false rejection rate (FRR)** and **false acceptance rate (FAR).**

***False Rejection Rate (FRR)*** This parameter measures how often a person, who should be recognized, is not recognized by the system. FRR is measured as the ratio of false rejection to the total number of attempts (in percentage).

***False Acceptance Rate (FAR)*** This parameter measures how often a person, who should not be recognized, is recognized by the system. FAR is measured as the ratio of false acceptance to the total number of attempts (in percentage).

### 14.5.6 Applications

Several applications of biometrics are already in use. In commercial environments, these include access to facilities, access to information systems, transaction at point-of-sales, and employee timekeeping. In the law enforcement system, they include investigations (using fingerprints or DNA) and forensic analysis. Border control and immigration control also use some biometric techniques.

## 14.6                    RECOMMENDED READING

The following books and websites give more details about subjects discussed in this chapter. The items enclosed in brackets refer to the reference list at the end of the book.

### Books

Entity authentication is discussed in [Sti06], [TW06], [Sal03], and [KPS02].

### WebSites

The following websites give more information about topics discussed in this chapter.
   http://en.wikipedia.org/wiki/Challenge-response_authentication
   http://en.wikipedia.org/wiki/Password-authenticated_key_agreement
   http://rfc.net/rfc2195.html

## *Key Terms*

biometrics
challenge-response authentication
claimant
dictionary attack
entity authentication

Feige-Fiat-Shamir protocol
Fiat-Shamir protocol
fixed password
Guillou-Quisquater protocol
identification

| | |
|---|---|
| false acceptance rate (FAR) | nonce |
| false rejection rate (FRR) | one-time password |
| password | something known |
| password-based authentication | something possessed |
| salting | verification |
| something inherent | zero-knowledge authentication |

## Summary

★ Entity authentication lets one party prove her identity to another. In entity authentication, a claimant proves her identity to the verifier using one of the three kinds of witnesses: something known, something possessed, or something inherent.

★ In password-based authentication, the claimant uses a string of characters as something she knows. Password-based authentication can be divided into two broad categories: fixed and one-time. Attacks on password-based authentication include eavesdropping, stealing a password, accessing the password file, guessing, and the dictionary attack.

★ In challenge-response authentication, the claimant proves that she knows a secret without actually sending it. Challenge-response authentication can use symmetric-key ciphers, keyed-hash functions, asymmetric-key ciphers, and digital signatures.

★ In zero-knowledge authentication, the claimant does not reveal her secret; she just proves that she knows it.

★ Biometrics is the measurement of physiological or behavioral features for identifying a person using something inherent to her. We can divide the biometric techniques into two broad categories: physiological and behavioral. Physiological techniques measure the physical traits of the human body for verification and identification. Behavioral techniques measure some traits in human behavior.

## Practice Set

### Review Questions

14.1 Distinguish between data-origin authentication and entity authentication.

14.2 List and define three kinds of identification witnesses in entity authentication.

14.3 Distinguish between fixed and one-time passwords.

14.4 What are some advantages and disadvantages of using long passwords?

14.5 Explain the general idea behind challenge-response entity authentication.

14.6 Define a nonce and its use in entity authentication.

14.7 Define a dictionary attack and how it can be prevented.

14.8 Distinguish between challenge-response and zero-knowledge entity authentications.

14.9 Define biometrics and distinguish between two the broad categories of the techniques.

14.10 Distinguish between the two accuracy parameters defined for biometric measurement in this chapter.

### Exercises

14.11 We discussed fixed and one-time passwords as two extremes. What about frequently changed passwords? How do you think this scheme can be implemented? What are the advantages and disadvantages?

**14.12** How can a system prevent a guessing attack on a password? How can a bank prevent PIN guessing if someone has found or stolen a bank card and tries to use it?

**14.13** Show two more exchanges of the authentication procedure in Fig. 14.4.

**14.14** What are some disadvantages of using the timestamp in Fig. 14.6?

**14.15** Can we repeat the three messages in Fig. 14.5 to achieve bidirectional authentication? Explain.

**14.16** Show how authentication in Fig. 14.5 can be done using a keyed-hash function.

**14.17** Show how authentication in Fig. 14.7 can be done using a keyed-hash function.

**14.18** Compare Fig. 14.5 and Fig. 14.9 and make a list of similarities and differences.

**14.19** Compare Fig. 14.7 and Fig. 14.10 and make a list of similarities and differences.

**14.20** Can we use a timestamp with an asymmetric-key cipher to achieve authentication? Explain.

**14.21** Compare and contrast Fig. 14.13, Fig. 14.15, and Fig. 14.16. Make a list of similarities and differences.

**14.22** Redo the cave example for the Feige-Fiat-Shamir protocol.

**14.23** For $p = 569$, $q = 683$, and $s = 157$, show three rounds of the Fiat-Shamir protocol by calculating the values and filling in the entries of a table.

**14.24** For $p = 683$, $q = 811$, $s_1 = 157$, and $s_2 = 43215$, show three rounds of the Feige-Fiat-Shamir protocol by calculating the values and filling in the entries of a table.

**14.25** For $p = 683$, $q = 811$, and $v = 157$, show three rounds of the Guillou-Quisquater protocol by calculating the values and filling in the entries of a table.

**14.26** Draw a digram to show the general idea behind the three protocols discussed in this chapter for zero-knowledge authentication.

**14.27** In the Fiat-Shamir protocol, what is the probability that a dishonest claimant correctly responds to the challenge 15 times in a row?

**14.28** In the Feige-Fiat-Shamir protocol, what is the probability that a dishonest claimant correctly responds to the challenge 15 times in a row?

**14.29** In the Guillou-Quisquater protocol, what is the probability that a dishonest claimant correctly responds to the challenge 15 times in a row if the value of the challenge is selected between 1 and 15?

**14.30** In the bidirectional approach to authentication in Fig. 14.10 if multiple session authentication is allowed, Eve intercepts the $R_B$ nonce from Bob (in the second session) and sends it as Alice's nonce for a second session. Bob, without checking that this nonce is the same as the one he sent, encrypts $R_B$ and puts it in a message with his nonce. Eve uses the encrypted $R_B$ and pretends that she is Alice, continuing with the first session and responding with the encrypted $R_B$. This is called a reflection attack. Show the steps in this scenario.

# 15

# Key Management

## Objectives

This chapter has several objectives:
- ☞ To explain the need for a key-distribution center (KDC)
- ☞ To show how a KDC can create a session key between two parties
- ☞ To show how two parties can use a symmetric-key agreement protocol to create a session key between themselves without using the services of a KDC
- ☞ To describe Kerberos as a KDC and an authentication protocol
- ☞ To explain the need for certification authorities (CAs) for public keys and how X.509 recommendation defines the format of certificates
- ☞ To introduce the idea of a Public-Key Infrastructure (PKI) and explain some of its duties

Previous chapters have discussed symmetric-key and asymmetric-key cryptography. However, we have not yet discussed how secret keys in symmetric-key cryptography, and public keys in asymmetric-key cryptography, are distributed and maintained. This chapter touches on these two issues.

We first discuss the distribution of symmetric keys using a trusted third party. Second, we show how two parties can establish a symmetric key between themselves without using a trusted third party. Third, we introduce Kerberos as both a KDC and an authentication protocol. Fourth, we discuss the certification of public keys using certification authorities (CAs) based on the X.509 recommendation. Finally, we briefly discuss the idea of a Public-Key Infrastructure (PKI) and mention some of its duties.

## 15.1    SYMMETRIC-KEY DISTRIBUTION

Symmetric-key cryptography is more efficient than asymmetric-key cryptography for enciphering large messages. Symmetric-key cryptography, however, needs a shared secret key between two parties.

If Alice needs to exchange confidential messages with $N$ people, she needs $N$ different keys. What if $N$ people need to communicate with each other? A total of $N(N-1)$ keys is needed if we require that Alice and Bob use two keys for bidirectional communication; only $N(N-1)/2$ keys are needed if we allow a key to be used for both directions. This means that if one million people need to communicate with each other, each person has almost one million different keys; in total, almost one trillion keys are needed. This is normally referred to as the $N^2$ problem because the number of required keys for $N$ entities is $N^2$.

The number of keys is not the only problem; the distribution of keys is another. If Alice and Bob want to communicate, they need a way to exchange a secret key; if Alice wants to communicate with one million people, how can she exchange one million keys with one million people? Using the Internet is definitely not a secure method. It is obvious that we need an efficient way to maintain and distribute secret keys.

## 15.1.1  Key-Distribution Center: KDC

A practical solution is the use of a trusted third party, referred to as a **key-distribution center (KDC)**. To reduce the number of keys, each person establishes a shared secret key with the KDC, as shown in Fig. 15.1.

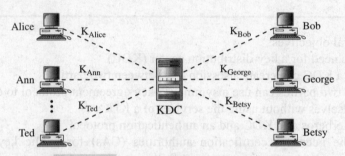

**Fig. 15.1**  *Key-distribution center (KDC)*

A secret key is established between the KDC and each member. Alice has a secret key with the KDC, which we refer to as $K_{Alice}$; Bob has a secret key with the KDC, which we refer to as $K_{Bob}$; and so on. Now the question is how Alice can send a confidential message to Bob. The process is as follows:

1.  Alice sends a request to the KDC stating that she needs a session (temporary) secret key between herself and Bob.
2.  The KDC informs Bob about Alice's request.
3.  If Bob agrees, a session key is created between the two.

The secret key between Alice and Bob that is established with the KDC is used to authenticate Alice and Bob to the KDC and to prevent Eve from impersonating either of them. We discuss how a session key is established between Alice and Bob later in the chapter.

***Flat Multiple KDCs***  When the number of people using a KDC increases, the system becomes unmanageable and a bottleneck can result. To solve the problem, we need to have multiple KDCs. We can divide the world into domains. Each domain can have one or more KDCs (for redundancy in case of failure). Now if Alice wants to send a confidential message to Bob, who belongs to another domain, Alice contacts her KDC, which in turn contacts the KDC in Bob's domain. The two KDCs can create a secret key between Alice and Bob. Figure 15.2 shows KDCs all at the same level. We call this flat multiple KDCs.

***Hierarchical Multiple KDCs***  The concept of flat multiple KDCs can be extended to a hierarchical system of KDCs, with one or more KDCs at the top of the hierarchy. For example, there can be local KDCs, national KDCs, and international KDCs. When Alice needs to communicate with Bob, who lives in another country, she sends her request to a local KDC; the local KDC relays the request to the national KDC; the national KDC relays the request to an international KDC. The request is then relayed all the way down to the local KDC where Bob lives. Figure 15.3 shows a configuration of hierarchical multiple KDCs.

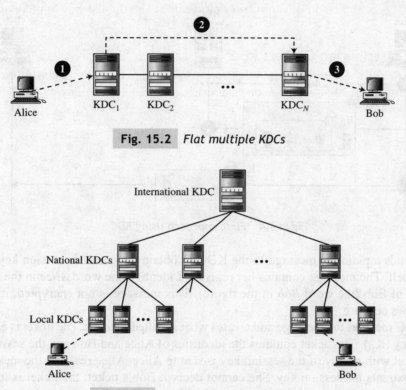

**Fig. 15.2** *Flat multiple KDCs*

**Fig. 15.3** *Hierarchical multiple KDCs*

### 15.1.2 Session Keys

A KDC creates a secret key for each member. This secret key can be used only between the member and the KDC, not between two members. If Alice needs to communicate secretly with Bob, she needs a secret key between herself and Bob. A KDC can create a **session key** between Alice and Bob, using their keys with the center. The keys of Alice and Bob are used to authenticate Alice and Bob to the center and to each other before the session key is established. After communication is terminated, the session key is no longer useful.

---

**A session symmetric key between two parties is used only once.**

---

Several different approaches have been proposed to create the session key using ideas discussed in Chapter 14 for entity authentication.

***A Simple Protocol Using a KDC***   Let us see how a KDC can create a session key $K_{AB}$ between Alice and Bob. Figure 15.4 shows the steps.

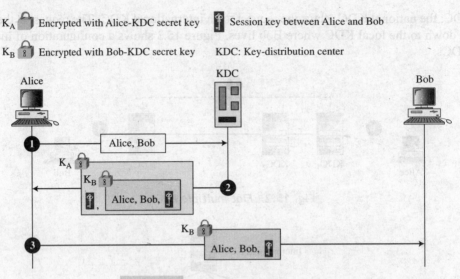

**Fig. 15.4** *First approach using KDC*

1. Alice sends a plaintext message to the KDC to obtain a symmetric session key between Bob and herself. The message contains her registered identity (the word *Alice* in the figure) and the identity of Bob (the word *Bob* in the figure). This message is not encrypted, it is public. The KDC does not care.

2. The KDC receives the message and creates what is called a **ticket.** The ticket is encrypted using Bob's key ($K_B$). The ticket contains the identities of Alice and Bob and the session key ($K_{AB}$). The ticket with a copy of the session key is sent to Alice. Alice receives the message, decrypts it, and extracts the session key. She cannot decrypt Bob's ticket; the ticket is for Bob, not for Alice. Note that this message contains a double encryption; the ticket is encrypted, and the entire message is also encrypted. In the second message, Alice is actually authenticated to the KDC, because only Alice can open the whole message using her secret key with KDC.

3. Alice sends the ticket to Bob. Bob opens the ticket and knows that Alice needs to send messages to him using $K_{AB}$ as the session key. Note that in this message, Bob is authenticated to the KDC because only Bob can open the ticket. Because Bob is authenticated to the KDC, he is also authenticated to Alice, who trusts the KDC. In the same way, Alice is also authenticated to Bob, because Bob trusts the KDC and the KDC has sent Bob the ticket that includes the identity of Alice.

Unfortunately, this simple protocol has a flaw. Eve can use the replay attack discussed previously. That is, she can save the message in step 3 and replay it later.

### Needham-Schroeder Protocol

Another approach is the elegant **Needham-Schroeder protocol,** which is a foundation for many other protocols. This protocol uses multiple challenge-response interactions between parties to achieve a flawless protocol. Needham and Schroeder uses two nonces: $R_A$ and $R_B$. Figure 15.5 shows the five steps used in this protocol.

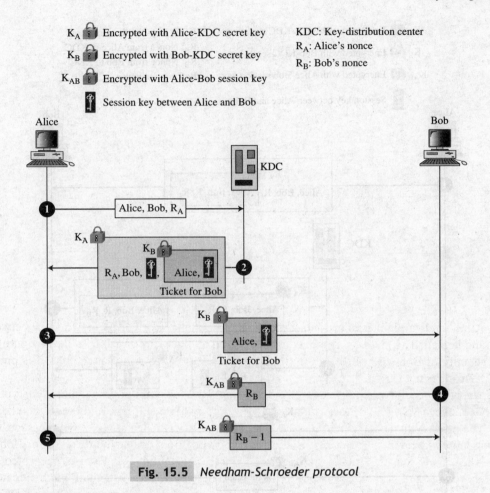

**Fig. 15.5** *Needham-Schroeder protocol*

We briefly describe each step:

1. Alice sends a message to the KDC that includes her nonce, $R_A$, her identity, and Bob's identity.
2. The KDC sends an encrypted message to Alice that includes Alice's nonce, Bob's identity, the session key, and an encrypted ticket for Bob. The whole message is encrypted with Alice's key.
3. Alice sends Bob's ticket to him.
4. Bob sends his challenge to Alice ($R_B$), encrypted with the session key.
5. Alice responds to Bob's challenge. Note that the response carries $R_B - 1$ instead of $R_B$.

**Otway-Rees Protocol** A third approach is the **Otway-Rees protocol,** another elegant protocol. Figure 15.6 shows this five-step protocol.

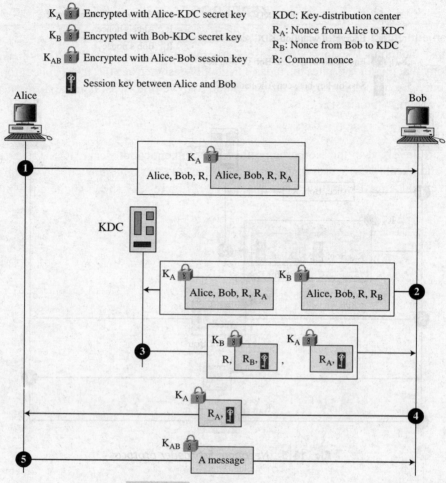

**Fig. 15.6** *Otway-Rees protocol*

The following briefly describes the steps.

1. Alice sends a message to Bob that includes a common nonce, R, the identities of Alice and Bob, and a ticket for KDC that includes Alice's nonce $R_A$ (a challenge for the KDC to use), a copy of the common nonce, R, and the identities of Alice and Bob.

2. Bob creates the same type of ticket, but with his own nonce $R_B$. Both tickets are sent to the KDC.

3. The KDC creates a message that contains R, the common nonce, a ticket for Alice and a ticket for Bob; the message is sent to Bob. The tickets contain the corresponding nonce, $R_A$ or $R_B$, and the session key, $K_{AB}$.

4. Bob sends Alice her ticket.

5. Alice sends a short message encrypted with her session key $K_{AB}$ to show that she has the session key.

## 15.2                  KERBEROS

**Kerberos** is an authentication protocol, and at the same time a KDC, that has become very popular. Several systems, including Windows 2000, use Kerberos. It is named after the three-headed dog in Greek mythology that guards the gates of Hades. Originally designed at MIT, it has gone through several versions. We only discuss version 4, the most popular, and we briefly explain the difference between version 4 and version 5 (the latest).

### 15.2.1   Servers

Three servers are involved in the Kerberos protocol: an authentication server (AS), a ticket-granting server (TGS), and a real (data) server that provides services to others. In our examples and figures, *Bob* is the real server and *Alice* is the user requesting service. Figure 15.7 shows the relationship between these three servers.

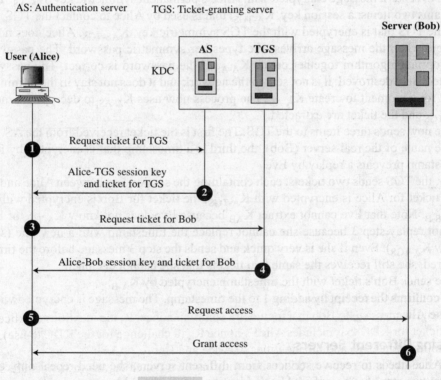

**Fig. 15.7** *Kerberos servers*

***Authentication Server (AS)***    The **authentication server (AS)** is the KDC in the Kerberos protocol. Each user registers with the AS and is granted a user identity and a password. The AS has a database with these identities and the corresponding passwords. The AS verifies the user, issues a session key to be used between Alice and the TGS, and sends a ticket for the TGS.

**Ticket-Granting Server (TGS)**  The **ticket-granting server (TGS)** issues a ticket for the real server (Bob). It also provides the session key ($K_{AB}$) between Alice and Bob. Kerberos has separated user verification from the issuing of tickets. In this way, though Alice verifies her ID just once with the AS, she can contact the TGS multiple times to obtain tickets for different real servers.

**Real Server**  The real server (Bob) provides services for the user (Alice). Kerberos is designed for a client-server program, such as FTP, in which a user uses the client process to access the server process. Kerberos is not used for person-to-person authentication.

## 15.2.2  Operation

A client process (Alice) can access a process running on the real server (Bob) in six steps, as shown in Fig. 15.8

1. Alice sends her request to the AS in plain text using her registered identity.
2. The AS sends a message encrypted with Alice's permanent symmetric key, $K_{A-AS}$. The message contains two items: a session key, $K_{A-TGS}$, that is used by Alice to contact the TGS, and a ticket for the TGS that is encrypted with the TGS symmetric key, $K_{AS-TGS}$. Alice does not know $K_{A-AS}$, but when the message arrives, she types her symmetric password. The password and the appropriate algorithm together create $K_{A-AS}$ if the password is correct. The password is then immediately destroyed; it is not sent to the network and it does not stay in the terminal. It is used only for a moment to create $K_{A-AS}$. The process now uses $K_{A-AS}$ to decrypt the message sent. $K_{A-TGS}$ and the ticket are extracted.
3. Alice now sends three items to the TGS. The first is the ticket received from the AS. The second is the name of the real server (Bob), the third is a timestamp that is encrypted by $K_{A-TGS}$. The timestamp prevents a replay by Eve.
4. Now, the TGS sends two tickets, each containing the session key between Alice and Bob, $K_{A-B}$. The ticket for Alice is encrypted with $K_{A-TGS}$; the ticket for Bob is encrypted with Bob's key, $K_{TGS-B}$. Note that Eve cannot extract $K_{AB}$ because Eve does not know $K_{A-TGS}$ or $K_{TGS-B}$. She cannot replay step 3 because she cannot replace the timestamp with a new one (she does not know $K_{A-TGS}$). Even if she is very quick and sends the step 3 message before the timestamp has expired, she still receives the same two tickets that she cannot decipher.
5. Alice sends Bob's ticket with the timestamp encrypted by $K_{A-B}$.
6. Bob confirms the receipt by adding 1 to the timestamp. The message is encrypted with $K_{A-B}$ and sent to Alice.

## 15.2.3  Using Different Servers

Note that if Alice needs to receive services from different servers, she need repeat only the last four steps. The first two steps have verified Alice's identity and need not be repeated. Alice can ask TGS to issue tickets for multiple servers by repeating steps 3 to 6.

**Kerberos Version 5**  The minor differences between version 4 and version 5 are briefly listed below:

1. Version 5 has a longer ticket lifetime.
2. Version 5 allows tickets to be renewed.
3. Version 5 can accept any symmetric-key algorithm.

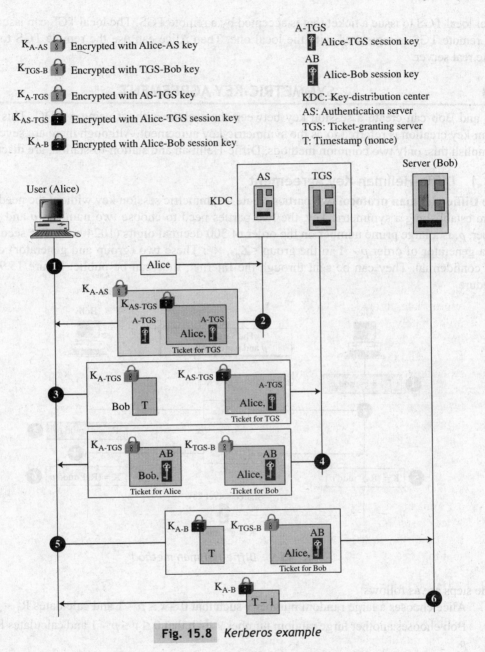

$K_{A\text{-}AS}$ 🔒 Encrypted with Alice-AS key

$K_{TGS\text{-}B}$ 🔒 Encrypted with TGS-Bob key

$K_{A\text{-}TGS}$ 🔒 Encrypted with AS-TGS key

$K_{AS\text{-}TGS}$ 🔒 Encrypted with Alice-TGS session key

$K_{A\text{-}B}$ 🔒 Encrypted with Alice-Bob session key

A-TGS 🔑 Alice-TGS session key

AB 🔑 Alice-Bob session key

KDC: Key-distribution center
AS: Authentication server
TGS: Ticket-granting server
T: Timestamp (nonce)

**Fig. 15.8** *Kerberos example*

4. Version 5 uses a different protocol for describing data types.
5. Version 5 has more overhead than version 4.

***Realms*** Kerberos allows the global distribution of ASs and TGSs, with each system called a *realm*. A user may get a ticket for a local server or a remote server. In the second case, for example, Alice may ask her local TGS to issue a ticket that is accepted by a remote TGS. The local TGS can issue this ticket if the remote TGS is registered with the local one. Then Alice can use the remote TGS to access the remote real server.

## 15.3                    SYMMETRIC-KEY AGREEMENT

Alice and Bob can create a session key between themselves without using a KDC. This method of session-key creation is referred to as the symmetric-key agreement. Although there are several ways to accomplish this, only two common methods, Diffie-Hellman and station-to-station, are discussed here.

### 15.3.1   Diffie-Hellman Key Agreement

In the **Diffie-Hellman protocol** two parties create a symmetric session key without the need of a KDC. Before establishing a symmetric key, the two parties need to choose two numbers $p$ and $g$. The first number, $p$, is a large prime number on the order of 300 decimal digits (1024 bits). The second number, $g$, is a generator of order $p - 1$ in the group $<\mathbf{Z}_{p*}, \times>$. These two (group and generator) do not need to be confidential. They can be sent through the Internet; they can be public. Figure 15.9 shows the procedure.

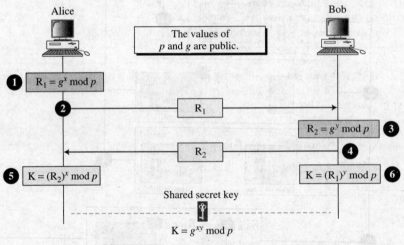

**Fig. 15.9** *Diffie-Hellman method*

The steps are as follows:
1. Alice chooses a large random number $x$ such that $0 \leq x \leq p - 1$ and calculates $R_1 = g^x \bmod p$.
2. Bob chooses another large random number $y$ such that $0 \leq y \leq p - 1$ and calculates $R_2 = g^y \bmod p$.
3. Alice sends $R_1$ to Bob. Note that Alice does not send the value of $x$; she sends only $R_1$.
4. Bob sends $R_2$ to Alice. Again, note that Bob does not send the value of $y$, he sends only $R_2$.
5. Alice calculates $K = (R_2)^x \bmod p$.
6. Bob also calculates $K = (R_1)^y \bmod p$.

K is the symmetric key for the session.

$$K = (g^x \bmod p)^y \bmod p = (g^y \bmod p)^x \bmod p = g^{xy} \bmod p$$

Bob has calculated $K = (R_1)^y \bmod p = (g^x \bmod p)^y \bmod p = g^{xy} \bmod p$. Alice has calculated $K = (R_2)^x \bmod p = (g^y \bmod p)^x \bmod = g^{xy} \bmod p$. Both have reached the same value without Bob knowing the value of $x$ and without Alice knowing the value of $y$.

---

**The symmetric (shared) key in the Diffie-Hellman method is $K = g^{xy} \bmod p$.**

---

**Example 15.1** Let us give a trivial example to make the procedure clear. Our example uses small numbers, but note that in a real situation, the numbers are very large. Assume that $g = 7$ and $p = 23$. The steps are as follows:

1. Alice chooses $x = 3$ and calculates $R_1 = 7^3 \bmod 23 = 21$.
2. Bob chooses $y = 6$ and calculates $R_2 = 7^6 \bmod 23 = 4$.
3. Alice sends the number 21 to Bob.
4. Bob sends the number 4 to Alice.
5. Alice calculates the symmetric key $K = 4^3 \bmod 23 = 18$.
6. Bob calculates the symmetric key $K = 21^6 \bmod 23 = 18$.

The value of K is the same for both Alice and Bob; $g^{xy} \bmod p = 7^{18} \bmod 35 = 18$.

---

**Example 15.2** Let us give a more realistic example. We used a program to create a random integer of 512 bits (the ideal is 1024 bits). The integer $p$ is a 159-digit number. We also choose $g$, $x$, and $y$ as shown below:

| $p$ | 76462429856349357218249376595503050747633809672694974892357377728609252356 66660755423637423309661180033338106194730130950414738700999178043654878858 07987581 |
|---|---|
| $g$ | 2 |
| $x$ | 557 |
| $y$ | 273 |

The following shows the values of $R_1$, $R_2$, and K.

| $R_1$ | 84492028420566550521617294749103509414343369852001266086286363106767361995 92808285867008021318592909451402175003199733129458360838219430659660201579 55354 |
|---|---|
| $R_2$ | 43526283870920037947074711489558162763638911626211555797512337921856631001 14357182083900401818764868417538311653426916302634211067215085896255201288 594143 |
| K | 15563800066452229059622582752327076527321804694442367852032040014640650088 79366512042574267766083279110171530386745612522131516109765842001204086433 617740 |

**Analysis of Diffie-Hellman**    The Diffie-Hellman concept, shown in Fig. 15.10, is simple but elegant. We can think of the secret key between Alice and Bob as made of three parts: $g$, $x$, and $y$. The first part is public. Everyone knows 1/3 of the key; $g$ is a public value. The other two parts must be added by Alice and Bob. Each of them add one part. Alice adds $x$ as the second part for Bob; Bob adds $y$ as the second part for Alice. When Alice receives the 2/3 completed key from Bob, she adds the last part, her $x$, to complete the key. When Bob receives the 2/3-completed key from Alice, he adds the last part, his $y$, to complete the key. Note that although the key in Alice's hand consists of $g$, $y$, and $x$ and the key in Bob's hand consists of $g$, $x$, and $y$, these two keys are the same because $g^{xy} = g^{yx}$.

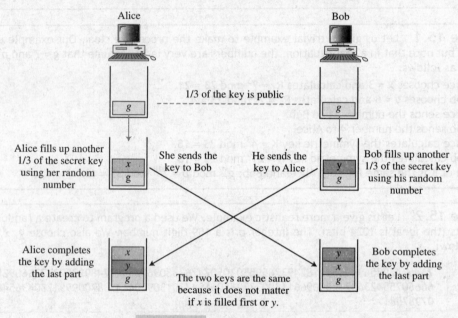

**Fig. 15.10**   *Diffie-Hellman idea*

Note also that although the two keys are the same, Alice cannot find the value $y$ used by Bob because the calculation is done in modulo $p$; Alice receives $g^y$ mod $p$ from Bob, not $g^y$. To know the value of $y$, Alice must use the discrete logarithm that we discussed in a previous chapter.

## Security of Diffie-Hellman

The Diffie-Hellman key exchange is susceptible to two attacks: the discrete logarithm attack and the man-in-the-middle attack.

**Discrete Logarithm Attack**    The security of the key exchange is based on the difficulty of the discrete logarithm problem. Eve can intercept $R_1$ and $R_2$. If she can find $x$ from $R_1 = g^x$ mod $p$ and $y$ from $R_2 = g^y$ mod $p$, then she can calculate the symmetric key $K = g^{xy}$ mod $p$. The secret key is not secret anymore. To make Diffie-Hellman safe from the discrete logarithm attack, the following are recommended.

1. The prime $p$ must be very large (more than 300 decimal digits).
2. The prime $p$ must be chosen such that $p - 1$ has at least one large prime factor (more than 60 decimal digits).

3. The generator must be chosen from the group $<\mathbf{Z}_{p*}, \times>$.
4. Bob and Alice must destroy $x$ and $y$ after they have calculated the symmetric key. The values of $x$ and $y$ must be used only once.

## Man-in-the-Middle Attack
The protocol has another weakness. Eve does not have to find the value of $x$ and $y$ to attack the protocol. She can fool Alice and Bob by creating two keys: one between herself and Alice, and another between herself and Bob. Figure 15.11 shows the situation.

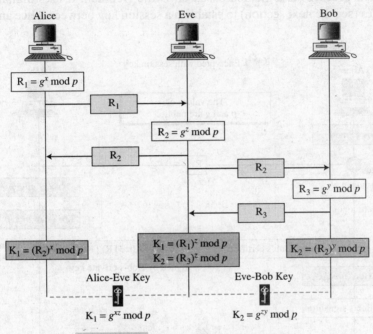

**Fig. 15.11** *Man-in-the-middle attack*

The following can happen:
1. Alice chooses $x$, calculates $R_1 = g^x \bmod p$, and sends $R_1$ to Bob.
2. Eve, the intruder, intercepts $R_1$. She chooses z, calculates $R_2 = g^z \bmod p$, and sends $R_2$ to both Alice and Bob.
3. Bob chooses $y$, calculates $R_3 = g^y \bmod p$, and sends $R_3$ to Alice. $R_3$ is intercepted by Eve and never reaches Alice.
4. Alice and Eve calculate $K_1 = g^{xz} \bmod p$, which becomes a shared key between Alice and Eve. Alice, however, thinks that it is a key shared between Bob and herself.
5. Eve and Bob calculate $K_2 = g^{zy} \bmod p$, which becomes a shared key between Eve and Bob. Bob, however, thinks that it is a key shared between Alice and himself.

In other words, two keys, instead of one, are created: one between Alice and Eve, one between Eve and Bob. When Alice sends data to Bob encrypted with $K_1$ (shared by Alice and Eve), it can be deciphered and read by Eve. Eve can send the message to Bob encrypted by $K_2$ (shared key between Eve and Bob); or she can even change the message or send a totally new message. Bob is fooled into believing that the message has come from Alice. A similar scenario can happen to Alice in the other direction.

This situation is called a **man-in-the-middle attack** because Eve comes in between and intercepts $R_1$, sent by Alice to Bob, and $R_3$, sent by Bob to Alice. It is also known as a **bucket brigade attack** because it resembles a short line of volunteers passing a bucket of water from person to person. The next method, based on the Diffie-Hellman uses authentication to thwart this attack.

## 15.3.2 Station-to-Station Key Agreement

The **station-to-station protocol** is a method based on Diffie-Hellman. It uses digital signatures with public-key certificates (see the next section) to establish a session key between Alice and Bob, as shown in Fig. 15.12.

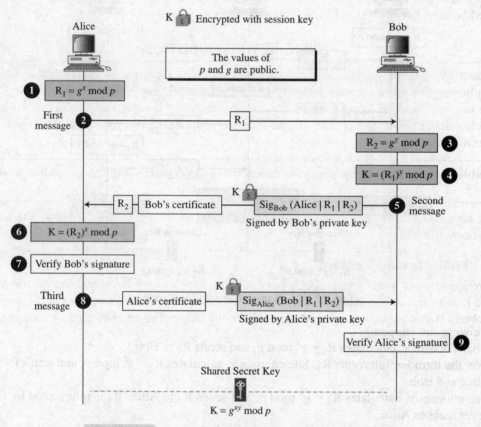

**Fig. 15.12** *Station-to-station key agreement method*

The following shows the steps:

❑ After calculating $R_1$, Alice sends $R_1$ to Bob (steps 1 and 2 in Fig. 15.12).

❑ After calculating $R_2$ and the session key, Bob concatenates Alice's ID, $R_1$, and $R_2$. He then signs the result with his private key. Bob now sends $R_2$, the signature, and his own public-key certificate to Alice. The signature is encrypted with the session key (steps 3, 4, and 5 in Fig. 15.12).

❑ After calculating the session key, if Bob's signature is verified, Alice concatenates Bob's ID, $R_1$, and $R_2$. She then signs the result with her own private key and sends it to Bob. The signature is encrypted with the session key (steps 6, 7, and 8 in Fig. 15.12).

❑ If Alice's signature is verified, Bob keeps the session key (step 9 in Fig. 15.12).

***Security of Station-to-Station Protocol*** The station-to-station protocol prevents man-in-the-middle attacks. After intercepting $R_1$, Eve cannot send her own $R_2$ to Alice and pretend it is coming from Bob because Eve cannot forge the private key of Bob to create the signature—the signature cannot be verified with Bob's public key defined in the certificate. In the same way, Eve cannot forge Alice's private key to sign the third message sent by Alice. The certificates, as we will see in the next section, are trusted because they are issued by trusted authorities.

## 15.4                PUBLIC-KEY DISTRIBUTION

In asymmetric-key cryptography, people do not need to know a symmetric shared key. If Alice wants to send a message to Bob, she only needs to know Bob's public key, which is open to the public and available to everyone. If Bob needs to send a message to Alice, he only needs to know Alice's public key, which is also known to everyone. In public-key cryptography, everyone shields a private key and advertises a public key.

---

**In public-key cryptography, everyone has access to everyone's public key; public keys are available to the public.**

---

Public keys, like secret keys, need to be distributed to be useful. Let us briefly discuss the way public keys can be distributed.

### 15.4.1   Public Announcement

The naive approach is to announce public keys publicly. Bob can put his public key on his website or announce it in a local or national newspaper. When Alice needs to send a confidential message to Bob, she can obtain Bob's public key from his site or from the newspaper, or even send a message to ask for it. Fig. 15.13 shows the situation.

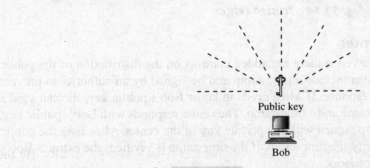

Public key

Bob

**Fig. 15.13** *Announcing a public key*

This approach, however, is not secure; it is subject to forgery. For example, Eve could make such a public announcement. Before Bob can react, damage could be done. Eve can fool Alice into sending her a message that is intended for Bob. Eve could also sign a document with a corresponding forged private key and make everyone believe it was signed by Bob. The approach is also vulnerable if Alice directly requests Bob's public key. Eve can intercept Bob's response and substitute her own forged public key for Bob's public key.

### 15.4.2 Trusted Center

A more secure approach is to have a trusted center retain a directory of public keys. The directory, like the one used in a telephone system, is dynamically updated. Each user can select a private and public key, keep the private key, and deliver the public key for insertion into the directory. The center requires that each user register in the center and prove his or her identity. The directory can be publicly advertised by the trusted center. The center can also respond to any inquiry about a public key. Figure 15.14 shows the concept.

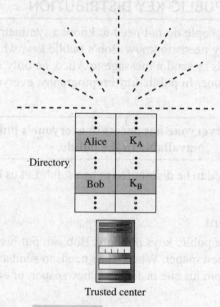

**Fig. 15.14** *Trusted center*

### 15.4.3 Controlled Trusted Center

A higher level of security can be achieved if there are added controls on the distribution of the public key. The public-key announcements can include a timestamp and be signed by an authority to prevent interception and modification of the response. If Alice needs to know Bob's public key, she can send a request to the center including Bob's name and a timestamp. The center responds with Bob's public key, the original request, and the timestamp signed with the private key of the center. Alice uses the public key of the center, known by all, to verify the timestamp. If the timestamp is verified, she extracts Bob's public key. Figure 15.15 shows one scenario.

### 15.4.4 Certification Authority

The previous approach can create a heavy load on the center if the number of requests is large. The alternative is to create **public-key certificates.** Bob wants two things; he wants people to know his public

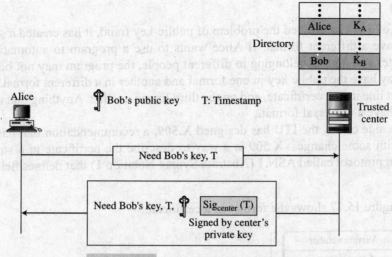

**Fig. 15.15** *Controlled trusted center*

key, and he wants no one to accept a forged public key as his. Bob can go to a **certification authority (CA),** a federal or state organization that binds a public key to an entity and issues a certificate. The CA has a well-known public key itself that cannot be forged. The CA checks Bob's identification (using a picture ID along with other proof). It then asks for Bob's public key and writes it on the certificate. To prevent the certificate itself from being forged, the CA signs the certificate with its private key. Now Bob can upload the signed certificate. Anyone who wants Bob's public key downloads the signed certificate and uses the center's public key to extract Bob's public key. Figure 15.16 shows the concept.

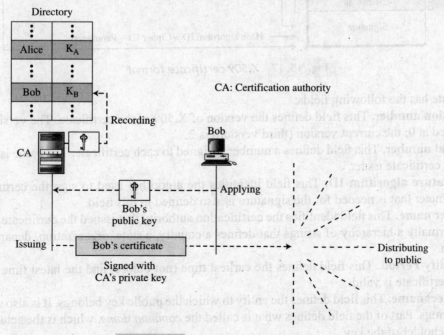

**Fig. 15.16** *Certification authority*

## 15.4.5 X.509

Although the use of a CA has solved the problem of public-key fraud, it has created a side-effect. Each certificate may have a different format. If Alice wants to use a program to automatically download different certificates and digests belonging to different people, the program may not be able to do this. One certificate may have the public key in one format and another in a different format. The public key may be on the first line in one certificate, and on the third line in another. Anything that needs to be used universally must have a universal format.

To remove this side effect, the ITU has designed **X.509,** a recommendation that has been accepted by the Internet with some changes. X.509 is a way to describe the certificate in a structured way. It uses a well-known protocol called ASN.1 (Abstract Syntax Notation 1) that defines fields familiar to C programmers.

***Certificate*** Figure 15.17 shows the format of a certificate.

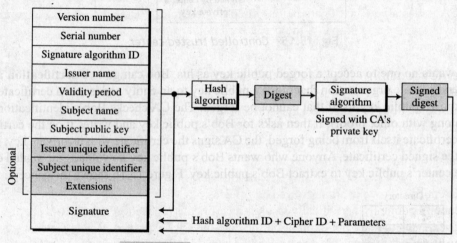

**Fig. 15.17** *X.509 certificate format*

A certificate has the following fields:

- ❏ **Version number.** This field defines the version of X.509 of the certificate. The version number started at 0; the current version (third version) is 2.
- ❏ **Serial number.** This field defines a number assigned to each certificate. The value is unique for each certificate issuer.
- ❏ **Signature algorithm ID.** This field identifies the algorithm used to sign the certificate. Any parameter that is needed for the signature is also defined in this field.
- ❏ **Issuer name.** This field identifies the certification authority that issued the certificate. The name is normally a hierarchy of strings that defines a country, a state, organization, department, and so on.
- ❏ **Validity Period.** This field defines the earliest time (not before) and the latest time (not after) the certificate is valid.
- ❏ **Subject name.** This field defines the entity to which the public key belongs. It is also a hierarchy of strings. Part of the field defines what is called the *common name,* which is the actual name of the beholder of the key.

❑ **Subject public key.** This field defines the owner's public key, the heart of the certificate. The field also defines the corresponding public-key algorithm (RSA, for example) and its parameters.

❑ **Issuer unique identifier.** This optional field allows two issuers to have the same *issuer* field value, if the *issuer unique identifiers* are different.

❑ **Subject unique identifier.** This optional field allows two different subjects to have the same *subject* field value, if the *subject unique identifiers* are different.

❑ **Extensions.** This optional field allows issuers to add more private information to the certificate.

❑ **Signature.** This field is made of three sections. The first section contains all other fields in the certificate. The second section contains the digest of the first section encrypted with the CA's public key. The third section contains the algorithm identifier used to create the second section.

**Certificate Renewal** Each certificate has a period of validity. If there is no problem with the certificate, the CA issues a new certificate before the old one expires. The process is like the renewal of credit cards by a credit card company; the credit card holder normally receives a renewed credit card before the one expires.

**Certificate Revocation** In some cases a certificate must be revoked before its expiration. Here are some examples:

a. The user's (subject's) private key (corresponding to the public key listed in the certificate) might have been comprised.

b. The CA is no longer willing to certify the user. For example, the user's certificate relates to an organization that she no longer works for.

c. The CA's private key, which can verify certificates, may have been compromised. In this case, the CA needs to revoke all unexpired certificates.

The revocation is done by periodically issuing a certificate revocation list (CRL). The list contains all revoked certificates that are not expired on the date the CRL is issued. When a user wants to use a certificate, she first needs to check the directory of the corresponding CA for the last certificate revocation list. Figure 15.18 shows the certificate revocation list.

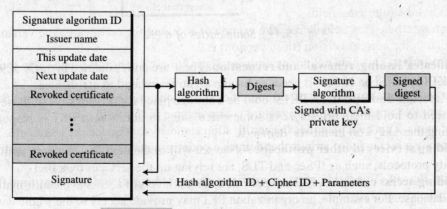

**Fig. 15.18** *Certificate revocation format*

A certificate revocation list has the following fields:

❑ **Signature algorithm ID.** This field is the same as the one in the certificate.
❑ **Issuer name.** This field is the same as the one in the certificate.
❑ **This update date.** This field defines when the list is released.
❑ **Next update date.** This field defines the next date when the new list will be released.
❑ **Revoked certificate.** This is a repeated list of all unexpired certificates that have been revoked. Each list contains two sections: user certificate serial number and revocation date.
❑ **Signature.** This field is the same as the one in the certificate list.

***Delta Revocation*** To make revocation more efficient, the delta certificate revocation list (delta CRL) has been introduced. A delta CRL is created and posted on the directory if there are changes after *this update date* and *next update date*. For example, if CRLs are issued every month, but there are revocations in between, the CA can create a delta CRL when there is a change during the month. However, a delta CRL contains only the changes made after the last CRL.

### 15.4.6 Public-Key Infrastructures (PKI)

**Public-Key Infrastructure (PKI)** is a model for creating, distributing, and revoking certificates based on the X.509. The Internet Engineering Task Force (see Appendix B) has created the Public-Key Infrastructure X.509 (PKIX).

***Duties*** Several duties have been defined for a PKI. The most important ones are shown in Fig. 15.19.

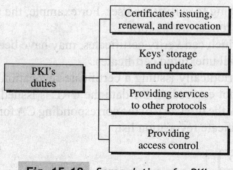

**Fig. 15.19** *Some duties of a PKI*

❑ **Certificates' issuing, renewal, and revocation.** These are duties defined in the X.509. Because the PKIX is based on X.509, it needs to handle all duties related to certificates.
❑ **Keys' storage and update.** A PKI should be a storage place for private keys of those members that need to hold their private keys somewhere safe. In addition, a PKI is responsible for updating these keys on members' demands.
❑ **Providing services to other protocols.** As we see will in the next few chapters, some Internet security protocols, such as IPSec and TLS, are relying on the services by a PKI.
❑ **Providing access control.** A PKI can provide different levels of access to the information stored in its database. For example, an organization PKI may provide access to the whole database for the top management, but limited access for employees.

## Trust Model

It is not possible to have just one CA issuing all certificates for all users in the world. There should be many CAs, each responsible for creating, storing, issuing, and revoking a limited number of certificates. The **trust model** defines rules that specify how a user can verify a certificate received from a CA.

*Hierarchical Model* In this model, there is a tree-type structure with a root CA. The root CA has a self-signed, self-issued certificate; it needs to be trusted by other CAs and users for the system to work. Figure 15.20 shows a trust model of this kind with three hierarchical levels. The number of levels can be more than three in a real situation.

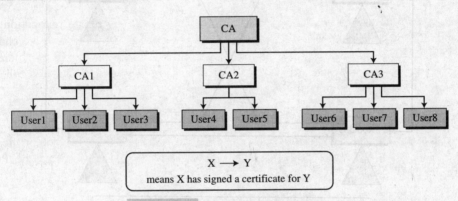

**Fig. 15.20** *PKI hierarchical model*

The figure shows that the CA (the root) has signed certificates for CA1, CA2, and CA3; CA1 has signed certificates for User1, User2, and User3; and so on. PKI uses the following notation to mean the certificate issued by authority X for entity Y.

$$X<<Y>>$$

**Example 15.3** Show how User1, knowing only the public key of the CA (the root), can obtain a verified copy of User3's public key.

**Solution** User3 sends a chain of certificates, CA<<CA1>> and CA1<<User3>>, to User1.
a. User1 validates CA<<CA1>> using the public key of CA.
b. User1 extracts the public key of CA1 from CA<<CA1>>.
c. User1 validates CA1<<User3>> using the public key of CA1.
d. User1 extracts the public key of User 3 from CA1<<User3>>.

**Example 15.4** Some Web browsers, such as Netscape and Internet Explorer, include a set of certificates from independent roots without a single, high-level, authority to certify each root. One can find the list of these roots in the Internet Explorer at *Tools/Internet Options/Contents/Certificate/Trusted roots* (using pull-down menu). The user then can choose any of this root and view the certificate.

*Mesh Model* The hierarchical model may work for an organization or a small community. A larger community may need several hierarchical structures connected together. One method is to use a mesh model to connect the roots together. In this model, each root is connected to every other root, as shown in Fig. 15.21.

Figure 15.21 shows that the mesh structure connects only roots together; each root has its own hierarchical structure, shown by a triangle. The certifications between the roots are cross-certificates; each root certifies all other roots, which means there are $N(N-1)$ certificates. In Fig. 15.21, there are 4 nodes, so we need $4 \times 3 = 12$ certificates. Note that each double-arrow line represents two certificates.

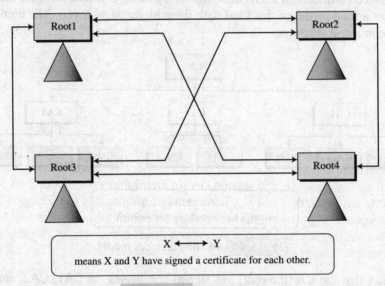

**Fig. 15.21** *Mesh model*

**Example 15.5** Alice is under the authority Root1; Bob is under the authority Root4. Show how Alice can obtain Bob's verified public key.

**Solution** Bob sends a chain of certificates from Root4 to Bob. Alice looks at the directory of Root1 to find Root1<<Root1>> and Root1<< Root4>> certificates. Using the process shown in Fig. 15.21, Alice can verify Bob's public key.

**Web of Trust** This model is used in Pretty Good Privacy, a security service for electronic mail discussed in Chapter 16.

## 15.5 HIJACKING

Hijacking or man-in-the-middle attack is a class of attacks where the hacker begins by listening in on the electronic conversation between two communicating hosts. This category of attack has both active and passive versions. The active versions of the man-in-the-middle attack are utilized to assume control of a communication's path to sabotage the normal functionality of the network. The attack may redirect the information to the hacker, modify the information to suit the attacker's need or prevent transmission of data.

One of the strongest and common forms of such attacks is the replay attack. This class of attacks may obtain the information being passed over the network through network sniffers, and can relay (or, replay) the information at a later time to obtain access of a certain system. For, example the attacker can obtain an encrypted message and may use to satisfy a protocol at a later time simply by relaying the information. Note that such attacks do not even need the decoding of the information.

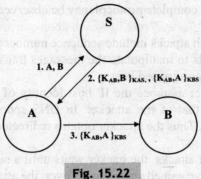

**Fig. 15.22**

Consider the above scenario, where *A* and *B* are two parties wishing to communicate. They intend to establish a short lived key, known as the session key for their future communications. They use a central server, who has long term keys $K_{AS}$ and $K_{BS}$ for communicating with *A* and *B* respectively.

A first sends the request of obtaining the session key for communicating with *B* to *S*. *S* sends back the session key $K_{AB}$, but in the encrypted form. *S* encrypts $K_{AB}$ and *B* with the long term key $K_{AS}$ (denoted by $\{K_{AB},B\}_{KAS}$). It also sends back $\{K_{AB},A\}_{KBS}$, which represents the encrypted form for $K_{AB}$, the session key and *A*.

A obtains the session key, $K_{AB}$ by decrypting the first part of the message received from C using its long term key $K_{AS}$. It passes the second part of the message, $\{K_{AB},A\}_{KBS}$ *B*, who can decrypt using the long term key $K_{BS}$ to obtain the session key $K_{AB}$.

It may be noted that here encryption is used for confidentiality of the session key and the integrity of the information using the identity of the parties in the message encrypted. This prevents masquerading or impersonation attacks. However replay attacks may still work against this protocol.

Replay attack can be performed by an attacker who knows a previous session key or old session key $K'_{AB}$. He can simply replay the old messages and thus can force the establishment of the old session key, which he is aware of. The attacker comes in between *A* and the server and sends back (replays) an old message to ensure that the old key is established. Note that *A* and *B* have no means of understanding or detecting this. The attack is depicted in Fig. 15.23.

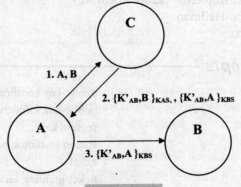

**Fig. 15.23**

In order to prevent such attacks sequence numbers, timestamps or nonces are used. A sequence number is sent by a party and it sent back by the receiver in encrypted form. The sender who transmitted the sequence number checks by decrypting the encrypted sequence number, whether it is the same which he transmitted. Since the sequence number is related to the time of the protocol, any replay of old data is detected by the sender. The complete protocol may be observed in the Needham and Schroeder's Protocol.

More complicated forms of such attacks include sequence number prediction, cache poisoning, DNS spoofing. They involve using tools to manipulate the messages transferred in the protocol to perform unintended action or masquerade as a trusted host.

In cache poisoning, the attacker assumes the IP host identity of a trusted host while substituting the attacker's MAC address for that of the attacker. In DNS spoofing attack, the attacker directly manipulates the DNS server entry. Thus the attacker obtains redirected connection requests and it starts communicating as a legal party.

In sequence number prediction attacks, the hacker waits until a session between two trusting hosts is under way. When the clients have gained access to a server, the attacker tries to obtain control of the session, by sniffing the IP addresses of the server and the client, the hacker performs a Denial of Service (DOS) attack on the client and stops it from communicating to the server. Finally it properly inserts a sequence of bogus packets according to the requirements by the underlying protocol. This is often done by using tools, like "Spoofit" and "rbone".

## 15.6     RECOMMENDED READING

The following books and websites give more details about subjects discussed in this chapter. The items enclosed in brackets refer to the reference list at the end of the book.

### Books

For further discussion of symmetric-key and asymmetric-key management, see [Sti06], [KPS02], [Sta06], [Rhe03], and [PHS03].
Protocols for Authentication and Key Establishment, by Anish Mathuria and Colin Boyd, Springer.

### WebSites

The following websites give more information about topics discussed in this chapter.
 http://en.wikipedia.org/wiki/Needham-Schroeder
 http://en.wikipedia.org/wiki/Otway-Rees
 http://en.wikipedia.org/wiki/Kerberos_%28protocol%29
 en.wikipedia.org/wiki/Diffie-Hellman
 www.ietf.org/rfc/rfc2631.txt

## *Key Terms and Concepts*

| | |
|---|---|
| authentication server (AS) | public-key certificate |
| bucket brigade attack | public-key infrastructure (PKI) |
| certification authority (CA) | session key |
| Diffie-Hellman protocol | station-to-station protocol |
| Kerberos | ticket |
| key-distribution center (KDC) | ticket-granting server (TGS) |

man-in-the-middle attack
Needham-Schroeder protocol
Otway-Rees protocol

trust model
X.509

# Summary

★ Symmetric-key cryptography needs a shared secret key between two parties. If $N$ people need to communicate with each other, $N(N-1)/2$ keys are needed. The number of keys is not the only problem; the distribution of keys is another.

★ A practical solution is the use of a trusted third party, referred to as a key-distribution center (KDC). A KDC can create a session (temporary) key between Alice and Bob using their keys with the center. The keys of Alice and Bob are used to authenticate Alice and Bob to the center.

★ Several different approaches have been proposed to create the session key using ideas discussed in Chapter 14 for entity authentication. Two of the most elegant ones are Needham-Schroeder protocol, which is a foundation for many other -protocols, and Otway-Rees Protocol.

★ Kerberos is both an authentication protocol and a KDC. Several systems, including Windows 2000, use Kerberos. Three servers are involved in the Kerberos protocol: an authentication server (AS), a ticket-granting server (TGS), and a real (data) server.

★ Alice and Bob can create a session key between themselves without using a KDC. This method of session-key creation is referred to as the symmetric-key agreement. We discussed two methods: Diffie-Hellman and station-to-station. The first is susceptible to the man-in-the-middle attack; the second is not.

★ Public keys, like secret keys, need to be distributed to be useful. Certificate authorities (CAs) provide certificates as proof of the ownership of public keys. X.509 is a recommendation that defines the structure of certificates issued by CAs.

★ Public Key Infrastructure (PKI) is a model for creating, distributing, and revoking certificates based on the X.509. The Internet Engineering Task Force has created the Public Key Infrastructure X.509 (PKIX). The duties of a PKI include certificate issuing, private key storage, services to other protocols, and access control. A PKI also defines trust models, the relationship between certificate authorities. The three trust models mentioned in this chapter are hierarchical, mesh, and web of trust.

# Practice Set

## Review Questions

**15.1** List the duties of a KDC.

**15.2** Define a session key and show how a KDC can create a session key between Alice and Bob.

**15.3** Define Kerberos and name its servers. Briefly explain the duties of each server.

**15.4** Define the Diffie-Hellman protocol and its purpose.

**15.5** Define the man-in-the-middle attack.

**15.6** Define the station-to-station protocol and mention its purpose.

**15.7** Define a certification authority (CA) and its relation to public-key cryptography.

**15.8** Define the X.509 recommendation and state its purpose.

**15.9** List the duties of a PKI.

**15.10** Define a trust model and mention some variations of this model discussed in this chapter.

## Exercises

**15.11** In Fig. 15.4, what happens if the ticket for Bob is not encrypted in step 2 with $K_B$, but is encrypted instead by $K_{AB}$ in step 3?

**15.12** Why is there a need for four nonces in the Needham-Schroeder protocol?

**15.13** In the Needham-Schroeder protocol, how is Alice authenticated by the KDC? How is Bob authenticated by the KDC? How is the KDC authenticated to Alice? How is the KDC authenticated to Bob? How is Alice authenticated to Bob? How is Bob authenticated to Alice?

**15.14** Can you explain why in the Needham-Schroeder protocol, Alice is the party that is in contact with the KDC, but in the Otway-Rees protocol, Bob is the party that is in contact with the KDC?

**15.15** There are four nonces ($R_A$, $R_B$, $R_1$, and $R_2$) in the Needham-Schroeder protocol, but only three nonces ($R_A$, $R_B$, and $R$) in the Otway-Rees protocol. Can you explain why there is a need for one extra nonce, $R_2$, in the first protocol?

**15.16** Why do you think we need only one timestamp in Kerberos instead of four nonces as in Needham-Schroeder or three nonces as in Otway-Rees?

**15.17** In the Diffie-Hellman protocol, $g = 7$, $p = 23$, $x = 3$, and $y = 5$.
   a.   What is the value of the symmetric key?
   b.   What is the value of $R_1$ and $R_2$?

**15.18** In the Diffie-Hellman protocol, what happens if $x$ and $y$ have the same value, that is, Alice and Bob have accidentally chosen the same number? Are $R_1$ and $R_2$ the same? Do the session keys calculated by Alice and Bob have the same value? Use an example to prove your claims.

**15.19** In a trivial (not secure) Diffie-Hellman key exchange, $p = 53$. Find an appropriate value for $g$.

**15.20** In station-to-station protocol, show that if the identity of the receiver is removed from the signature, the protocol becomes vulnerable to the man-in-the-middle attack.

**15.21** Discuss the trustworthiness of root certificates provided by browsers.

# PART IV

# Network Security

Part Four focuses on the subject that is the ultimate goal of the book: using cryptography to create secure networks. This part assumes that the reader has previous knowledge of the Internet architecture and the TCP/IP Protocol Suite. Appendix C can be used as a quick review in this case. Readers are also referred to [For06] on the reference list for further study. Each chapter in this part is dedicated to the discussion of security in one of the three layers of the TCP/IP Protocol Suite: application layer, transport layer, and network layer. Chapter 16 discusses security at the application layer. Chapter 17 discusses security at the transport layer. Chapter 18 discusses security at the network layer. Chapter 19 discusses security at system's level.

## Chapter 16: Security at the Application Layer: PGP and S/MIME

Chapter 16 discusses two protocols that provide security for electronic mail (e-mail). Pretty Good Privacy (PGP) is a protocol that is common for personal e-mail exchange. Secure/Multipurpose Internet Mail Extension (S/MIME) is a protocol that is common in commercial e-mail systems.

## Chapter 17: Security at the Transport Layer: SSL and TLS

Chapter 17 first shows the need for security services at the transport layer of the Internet model. It then shows how security at the transport level can be provided using one of the two protocols: Secure Sockets Layer (SSL) and Transport Layer Security (TLS). The second protocol is the new version of the first.

## Chapter 18: Security at the Network Layer: IPSec

Chapter 18 is devoted to the only common security protocol at the network layer: IPSec. The chapter defines the architecture of IPSec and discusses the application of IPSec in transport and tunnel modes. The chapter also discusses other auxiliary protocols, such as IKE, that are used by IPSec, defines Internet Key Exchange, and explains how it is used by IPSec.

## Chapter 19: System Security

Chapter 19 presents the concepts of system security. It starts with the definitions of systems and the functionalities of its various components in providing security. It discusses at length about buffer overflows and its possible usage in triggering malicious programs. The chapter presents a detailed overview on malicious programs, like viruses, worms, Trojans, etc., and clarifies the differences between them.

The chapter also provides an overview of the UNIX password system and the underlying concepts. Finally, it concludes with important concepts of firewalls and Intrusion Detection Systems (IDS) and their usage in protecting the security of systems.

# 16

# Security at the Application Layer: PGP and S/MIME

## Objectives

This chapter has several objectives:

☞ To explain the general structure of an e-mail application program
☞ To discuss how PGP can provide security services for e-mail
☞ To discuss how S/MIME can provide security services for e-mail
☞ To define trust mechanism in both PGP and S/MIME
☞ To show the structure of messages exchanged in PGP and S/MIME

This chapter discusses two protocols providing security services for e-mails: Pretty Good Privacy (PGP) and Secure/Multipurpose Internet Mail Extension (S/MIME). Understanding each of these protocols requires the general understanding of the e-mail system. We first discuss the structure of electronic mail. We then show how PGP and S/MIME can add security services to this structure. Emphasis is on how PGP and S/MIME can exchange cryptographic algorithms, secret keys, and certificates without establishing a session between Alice and Bob.

## 16.1                                         E-MAIL

Let us first discuss the **electronic mail (e-mail)** system in general.

### 16.1.1  E-mail Architecture

Figure 16.1 shows the most common scenario in a one-way e-mail exchange.

Assume that Alice is working in an organization that runs an e-mail server; every employee is connected to the e-mail server through a LAN. Or alternatively, Alice could be connected to the e-mail server of an ISP through a WAN (telephone line or cable line). Bob is also in one of the above two situations.

The administrator of the e-mail server at Alice's site has created a queuing system that sends e-mail to the Internet one by one. The administrator of the e-mail server at Bob's site has created a mailbox for every user connected to the server; the mailbox holds the received messages until they are retrieved by the recipient.

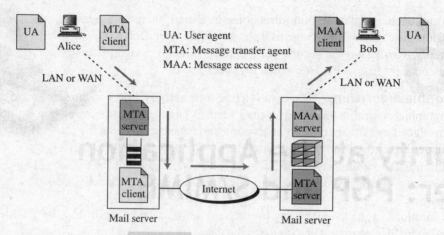

**Fig. 16.1** *E-mail architecture*

When Alice needs to send a message to Bob, she invokes a **user agent (UA)** program to prepare the message. She then uses another program, a **message transfer agent (MTA),** to send the message to the mail server at her site. Note that the MTA is a client/server program with the client installed at Alice's computer and the server installed at the mail server.

The message received at the mail server at Alice's site is queued with all other messages; each goes to its corresponding destination. In Alice's case, her message goes to the mail server at Bob's site. A client/server MTA is responsible for the e-mail transfer between the two servers. When the message arrives at the destination mail server, it is stored in Bob's mailbox, a special file that holds the message until it is retrieved by Bob.

When Bob needs to retrieve his messages, including the one sent by Alice, he invokes another program, which we call a **message access agent (MAA).** The MAA is also designed as a client/server program with the client installed at Bob's computer and the server installed at the mail server.

There are several important points about the architecture of the e-mail system.

a.  The sending of an e-mail from Alice to Bob is a store-retrieve activity. Alice can send an e-mail today; Bob, being busy, may check his e-mail three days later. During this time, the e-mail is stored in Bob's mailbox until it is retrieved.

b.  The main communication between Alice and Bob is through two application programs: the MTA client at Alice's computer and the MAA client at Bob's computer.

c.  The MTA client program is a *push* program; the client pushes the message when Alice needs to send it. The MAA client program is a *pull* program; the client pulls the messages when Bob is ready to retrieve his e-mail.

d.  Alice and Bob cannot directly communicate using an MTA client at the sender site and an MTA server at the receiver site. This requires that the MTA server be running all the time, because Bob does not know when a message will arrive. This is not practical, because Bob probably turns off his computer when he does not need it.

## 16.1.2  E-mail Security

Sending an e-mail is a one-time activity. The nature of this activity is different from those we will see in the next two chapters. In IPSec or SSL, we assume that the two parties create a session between themselves and exchange data in both directions. In e-mail, there is no session. Alice and Bob cannot create a session. Alice sends a message to Bob; sometime later, Bob reads the message and may or may not send a reply. We discuss the security of a unidirectional message because what Alice sends to Bob is totally independent from what Bob sends to Alice.

***Cryptographic Algorithms*** If e-mail is a one-time activity, how can the sender and receiver agree on a cryptographic algorithm to use for e-mail security? If there is no session and no handshaking to negotiate the algorithms for encryption/decryption and hashing, how can the receiver know which algorithm the sender has chosen for each purpose?

One solution is for the underlying protocol to select one algorithm for each cryptographic operation and to force Alice to use only those algorithms. This solution is very restrictive and limits the capabilities of the two parties.

A better solution is for the underlying protocol to define a set of algorithms for each operation that the user used in his/her system. Alice includes the name (or identifiers) of the algorithms she has used in the e-mail. For example, Alice can choose triple DES for encryption/decryption and MD5 for hashing. When Alice sends a message to Bob, she includes the corresponding identifiers for triple DES and MD5 in her message. Bob receives the message and extracts the identifiers first. He then knows which algorithm to use for decryption and which one for hashing.

---

**In e-mail security, the sender of the message needs to include the name or identifiers of the algorithms used in the message.**

---

***Cryptographic Secrets*** The same problem for the cryptographic algorithms applies to the cryptographic secrets (keys). If there is no negotiation, how can the two parties establish secrets between themselves? Alice and Bob could use asymmetric-key algorithms for authentication and encryption, which do not require the establishment of a symmetric key. However, as we have discussed, the use of asymmetric-key algorithms is very inefficient for the encryption/decryption of a long message.

Most e-mail security protocols today require that encryption/decryption be done using a symmetric-key algorithm and a one-time secret key sent with the message. Alice can create a secret key and send it with the message she sends to Bob. To protect the secret key from interception by Eve, the secret key is encrypted with Bob's public key. In other words, the secret key itself is encrypted.

---

**In e-mail security, the encryption/decryption is done using a symmetric-key algorithm, but the secret key to decrypt the message is encrypted with the public key of the receiver and is sent with the message.**

---

***Certificates*** One more issue needs to be considered before we discuss any e-mail security protocol in particular. It is obvious that some public-key algorithms must be used for e-mail security. For example, we need to encrypt the secret key or sign the message. To encrypt the secret key, Alice needs Bob's public key; to verify a signed message, Bob needs Alice's public key. So, for sending a small authenticated and confidential message, two public keys are needed. How can Alice be assured of Bob's public key, and how can Bob be assured of Alice's public key? Each e-mail security protocol has a different method of certifying keys.

## 16.2                    PGP

The first protocol discussed in this chapter is called **Pretty Good Privacy (PGP)**. PGP was invented by Phil Zimmermann to provide e-mail with privacy, integrity, and authentication. PGP can be used to create a secure e-mail message or to store a file securely for future retrieval.

### 16.2.1   Scenarios

Let us first discuss the general idea of PGP, moving from a simple scenario to a complex one. We use the term "Data" to show the message or file prior to processing.

*Plaintext*    The simplest scenario is to send the e-mail message (or store the file) in plaintext as shown in Fig. 16.2. There is no message integrity or confidentiality in this scenario. Alice, the sender, composes a message and sends it to Bob, the receiver. The message is stored in Bob's mailbox until it is retrieved by him.

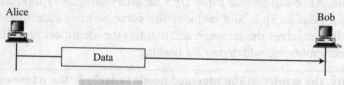

**Fig. 16.2** *A plaintext message*

*Message Integrity*    Probably the next improvement is to let Alice sign the message. Alice creates a digest of the message and signs it with her private key. When Bob receives the message, he verifies the message by using Alice's public key. Two keys are needed for this scenario. Alice needs to know her private key; Bob needs to know Alice's public key. Figure 16.3 shows the situation.

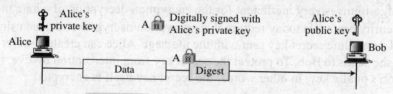

**Fig. 16.3** *An authenticated message*

*Compression*    A further improvement is to compress the message and digest to make the packet more compact. This improvement has no security benefit, but it eases the traffic. Figure 16.4 shows the new scenario.

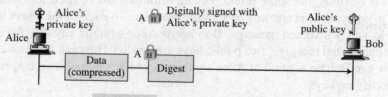

**Fig. 16.4** *A compressed message*

## Confidentiality with One-Time Session Key

As we discussed before, confidentiality in an e-mail system can be achieved using conventional encryption with a one-time session key. Alice can create a session key, use the session key to encrypt the message and the digest, and send the key itself with the message. However, to protect the session key, Alice encrypts it with Bob's public key. Figure 16.5 shows the situation.

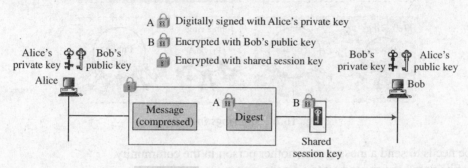

**Fig. 16.5** *A confidential message*

When Bob receives the packet, he first decrypts the key, using his private key to remove the key. He then uses the session key to decrypt the rest of the message. After decompressing the rest of the message, Bob creates a digest of the message and checks to see if it is equal to the digest sent by Alice. If it is, then the message is authentic.

**Code Conversion**    Another service provided by PGP is code conversion. Most e-mail systems allow the message to consist of only ASCII characters. To translate other characters not in the ASCII set, PGP uses Radix-64 conversion. Each character to be sent (after encryption) is converted to Radix-64 code, which is discussed later in the chapter.

**Segmentation**    PGP allows segmentation of the message after it has been converted to Radix-64 to make each transmitted unit the uniform size as allowed by the underlying e-mail protocol.

### 16.2.2  Key Rings

In all previous scenarios, we assumed that Alice needs to send a message only to Bob. That is not always the case. Alice may need to send messages to many people; she needs **key rings.** In this case, Alice needs a ring of public keys, with a key belonging to each person with whom Alice needs to correspond (send or receive messages). In addition, the PGP designers specified a ring of private/public keys. One reason is that Alice may wish to change her pair of keys from time to time. Another reason is that Alice may need to correspond with different groups of people (friends, colleagues, and so on). Alice may wish to use a different key pair for each group. Therefore, each user needs to have two sets of rings: a ring of private/public keys and a ring of public keys of other people. Figure 16.6 shows a community of four people, each having a ring of pairs of private/public keys and, at the same time, a ring of public keys belonging to other people in the community.

Alice, for example, has several pairs of private/public keys belonging to her and public keys belonging to other people. Note that everyone can have more than one public key. Two cases may arise.

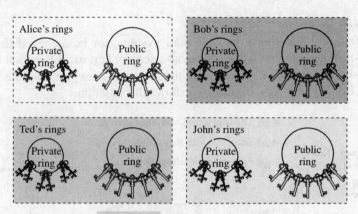

**Fig. 16.6**  *Key rings in PGP*

1. Alice needs to send a message to another person in the community.
   a. She uses her private key to sign the digest.
   b. She uses the receiver's public key to encrypt a newly created session key.
   c. She encrypts the message and signed digest with the session key created.
2. Alice receives a message from another person in the community.
   a. She uses her private key to decrypt the session key.
   b. She uses the session key to decrypt the message and digest.
   c. She uses her public key to verify the digest.

## PGP Algorithms

The following algorithms are used in PGP.

*Public-Key Algorithms*  The public-key algorithms that are used for signing the digests or encrypting the messages are listed in Table 16.1.

**Table 16.1**  *Public-key algorithms*

| ID | Description |
|---|---|
| 1 | RSA (encryption or signing) |
| 2 | RSA (for encryption only) |
| 3 | RSA (for signing only) |
| 16 | ElGamal (encryption only) |
| 17 | DSS |
| 18 | Reserved for elliptic curve |
| 19 | Reserved for ECDSA |
| 20 | ElGamal (for encryption or signing) |
| 21 | Reserved for Diffie-Hellman |
| 100–110 | Private algorithms |

*Symmetric-Key Algorithms*  The symmetric-key algorithms that are used for conventional encrypting are shown in Table 16.2.

**Table 16.2** *Symmetric-key algorithms*

| ID | Description |
|---------|---------------------|
| 0 | No Encryption |
| 1 | IDEA |
| 2 | Triple DES |
| 3 | CAST-128 |
| 4 | Blowfish |
| 5 | SAFER-SK128 |
| 6 | Reserved for DES/SK |
| 7 | Reserved for AES-128 |
| 8 | Reserved for AES-192 |
| 9 | Reserved for AES-256 |
| 100–110 | Private algorithms |

**Hash Algorithms** The hash algorithms that are used for creating hashes in PGP are shown in Table 16.3.

**Table 16.3** *Hash Algorithms*

| ID | Description |
|---------|-----------------------------|
| 1 | MD5 |
| 2 | SHA-1 |
| 3 | RIPE-MD/160 |
| 4 | Reserved for double-width SHA |
| 5 | MD2 |
| 6 | TIGER/192 |
| 7 | Reserved for HAVAL |
| 100–110 | Private algorithms |

**Compression Algorithms** The compression algorithms that are used for compressing text are shown in Table 16.4.

**Table 16.4** *Compression methods*

| ID | Description |
|---------|-----------------|
| 0 | Uncompressed |
| 1 | ZIP |
| 2 | ZLIP |
| 100–110 | Private methods |

## 16.2.3 PGP Certificates

PGP, like other protocols we have seen so far, uses certificates to authenticate public keys. However, the process is totally different.

***X.509 Certificates*** Protocols that use X.509 certificates depend on the hierarchical structure of the trust. There is a predefined chain of trust from the root to any certificate. Every user fully trusts the authority of the CA at the root level (prerequisite). The root issues certificates for the CAs at the second level, a second level CA issues a certificate for the third level, and so on. Every party that needs to be trusted presents a certificate from some CA in the tree. If Alice does not trust the certificate issuer for Bob, she can appeal to a higher-level authority up to the root (which must be trusted for the system to work). In other words, there is one single path from a fully trusted CA to a certificate.

---

**In X.509, there is a single path from the fully trusted authority to any certificate.**

---

***PGP Certificates*** In PGP, there is no need for CAs; anyone in the ring can sign a certificate for anyone else in the ring. Bob can sign a certificate for Ted, John, Anne, and so on. There is no hierarchy of trust in PGP; there is no tree. The lack of hierarchical structure may result in the fact that Ted may have one certificate from Bob and another certificate from Liz. If Alice wants to follow the line of certificates for Ted, there are two paths: one starts from Bob and one starts from Liz. An interesting point is that Alice may fully trust Bob, but only partially trust Liz. There can be multiple paths in the line of trust from a fully or partially trusted authority to a certificate. In PGP, the issuer of a certificate is usually called an *introducer*.

---

**In PGP, there can be multiple paths from fully or partially trusted authorities to any subject.**

---

### Trusts and Legitimacy

The entire operation of PGP is based on introducer trust, the certificate trust, and the legitimacy of the public keys.

***Introducer Trust Levels*** With the lack of a central authority, it is obvious that the ring cannot be very large if every user in the PGP ring of users has to fully trust everyone else. (Even in real life we cannot fully trust everyone that we know.) To solve this problem, PGP allows different levels of trust. The number of levels is mostly implementation dependent, but for simplicity, let us assign three levels of trust to any introducer: *none, partial,* and *full.* The introducer trust level specifies the trust levels issued by the introducer for other people in the ring. For example, Alice may fully trust Bob, partially trust Anne, and not trust John at all. There is no mechanism in PGP to determine how to make a decision about the trustworthiness of the introducer; it is up to the user to make this decision.

***Certificate Trust Levels*** When Alice receives a certificate from an introducer, she stores the certificate under the name of the subject (certified entity). She assigns a level of trust to this certificate. The certificate trust level is normally the same as the introducer trust level that issued the certificate. Assume that Alice fully trusts Bob, partially trusts Anne and Janette, and has no trust in John. The following scenarios can happen.

1. Bob issues two certificates, one for Linda (with public key K1) and one for Lesley (with public key K2). Alice stores the public key and certificate for Linda under Linda's name and assigns

a *full* level of trust to this certificate. Alice also stores the certificate and public key for Lesley under Lesley's name and assigns a full level of trust to this certificate.

2. Anne issues a certificate for John (with public key K3). Alice stores this certificate and public key under John's name, but assigns a *partial* level for this certificate.

3. Janette issues two certificates, one for John (with public key K3) and one for Lee (with public key K4). Alice stores John's certificate under his name and Lee's certificate under his name, each with a *partial* level of trust. Note that John now has two certificates, one from Anne and one from Janette, each with a *partial* level of trust.

4. John issues a certificate for Liz. Alice can discard or keep this certificate with a signature trust of *none*.

**Key Legitimacy**    The purpose of using introducer and certificate trusts is to determine the legitimacy of a public key. Alice needs to know how legitimate the public keys of Bob, John, Liz, Anne, and so on are. PGP defines a very clear procedure for determining key legitimacy. The level of the key legitimacy for a user is the weighted trust levels of that user. For example, suppose we assign the following weights to certificate trust levels:

1. A weight of 0 to a nontrusted certificate
2. A weight of 1/2 to a certificate with partial trust
3. A weight of 1 to a certificate with full trust

Then to fully trust an entity, Alice needs one fully trusted certificate or two partially trusted certificates for that entity. For example, Alice can use John's public key in the previous scenario because both Anne and Janette have issued a certificate for John, each with a certificate trust level of 1/2. Note that the legitimacy of a public key belonging to an entity does not have anything to do with the trust level of that person. Although Bob can use John's public key to send a message to him, Alice cannot accept any certificate issued by John because, for Alice, John has a trust level of *none*.

**Starting the Ring**    You might have realized a problem with the above discussion. What if nobody sends a certificate for a fully or partially trusted entity? For example, how can the legitimacy of Bob's public key be determined if no one has sent a certificate for Bob? In PGP, the key legitimacy of a trusted or partially trusted entity can be also determined by other methods.

1. Alice can physically obtain Bob's public key. For example, Alice and Bob can meet personally and exchange a public key written on a piece of paper or to a disk.

2. If Bob's voice is recognizable to Alice, Alice can call him and obtain his public key on the phone.

3. A better solution proposed by PGP is for Bob to send his public key to Alice by e-mail. Both Alice and Bob make a 16-byte MD5 (or 20-byte SHA-1) digest from the key. The digest is normally displayed as eight groups of 4 digits (or ten groups of 4 digits) in hexadecimal and is called a *fingerprint*. Alice can then call Bob and verify the fingerprint on the phone. If the key is altered or changed during the e-mail transmission, the two fingerprints do not match. To make it even more convenient, PGP has created a list of words, each representing a 4-digit combination. When Alice calls Bob, Bob can pronounce the eight words (or ten words) for Alice. The words are carefully chosen by PGP to avoid those similar in pronunciation; for example, if *sword* is in the list, *word* is not.

4. In PGP, nothing prevents Alice from getting Bob's public key from a CA in a separate procedure. She can then insert the public key in the public key ring.

## Key Ring Tables

Each user, such as Alice, keeps track of two key rings: one private-key ring and one public key ring. PGP defines a structure for each of these key rings in the form of a table.

***Private Key Ring Table*** Figure 16.7 shows the format of a private key ring table.

| User ID | Key ID | Public key | Encrypted private key | Timestamp |
|---------|--------|------------|-----------------------|-----------|
| ⋮ | ⋮ | ⋮ | ⋮ | ⋮ |

Private ring

**Fig. 16.7** *Format of private key ring table*

❑ **User ID.** The user ID is usually the e-mail address of the user. However, the user may designate a unique e-mail address or alias for each key pair. The table lists the user ID associated with each pair.

❑ **Key ID.** This column uniquely defines a public key among the user's public keys. In PGP, the key ID for each pair is the first (least significant) 64 bits of the public key. In other words, the key ID is calculated as (key mod $2^{64}$). The key ID is needed for the operation of PGP because Bob may have several public keys belonging to Alice in his public key ring. When he receives a message from Alice, Bob must know which key ID to use to verify the message. The key ID, which is sent with the message, as we will see shortly, enables Bob to use a specific public key for Alice from his public ring. You might ask why the entire public key is not sent. The answer is that in public-key cryptography, the size of the public key may be very long. Sending just 8 bytes reduces the size of the message.

❑ **Public Key.** This column just lists the public key belonging to a particular private key/public key pair.

❑ **Encrypted Private Key.** This column shows the encrypted value of the private key in the private key/public key pair. Although Alice is the only person accessing her private ring, PGP saves only the encrypted version of the private key. We will see later how the private key is encrypted and decrypted.

❑ **Timestamp.** This column holds the date and time of the key pair creation. It helps the user decide when to purge old pairs and when to create new ones.

---

**Example 16.1** Let us show a private key ring table for Alice. We assume that Alice has only two user IDs, *alice@some.com* and *alice@anet.net*. We also assume that Alice has two sets of private/public keys, one for each user ID. Table 16.5 shows the private key ring table for Alice.

**Table 16.5** *Private key ring table for Example 1*

| User ID | Key ID | Public Key | Encrypted Private Key | Timestamp |
|---------|--------|------------|-----------------------|-----------|
| alice@anet.net | AB13...45 | AB13...45...59 | **32452398...23** | 031505-16:23 |
| alice@some.com | FA23...12 | FA23...12...22 | **564A4923...23** | 031504-08:11 |

Note that although the values of key ID, public key, and private key are shown in hexadecimal, and *ddmmyy-time* format is used for the timestamp, these formats are only for presentation and may be different in an actual implementation.

## Public Key Ring Table

*Public Key Ring Table*    Figure 16.8 shows the format of a public key ring table.

| User ID | Key ID | Public key | Producer trust | Certificate(s) | Certificate trust(s) | Key Legitimacy | Timestamp |
|---------|--------|------------|----------------|----------------|----------------------|----------------|-----------|
| ⋮ | ⋮ | ⋮ | ⋮ | ⋮ | ⋮ | ⋮ | ⋮ |

Public ring

**Fig. 16.8**  *Format of a public key ring table*

❏ **User ID.** As in the private key ring table, the user ID is usually the e-mail address of the entity.

❏ **Key ID.** As in the private key ring table, the key ID is the first (least significant) 64 bits of the public key.

❏ **Public Key.** This is the public key of the entity.

❏ **Producer Trust.** This column defines the producer level of trust. In most implementations, it can only be of one of three values: none, partial, or full.

❏ **Certificate(s).** This column holds the certificate or certificates signed by other entities for this entity. A user ID may have more than one certificate.

❏ **Certificate Trust(s).** This column represents the certificate trust or trusts. If Anne sends a certificate for John, PGP searches the row entry for Anne, finds the value of the producer trust for Anne, copies that value, and inserts it in the certificate trust field in the entry for John.

❏ **Key Legitimacy.** This value is calculated by PGP based on the value of the certificate trust and the predefined weight for each certificate trust.

❏ **Timestamp.** This column holds the date and time of the column creation.

**Example 16.2**    A series of steps will show how a public key ring table is formed for Alice.

1.  Start with one row, Alice herself, as shown in Table 16.6. Use N (none), P (partial), and F (full) for the levels of trust. For simplicity, also assume that everyone (including Alice) has only one user ID.

**Table 16.6**  *Example 2, starting table*

| User ID | Key ID | Public key | Prod. trust | Certificate | Cert. trust | Key legit. | Time-stamp |
|---------|--------|------------|-------------|-------------|-------------|------------|------------|
| Alice... | AB... | AB....... | F | | | F | ........ |

Note that, based on this table, we assume that Alice has issued a certificate for herself (implicitly). Alice of course trusts herself fully. The producer level of trust is also *full* and so is the key legitimacy. Although Alice never uses this first row, it is needed for the operation of PGP.

2.  Now Alice adds Bob to the table. Alice fully trusts Bob, but to obtain his public key, she asks Bob to send the public key by e-mail as well as his fingerprint. Alice then calls Bob to check the fingerprint. Table 16.7 shows this new event.

**Table 16.7**  *Example 2, after Bob is added to the table*

| User ID | Key ID | Public key | Prod. trust | Certificate | Cert. trust | Key legit. | Time-stamp |
|---------|--------|------------|-------------|-------------|-------------|------------|------------|
| Alice... | AB... | AB........ | F | | | F | ........ |
| Bob... | 12... | 12........ | F | | | F | ........ |

Note that the value of the producer trust is *full* for Bob because Alice fully trusts Bob. The value of the certificate field is empty, which shows that this key has been received indirectly, and not by a certificate.

3. Now Alice adds Ted to the table. Ted is fully trusted. However, for this particular user, Alice does not have to call Ted. Instead, Bob, who knows Ted's public key, sends Alice a certificate that includes Ted's public key, as shown in Table 16.8.

**Table 16.8** *Example 2, after Ted is added to the table*

| User ID | Key ID | Public key | Prod.trust | Certificate | Cert. trust | Key legit. | Time-stamp |
|---------|--------|------------|------------|-------------|-------------|------------|------------|
| Alice... | AB... | AB........ | F | | | F | ........ |
| Bob... | 12... | 12........ | F | | | F | ........ |
| Ted... | 48... | 48........ | F | Bob's | F | F | ........ |

Note that the value of certificate field shows that the certificate was received from Bob. The value of the certificate trust is copied by PGP from Bob's producer trust field. The value of the key legitimacy field is the value of the certificate trust multiplied by 1 (the weight).

4. Now Alice adds Anne to the list. Alice partially trusts Anne, but Bob, who is fully trusted, sends a certificate for Anne. Table 16.9 shows the new event.

**Table 16.9** *Example 2, after Anne is added to the table*

| User ID | Key ID | Public key | Prod. trust | Certificate | Cert. trust | Key legit. | Time-stamp |
|---------|--------|------------|-------------|-------------|-------------|------------|------------|
| Alice... | AB... | AB........ | F | | | F | ........ |
| Bob... | 12... | 12........ | F | | | F | ........ |
| Ted... | 48... | 48........ | F | Bob's | F | F | ........ |
| Anne... | 71... | 71........ | P | Bob's | F | F | ........ |

Note that the producer trust value for Anne is partial, but the certificate trust and key legitimacy is full.

5. Now Anne introduces John, who is not trusted by Alice. Table 16.10 shows the new event.

**Table 16.10** *Example 2, after John is added to the table*

| User ID | Key ID | Public key | Prod. trust | Certificate | Cert. trust | Key legit. | Time-stamp |
|---------|--------|------------|-------------|-------------|-------------|------------|------------|
| Alice... | AB... | AB........ | F | | | F | ........ |
| Bob... | 12... | 12........ | F | | | F | ........ |
| Ted... | 48... | 48........ | F | Bob's | F | F | ........ |
| Anne... | 71... | 71........ | P | Bob's | F | F | ........ |
| John... | 31... | 31........ | N | Anne's | P | P | ........ |

Note that PGP has copied the value of Anne's producer trust (P) to the certificate trust field for John. The value of the key legitimacy field for John is 1/2 (P) at this moment, which means that Alice must not use John's key until it changes to 1 (F).

6. Now Janette, who is unknown to Alice, sends a certificate for Lee. Alice totally ignores this certificate because she does not know Janette.

7.  Now Ted sends a certificate for John (John, who is trusted by Ted, has probably asked Ted to send this certificate). Alice looks at the table and finds John's user ID with the corresponding key ID and public key. Alice does not add another row to the table; she just modifies the table as shown in Table 16.11.

    Because John has two certificates in Alice's table and his key legitimacy value is 1, Alice can use his key. But John is still untrustworthy. Note that Alice can continue to add entries to the table.

**Table 16.11** *Example 2, after one more certificate received for John*

| User ID | Key ID | Public key | Prod. trust | Certificate | Cert. trust | Key legit. | Time-stamp |
|---------|--------|------------|-------------|-------------|-------------|------------|------------|
| Alice... | AB... | AB........ | F | | | F | ........ |
| Bob... | 12... | 12........ | F | | | F | ........ |
| Ted... | 48... | 48........ | F | Bob's | F | F | ........ |
| Anne... | 71... | 71........ | P | Bob's | F | F | ........ |
| John... | 31... | 31........ | N | Anne's Ted's | PF | F | ........ |

## 16.2.4 Trust Model in PGP

As Zimmermann has proposed, we can create a trust model for any user in a ring with the user as the center of activity. Such a model can look like the one shown in Fig. 16.9. The figure shows the trust model for Alice at some moment. The diagram may change with any changes in the public key ring table.

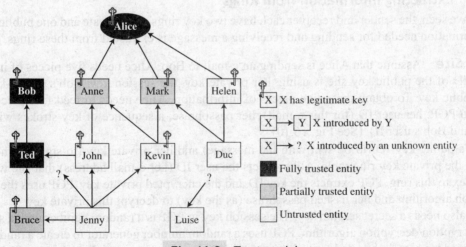

**Fig. 16.9** *Trust model*

Let us elaborate on the figure. Fig. 16.9 shows that there are three entities in Alice's ring with full trust (Alice herself, Bob, and Ted). The figure also shows three entities with partial trust (Anne, Mark, and Bruce). There are also six entities with no trust. Nine entities have a legitimate key. Alice can encrypt a message to any one of these entities or verify a signature received from one of these entities (Alice's key is never used in this model). There are also three entities that do not have any legitimate keys with Alice.

Bob, Anne, and Mark have made their keys legitimate by sending their keys by e-mail and verifying their fingerprints by phone. Helen, on the other hand, has sent a certificate from a CA because she is not trusted by Alice and verification on the phone is not possible. Although Ted is fully trusted, he has given Alice a certificate signed by Bob. John has sent Alice two certificates, one signed by Ted and one by Anne. Kevin has sent two certificates to Alice, one signed by Anne and one by Mark. Each of these certificates gives Kevin half a point of legitimacy; therefore, Kevin's key is legitimate. Duc has sent two certificates to Alice, one signed by Mark and the other by Helen. Since Mark is half-trusted and Helen is not trusted, Duc does not have a legitimate key. Jenny has sent four certificates, one signed by a half-trusted entity, two by untrusted entities, and one by an unknown entity. Jenny does not have enough points to make her key legitimate. Luise has sent one certificate signed by an unknown entity. Note that Alice may keep Luise's name in the table in case future certificates for Luise arrive.

*Web of Trust*  PGP can eventually make a **web of trust** between a group of people. If each entity introduces more entities to other entities, the public key ring for each entity gets larger and larger and entities in the ring can send secure e-mail to each other.

## 16.2.5  Key Revocation

It may become necessary for an entity to revoke his or her public key from the ring. This may happen if the owner of the key feels that the key is compromised (stolen, for example) or just too old to be safe. To revoke a key, the owner can send a revocation certificate signed by herself. The revocation certificate must be signed by the old key and disseminated to all the people in the ring that use that public key.

## 16.2.6  Extracting Information from Rings

As we have seen, the sender and receiver each have two key rings, one private and one public. Let us see how information needed for sending and receiving a message is extracted from these rings.

*Sender Site*  Assume that Alice is sending an e-mail to Bob. Alice needs five pieces of information: the key ID of the public key she is using, her private key, the session key, Bob's public-key ID, and Bob's public key. To obtain these five pieces of information, Alice needs to feed four pieces of information to PGP: her user ID (for this e-mail), her passphrase, a sequence of key strokes with possible pauses, and Bob's user ID. (See Fig. 16.10)

Alice's public-key ID (to be sent with the message) and her private key (to sign the message) are stored in the private key ring table. Alice selects the user ID (her e-mail address) that she wants to use as an index to this ring. PGP extracts the key ID and the encrypted private key. PGP uses the predefined decryption algorithm and her hashed passphrase (as the key) to decrypt this private key.

Alice also needs a secret session key. The session key in PGP is a random number with a size defined in the encryption/decryption algorithm. PGP uses a random number generator to create a random session key; the seed is a set of arbitrary keystrokes typed by Alice on her keyboard. Each key stroke is converted to 8 bits and each pause between the keystrokes is converted to 32 bits. The combination goes through a complex random number generator to create a very reliable random number as the session key. Note that the session key in PGP is a one-time random key (see Appendix K) and used only once.

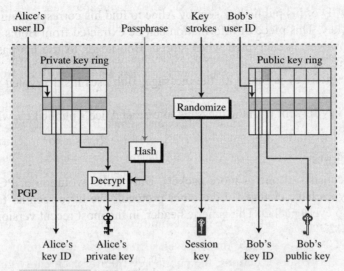

**Fig. 16.10** *Extracting information at the sender site*

Alice also needs Bob's key ID (to be sent with the message) and Bob's public key (to encrypt the session key). These two pieces of information are extracted from the public key ring table using Bob's user ID (his e-mail address).

***Receiver Site*** At the receiver site, Bob needs three pieces of information: Bob's private key (to decrypt the session key), the session key (to decrypt the data), and Alice's public key (to verify the signature). See Fig. 16.11.

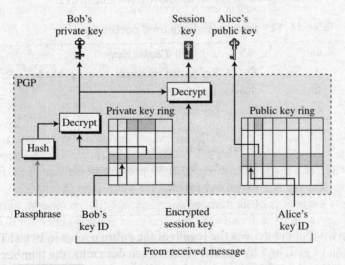

**Fig. 16.11** *Extracting information at the receiver site*

Bob uses the key ID of his public key sent by Alice to find his corresponding private key needed to decrypt the session key. This piece of information can be extracted from Bob's private key ring table. The private key, however, is encrypted when stored. Bob needs to use his passphrase and the hash function to decrypt it.

The encrypted session key is sent with the message; Bob uses his decrypted private key to decrypt the session key.

Bob uses Alice's key ID sent with the message to extract Alice's public key, which is stored in Bob's public key ring table.

### 16.2.7   PGP Packets

A message in PGP consists of one or more packets. During the evolution of PGP, the format and the number of packet types have changed. Like other protocols we have seen so far, PGP has a generic header that applies to every packet. The generic header, in the most recent version, has only two fields, as shown in Fig. 16.12.

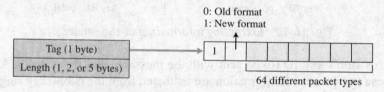

**Fig. 16.12**   *Format of packet header*

❑   **Tag.** The recent format for this field defines a tag as an 8-bit flag; the first bit (most significant) is always 1. The second bit is 1 if we are using the latest version. The remaining six bits can define up to 64 different packet types, as shown in Table 16.12.

**Table 16.12**   *Some commonly used packet types*

| Value | Packet type |
|---|---|
| 1 | Session key packet encrypted using a public key |
| 2 | Signature packet |
| 5 | Private-key packet |
| 6 | Public-key packet |
| 8 | Compressed data packet |
| 9 | Data packet encrypted with a secret key |
| 11 | Literal data packet |
| 13 | User ID packet |

❑   **Length.** The length field defines the length of the entire packet in bytes. The size of this field is variable; it can be 1, 2, or 5 bytes. The receiver can determine the number of bytes of the length field by looking at the value of the byte immediately following the tag field.

a.   If the value of the byte after the tag field is less than 192, the length field is only one byte. The length of the body (packet minus header) is calculated as:

$$\text{body length} = \text{first byte}$$

b.   If the value of the byte after the tag field is between 192 and 223 (inclusive), the length field is two bytes. The length of the body can be calculated as:

$$\text{body length} = (\text{first byte} - 192) << 8 + \text{second byte} + 192$$

c.   If the value of the byte after the tag field is between 224 and 254 (inclusive), the length field is one byte. This type of length field defines only the length of part of the body (partial body length). The partial body length can be -calculated as:

$$\text{partial body length} = 1 << (\text{first byte \& 0x1F})$$

Note that the formula means $1 \times 2^{(\text{first byte \& 0x1F})}$. The power is actually the value of the five rightmost bits. Because the field is between 224 and 254, inclusive, the value of the five rightmost bits is between 0 and 30, inclusive. In other words, the partial body length can be between one ($2^0$) and 1,073,741,824 ($2^{30}$). When a packet becomes several partial bodies, the partial body length is applicable. Each partial body length defines one part of the length. The last length field cannot be a partial body length definer. For example, if a packet has four parts, it can have three partial length fields and one length field of another type.

d.   If the value of the byte after the tag field is 255, the length field consists of five bytes. The length of the body is calculated as:

$$\text{Body length} = \text{second byte} << 24 \mid \text{third byte} << 16 \mid \text{fourth byte} << 8 \mid \text{fifth byte}$$

**Literal Data Packet**   The literal data packet is the packet that carries or holds the actual data that is being transmitted or stored. This packet is the most elementary type of message; that is, it cannot carry any other packet. The format of the packet is shown in Fig. 16.13.

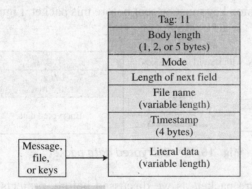

**Fig. 16.13**   *Literal data packet*

❑   **Mode.** This one-byte field defines how data is written to the packet. The value of this field can be "b" for binary, "t" for text, or any other locally defined value.

❑   **Length of next field.** This one-byte field defines the length of the next field (file name field).

❑   **File name.** This variable-length field defines the name of the file or message as an ASCII string.

❑ **Timestamp.** This four-byte field defines the time of creation or last modification of the message. The value can be 0, which means that the user chooses not to specify a time.

❑ **Literal data.** This variable-length field carries the actual data (file or message) in text or binary (depending on the value of the mode field).

*Compressed Data Packet* This packet carries compressed data packets. Figure 16.14 shows the format of a compressed data packet.

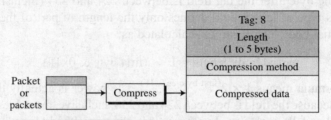

**Fig. 16.14** *Compressed data packet*

❑ **Compression method.** This one-byte field defines the compression method used to compress the data (next field). The values defined for this field so far are 1 (ZIP) and 2 (ZLIP). Also, an implementation can use other experimental compression methods. ZIP is discussed in Appendix M.

❑ **Compressed data.** This variable-length field carries the data after compression. Note that the data in this field can be one packet or the concatenation of two or more packets. The common situation is a single literal data packet or a combination of a signature packet followed by a literal data packet.

*Data Packet Encrypted with Secret Key* This packet carries data from one packet or a combination of packets that have been encrypted using a conventional symmetric-key algorithm. Note that a packet carrying the one-time session key must be sent before this packet. Figure 16.15 shows the format of the encrypted data packet.

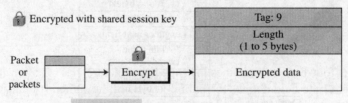

**Fig. 16.15** *Encrypted data packet*

*Signature Packet* A signature packet, as we discussed before, protects the integrity of the data. Figure 16.16 shows the format of the signature packet.

❑ **Version.** This one-byte field defines the PGP version that is being used.

❑ **Length.** This field was originally designed to show the length of the next two fields, but because the size of these fields is now fixed, the value of this field is 5.

❑ **Signature type.** This one-byte field defines the purpose of the signature, the document it signs. Table 16.13 shows some signature types.

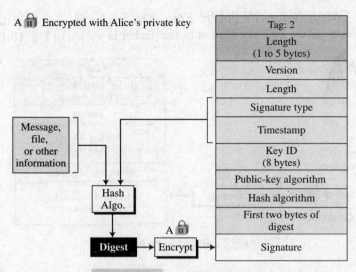

**Fig. 16.16** *Signature packet*

**Table 16.13** *Some signature values*

| Value | Signature |
|-------|-----------|
| 0x00 | Signature of a binary document (message or file). |
| 0x01 | Signature of a text document (message or file). |
| 0x10 | Generic certificate of a user ID and public-key packet. The signer does not make any particular assertion about the owner of the key. |
| 0x11 | Personal certificate of a user ID and public-key packet. No verification is done on the owner of the key. |
| 0x12 | Casual certificate of a User ID and public-key packet. Some casual verification done on the owner of the key. |
| 0x13 | Positive certificate of a user ID and public-key packet. Substantial verification done. |
| 0x30 | Certificate revocation signature. This removes an earlier certificate (0x10 through 0x13). |

❑ **Timestamp.** This four-byte field defines the time the signature was calculated.

❑ **Key ID.** This eight-byte field defines the public-key ID of the signer. It indicates to the verifier which signer public key should be used to decrypt the digest.

❑ **Public-key algorithm.** This one-byte field gives the code for the public-key algorithm used to encrypt the digest. The verifier uses the same algorithm to decrypt the digest.

❑ **Hash algorithm.** This one-byte field gives the code for the hash algorithm used to create the digest.

❑ **First two bytes of message digest.** These two bytes are used as a kind of checksum. They ensure that the receiver is using the right key ID to decrypt the digest.

❑ **Signature.** This variable-length field is the signature. It is the encrypted digest signed by the sender.

## Session-Key Packet Encrypted with Public Key

This packet is used to send the session key encrypted with the receiver public key. The format of the packet is shown in Fig. 16.17.

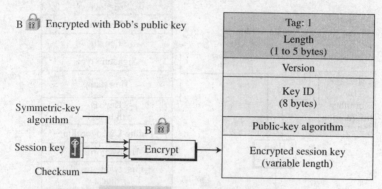

**Fig. 16.17** *Session-key packet*

❑ **Version.** This one-byte field defines the PGP version being used.
❑ **Key ID.** This eight-byte field defines the public-key ID of the sender. It indicates to the receiver which sender public key should be used to decrypt the session key.
❑ **Public-key algorithm.** This one-byte field gives the code for the public-key algorithm used to encrypt the session key. The receiver uses the same algorithm to decrypt the session key.
❑ **Encrypted session.** This variable-length field is the encrypted value of the session key created by the sender and sent to the receiver. The encryption is done on the following:
  a.  One-octet symmetric encryption algorithm
  b.  The session key
  c.  A two-octet checksum equal to the sum of the preceding session-key octets

## Public-Key Packet

This packet contains the public key of the sender. The format of the packet is shown in Fig. 16.18.

| Tag: 6 |
| Length (1 to 5 bytes) |
| Version |
| Key ID (8 bytes) |
| Public-key algorithm |

**Fig. 16.18** *Public-key packet*

❑ **Version.** This one-byte field defines the PGP version of the PGP being used.
❑ **Timestamp.** This four-byte field defines the time the key was created.

❏ **Validity.** This two-byte field shows the number of days the key is valid. If the value is 0, it means the key does not expire.

❏ **Public-key algorithm.** This one-byte field gives the code for the public-key algorithm.

❏ **Public key.** This variable-length field holds the public key itself. Its contents depend on the public-key algorithm used.

*User ID Packet*   This packet identifies a user and can normally associate the user ID contents with a public key of the sender. Figure 16.19 shows the format of the user ID packet. Note that the length field of the general header is only one byte.

| Tag: 13 |
| :---: |
| Length (1 byte) |
| User ID |

**Fig. 16.19**   *User ID packet*

❏ **User ID.** This variable-length string defines the user ID of the sender. It is normally the name of the user followed by an e-mail address.

## 16.2.8   PGP Messages

A message in PGP is a combination of sequenced and/or nested packets. Even though not all combinations of packets can make a message, the list of combinations is still long. In this section, we give a few examples to show the idea.

*Encrypted Message*   An encrypted message can be a sequence of two packets, a session-key packet and a symmetrically encrypted packet. The latter is normally a nested packet. Figure 16.20 shows this combination.

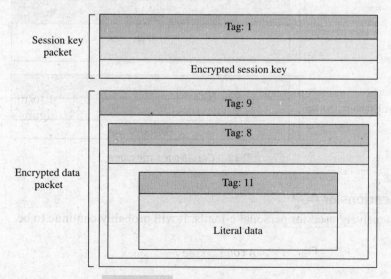

**Fig. 16.20**   *Encrypted message*

Note that the session-key packet is just a single packet. The encrypted data packet, however, is made of a compressed packet. The compressed packet is made of a literal data packet. The last one holds the literal data.

**Signed Message**   A signed message can be the combination of a signature packet and a literal packet, as shown in Fig. 16.21.

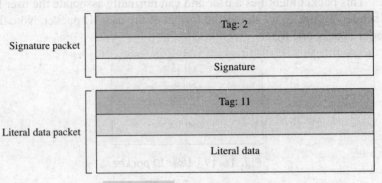

**Fig. 16.21**   *Signed message*

**Certificate Message**   Although a certificate can take many forms, one simple example is the combination of a user ID packet and a public-key packet as shown in Fig. 16.22. The signature is then calculated on the concatenation of the key and user ID.

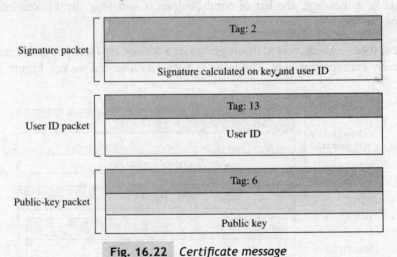

**Fig. 16.22**   *Certificate message*

## 16.2.9   Applications of PGP

PGP has been extensively used for personal e-mails. It will probably continue to be.

## 16.3                                                S/MIME

Another security service designed for electronic mail is **Secure/Multipurpose Internet Mail Extension (S/MIME).** The protocol is an enhancement of the **Multipurpose Internet Mail Extension (MIME)** protocol. To better understand S/MIME, first we briefly describe MIME. Next, S/MIME is discussed as the extension to MIME.

### 16.3.1   MIME

Electronic mail has a simple structure. Its simplicity, however, comes with a price. It can send messages only in NVT 7-bit ASCII format. In other words, it has some limitations. For example, it cannot be used for languages that are not supported by 7-bit ASCII characters (such as Arabic, Chinese, French, German, Hebrew, Japanese, and Russian). Also, it cannot be used to send binary files or video or audio data.

Multipurpose Internet Mail Extensions (MIME) is a supplementary protocol that allows non-ASCII data to be sent through e-mail. MIME transforms non-ASCII data at the sender site to NVT ASCII data and delivers it to the client MTA to be sent through the Internet. The message at the receiving side is transformed back to the original data.

We can think of MIME as a set of software functions that transform non-ASCII data to ASCII data, and vice versa, as shown in Fig. 16.23.

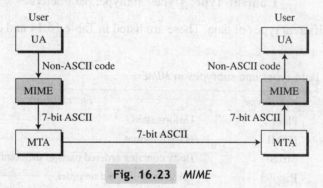

**Fig. 16.23**   *MIME*

MIME defines five headers that can be added to the original e-mail header section to define the transformation parameters:
1. MIME-Version
2. Content-Type
3. Content-Transfer-Encoding
4. Content-Id
5. Content-Description

Figure 16.24 shows the MIME headers. We will describe each header in detail.

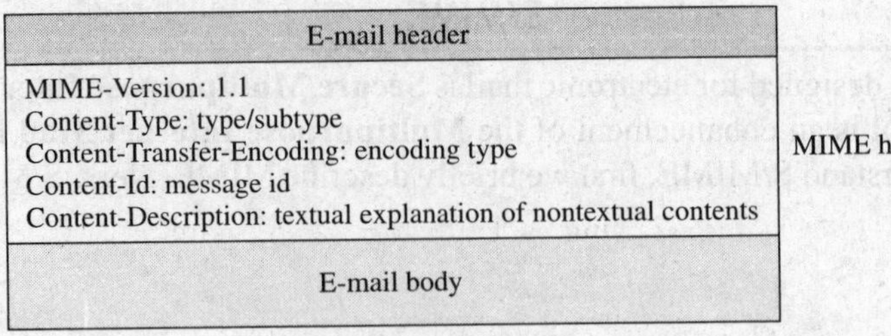

```
┌─────────────────────────────────────────────────────────┐
│                      E-mail header                       │
├─────────────────────────────────────────────────────────┤
│  MIME-Version: 1.1                                       │
│  Content-Type: type/subtype                              │
│  Content-Transfer-Encoding: encoding type                │   MIME headers
│  Content-Id: message id                                  │
│  Content-Description: textual explanation of nontextual contents │
├─────────────────────────────────────────────────────────┤
│                       E-mail body                        │
└─────────────────────────────────────────────────────────┘
```

**Fig. 16.24** *MIME header*

***MIME-Version***   This header defines the version of MIME used. The current version is 1.1.

**MIME-Version: 1.1**

***Content-Type***   This header defines the type of data used in the body of the message. The content type and the content subtype are separated by a slash. Depending on the subtype, the header may contain other parameters.

**Content-Type:** <type / subtype; parameters>

MIME allows seven different types of data. These are listed in Table 16.14 and described in more detail below.

**Table 16.14** *Data types and subtypes in MIME*

| Type | Subtype | Description |
|------|---------|-------------|
| | Plain | Unformatted. |
| | HTML | HTML format. |
| Multipart | Mixed | Body contains ordered parts of different data types. |
| | Parallel | Same as above, but no order. |
| | Digest | Similar to Mixed, but the default is message/RFC822. |
| | Alternative | Parts are different versions of the same message. |
| Message | RFC822 | Body is an encapsulated message. |
| | Partial | Body is a fragment of a bigger message. |
| | External-Body | Body is a reference to another message. |
| Image | JPEG | Image is in JPEG format. |
| | GIF | Image is in GIF format. |
| Video | MPEG | Video is in MPEG format. |
| Audio | Basic | Single channel encoding of voice at 8 KHz. |
| Application | PostScript | Adobe PostScript. |
| | Octet-stream | General binary data (eight-bit bytes). |

❏ **Text.** The original message is in 7-bit ASCII format and no transformation by MIME is needed. There are two subtypes currently used, *plain* and *HTML*.

❏ **Multipart.** The body contains multiple, independent parts. The multipart header needs to define the boundary between each part. A parameter is used for this purpose. The parameter is a string token that comes before each part; it is on a separate line by itself and is preceded by two hyphens. The body is terminated using the boundary token, again preceded by two hyphens, and then terminated with two hyphens.

Four subtypes are defined for this type: *mixed, parallel, digest,* and *alternative*. In the mixed subtype, the parts must be presented to the recipient in the exact order as in the message. Each part has a different type and is defined at the boundary. The parallel subtype is similar to the mixed subtype, except that the order of the parts is unimportant. The digest subtype is also similar to the mixed subtype except that the default type/subtype is message/RFC822, as defined below. In the alternative subtype, the same message is repeated using different formats. The following is an example of a multipart message using a mixed subtype:

**Content-Type: multipart/mixed; boundary=xxxx**

**—xxxx**
**Content-Type: text/plain;**
·············································
**—xxxx**
**Content-Type: image/gif;**
·············································
**—xxxx—**

❏ **Message.** In the message type, the body is itself an entire mail message, a part of a mail message, or a pointer to a message. Three subtypes are currently used: *RFC822, partial,* and *external-body*. The subtype RFC822 is used if the body is encapsulating another message (including header and the body). The partial subtype is used if the original message has been fragmented into different mail messages and this mail message is one of the fragments. The fragments must be reassembled at the destination by MIME. Three parameters must be added: *id, number,* and the *total*. The id identifies the message and is present in all the fragments. The number defines the sequence order of the fragment. The total defines the number of fragments that comprise the original message. The following is an example of a message with three fragments:

**Content-Type: message/partial;**
**id="forouzan@challenger.atc.fhda.edu";**
**number=1;**
**total=3;**


·····················
·····················

The subtype external-body indicates that the body does not contain the actual message but is only a reference (pointer) to the original message. The parameters following the subtype define how to access the original message. The following is an example:

> **Content-Type: message/external-body;**
> **name="report.txt";**
> **site="fhda.edu";**
> **access-type="ftp";**
> ........................
> ........................

❑ **Image.** The original message is a stationary image, indicating that there is no animation. The two currently used subtypes are *Joint Photographic Experts Group (JPEG),* which uses image compression, and *Graphics Interchange -Format (GIF)*.

❑ **Video.** The original message is a time-varying image (animation). The only subtype is Moving Picture Experts Group (*MPEG*). If the animated image contains sounds, it must be sent separately using the audio content type.

❑ **Audio.** The original message is sound. The only subtype is basic, which uses 8 kHz standard audio data.

❑ **Application.** The original message is a type of data not previously defined. There are only two subtypes used currently: *PostScript* and *octet-stream.* PostScript is used when the data are in Adobe PostScript format. Octet-stream is used when the data must be interpreted as a sequence of 8-bit bytes (binary file).

## Content-Transfer-Encoding

This header defines the method used to encode the messages into 0s and 1s for transport:

> **Content-Transfer-Encoding: <type>**

The five types of encoding methods are listed in Table 16.15.

**Table 16.15**  *Content-transfer-encoding*

| Type | Description |
|---|---|
| 7bit | NVT ASCII characters and short lines. |
| 8bit | Non-ASCII characters and short lines. |
| Binary | Non-ASCII characters with unlimited-length lines. |
| Radix-64 | 6-bit blocks of data are encoded into 8-bit ASCII characters using Radix-64 conversion. |
| Quoted-printable | Non-ASCII characters are encoded as an equal sign followed by an ASCII code. |

❑ **7bit.** This is 7-bit NVT ASCII encoding. Although no special transformation is needed, the length of the line should not exceed 1,000 characters.

❑ **8bit.** This is 8-bit encoding. Non-ASCII characters can be sent, but the length of the line still should not exceed 1,000 characters. MIME does not do any encoding here; the underlying SMTP protocol must be able to transfer 8-bit non-ASCII characters. It is, therefore, not recommended. Radix-64 and quoted-printable types are preferable.

❑ **Binary.** This is 8-bit encoding. Non-ASCII characters can be sent, and the length of the line can exceed 1,000 characters. MIME does not do any encoding here; the underlying SMTP protocol must be able to transfer binary data. It is, therefore, not recommended. Radix-64 and quoted-printable types are preferable.

❑ **Radix-64.** This is a solution for sending data made of bytes when the highest bit is not necessarily zero. Radix-64 transforms this type of data to printable characters, which can then be sent as ASCII characters or any type of character set supported by the underlying mail transfer mechanism.

Radix-64 divides the binary data (made of streams of bits) into 24-bit blocks. Each block is then divided into four sections, each made of 6 bits (see Fig. 16.25).

Each 6-bit section is interpreted as one character according to Table 16.16.

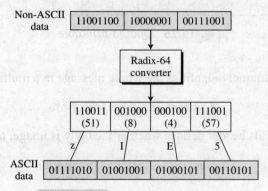

**Fig. 16.25** *Radix-64 conversion*

**Table 16.16** *Radix-64 encoding table*

| Value | Code | Value | Code | Value | Code | Value | Code | Value | Code | Value | Code |
|-------|------|-------|------|-------|------|-------|------|-------|------|-------|------|
| 0 | A | 11 | L | 22 | W | 33 | h | 44 | s | 55 | 3 |
| 1 | B | 12 | M | 23 | X | 34 | i | 45 | t | 56 | 4 |
| 2 | C | 13 | N | 24 | Y | 35 | j | 46 | u | 57 | 5 |
| 3 | D | 14 | O | 25 | Z | 36 | k | 47 | v | 58 | 6 |
| 4 | E | 15 | P | 26 | a | 37 | l | 48 | w | 59 | 7 |
| 5 | F | 16 | Q | 27 | b | 38 | m | 49 | x | 60 | 8 |
| 6 | G | 17 | R | 28 | c | 39 | n | 50 | y | 61 | 9 |
| 7 | H | 18 | S | 29 | d | 40 | o | 51 | z | 62 | + |
| 8 | I | 19 | T | 30 | e | 41 | p | 52 | 0 | 63 | / |
| 9 | J | 20 | U | 31 | f | 42 | q | 53 | 1 | | |
| 10 | K | 21 | V | 32 | g | 43 | r | 54 | 2 | | |

❑ **Quoted-printable.** Radix-64 is a redundant encoding scheme; that is, 24 bits become four characters, and eventually are sent as 32 bits. We have an overhead of 25 percent. If the data consist mostly of ASCII characters with a small non-ASCII portion, we can use **quoted-printable** encoding. If a character is ASCII, it is sent as is. If a character is not ASCII, it is sent as three characters. The first character is the equal sign (=). The next two characters are the hexadecimal representations of the byte. Figure 16.26 shows an example.

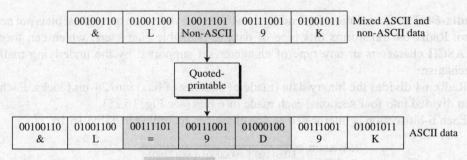

**Fig. 16.26** *Quoted-printable*

**Content-Id** This header uniquely identifies the whole message in a multiple message environment.

> **Content-Id:** id=<content-id>

**Content-Description** This header defines whether the body is image, audio, or video.

> **Content-Description:** <description>

### 16.3.2 S/MIME

S/MIME adds some new content types to include security services to the MIME. All of these new types include the parameter "application/pkcs7-mime," in which "pkcs" defines "Public Key Cryptography Specification."

#### Cryptographic Message Syntax (CMS)

To define how security services, such as confidentiality or integrity, can be added to MIME content types, S/MIME has defined **Cryptographic Message Syntax (CMS).** The syntax in each case defines the exact encoding scheme for each content type. The following describe the type of message and different subtypes that are created from these messages. For details, the reader is referred to RFC 3369 and 3370.

**Data Content Type** This is an arbitrary string. The object created is called *Data*.

**Signed-Data Content Type** This type provides only integrity of data. It contains any type and zero or more signature values. The encoded result is an *object* called *signedData*. Figure 16.27 shows the process of creating an object of this type. The following are the steps in the process:

1. For each signer, a message digest is created from the content using the specific hash algorithm chosen by that signer.
2. Each message digest is signed with the private key of the signer.
3. The content, signature values, certificates, and algorithms are then collected to create the *signedData* object.

**Enveloped-Data Content Type** This type is used to provide privacy for the message. It contains any type and zero or more encrypted keys and certificates. The encoded result is an *object* called *envelopedData*. Figure 16.28 shows the process of creating an object of this type.

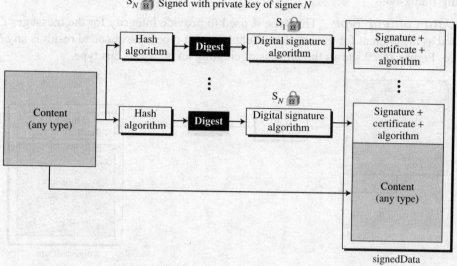

S₁ 🔒 Signed with private key of signer 1

Sₙ 🔒 Signed with private key of signer N

**Fig. 16.27** *Signed-data content type*

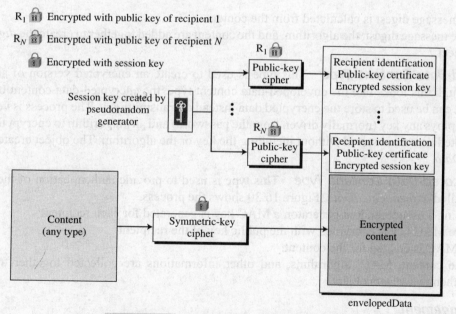

R₁ 🔒 Encrypted with public key of recipient 1

Rₙ 🔒 Encrypted with public key of recipient N

🔒 Encrypted with session key

**Fig. 16.28** *Enveloped-data content type*

1. A pseudorandom session key is created for the symmetric-key algorithms to be used.
2. For each recipient, a copy of the session key is encrypted with the public key of each recipient.
3. The content is encrypted using the defined algorithm and created session key.

4. The encrypted contents, encrypted session keys, algorithm used, and certificates are encoded using Radix-64.

***Digested-Data Content Type*** This type is used to provide integrity for the message. The result is normally used as the content for the enveloped-data content type. The encoded result is an *object* called *digestedData*. Figure 16.29 shows the process of creating an object of this type.

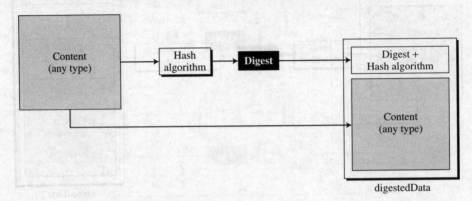

**Fig. 16.29** *Digest-data content type*

1. A message digest is calculated from the content.
2. The message digest, the algorithm, and the content are added together to create the *digestedData* object.

***Encrypted-Data Content Type*** This type is used to create an encrypted version of any content type. Although this looks like the enveloped-data content type, the encrypted-data content type has no recipient. It can be used to store the encrypted data instead of transmitting it. The process is very simple, the user employs any key (normally driven from the password) and any algorithm to encrypt the content. The encrypted content is stored without including the key or the algorithm. The object created is called *encryptedData*.

***Authenticated-Data Content Type*** This type is used to provide authentication of the data. The object is called *authenticatedData*. Figure 16.30 shows the process.

1. Using a pseudorandom generator, a MAC key is generated for each recipient.
2. The MAC key is encrypted with the public key of the recipient.
3. A MAC is created for the content.
4. The content, MAC, algorithms, and other informations are collected together to form the authenticatedData object.

### Key Management

The key management in S/MIME is a combination of key management used by X.509 and PGP. S/MIME uses public-key certificates signed by the certificate authorities defined by X.509. However, the user is responsible to maintain the web of trust to verify signatures as defined by PGP.

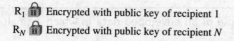

R$_1$   Encrypted with public key of recipient 1

R$_N$   Encrypted with public key of recipient $N$

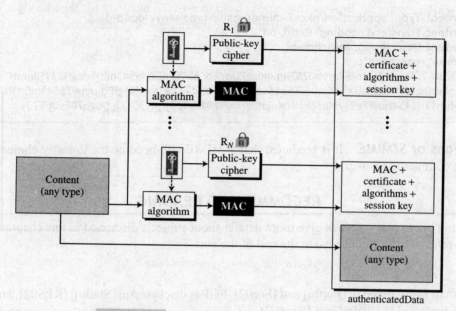

authenticatedData

**Fig. 16.30**   *Authenticated-data content type*

***Cryptographic Algorithms***   S/MIME defines several cryptographic algorithms as shown in Table 16.17. The term "must" means an absolute requirement; the term "should" means recommendation.

**Table 16.17**   *Cryptographic algorithm for S/MIME*

| Algorithm | Sender must support | Receiver must support | Sender should support | Receiver should support |
|---|---|---|---|---|
| Content-encryption algorithm | Triple DES | Triple DES | | 1. AES<br>2. RC2/40 |
| Session-key encryption algorithm | RSA | RSA | Diffie-Hellman | Diffie-Hellman |
| Hash algorithm | SHA-1 | SHA-1 | | MD5 |
| Digest-encryption algorithm | DSS | DSS | RSA | RSA |
| Message-authentication algorithm | | HMAC with SHA-1 | | |

**Example 16.3** The following shows an example of an enveloped-data in which a small message is encrypted using triple DES.

> **Content-Type: application/pkcs7-mime; mime-type=enveloped-data**
> **Content-Transfer-Encoding: Radix-64**
> **Content-Description: attachment**
> **name="report.txt";**
> cb32ut67f4bhijHU21oi87eryb0287hmnklsgFDoY8bc659GhIGfH6543mhjkdsaH23YjBnmN
> ybmlkzjhgfdyhGe23Kjk34XiuD678Es16se09jy76jHuytTMDcbnmlkjgfFdiuyu678543m0n3h
> G34un12P2454Hoi87e2ryb0H2MjN6KuyrlsgFDoY897fk923jljk1301XiuD6gh78EsUyT23y

*Applications of S/MIME* It is predicted that S/MIME will become the industry choice to provide security for commercial e-mail.

## 16.4           RECOMMENDED READING

The following books and websites give more details about subjects discussed in this chapter. The items in brackets refer to the reference list at the end of the text.

### Books

Electronic mail is discussed in [For06] and [For07]. PGP is discussed in [Sta06], [KPS02], and [Rhe03]. S/MIME is discussed in [Sta06] and [Rhe03].

### WebSites

The following websites give more information about topics discussed in this chapter.
    http://axion.physics.ubc.ca/pgp-begin.html
    csrc.nist.gov/publications/nistpubs/800-49/sp800-49.pdf
    www.faqs.org/rfcs/rfc2632.html

## *Key Terms*

| | |
|---|---|
| Cryptographic Message Syntax (CMS) | quoted-printable |
| electronic mail (e-mail) | Radix-64 encoding |
| key ring | Secure/Multipurpose Internet Mail |
| message access agent (MAA) | Extension (S/MIME) |
| message transfer agent (MTA) | user agent (UA) |
| Multipurpose Internet Mail Extension (MIME) | web of trust |
| Pretty Good Privacy (PGP) | |

## *Summary*

★   Because there is no session in e-mail communication, the sender of the message needs to include the name or identifiers of the algorithms used in the message. In e-mail communication, encryption/decryption is done using a symmetric-key algorithm, but the secret key to decrypt the message is encrypted with the public key of the receiver and is sent with the message.

★   The first protocol discussed in this chapter is called Pretty Good Privacy (PGP), which was invented by Phil Zimmermann to provide e-mail with privacy, integrity, and authentication. PGP can be used to create a secure e-mail message or to store a file securely for future retrieval.

★   In PGP, Alice needs a ring of public keys for each person with whom Alice needs to correspond. She also needs a ring of private/public keys belonging to her.

★   In PGP, there is no need for CAs; anyone in the ring can sign a certificate for anyone else in the ring. There is no hierarchy of trust in PGP; there is no tree. There can be multiple paths from fully or partially trusted authorities to any subject.

★   The entire operation of PGP is based on introducer trust, levels of trust, and the legitimacy of the public keys. PGP makes a web of trust between a group of people.

★   PGP has defined several packet types: literal data packet, compressed data packet, data packet encrypted with secret key, signature packet, session-key packet encrypted with public key, public-key packet, and user ID packet.

★   In PGP, we can have several types of messages: encrypted message, signed message, and certificate message.

★   Another security service designed for electronic mail is Secure/Multipurpose Internet Mail Extension (S/MIME). The protocol is an enhancement of the Multipurpose Internet Mail Extension (MIME) protocol, which is a supplementary protocol that allows non-ASCII data to be sent through e-mail. S/MIME adds some new content types to MIME to provide security services.

★   Cryptographic Message Syntax (CMS) has defined several message types that produce new content types to be added to MIME. This chapter mentioned several message types, including data content type, signed-data content type, enveloped-data content type, digested-data content type, encrypted-data content type, and authenticated-data content type.

★   The key management in S/MIME is a combination of key management used by X.509 and PGP. S/MIME uses public-key certificates signed by the certificate authorities.

# *Practice Set*

## Review Questions

**16.1**   Explain how Bob finds out what cryptographic algorithms Alice has used when he receives a PGP message from her.

**16.2**   Explain how Bob finds out what cryptographic algorithms Alice has used when he receives an S/MIME message from her.

**16.3**   In PGP, explain how Bob and Alice exchange the secret key for encrypting messages.

**16.4**   In S/MIME, explain how Bob and Alice exchange the secret key for encrypting messages.

**16.5**   Compare and contrast the nature of certificates in PGP and S/MIME. Explain the web of trust made from certificates in PGP and in S/MIME.

**16.6**   Name seven types of packets used in PGP and explain their purposes.

**16.7**   Name three types of messages in PGP and explain their purposes.

**16.8**   Name all content types defined by CMS and their purposes.

**16.9**   Compare and contrast key management in PGP and S/MIME.

## Exercises

**16.10** Bob receives a PGP message. How can he find out the type of the packet if the tag value is

    a.  8

    b.  9

    c.  2

**16.11** In PGP, can an e-mail message use two different public-key algorithms for encryption and signing? How is this defined in a message sent from Alice to Bob?

**16.12** Answer the following questions about tag values in PGP:

    a.  Can a packet with a tag value of 1 contain another packet?

    b.  Can a packet with a tag value of 6 contain another packet?

**16.13** What types of a packet should be sent in PGP to provide the following security services:

    a.  Confidentiality

    b.  Message integrity

    c.  Authentication

    d.  Nonrepudiation

    e.  Combination of a and b

    f.  Combination of a and c

    g.  Combination of a, b, and c

    h.  Combination of a, b, c, and d.

**16.14** What content type in S/MIME provides the following security services:

    a.  confidentiality

    b.  message integrity

    c.  authentication

    d.  nonrepudiation

    e.  combination of a and b

    f.  combination of a and c

    g.  combination of a, b, and c

    h.  combination of a, b, c, and d.

**16.15** Make a table to compare and contrast the symmetric-key cryptographic algorithms used in PGP and S/MIME.

**16.16** Make a table to compare and contrast the asymmetric-key cryptographic algorithms used in PGP and S/MIME.

**16.17** Make a table to compare and contrast the hash algorithms used in PGP and S/MIME.

**16.18** Make a table to compare and contrast the digital signature algorithms used in PGP and S/MIME.

**16.19** Encode the message "This is a test" using the following encoding scheme:

    a.  Radix-64

    b.  Quoted-printable

# 17

# Security at the Transport Layer: SSL and TLS

## Objectives

This chapter has several objectives:

☞ To discuss the need for security services at the transport layer of the Internet model
☞ To discuss the general architecture of SSL
☞ To discuss the general architecture of TLS
☞ To compare and contrast SSL and TLS

Transport layer security provides end-to-end security services for applications that use a reliable transport layer protocol such as TCP. The idea is to provide security services for transactions on the Internet. For example, when a customer shops online, the following security services are desired:

1.  The customer needs to be sure that the server belongs to the actual vendor, not an impostor. The customer does not want to give an impostor her credit card number (entity authentication).
2.  The customer and the vendor need to be sure that the contents of the message are not modified during transmission (message integrity).
3.  The customer and the vendor need to be sure that an impostor does not intercept sensitive information such as a credit card number (confidentiality).

Two protocols are dominant today for providing security at the transport layer: the **Secure Sockets Layer (SSL) Protocol** and the **Transport Layer Security (TLS) Protocol.** The latter is actually an IETF version of the former. We first discuss SSL, then TLS, and then compare and contrast the two. Figure 17.1 shows the position of SSL and TLS in the Internet model.

One of the goals of these protocols is to provide server and client authentication, data confidentiality, and data integrity. Application-layer client/server programs, such as **Hypertext Transfer Protocol (HTTP),** that use the services of TCP can

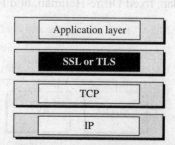

**Fig. 17.1** *Location of SSL and TLS in the Internet model*

encapsulate their data in SSL packets. If the server and client are capable of running SSL (or TLS) programs then the client can use the URL *https://...* instead of *http://...* to allow HTTP messages to be encapsulated in SSL (or TLS) packets. For example, credit card numbers can be safely transferred via the Internet for online shoppers.

## 17.1               SSL ARCHITECTURE

SSL is designed to provide security and compression services to data generated from the application layer. Typically, SSL can receive data from any application layer protocol, but usually the protocol is HTTP. The data received from the application is compressed (optional), signed, and encrypted. The data is then passed to a reliable transport layer protocol such as TCP. Netscape developed SSL in 1994. Versions 2 and 3 were released in 1995. In this chapter, we discuss SSLv3.

### 17.1.1    Services

SSL provides several services on data received from the application layer.

*Fragmentation*    First, SSL divides the data into blocks of $2^{14}$ bytes or less.

*Compression*    Each fragment of data is compressed using one of the lossless compression methods negotiated between the client and server. This service is optional.

*Message Integrity*    To preserve the integrity of data, SSL uses a keyed-hash function to create a MAC.

*Confidentiality*    To provide confidentiality, the original data and the MAC are encrypted using symmetric-key cryptography.

*Framing*    A header is added to the encrypted payload. The payload is then passed to a reliable transport layer protocol.

### 17.1.2    Key Exchange Algorithms

As we will see later, to exchange an authenticated and confidential message, the client and the server each need six cryptographic secrets (four keys and two initialization vectors). However, to create these secrets, one pre-master secret must be established between the two parties. SSL defines six key-exchange methods to establish this pre-master secret: NULL, RSA, anonymous Diffie-Hellman, ephemeral Diffie-Hellman, fixed Diffie-Hellman, and Fortezza, as shown in Fig. 17.2.

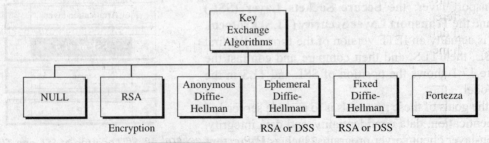

**Fig. 17.2** *Key-exchange methods*

***NULL*** There is no key exchange in this method. No pre-master secret is established between the client and the server.

---

**Both client and server need to know the value of the pre-master secret.**

---

***RSA*** In this method, the pre-master secret is a 48-byte random number created by the client, encrypted with the server's RSA public key, and sent to the server. The server needs to send its RSA encryption/decryption certificate. Figure 17.3 shows the idea.

**Fig. 17.3** *RSA key exchange; server public key*

***Anonymous Diffie-Hellman*** This is the simplest and most insecure method. The pre-master secret is established between the client and server using the Diffie-Hellman (DH) protocol. The Diffie-Hellman half-keys are sent in plaintext. It is called **anonymous Diffie-Hellman** because neither party is known to the other. As we have discussed, the most serious disadvantage of this method is the man-in-the-middle attack. Figure 17.4 shows the idea.

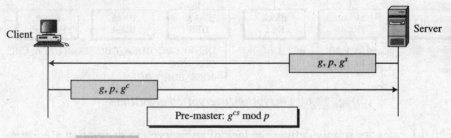

**Fig. 17.4** *Anonymous Diffie-Hellman key exchange*

***Ephemeral Diffie-Hellman*** To thwart the man-in-the-middle attack, the **ephemeral Diffie-Hellman** key exchange can be used. Each party sends a Diffie-Hellman key signed by its private key. The receiving party needs to verify the signature using the public key of the sender. The public keys for verification are exchanged using either RSA or DSS digital signature certificates. Figure 17.5 shows the idea.

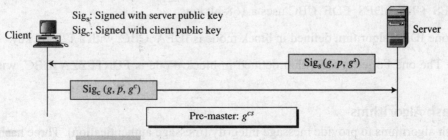

**Fig. 17.5** *Ephemeral Diffie-Hellman key exchange*

***Fixed Diffie-Hellman*** Another solution is the **fixed Diffie-Hellman** method. All entities in a group can prepare fixed Diffie-Hellman parameters (g and p). Then each entity can create a fixed Diffie-Hellman half-key ($g^x$). For additional security, each individual half-key is inserted into a certificate verified by a certification authority (CA). In other words, the two parties do not directly exchange the half-keys; the CA sends the half-keys in an RSA or DSS special certificate. When the client needs to calculate the pre-master, it uses its own fixed half-key and the server half-key received in a certificate. The server does the same, but in the reverse order. Note that no key-exchange messages are passed in this method; only certificates are exchanged.

***Fortezza*** **Fortezza** (derived from the Italian word for fortress) is a registered trademark of the U.S. National Security Agency (NSA). It is a family of security protocols developed for the Defense Department. We do not discuss Fortezza in this text because of its complexity.

### 17.1.3 Encryption/Decryption Algorithms

There are several choices for the encryption/decryption algorithm. We can divide the algorithms into 6 groups as shown in Fig. 17.6. All block protocols use an 8-byte initialization vector (IV) except for Fortezza, which uses a 20-byte IV.

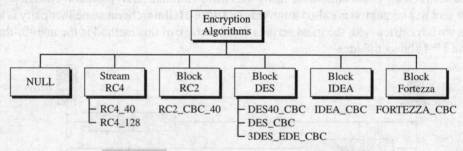

**Fig. 17.6** *Encryption/decryption algorithms*

***NULL*** The NULL category simply defines the lack of an encryption/decryption algorithm.

***Stream RC*** Two RC algorithms are defined in stream mode: RC4-40 (40-bit key) and RC4-128 (128-bit key).

***Block RC*** One RC algorithm is defined in block mode: RC2_CBC_40 (40-bit key).

***DES*** All DES algorithms are defined in block mode. DES40_CBC uses a 40-bit key. Standard DES is defined as DES_CBC. 3DES_EDE_CBC uses a 168-bit key.

***IDEA*** The one IDEA algorithm defined in block mode is IDEA_CBC, with a 128-bit key.

***Fortezza*** The one Fortezza algorithm defined in block mode is FORTEZZA_CBC, with a 96-bit key.

### 17.1.4 Hash Algorithms

SSL uses hash algorithms to provide message integrity (message authentication). Three hash functions are defined, as shown in Fig. 17.7.

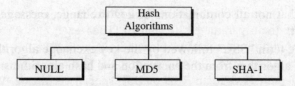

**Fig. 17.7** *Hash algorithms for message integrity*

***Null*** The two parties may decline to use an algorithm. In this case, there is no hash function and the message is not authenticated.

***MD5*** The two parties may choose MD5 as the hash algorithm. In this case, a 128-key MD5 hash algorithm is used.

***SHA-1*** The two parties may choose SHA as the hash algorithm. In this case, a 160-bit SHA-1 hash algorithm is used.

## 17.1.5 Cipher Suite

The combination of key exchange, hash, and encryption algorithms defines a **cipher suite** for each SSL session. Table 17.1 shows the suites used in the United States. We have not included those that

**Table 17.1** *SSL cipher suite list*

| Cipher suite | Key Exchange | Encryption | Hash |
|---|---|---|---|
| SSL_NULL_WITH_NULL_NULL | NULL | NULL | NULL |
| SSL_RSA_WITH_NULL_MD5 | RSA | NULL | MD5 |
| SSL_RSA_WITH_NULL_SHA | RSA | NULL | SHA-1 |
| SSL_RSA_WITH_RC4_128_MD5 | RSA | RC4 | MD5 |
| SSL_RSA_WITH_RC4_128_SHA | RSA | RC4 | SHA-1 |
| SSL_RSA_WITH_IDEA_CBC_SHA | RSA | IDEA | SHA-1 |
| SSL_RSA_WITH_DES_CBC_SHA | RSA | DES | SHA-1 |
| SSL_RSA_WITH_3DES_EDE_CBC_SHA | RSA | 3DES | SHA-1 |
| SSL_DH_anon_WITH_RC4_128_MD5 | DH_anon | RC4 | MD5 |
| SSL_DH_anon_WITH_DES_CBC_SHA | DH_anon | DES | SHA-1 |
| SSL_DH_anon_WITH_3DES_EDE_CBC_SHA | DH_anon | 3DES | SHA-1 |
| SSL_DHE_RSA_WITH_DES_CBC_SHA | DHE_RSA | DES | SHA-1 |
| SSL_DHE_RSA_WITH_3DES_EDE_CBC_SHA | DHE_RSA | 3DES | SHA-1 |
| SSL_DHE_DSS_WITH_DES_CBC_SHA | DHE_DSS | DES | SHA-1 |
| SSL_DHE_DSS_WITH_3DES_EDE_CBC_SHA | DHE_DSS | 3DES | SHA-1 |
| SSL_DH_RSA_WITH_DES_CBC_SHA | DH_RSA | DES | SHA-1 |
| SSL_DH_RSA_WITH_3DES_EDE_CBC_SHA | DH_RSA | 3DES | SHA-1 |
| SSL_DH_DSS_WITH_DES_CBC_SHA | DH_DSS | DES | SHA-1 |
| SSL_DH_DSS_WITH_3DES_EDE_CBC_SHA | DH_DSS | 3DES | SHA-1 |
| SSL_FORTEZZA_DMS_WITH_NULL_SHA | Fortezza | NULL | SHA-1 |
| SSL_FORTEZZA_DMS_WITH_FORTEZZA_CBC_SHA | Fortezza | Fortezza | SHA-1 |
| SSL_FORTEZZA_DMS_WITH_RC4_128_SHA | Fortezza | RC4 | SHA-1 |

are used for export. Note that not all combinations of key exchange, message integrity, and message authentication are in the list.

Each suite starts with the term "SSL" followed by the key exchange algorithm. The word "WITH" separates the key exchange algorithm from the encryption and hash algorithms. For example,

**SSL_DHE_RSA_WITH_DES_CBC_SHA**

defines DHE_RSA (ephemeral Diffie-Hellman with RSA digital signature) as the key exchange with DES_CBC as the encryption algorithm and SHA as the hash algorithm. Note that *DH* is fixed Diffie-Hellman, *DHE* is ephemeral Diffie-Hellman, and *DH-anon* is anonymous Diffie-Hellman.

### 17.1.6 Compression Algorithms

As we said before, compression is optional in SSLv3. No specific compression algorithm is defined for SSLv3. Therefore, the default compression method is NULL. However, a system can use whatever compression algorithm it desires.

### 17.1.7 Cryptographic Parameter Generation

To achieve message integrity and confidentiality, SSL needs six cryptographic secrets, four keys and two IVs. The client needs one key for message authentication (HMAC), one key for encryption, and one IV for block encryption. The server needs the same. SSL requires that the keys for one direction be different from those for the other direction. If there is an attack in one direction, the other direction is not affected. The parameters are generated using the following procedure:

1. The client and server exchange two random numbers; one is created by the client and the other by the server.
2. The client and server exchange one pre-master secret using one of the key-exchange algorithms we discussed previously.
3. A 48-byte **master secret** is created from the **pre-master secret** by applying two hash functions (SHA-1 and MD5), as shown in Fig. 17.8.

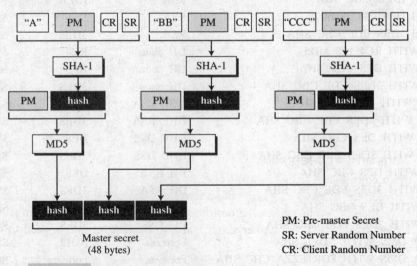

PM: Pre-master Secret
SR: Server Random Number
CR: Client Random Number

**Fig. 17.8** *Calculation of master secret from pre-master secret*

4. The master secret is used to create variable-length **key material** by applying the same set of hash functions and prepending with different constants as shown in Fig. 17.9.

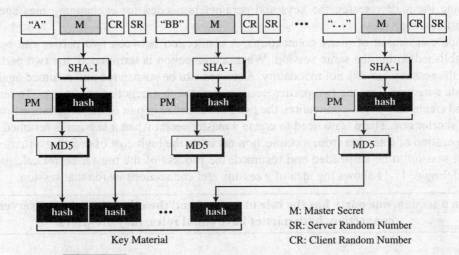

M: Master Secret
SR: Server Random Number
CR: Client Random Number

**Fig. 17.9** *Calculation of key material from master secret*

The module is repeated until key material of adequate size is created. Note that the length of the key material block depends on the cipher suite selected and the size of keys needed for this suite.

5. Six different keys are extracted from the key material, as shown in Fig. 17.10

Auth. Key: Authentication Key
Enc. Key: Encryption Key
IV: Initialization Vector

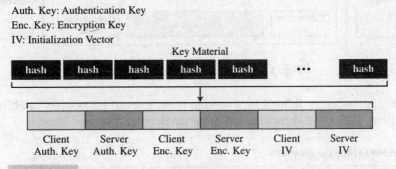

**Fig. 17.10** *Extractions of cryptographic secrets from key material*

## 17.1.8  Sessions and Connections

SSL differentiates a **connection** from a **session.** Let us elaborate on these two terms here. A session is an association between a client and a server. After a session is established, the two parties have common information such as the session identifier, the certificate authenticating each of them (if necessary), the compression method (if needed), the cipher suite, and a master secret that is used to create keys for message authentication encryption.

For two entities to exchange data, the establishment of a session is necessary, but not sufficient; they need to create a connection between themselves. The two entities exchange two random numbers and create, using the master secret, the keys and parameters needed for exchanging messages involving authentication and privacy.

A session can consist of many connections. A connection between two parties can be terminated and reestablished within the same session. When a connection is terminated, the two parties can also terminate the session, but it is not mandatory. A session can be suspended and resumed again.

To create a new session, the two parties need to go through a negotiation process. To resume an old session and create only a new connection, the two parties can skip part of the negotiation process and go through a shorter one. There is no need to create a master secret when a session is resumed.

The separation of a session from a connection prevents the high cost of creating a master secret. By allowing a session to be suspended and resumed, the process of the master secret calculation can be eliminated. Figure 17.11 shows the idea of a session and connections inside that session.

> **In a session, one party has the role of a client and the other the role of a server; in a connection, both parties have equal roles, they are peers.**

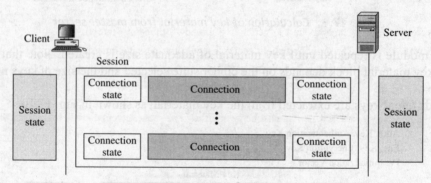

**Fig. 17.11**  *A session and connections*

***Session State***    A session is defined by a session state, a set of parameters established between the server and the client. Table 17.2 shows the list of parameters for a session state.

**Table 17.2**  *Session state parameters*

| Parameter | Description |
|---|---|
| Session ID | A server-chosen 8-bit number defining a session. |
| Peer Certificate | A certificate of type X509.v3. This parameter may by empty (null). |
| Compression Method | The compression method. |
| Cipher Suite | The agreed-upon cipher suite. |
| Master Secret | The 48-byte secret. |
| Is resumable | A yes-no flag that allows new connections in an old session. |

***Connection State***    A connection is defined by a connection state, a set of parameters established between two peers. Table 17.3 shows the list of parameters for a connection state.

SSL uses two attributes to distinguish cryptographic secrets: *write* and *read*. The term *write* specifies the key used for signing or encrypting outbound messages. The term *read* specifies the key used for verifying or decrypting inbound messages. Note that the *write* key of the client is the same as the *read* key of the server; the *read* key of the client is the same as the *write* key of the server.

---

**The client and the server have six different cryptography secrets: three *read* secrets and three *write* secrets.**
**The *read* secrets for the client are the same as the write secrets for the server and vice versa.**

---

**Table 17.3**  *Connection state parameters*

| Parameter | Description |
|---|---|
| Server and client random numbers | A sequence of bytes chosen by the server and client for each connection. |
| Server write MAC secret | The outbound server MAC key for message integrity. The server uses it to sign; the client uses it to verify. |
| Client write MAC secret | The outbound client MAC key for message integrity. The client uses it to sign; the server uses it to verify. |
| Server write secret | The outbound server encryption key for message integrity. |
| Client write secret | The outbound client encryption key for message integrity. |
| Initialization vectors | The block ciphers in CBC mode use initialization vectors (IVs). One initialization vector is defined for each cipher key during the negotiation, which is used for the first block exchange. The final cipher text from a block is used as the IV for the next block. |
| Sequence numbers | Each party has a sequence number. The sequence number starts from 0 and increments. It must not exceed $2^{64} - 1$. |

# 17.2            FOUR PROTOCOLS

We have discussed the idea of SSL without showing how SSL accomplishes its tasks. SSL defines four protocols in two layers, as shown in Fig. 17.12. The Record Protocol is the carrier. It carries messages from three other protocols as well as the data coming from the application layer. Messages from the

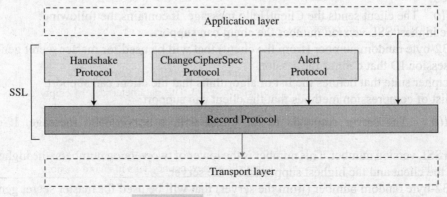

**Fig. 17.12** *Four SSL protocols*

Record Protocol are payloads to the transport layer, normally TCP. The Handshake Protocol provides security parameters for the Record Protocol. It establishes a cipher set and provides keys and security parameters. It also authenticates the server to the client and the client to the server if needed. The ChangeCipherSpec Protocol is used for signalling the readiness of cryptographic secrets. The Alert Protocol is used to report abnormal conditions. We will briefly discuss these protocols in this section.

### 17.2.1 Handshake Protocol

The **Handshake Protocol** uses messages to negotiate the cipher suite, to authenticate the server to the client and the client to the server if needed, and to exchange information for building the cryptographic secrets. The handshaking is done in four phases, as shown in Fig. 17.13.

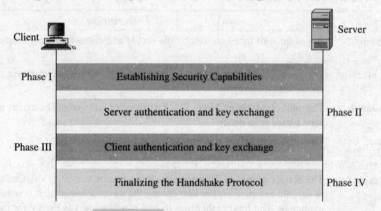

**Fig. 17.13**  *Handshake Protocol*

### *Phase I: Establishing Security Capability*

In Phase I, the client and the server announce their security capabilities and choose those that are convenient for both. In this phase, a session ID is established and the cipher suite is chosen. The parties agree upon a particular compression method. Finally, two random numbers are selected, one by the client and one by the server, to be used for creating a master secret as we saw before. Two messages are exchanged in this phase: ClientHello and ServerHello messages. Figure 17.14 gives additional details about Phase I.

*ClientHello*   The client sends the ClientHello message. It contains the following:
  a.   The highest SSL version number the client can support.
  b.   A 32-byte random number (from the client) that will be used for master secret generation.
  c.   A session ID that defines the session.
  d.   A cipher suite that defines the list of algorithms that the client can support.
  e.   A list of compression methods that the client can support.

*ServerHello*   The server responds to the client with a ServerHello message. It contains the following:
  a.   An SSL version number. This number is the lower of two version numbers: the highest supported by the client and the highest supported by the server.
  b.   A 32-byte random number (from the server) that will be used for master secret generation.

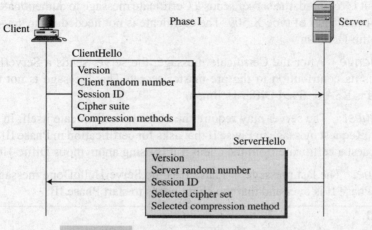

**Fig. 17.14** *Phase I of Handshake Protocol*

c. A session ID that defines the session.
d. The selected cipher set from the client list.
e. The selected compression method from the client list.

**After Phase I, the client and server know the following:**
❑ *The version of SSL*
❑ *The algorithms for key exchange, message authentication, and encryption*
❑ *The compression method*
❑ *The two random numbers for key generation*

## Phase II: Server Key Exchange and Authentication

In phase II, the server authenticates itself if needed. The sender may send its certificate, its public key, and may also request certificates from the client. At the end, the server announces that the serverHello process is done. Figure 17.15 gives additional details about Phase II.

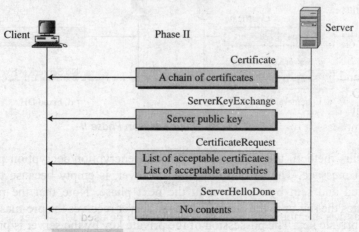

**Fig. 17.15** *Phase II of Handshake Protocol*

*Certificate* If it is required, the server sends a Certificate message to authenticate itself. The message includes a list of certificates of type X.509. The certificate is not needed if the key-exchange algorithm is anonymous Diffie-Hellman.

*ServerKeyExchange* After the Certificate message, the server sends a ServerKey-Exchange message that includes its contribution to the pre-master secret. This message is not required if the key-exchange method is RSA or fixed Diffie-Hellman.

*CertificateRequest* The server may require the client to authenticate itself. In this case, the server sends a CertificateRequest message in Phase II that asks for certification in Phase III from the client. The server cannot request a certificate from the client if it is using anonymous Diffie-Hellman.

*ServerHelloDone* The last message in Phase II is the ServerHelloDone message, which is a signal to the client that Phase II is over and that the client needs to start Phase III.

---

**After Phase II,**
- ❏ *The server is authenticated to the client.*
- ❏ *The client knows the public key of the server if required.*

---

Let us elaborate on the server authentication and the key exchange in this phase. The first two messages in this phase are based on the key-exchange method. Figure 17.16 shows four of six methods we discussed before. We have not included the NULL method because there is no exchange. We have not included the Fortezza method because we do not discuss it in depth in this book.

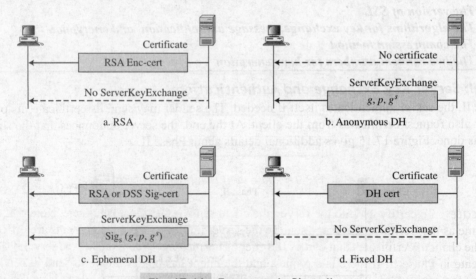

**Fig. 17.16** *Four cases in Phase II*

- ❏ **RSA.** In this method, the server sends its RSA encryption/decryption public-key certificate in the first message. The second message, however, is empty because the pre-master secret is generated and sent by the client in the next phase. Note that the public-key certificate authenticates the server to the client. When the server receives the pre-master secret, it decrypts it with its private key. The possession of the private key by the server is proof that the server is the entity that it claims to be in the public-key certificate sent in the first message.

❏ **Anonymous DH.** In this method, there is no Certificate message. An anonymous entity does not have a certificate. In the ServerKeyExchange message, the server sends the Diffie-Hellman parameters and its half-key. Note that the server is not authenticated in this method.

❏ **Ephemeral DH.** In this method, the server sends either an RSA or a DSS digital signature certificate. The private key associated with the certificate allows the server to sign a message; the public key allows the recipient to verify the signature. In the second message, the server sends the Diffie-Hellman parameters and the half-key signed by its private key. Other text is also sent. The server is authenticated to the client in this method, not because it sends the certificate, but because it signs the parameters and keys with its private key. The possession of the private key is proof that the server is the entity that it claims to be in the certificate. If an impostor copies and sends the certificate to the client, pretending that it is the server claimed in the certificate, it cannot sign the second message because it does not have the private key.

❏ **Fixed DH.** In this method, the server sends an RSA or DSS digital signature certificate that includes its registered DH half-key. The second message is empty. The certificate is signed by the CA's private key and can be verified by the client using the CA's public key. In other words, the CA is authenticated to the client and the CA claims that the half-key belongs to the server.

**Phase III: Client Key Exchange and Authentication** Phase III is designed to authenticate the client. Up to three messages can be sent from the client to the server, as shown in Fig. 17.17.

**Fig. 17.17** *Phase III of Handshake Protocol*

*Certificate* To certify itself to the server, the client sends a Certificate message. Note that the format is the same as the Certificate message sent by the server in Phase II, but the contents are different. It includes the chain of certificates that certify the client. This message is sent only if the server has requested a certificate in Phase II. If there is a request and the client has no certificate to send, it sends an Alert message (part of the Alert Protocol to be discussed later) with a warning that there is no certificate. The server may continue with the session or may decide to abort.

*ClientKeyExchange* After sending the Certificate message, the client sends a ClientKeyExchange message, which includes its contribution to the pre-master secret. The contents of this message are based on the key-exchange algorithm used. If the method is RSA, the client creates the entire pre-master secret and encrypts it with the RSA public key of the server. If the method is anonymous or ephemeral Diffie-Hellman, the client sends its Diffie-Hellman half-key. If the method is Fortezza, the client sends the Fortezza parameters. The contents of this message are empty if the method is fixed Diffie-Hellman.

*CertificateVerify*   If the client has sent a certificate declaring that it owns the public key in the certificate, it needs to prove that it knows the corresponding private key. This is needed to thwart an impostor who sends the certificate and claims that it comes from the client. The proof of private-key possession is done by creating a message and signing it with the private key. The server can verify the message with the public key already sent to ensure that the certificate actually belongs to the client. Note that this is possible if the certificate has a signing capability; a pair of keys, public and private, is involved. The certificate for fixed Diffie-Hellman cannot be verified this way.

---

**After Phase III,**
- ❏ *The client is authenticated for the server.*
- ❏ *Both the client and the server know the pre-master secret.*

---

Let us elaborate on the client authentication and the key exchange in this phase. The three messages in this phase are based on the key-exchange method. Figure 17.18 shows four of the six methods we discussed before. Again, we have not included the NULL method or the Fortezza method.

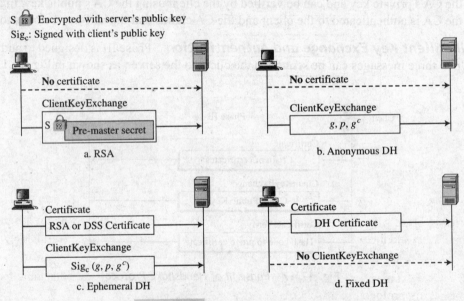

**Fig. 17.18**   *Four cases in Phase III*

- ❏ **RSA.** In this case, there is no Certificate message unless the server has explicitly requested one in Phase II. The ClientKeyExchange method includes the pre-master key encrypted with the RSA public key received in Phase II.
- ❏ **Anonymous DH.** In this method, there is no Certificate message. The server does not have the right to ask for the certificate (in Phase II) because both the client and the server are anonymous. In the ClientKeyExchange message, the server sends the Diffie-Hellman parameters and its half-key. Note that the client is not authenticated to the server in this method.
- ❏ **Ephemeral DH.** In this method, the client usually has a certificate. The server needs to send its RSA or DSS certificate (based on the agreed-upon cipher set). In the ClientKeyExchange message, the client signs the DH parameters and its half-key and sends them. The client is

authenticated to the server by signing the second message. If the client does not have the certificate, and the server asks for it, the client sends an Alert message to warn the client. If this is acceptable to the server, the client sends the DH parameters and key in plaintext. Of course, the client is not authenticated to the server in this situation.

❑ **Fixed DH.** In this method, the client usually sends a DH certificate in the first message. Note that the second message is empty in this method. The client is authenticated to the server by sending the DH certificate.

## Phase IV: Finalizing and Finishing

In Phase IV, the client and server send messages to change cipher specification and to finish the handshaking protocol. Four messages are exchanged in this phase, as shown in Fig. 17.19.

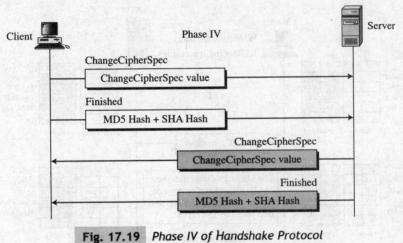

**Fig. 17.19** *Phase IV of Handshake Protocol*

*ChangeCipherSpec*  The client sends a ChangeCipherSpec message to show that it has moved all of the cipher suite set and the parameters from the pending state to the active state. This message is actually part of the ChangeCipherSpec Protocol that we will discuss later.

*Finished*  The next message is also sent by the client. It is a Finished message that announces the end of the handshaking protocol by the client.

*ChangeCipherSpec*  The server sends a ChangeCipherSpec message to show that it has also moved all of the cipher suite set and parameters from the pending state to the active state. This message is part of the ChangeCipherSpec Protocol, which will be discussed later.

---

**After Phase IV, the client and server are ready to exchange data.**

---

*Finished*  Finally, the server sends a Finished message to show that handshaking is totally completed.

## 17.2.2  ChangeCipherSpec Protocol

We have seen that the negotiation of the cipher suite and the generation of cryptographic secrets are formed gradually during the Handshake Protocol. The question now is: When can the two parties use these parameter secrets? SSL mandates that the parties cannot use these parameters or secrets until they have sent or received a special message, the ChangeCipherSpec message, which is exchanged during the Handshake protocol and defined in the ChangeCipherSpec Protocol. The reason is that the issue is not just sending or receiving a message. The sender and the receiver need two states, not one. One state, the pending state, keeps track of the parameters and secrets. The other state, the active state, holds parameters and secrets used by the Record Protocol to sign/verify or encrypt/decrypt messages. In addition, each state holds two sets of values: *read* (inbound) and *write* (outbound).

The ChangeCipherSpec Protocol defines the process of moving values between the pending and active states. Figure 17.20 shows a hypothetical situation, with hypothetical values, to show the concept. Only a few parameters are shown. Before the exchange of any ChangeCipherSpec messages, only the pending columns have values.

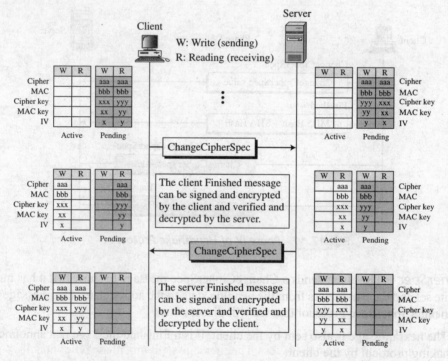

**Fig. 17.20** *Movement of parameters from pending state to active state*

First the client sends a ChangeCipherSpec message. After the client sends this message, it moves the write (outbound) parameters from pending to active. The client can now use these parameters to sign or encrypt outbound messages. After the receiver receives this message, it moves the read (inbound) parameters from the pending to the active state. Now the server can verify and decrypt messages. This means that the Finished message sent by the client can be signed and encrypted by the client and verified and decrypted by the server.

The server sends the ChangeCipherSpec message after receiving the Finish message from the client. After sending this message it moves the write (outbound) parameters from pending to active. The server can now use these parameters to sign or encrypt outbound messages. After the client receives this message, it moves the read (inbound) parameters from the pending to the active state. Now the client can verify and decrypt messages.

Of course, after the exchanged Finished messages, both parties can communicate in both directions using the read/write active parameters.

### 17.2.3 Alert Protocol

SSL uses the **Alert Protocol** for reporting errors and abnormal conditions. It has only one message type, the Alert message, that describes the problem and its level (warning or fatal). Table 17.4 shows the types of Alert messages defined for SSL.

**Table 17.4** *Alerts defined for SSL*

| Value | Description | Meaning |
|-------|-------------|---------|
| 0 | *CloseNotify* | Sender will not send any more messages. |
| 10 | *UnexpectedMessage* | An inappropriate message received. |
| 20 | *BadRecordMAC* | An incorrect MAC received. |
| 30 | *DecompressionFailure* | Unable to decompress appropriately. |
| 40 | *HandshakeFailure* | Sender unable to finalize the handshake. |
| 41 | *NoCertificate* | Client has no certificate to send. |
| 42 | *BadCertificate* | Received certificate corrupted. |
| 43 | *UnsupportedCertificate* | Type of received certificate is not supported. |
| 44 | *CertificateRevoked* | Signer has revoked the certificate. |
| 45 | *CertificateExpired* | Certificate expired. |
| 46 | *CertificateUnknown* | Certificate unknown. |
| 47 | *IllegalParameter* | An out-of-range or inconsistent field. |

### 17.2.4 Record Protocol

The **Record Protocol** carries messages from the upper layer (Handshake Protocol, ChangeCipherSpec Protocol, Alert Protocol, or application layer). The message is fragmented and optionally compressed; a MAC is added to the compressed message using the negotiated hash algorithm. The compressed fragment and the MAC are encrypted using the negotiated encryption algorithm. Finally, the SSL header is added to the encrypted message. Figure 17.21 shows this process at the sender. The process at the receiver is reversed.

Note, however, that this process can only be done when the cryptographic parameters are in the active state. Messages sent before the movement from pending to active are neither signed nor encrypted. However, in the next sections, we will see some messages in the Handshake Protocol that use some defined hash values for message integrity.

***Fragmentation/Combination***   At the sender, a message from the application layer is fragmented into blocks of $2^{14}$ bytes, with the last block possibly less than this size. At the receiver, the fragments are combined together to make a replica of the original message.

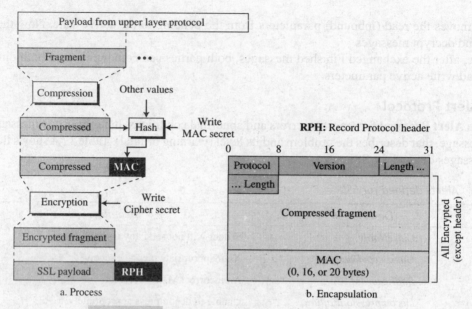

**Fig. 17.21** *Processing done by the Record Protocol*

***Compression/Decompression*** At the sender, all application layer fragments are compressed by the compression method negotiated during the handshaking. The compression method needs to be lossless (the decompressed fragment must be an exact replica of the original fragment). The size of the fragment must not exceed 1024 bytes. Some compression methods work only on a predefined block size and if the size of the block is less than this, some padding is added. Therefore, the size of the compressed fragment may be greater than the size of the original fragment. At the receiver, the compressed fragment is decompressed to create a replica of the original. If the size of the decompressed fragment exceeds $2^{14}$, a fatal decompression Alert message is issued. Note that compression/decompression is optional in SSL.

***Signing/Verifying*** At the sender, the authentication method defined during the handshake (NULL, MD5, or SHA-1) creates a signature (MAC), as shown in Fig. 17.22.

The hash algorithm is applied twice. First, a hash is created from the concatenations of the following values:

a. The MAC write secret (authentication key for the outbound message)
b. Pad-1, which is the byte 0x36 repeated 48 times for MD5 and 40 times for SHA-1
c. The sequence number for this message
d. The compressed type, which defines the upper-layer protocol that provided the compressed fragment
e. The compressed length, which is the length of the compressed fragment
f. The compressed fragment itself

Second, the final hash (MAC) is created from the concatenation of the following values:

a. The MAC write secret
b. Pad-2, which is the byte 0x5C repeated 48 times for MD5 and 40 times for SHA-1
c. The hash created from the first step

At the receiver, the verifying is done by calculating a new hash and comparing it to the received hash.

Pad-1: Byte 0x36 (00110110) repeated 48 times for MD5 and 40 times for SHA-1
Pad-2: Byte 0x5C (01011100) repeated 48 times for MD5 and 40 times for SHA-1

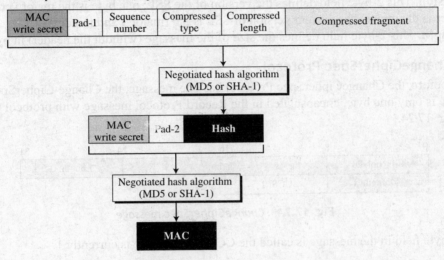

**Fig. 17.22** *Calculation of MAC*

***Encryption/Decryption*** At the sender, the compressed fragment and the hash are encrypted using the cipher write secret. At the receiver, the received message is decrypted using the cipher read secret. For block encryption, padding is added to make the size of the encryptable message a multiple of the block size.

***Framing/Deframing*** After the encryption, the Record Protocol header is added at the sender. The header is removed at the receiver before decryption.

## 17.3    SSL MESSAGE FORMATS

As we have discussed, messages from three protocols and data from the application layer are encapsulated in the Record Protocol messages. In other words, the Record Protocol message encapsulates messages from four different sources at the sender site. At the receiver site, the Record Protocol decapsulates the messages and delivers them to different destinations. The Record Protocol has a general header that is added to each message coming from the sources, as shown in Fig. 17.23.

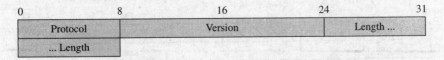

**Fig. 17.23** *Record Protocol general header*

The fields in this header are listed below.

- ❏ **Protocol.** This 1-byte field defines the source or destination of the encapsulated message. It is used for multiplexing and demultiplexing. The values are 20 (ChangeCipherSpec Protocol), 21 (Alert Protocol), 22 (Handshake Protocol), and 23 (data from the application layer).
- ❏ **Version.** This 2-byte field defines the version of the SSL; one byte is the major version and the other is the minor. The current version of SSL is 3.0 (major 3 and minor 0).
- ❏ **Length.** This 2-byte field defines the size of the message (without the header) in bytes.

### 17.3.1 ChangeCipherSpec Protocol

As we said before, the ChangeCipherSpec Protocol has one message, the Change-CipherSpec message. The message is only one byte, encapsulated in the Record Protocol message with protocol value 20, as shown in Fig. 17.24.

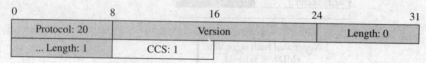

**Fig. 17.24** *ChangeCipherSpec message*

The one-byte field in the message is called the CCS and its value is currently 1.

### 17.3.2 Alert Protocol

The Alert Protocol, as we discussed before, has one message that reports errors in the process. Figure 17.25 shows the encapsulation of this single message in the Record Protocol with protocol value 21.

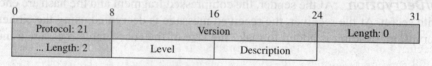

**Fig. 17.25** *Alert message*

The two fields of the Alert message are listed below.

- ❏ **Level.** This one-byte field defines the level of the error. Two levels have been defined so far: warning and fatal.
- ❏ **Description.** The one-byte description defines the type of error.

### 17.3.3 Handshake Protocol

Several messages have been defined for the Handshake Protocol. All of these messages have the four-byte generic header shown in Fig. 17.26. The figure shows the Record Protocol header and the generic header for the Handshake Protocol. Note that the value of the protocol field is 22.

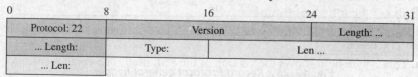

**Fig. 17.26** *Generic header for Handshake Protocol*

❑ **Type.** This one-byte field defines the type of message. So far ten types have been defined as listed in Table 17.5.

**Table 17.5** *Types of Handshake messages*

| Type | Message |
|------|---------|
| 0 | HelloRequest |
| 1 | ClientHello |
| 2 | ServerHello |
| 11 | Certificate |
| 12 | ServerKeyExchange |
| 13 | CertificateRequest |
| 14 | ServerHelloDone |
| 15 | CertificateVerify |
| 16 | ClientKeyExchange |
| 20 | Finished |

❑ **Length (Len).** This three-byte field defines the length of the message (excluding the length of the type and length field). The reader may wonder why we need two length fields, one in the general Record header and one in the generic header for the Handshake messages. The answer is that a Record message may carry two Handshake messages at the same time if there is no need for another message in between.

***HelloRequest Message*** The HelloRequest message, which is rarely used, is a request from the server to the client to restart a session. This may be needed if the server feels that something is wrong with the session and a fresh session is needed. For example, if the session becomes so long that it threatens the security of the session, the server may send this message. The client then needs to send a ClientHello message and negotiate the security parameters. Figure 17.27 shows the format of this message. It is four bytes with a type value of 0. The message has no body, so the value of the length field is also 0.

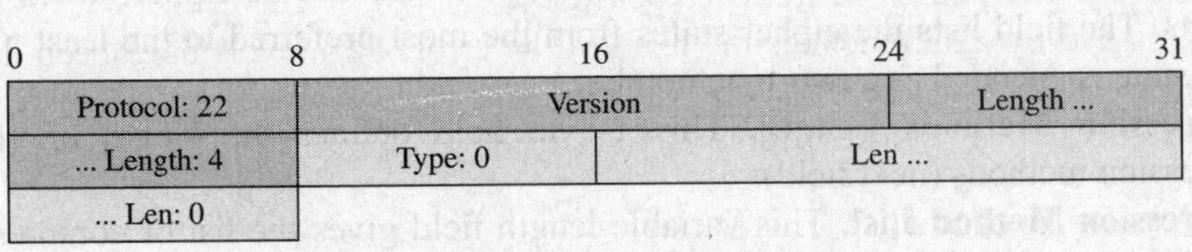

**Fig. 17.27** *HelloRequest message*

***ClientHello Message*** The ClientHello message is the first message exchanged during handshaking. Figure 17.28 shows the format of the message.

The type and length fields are as discussed previously. The following is a brief description of the other fields.

❑ **Version.** This 2-byte field shows the version of the SSL used. The version is 3.0 for SSL and 3.1 for TLS. Note that the version value, for example, 3.0, is stored in two bytes: 3 in the first byte and 0 in the second.

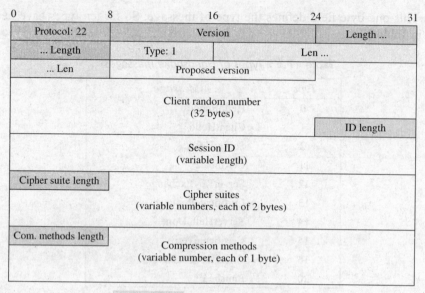

**Fig. 17.28** *ClientHello message*

❑ **Client Random Number.** This 32-byte field is used by the client to send the client random number, which creates security parameters.

❑ **Session ID Length.** This 1-byte field defines the length of the session ID (next field). If there is no session ID, the value of this field is 0.

❑ **Session ID.** The value of this variable-length field is 0 when the client starts a new session. The session ID is initiated by the server. However, if a client wants to resume a previously stopped session, it can include the previously-defined session ID in this field. The protocol defines a maximum of 32 bytes for the session ID.

❑ **Cipher Suite Length.** This 2-byte field defines the length of the client-proposed cipher suite list (next field).

❑ **Cipher Suite List.** This variable-length field gives the list of cipher suites that the client supports. The field lists the cipher suites from the most preferred to the least preferred. Each cipher suite is encoded as a two-byte number.

❑ **Compression Methods Length.** This 1-byte field defines the length of client-proposed compression methods (next field).

❑ **Compression Method List.** This variable-length field gives the list of compression methods that the client supports. The field lists the methods from the most preferred to the least preferred. Each method is encoded as a one-byte number. So far, the only method is the *NULL* method (no compression). In this case, the value of the compression method length is 1 and the compression method list has only one element with the value of 0.

**ServerHello Message**  The ServerHello message is the server response to the ClientHello message. The format is similar to the ClientHello message, but with fewer fields. Figure 17.29 shows the format of the message.

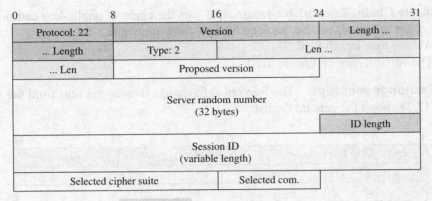

**Fig. 17.29** *ServerHello message*

The version field is the same. The server random number field defines a value selected by the server. The session ID length and the session ID field are the same as those in the ClientHello message. However, the session ID is usually blank (and the length is usually set to 0) unless the server is resuming an old session. In other words, if the server allows a session to resume, it inserts a value in the session ID field to be used by the client (in the ClientHello message) if the client wishes to reopen an old session.

The selected cipher suite field defines the single cipher suite selected by the server from the list sent by the client. The compression method field defines the method selected by the server from the list sent by the client.

**Certificate Message** The Certificate message can be sent by the client or the server to list the chain of public-key certificates. Figure 17.30 shows the format.

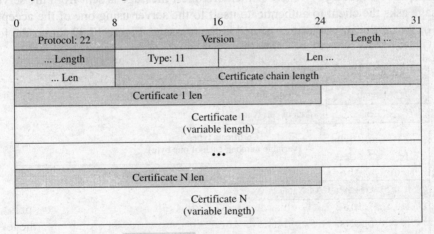

**Fig. 17.30** *Certificate message*

The value of the type field is 11. The body of the message includes the following fields:

❑ **Certificate Chain Length.** This three-byte field shows the length of the certificate chain. This field is redundant because its value is always 3 less than the value of the length field.

❑ **Certificate Chain.** This variable-length field lists the chain of public-key certificates that the client or the server carries. For each certificate, there are two sub-fields:

a. A three-byte length field

b. The variable-size certificate itself

***ServerKeyExchange Message*** The ServerKeyExchange message is sent from the server to the client. Figure 17.31 shows the general format.

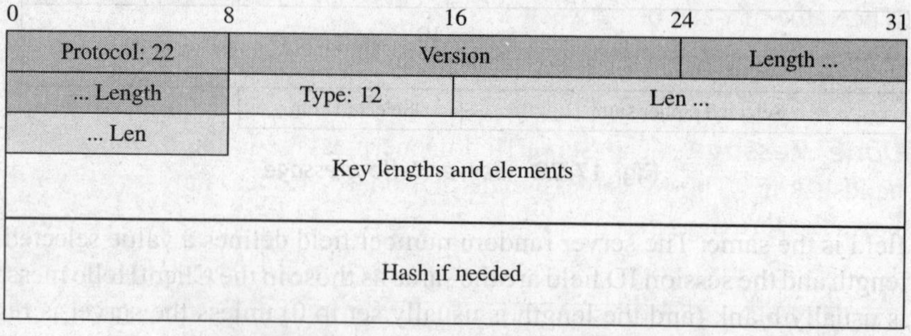

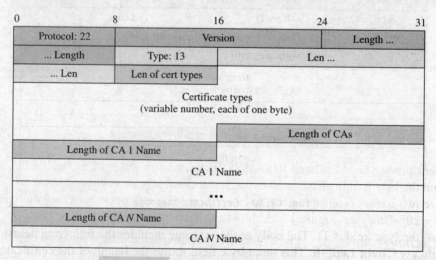

**Fig. 17.31** *ServerKeyExchange message*

The message contains the keys generated by the server. The format of the message is dependent on the cipher suite selected in the previous message. The client that receives the message needs to interpret the message according to the previous information. If the server has sent a certificate message, then the message also contains a signed parameter.

***CertificateRequest Message*** The CertificateRequest message is sent from the server to the client. The message asks the client to authenticate itself to the server using one of the acceptable certificates and one of the certificate authorities named in the message. Figure 17.32 shows the format.

**Fig. 17.32** *CertificateRequest message*

The value of the type field is 13. The body of the message includes the following fields:

❏ **Len of Cert Types.** This one-byte field shows the length of the certificate types.
❏ **Certificates Types.** This variable-length field gives the list of the public-key certificate types that the server accepts. Each type is one byte.
❏ **Length of CAs.** This two-byte field gives the length of the certificate authorities (the rest of the packet).
❏ **Length of CA $x$ Name.** This two-byte field defines the length of the $x$th certificate authority name. The value of $x$ can be between 1 to $N$.
❏ **CA $x$ Name.** This variable-length field defines the name of the $x$th certificate authority. The value of $x$ can be between 1 to $N$.

**ServerHelloDone Message** The ServerHelloDone message is the last message sent in the second phase of handshaking. The message signals that phase II does not carry any extra information. Figure 17.33 shows the format.

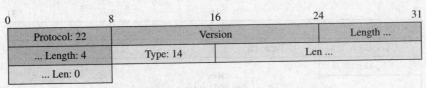

**Fig. 17.33** *ServerHelloDone message*

**CertificateVerify Message** The CertificateVerify message is the last message of Phase III. In this message, the client proves that it actually owns the private key related to its public-key certificate. To do so, the client creates a hash of all handshake messages sent before this message, and signs them using the MD5 or SHA-1 algorithm based on the certificate type of the client. Figure 17.34 shows the format.

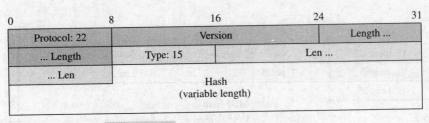

**Fig. 17.34** *CertificateVerify message*

If the client private key is related to a DSS certificate, then the hash is based only on the SHA-1 algorithm and the length of the hash is 20 bytes. If the client private key is related to an RSA certificate, then there are two hashes (concatenated), one based on MD5 and the other based on SHA-1. The total length is $16 + 20 = 36$ bytes. Figure 17.35 shows the hash calculation.

**ClientKeyExchange Message** The ClientKeyExchange is the second message sent during the third phase of handshaking. In this message, the client provides the keys. The format of the message depends on the specific key exchange algorithms selected by two parties. Figure 17.36 shows the general idea.

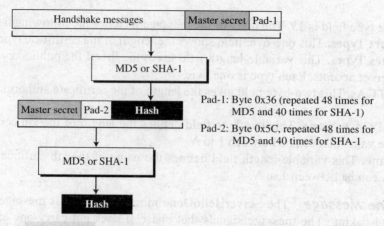

**Fig. 17.35**  *Hash calculation for CertificateVerify message*

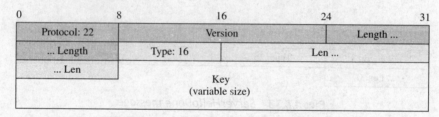

**Fig. 17.36**  *ClientKeyExchange message*

***Finished Message***  The Finished message shows that the negotiation is over. It contains all of the messages exchanged during handshaking, followed by the sender role, the master secret, and the padding. The exact format depends on the type of cipher suite used. The general format is shown in Fig. 17.37.

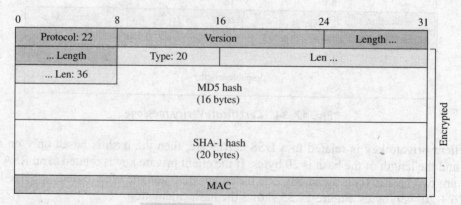

**Fig. 17.37**  *Finished message*

Figure 17.37 shows that there is a concatenation of two hashes in the message. Figure 17.38 shows how each is calculated.

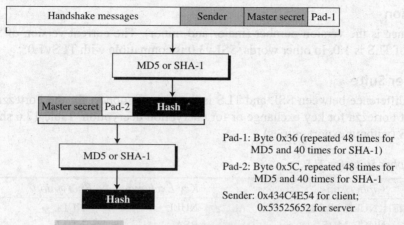

Pad-1: Byte 0x36 (repeated 48 times for MD5 and 40 times for SHA-1)

Pad-2: Byte 0x5C, repeated 48 times for MD5 and 40 times for SHA-1

Sender: 0x434C4E54 for client; 0x53525652 for server

**Fig. 17.38** *Hash calculation for Finished message*

Note that when the client or server sends the Finished message, it has already sent the ChangeCipherSpec message. In other words, the write cryptographic secrets are in the active state. The client or the server can treat the Finished message like a data fragment coming from the application layer. The Finished message can be authenticated (using the MAC in the cipher suite) and encrypted (using the encryption algorithm in the cipher suite).

### 17.3.4 Application Data

The Record Protocol adds a signature (MAC) at the end of the (possibly compressed) fragment coming from the application layer and then encrypts the fragment and the MAC. After adding the general header with protocol value 23, the Record message is transmitted. Note that the general header is not encrypted. Figure 17.39 shows the format.

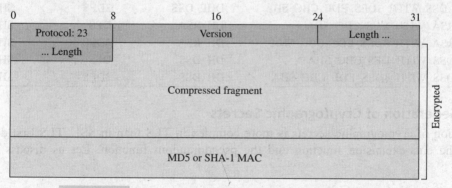

**Fig. 17.39** *Record Protocol message for application data*

## 17.4                TRANSPORT LAYER SECURITY

The Transport Layer Security (TLS) protocol is the IETF standard version of the SSL protocol. The two are very similar, with slight differences. Instead of describing TLS in full, we highlight the differences between TLS and SSL protocols in this section.

### 17.4.1 Version

The first difference is the version number (major and minor). The current version of SSL is 3.0; the current version of TLS is 1.0. In other words, SSLv3.0 is compatible with TLSv1.0.

### 17.4.2 Cipher Suite

Another minor difference between SSL and TLS is the lack of support for the Fortezza method. TLS does not support Fortezza for key exchange or for encryption/decryption. Table 17.6 shows the cipher suite list for TLS (without export entries).

**Table 17.6** *Cipher Suite for TLS*

| Cipher suite | Key Exchange | Encryption | Hash |
|---|---|---|---|
| TLS_NULL_WITH_NULL_NULL | NULL | NULL | NULL |
| TLS_RSA_WITH_NULL_MD5 | RSA | NULL | MD5 |
| TLS_RSA_WITH_NULL_SHA | RSA | NULL | SHA-1 |
| TLS_RSA_WITH_RC4_128_MD5 | RSA | RC4 | MD5 |
| TLS_RSA_WITH_RC4_128_SHA | RSA | RC4 | SHA-1 |
| TLS_RSA_WITH_IDEA_CBC_SHA | RSA | IDEA | SHA-1 |
| TLS_RSA_WITH_DES_CBC_SHA | RSA | DES | SHA-1 |
| TLS_RSA_WITH_3DES_EDE_CBC_SHA | RSA | 3DES | SHA-1 |
| TLS_DH_anon_WITH_RC4_128_MD5 | DH_anon | RC4 | MD5 |
| TLS_DH_anon_WITH_DES_CBC_SHA | DH_anon | DES | SHA-1 |
| TLS_DH_anon_WITH_3DES_EDE_CBC_SHA | DH_anon | 3DES | SHA-1 |
| TLS_DHE_RSA_WITH_DES_CBC_SHA | DHE_RSA | DES | SHA-1 |
| TLS_DHE_RSA_WITH_3DES_EDE_CBC_SHA | DHE_RSA | 3DES | SHA-1 |
| TLS_DHE_DSS_WITH_DES_CBC_SHA | DHE_DSS | DES | SHA-1 |
| TLS_DHE_DSS_WITH_3DES_EDE_CBC_SHA | DHE_DSS | 3DES | SHA-1 |
| TLS_DH_RSA_WITH_DES_CBC_SHA | DH_RSA | DES | SHA-1 |
| TLS_DH_RSA_WITH_3DES_EDE_CBC_SHA | DH_RSA | 3DES | SHA-1 |
| TLS_DH_DSS_WITH_DES_CBC_SHA | DH_DSS | DES | SHA-1 |
| TLS_DH_DSS_WITH_3DES_EDE_CBC_SHA | DH_DSS | 3DES | SHA-1 |

### 17.4.3 Generation of Cryptographic Secrets

The generation of cryptographic secrets is more complex in TLS than in SSL. TLS first defines two functions: the data-expansion function and the pseudorandom function. Let us discuss these two functions.

***Data-Expansion Function*** The **data-expansion function** uses a predefined HMAC (either MD5 or SHA-1) to expand a secret into a longer one. This function can be considered a multiple-section function, where each section creates one hash value. The extended secret is the concatenation of the hash values. Each section uses two HMACs, a secret and a seed. The data-expansion function is the chaining of as many sections as required. However, to make the next section dependent on the previous, the second seed is actually the output of the first HMAC of the previous section as shown in Fig. 17.40.

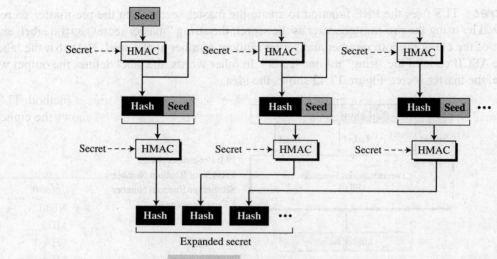

**Fig. 17.40** *Data-expansion function*

## 17.4.4 Pseudorandom Function (PRF)

TLS defines a **pseudorandom function** (**PRF**) to be the combination of two data-expansion functions, one using MD5 and the other SHA-1. PRF takes three inputs, a secret, a label, and a seed. The label and seed are concatenated and serve as the seed for each data-expansion function. The secret is divided into two halves; each half is used as the secret for each data-expansion function. The output of two data-expansion functions is exclusive-ored together to create the final expanded secret. Note that because the hashes created from MD5 and SHA-1 are of different sizes, extra sections of MD5-based functions must be created to make the two outputs the same size. Figure 17.41 shows the idea of PRF.

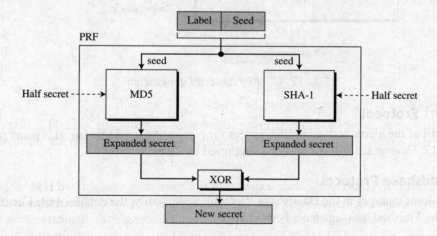

**Fig. 17.41** *PRF*

***Pre-master Secret*** The generation of the pre-master secret in TLS is exactly the same as in SSL.

***Master Secret*** TLS uses the PRF function to create the master secret from the pre-master secret. This is achieved by using the pre-master secret as the secret, the string "master secret" as the label, and concatenation of the client random number and server random number as the seed. Note that the label is actually the ASCII code of the string "master secret". In other words, the label defines the output we want to create, the master secret. Figure 17.42 shows the idea.

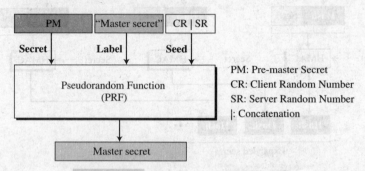

**Fig. 17.42** *Master secret generation*

***Key Material*** TLS uses the PRF function to create the key material from the master secret. This time the secret is the master secret, the label is the string "key expansion", and the seed is the concatenation of the server random number and the client random number, as shown in Fig. 17.43.

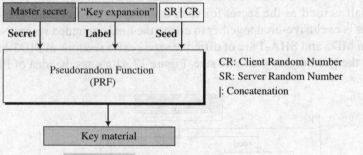

**Fig. 17.43** *Key material generation*

### 17.4.5 Alert Protocol

TLS supports all of the alerts defined in SSL except for *NoCertificate*. TLS also adds some new ones to the list. Table 17.7 shows the full list of alerts supported by TLS.

### 17.4.6 Handshake Protocol

TLS has made some changes in the Handshake Protocol. Specifically, the details of the CertificateVerify message and the Finished message have been changed.

***CertificateVerify Message*** In SSL, the hash used in the CertificateVerify message is the two-step hash of the handshake messages plus a pad and the master secret. TLS has simplified the process. The hash in the TLS is only over the handshake messages, as shown in Fig. 17.44.

**Table 17.7**  *Alerts defined for TLS*

| Value | Description | Meaning |
|---|---|---|
| 0 | *CloseNotify* | Sender will not send any more messages. |
| 10 | *UnexpectedMessage* | An inappropriate message received. |
| 20 | *BadRecordMAC* | An incorrect MAC received. |
| 21 | *DecryptionFailed* | Decrypted message is invalid. |
| 22 | *RecordOverflow* | Message size is more than $2^{14} + 2048$. |
| 30 | *DecompressionFailure* | Unable to decompress appropriately. |
| 40 | *HandshakeFailure* | Sender unable to finalize the handshake. |
| 42 | *BadCertificate* | Received certificate corrupted. |
| 43 | *UnsupportedCertificate* | Type of received certificate is not supported. |
| 44 | *CertificateRevoked* | Signer has revoked the certificate. |
| 45 | *CertificateExpired* | Certificate has expired. |
| 46 | *CertificateUnknown* | Certificate unknown. |
| 47 | *IllegalParameter* | A field out of range or inconsistent with others. |
| 48 | *UnknownCA* | CA could not be identified. |
| 49 | *AccessDenied* | No desire to continue with negotiation. |
| 50 | *DecodeError* | Received message could not be decoded. |
| 51 | *DecryptError* | Decrypted ciphertext is invalid. |
| 60 | *ExportRestriction* | Problem with U.S. restriction compliance. |
| 70 | *ProtocolVersion* | The protocol version is not supported. |
| 71 | *InsufficientSecurity* | More secure cipher suite needed. |
| 80 | *InternalError* | Local error. |
| 90 | *UserCanceled* | The party wishes to cancel the negotiation. |
| 100 | *NoRenegotiation* | The server cannot renegotiate the handshake. |

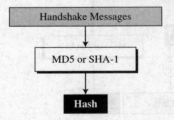

**Fig. 17.44**  *Hash for CertificateVerify message in TLS*

**Finished Message**  The calculation of the hash for the Finished message has also been changed. TLS uses the PRF to calculate two hashes used for the Finished message, as shown in Fig. 17.45.

## 17.4.7 Record Protocol

The only change in the Record Protocol is the use of HMAC for signing the message. TLS uses the MAC, as defined in Chapter 11, to create the HMAC. TLS also adds the protocol version (called Compressed version) to the text to be signed. Figure 17.46 shows how the HMAC is formed.

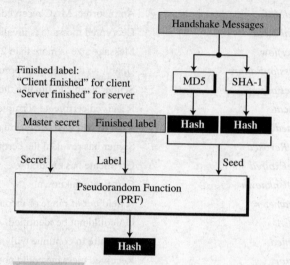

Finished label:
"Client finished" for client
"Server finished" for server

**Fig. 17.45** *Hash for Finished message in TLS*

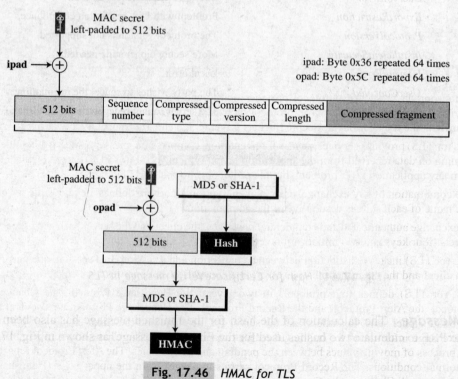

ipad: Byte 0x36 repeated 64 times
opad: Byte 0x5C repeated 64 times

**Fig. 17.46** *HMAC for TLS*

## 17.5 RECOMMENDED READING

The following books and websites give more details about subjects discussed in this chapter. The items enclosed in brackets refer to the reference list at the end of the book.

### Books

[Res01], [Tho00], [Sta06], [Rhe03], and [PHS03] discuss SSL and TLS.

### WebSites

The following website give more information about topics discussed in this chapter.
   http://www.ietf.org/rfc/rfc2246.txt

## Key Terms

| | |
|---|---|
| Alert Protocol | Hypertext Transfer Protocol (HTTP) |
| anonymous Diffie-Hellman | key material |
| ChangeCipherSpec Protocol | master secret |
| cipher suite | pre-master secret |
| connection | pseudorandom function (PRF) |
| data-expansion function | Record Protocol |
| ephemeral Diffie-Hellman | Secure Sockets Layer (SSL) Protocol |
| fixed Diffie-Hellman | session |
| Fortezza | Transport Layer Security (TLS) Protocol |
| Handshake Protocol | |

## Summary

★ A transport layer security protocol provides end-to-end security services for applications that use the services of a reliable transport layer protocol such as TCP. Two protocols are dominant today for providing security at the transport layer: Secure Sockets Layer (SSL) and Transport Layer Security (TLS).

★ SSL (or TLS) provides services such as fragmentation, compression, message integrity, confidentiality, and framing on data received from the application layer. Typically, SSL (or TLS) can receive application data from any application layer protocol, but the protocol is normally HTTP.

★ The combination of key exchange, hash, and encryption algorithm defines a cipher suite for each session. The name of each suite is descriptive of the combination.

★ To exchange authenticated and confidential messages, the client and the server each need six cryptographic secrets (four keys and two initialization vectors).

★ SSL (or TLS) makes a distinction between a connection and a session. In a session, one party has the role of a client and the other the role of a server; in a connection, both parties have equal roles, they are peers.

★ SSL (or TLS) defines four protocols in two layers: the Handshake Protocol, the ChangeCipherSpec Protocol, the Alert Protocol, and the Record Protocol. The Handshake Protocol uses several messages to negotiate cipher suite, to authenticate the server for the client and the client for the server if needed, and to exchange information for building the cryptographic secrets. The ChangeCipherSpec protocol defines the process of moving values between the pending and active states. The Alert Protocol reports errors and abnormal conditions. The Record Protocol carries messages from the upper layer (Handshake Protocol, Alert Protocol, ChangeCipherSpec Protocol, or application layer).

# Practice Set

## Review Questions

**17.1** List services provided by SSL or TLS.

**17.2** Describe how master secret is created from pre-master secret in SSL.

**17.3** Describe how master secret is created from pre-master secret in TLS.

**17.4** Describe how key materials are created from master secret in SSL.

**17.5** Describe how key materials are created from master secret in TLS.

**17.6** Distinguish between a session and a connection.

**17.7** List and give the purpose of four protocols defined in SSL or TLS.

**17.8** Define the goal of each phase in the Handshake protocol.

**17.9** Compare and contrast the Handshake protocols in SSL and TLS.

**17.10** Compare and contrast the Record protocols in SSL and TLS.

## Exercises

**17.11** What is the length of the key material if the cipher suite is one of the following:
  a. SSL_RSA_WITH_NULL_MD5
  b. SSL_RSA_WITH_NULL_SHA
  c. TLS_RSA_WITH_DES_CBC_SHA
  d. TLS_RSA_WITH_3DES_EDE_CBC_SHA
  e. TLS_DHE_RSA_WITH_DES_CBC_SHA
  f. TLS_DH_RSA_WITH_3DES_EDE_CBC_SHA

**17.12** Show the number of repeated modules needed for each case in Exercise 11 (see Fig. 17.9).

**17.13** Compare the calculation of the master secret in SSL with that in TLS. In SSL, the pre-master is included three times in the calculation, in TLS only once. Which calculation is more efficient in terms of space and time?

**17.14** Compare the calculation of the key material in SSL and TLS. Answer the following questions:
  a. Which calculation provides more security?
  b. Which calculation is more efficient in terms of space and time?

**17.15** The calculation of key material in SSL requires several iterations, the one for TLS does not. How can TLS calculate key material of variable length?

**17.16** When a session is resumed with a new connection, SSL does not require the full handshaking process. Show the messages that need to be exchanged in a partial handshaking.

**17.17** When a session is resumed, which of the following cryptographic secrets need to be recalculated?
  a. Pre-master secret
  b. Master secret
  c. Authentication keys
  d. Encryption keys
  e. IVs

**17.18** In Fig. 17.20, what happens if the server sends the ChangeCipherSpec message, but the client does not? Which messages in the Handshake Protocol can follow? Which cannot?

**17.19** Compare the calculation of MAC in SSL and TLS (see Fig. 17.22 and Fig. 17.26). Which one is more efficient?

**17.20** Compare the calculation of the hash for CertificateVerify messages in SSL and TLS (see Fig. 17.35 and Fig. 17.44). Which one is more efficient?

**17.21** Compare the calculation of the hash for Finished messages in SSL and TLS (see Fig. 17.38 and Fig. 17.45). Answer the following questions:

a. Which one is more secure?

b. Which one is more efficient?

**17.22** TLS uses PRF for all hash calculations except for CertificateVerify message. Give a reason for this exception.

**17.23** Most protocols have a formula to show the calculations of cryptographic secrets and hashes. For example, in SSL, the calculation of the master secret (see Fig. 17.8) is as follows (concatenation is designated by a bar):

Master Secret = MD5 (pre-master | SHA-1 ("A" | pre-master | CR | SR)) |

MD5 (pre-master | SHA-1 ("A" | pre-master | CR | SR)) |

MD5 (pre-master | SHA-1 ("A" | pre-master | CR | SR))

Show the formula for the following:

a. Key material in SSL (Fig. 17.9)

b. MAC in SSL (Fig. 17.22)

c. Hash calculation for CertificateVerify message in SSL (Fig. 17.35)

d. Hash calculation for Finished message in SSL (Fig. 17.38)

e. Data expansion in TLS (Fig. 17.40)

f. PRF in TLS (Fig. 17.41)

g. Master secret in TLS (Fig. 17.42)

h. Key material in TLS (Fig. 17.43)

i. Hash calculation for CertificateVerify message in TLS (Fig. 17.44)

j. Hash calculation for Finished message in TLS (Fig. 17.45)

k. MAC in TLS (Fig. 17.46)

**17.24** Show how SSL or TLS reacts to a replay attack. That is, show how SSL or TLS responds to an attacker that tries to replay one or more handshake messages.

**17.25** Show how SSL or TLS reacts to a brute-force attack. Can an intruder use an exhaustive computer search to find the encryption key in SSL or TLS? Which protocol is more secure in this respect, SSL or TLS?

**17.26** What is the risk of using short-length keys in SSL or TLS? What type of attack can an intruder try if the keys are short?

**17.27** Is SSL or TLS more secure to a man-in-the-middle attack? Can an intruder create key material between the client and herself and between the server and herself?

# 18

# Security at the Network Layer: IPSec

## Objectives

This chapter has several objectives:
- ☞ To define the architecture of IPSec
- ☞ To discuss the application of IPSec in transport and tunnel modes
- ☞ To discuss how IPSec can be used to provide only authentication
- ☞ To discuss how IPSec can be used to provide both confidentiality and authentication
- ☞ To define Security Association and explain how it is implemented for IPSec
- ☞ To define Internet Key Exchange and explain how it is used by IPSec

The two previous chapters have discussed the security at the application layer and transport layer. However, security at the above two layers may not be enough in some cases. First, not all client/server programs are protected at the application layer; for example, PGP and S/MIME protect only electronic mail. Second, not all client/server programs at the application layer use the service of TCP to be protected by SSL or TLS; some programs use the service of UDP. Third, many applications, such as routing protocols, directly use the service of IP; they need security services at the IP layer.

**IP Security (IPSec)** is a collection of protocols designed by the Internet Engineering Task Force (IETF) to provide security for a packet at the network level. The network layer in the Internet is often referred to as the Internet Protocol or IP layer. IPSec helps create authenticated and confidential packets for the IP layer as shown in Fig. 18.1.

IPSec can be useful in several areas. First, it can enhance the security of those client/server programs, such as electronic mail, that use their own security protocols. Second, it can enhance the security of those client/server programs, such as HTTP, that use the security services provided at the transport layer. It can provide security for those client/server programs that do not use the security services provided at the transport layer. It can provide security for node-to-node communication programs such as routing protocols.

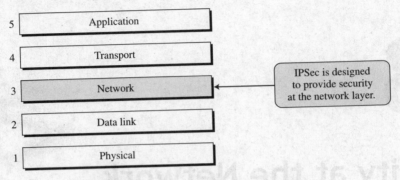

**Fig. 18.1** *TCP/IP protocol suite and IPSec*

## 18.1            TWO MODES

IPSec operates in one of two different modes: transport mode or tunnel mode.

### 18.1.1   Transport Mode

In **transport mode,** IPSec protects what is delivered from the transport layer to the network layer. In other words, transport mode protects the network layer payload, the payload to be encapsulated in the network layer, as shown in Fig. 18.2.

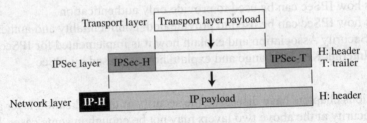

**Fig. 18.2** *IPSec in transport mode*

Note that transport mode does not protect the IP header. In other words, transport mode does not protect the whole IP packet; it protects only the packet from the transport layer (the IP layer payload). In this mode, the IPSec header (and trailer) are added to the information coming from the transport layer. The IP header is added later.

---

**IPSec in transport mode does not protect the IP header; it only protects the information coming from the transport layer.**

---

Transport mode is normally used when we need host-to-host (end-to-end) protection of data. The sending host uses IPSec to authenticate and/or encrypt the payload delivered from the transport layer. The receiving host uses IPSec to check the authentication and/or decrypt the IP packet and deliver it to the transport layer. Figure 18.3 shows this concept.

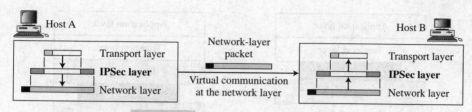

**Fig. 18.3** *Transport mode in action*

## 18.1.2 Tunnel Mode

In **tunnel mode,** IPSec protects the entire IP packet. It takes an IP packet, including the header, applies IPSec security methods to the entire packet, and then adds a new IP header, as shown in Fig. 18.4.

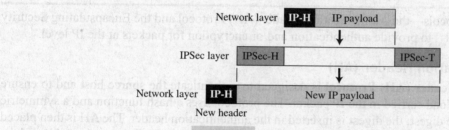

**Fig. 18.4** *IPSec in tunnel mode*

The new IP header, as we will see shortly, has different information than the original IP header. Tunnel mode is normally used between two routers, between a host and a router, or between a router and a host, as shown in Fig. 18.5. In other words, tunnel mode is used when either the sender or the receiver is not a host. The entire original packet is protected from intrusion between the sender and the receiver, as if the whole packet goes through an imaginary tunnel.

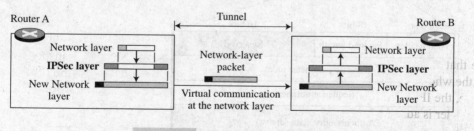

**Fig. 18.5** *Tunnel mode in action*

---

**IPSec in tunnel mode protects the original IP header.**

---

## 18.1.3 Comparison

In transport mode, the IPSec layer comes between the transport layer and the network layer. In tunnel mode, the flow is from the network layer to the IPSec layer and then back to the network layer again. Figure 18.6 compares the two modes.

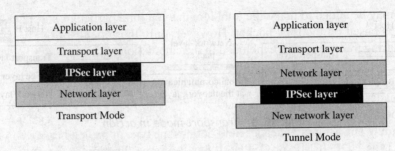

**Fig. 18.6**   *Transport mode versus tunnel mode*

## 18.2   TWO SECURITY PROTOCOLS

IPSec defines two protocols—the Authentication Header (AH) Protocol and the Encapsulating Security Payload (ESP) Protocol—to provide authentication and/or encryption for packets at the IP level.

### 18.2.1   Authentication Header (AH)

The **Authentication Header (AH) Protocol** is designed to authenticate the source host and to ensure the integrity of the payload carried in the IP packet. The protocol uses a hash function and a symmetric key to create a message digest; the digest is inserted in the authentication header. The AH is then placed in the appropriate location, based on the mode (transport or tunnel). Figure 18.7 shows the fields and the position of the authentication header in transport mode.

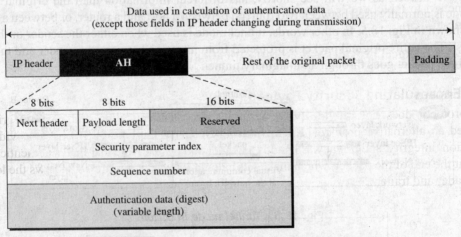

**Fig. 18.7**   *Authentication Header (AH) protocol*

When an IP datagram carries an authentication header, the original value in the protocol field of the IP header is replaced by the value 51. A field inside the authentication header (the next header field) holds the original value of the protocol field (the type of payload being carried by the IP datagram). The addition of an authentication header follows these steps:

1.   An authentication header is added to the payload with the authentication data field set to 0.

2. Padding may be added to make the total length even for a particular hashing algorithm.
3. Hashing is based on the total packet. However, only those fields of the IP header that do not change during transmission are included in the calculation of the message digest (authentication data).
4. The authentication data are inserted in the authentication header.
5. The IP header is added after changing the value of the protocol field to 51.

A brief description of each field follows:

❑ **Next header.** The 8-bit next header field defines the type of payload carried by the IP datagram (such as TCP, UDP, ICMP, or OSPF). It has the same function as the protocol field in the IP header before encapsulation. In other words, the process copies the value of the protocol field in the IP datagram to this field. The value of the protocol field in the new IP datagram is now set to 51 to show that the packet carries an authentication header.

❑ **Payload length.** The name of this 8-bit field is misleading. It does not define the length of the payload; it defines the length of the authentication header in 4-byte multiples, but it does not include the first 8 bytes.

❑ **Security parameter index.** The 32-bit security parameter index (SPI) field plays the role of a virtual circuit identifier and is the same for all packets sent during a connection called a Security Association (discussed later).

❑ **Sequence number.** A 32-bit sequence number provides ordering information for a sequence of datagrams. The sequence numbers prevent a playback. Note that the sequence number is not repeated even if a packet is retransmitted. A sequence number does not wrap around after it reaches $2^{32}$; a new connection must be established.

❑ **Authentication data.** Finally, the authentication data field is the result of applying a hash function to the entire IP datagram except for the fields that are changed during transit (e.g., time-to-live).

**The AH protocol provides source authentication and data integrity, but not privacy.**

## 18.2.2 Encapsulating Security Payload (ESP)

The AH protocol does not provide privacy, only source authentication and data integrity. IPSec later defined an alternative protocol, **Encapsulating Security Payload (ESP),** that provides source authentication, integrity, and privacy. ESP adds a header and trailer. Note that ESP's authentication data are added at the end of the packet, which makes its calculation easier. Figure 18.8 shows the location of the ESP header and trailer.

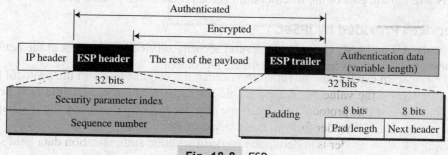

**Fig. 18.8** *ESP*

When an IP datagram carries an ESP header and trailer, the value of the protocol field in the IP header is 50. A field inside the ESP trailer (the next-header field) holds the original value of the protocol field (the type of payload being carried by the IP datagram, such as TCP or UDP). The ESP procedure follows these steps:

1. An ESP trailer is added to the payload.
2. The payload and the trailer are encrypted.
3. The ESP header is added.
4. The ESP header, payload, and ESP trailer are used to create the authentication data.
5. The authentication data are added to the end of the ESP trailer.
6. The IP header is added after changing the protocol value to 50.

The fields for the header and trailer are as follows:

❏ **Security parameter index.** The 32-bit security parameter index field is similar to that defined for the AH protocol.

❏ **Sequence number.** The 32-bit sequence number field is similar to that defined for the AH protocol.

❏ **Padding.** This variable-length field (0 to 255 bytes) of 0s serves as padding.

❏ **Pad length.** The 8-bit pad-length field defines the number of padding bytes. The value is between 0 and 255; the maximum value is rare.

❏ **Next header.** The 8-bit next-header field is similar to that defined in the AH protocol. It serves the same purpose as the protocol field in the IP header before encapsulation.

❏ **Authentication data.** Finally, the authentication data field is the result of applying an authentication scheme to parts of the datagram. Note the difference between the authentication data in AH and ESP. In AH, part of the IP header is included in the calculation of the authentication data; in ESP, it is not.

---

**ESP provides source authentication, data integrity, and privacy.**

---

### 18.2.3  IPv4 and IPv6

IPSec supports both IPv4 and IPv6. In IPv6, however, AH and ESP are part of the extension header.

### 18.2.4  AH versus ESP

The ESP protocol was designed after the AH protocol was already in use. ESP does whatever AH does with additional functionality (privacy). The question is, Why do we need AH? The answer is that we don't. However, the implementation of AH is already included in some commercial products, which means that AH will remain part of the Internet until these products are phased out.

### 18.2.5  Services Provided by IPSec

The two protocols, AH and ESP, can provide several security services for packets at the network layer. Table 18.1 shows the list of services available for each protocol.

**Table 18.1** *IPSec services*

| Services | AH | ESP |
|---|---|---|
| Access control | yes | yes |
| Message authentication (message integrity) | yes | yes |
| Entity authentication (data source authentication) | yes | yes |
| Confidentiality | **no** | yes |
| Replay attack protection | yes | yes |

**Access Control**    IPSec provides access control indirectly using a Security Association Database (SAD), as we will see in the next section. When a packet arrives at a destination, and there is no Security Association already established for this packet, the packet is discarded.

**Message Integrity**    Message integrity is preserved in both AH and ESP. A digest of data is created and sent by the sender to be checked by the receiver.

**Entity Authentication**    The Security Association and the keyed-hash digest of the data sent by the sender authenticate the sender of the data in both AH and ESP.

**Confidentiality**    The encryption of the message in ESP provides confidentiality. AH, however, does not provide confidentiality. If confidentiality is needed, one should use ESP instead of AH.

**Replay Attack Protection**    In both protocols, the replay attack is prevented by using sequence numbers and a sliding receiver window. Each IPSec header contains a unique sequence number when the Security Association is established. The number starts from 0 and increases until the value reaches $2^{32} - 1$ (the size of the sequence number field is 32 bits). When the sequence number reaches the maximum, it is reset to 0 and, at the same time, the old Security Association (see the next section) is deleted and a new one is established. To prevent processing duplicate packets, IPSec mandates the use of a fixed-size window at the receiver. The size of the window is determined by the receiver with a default value of 64. Figure 18.9 shows a replay window. The window is of a fixed size, W. The shaded packets signify received packets that have been checked and authenticated.

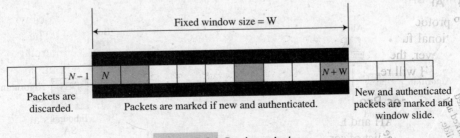

**Fig. 18.9**    *Replay window*

When a packet arrives at the receiver, one of three things can happen, depending on the value of the sequence number.

1.  The sequence number of the packet is less than $N$. This puts the packet to the left of the window. In this case, the packet is discarded. It is either a duplicate or its arrival time has expired.
2.  The sequence number of the packet is between $N$ and $(N + W - 1)$, inclusive. This puts the packet inside the window. In this case, if the packet is new (not marked) and it passes the authentication test, the sequence number is marked and the packet is accepted. Otherwise, it is discarded.
3.  The sequence number of the packet is greater than $(N + W - 1)$. This puts the packet to the right of the window. In this case, if the packet is authenticated, the corresponding sequence number is marked and the window slides to the right to cover the newly marked sequence number. Otherwise, the packet is discarded. Note that it may happen that a packet arrives with a sequence number much larger than $(N + W)$ (very far from the right edge of the window). In this case, the sliding of the window may cause many unmarked numbers to fall to the left of the window. These packets, when they arrive, will never be accepted; their time has expired. For example, in Fig. 18.9, if a packet arrives with sequence number $(N + W + 3)$, the window slides and the left edge will be at the beginning of $(N + 3)$. This means the sequence number $(N + 2)$ is now out of the window. If a packet arrives with this sequence number, it will be discarded.

## 18.3  SECURITY ASSOCIATION

Security Association is a very important aspect of IPSec. IPSec requires a logical relationship, called a **Security Association (SA)**, between two hosts. This section first discusses the idea and then shows how it is used in IPSec.

### 18.3.1  Idea of Security Association

A Security Association is a contract between two parties; it creates a secure channel between them. Let us assume that Alice needs to unidirectionally communicate with Bob. If Alice and Bob are interested only in the confidentiality aspect of security, they can get a shared secret key between themselves. We can say that there are two Security Associations (SAs) between Alice and Bob; one outbound SA and one inbound SA. Each of them stores the value of the key in a variable and the name of the encryption/ decryption algorithm in another. Alice uses the algorithm and the key to encrypt a message to Bob; Bob uses the algorithm and the key when he needs to decrypt the message received from Alice. Figure 18.10 shows a simple SA.

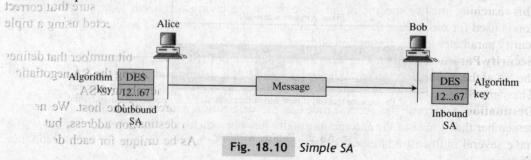

**Fig. 18.10**  *Simple SA*

The Security Associations can be more involved if the two parties need message integrity and authentication. Each association needs other data such as the algorithm for message integrity, the key, and other parameters. It can be much more complex if the parties need to use specific algorithms and specific parameters for different protocols, such as IPSec AH or IPSec ESP.

## 18.3.2  Security Association Database (SAD)

A Security Association can be very complex. This is particularly true if Alice wants to send messages to many people and Bob needs to receive messages from many people. In addition, each site needs to have both inbound and outbound SAs to allow bidirectional communication. In other words, we need a set of SAs that can be collected into a database. This database is called the **Security Association Database (SAD).** The database can be thought of as a two-dimensional table with each row defining a single SA. Normally, there are two SADs, one inbound and one outbound. Figure 18.11 shows the concept of outbound and inbound SADs for one entity.

| Index | SN | OF | ARW | AH/ESP | LT | Mode | MTU |
|---|---|---|---|---|---|---|---|
| < SPI, DA, P > | | | | | | | |
| < SPI, DA, P > | | | | | | | |
| < SPI, DA, P > | | | | | | | |
| < SPI, DA, P > | | | | | | | |

Security Association Database

**Legend:**

| | |
|---|---|
| SPI: Security Parameter Index | SN: Sequence Number |
| DA: Destination Address | OF: Overflow Flag |
| AH/ESP: Information for either one | ARW: Anti-Replay Window |
| P: Protocol | LT: Lifetime |
| Mode: IPSec Mode Flag | MTU: Path MTU (Maximum Transfer Unit) |

**Fig. 18.11**  *SAD*

When a host needs to send a packet that must carry an IPSec header, the host needs to find the corresponding entry in the outbound SAD to find the information for applying security to the packet. Similarly, when a host receives a packet that carries an IPSec header, the host needs to find the corresponding entry in the inbound SAD to find the information for checking the security of the packet. This searching must be specific in the sense that the receiving host needs to be sure that correct information is used for processing the packet. Each entry in an inbound SAD is selected using a triple index: security parameter index, destination address, and protocol.

❑ **Security Parameter Index.** The security parameter index (SPI) is a 32-bit number that defines the SA at the destination. As we will see later, the SPI is determined during the SA negotiation. The same SPI is included in all IPSec packets belonging to the same inbound SA.

❑ **Destination Address.** The second index is the destination address of the host. We need to remember that a host in the Internet normally has one unicast destination address, but it may have several multicast addresses. IPSec requires that the SAs be unique for each destination address.

❑ **Protocol.** IPSec has two different security protocols: AH and ESP. To separate the parameters and information used for each protocol, IPSec requires that a destination define a different SA for each protocol.

The entries for each row are called the SA parameters. Typical parameters are shown in Table 18.2.

**Table 18.2** *Typical SA Parameters*

| | |
|---|---|
| Sequence Number Counter | This is a 32-bit value that is used to generate sequence numbers for the AH or ESP header. |
| Sequence Number Overflow | This is a flag that defines a station's options in the event of a sequence number overflow. |
| Anti-Replay Window | This detects an inbound replayed AH or ESP packet. |
| AH Information | This section contains information for the AH protocol:<br>1. Authentication algorithm<br>2. Keys<br>3. Key lifetime<br>4. Other related parameters |
| ESP Information | This section contains information for the ESP protocol:<br>1. Encryption algorithm<br>2. Authentication algorithm<br>3. Keys<br>4. Key lifetime<br>5. Initiator vectors<br>6. Other related parameters |
| SA Lifetime | This defines the lifetime for the SA. |
| IPSec Mode | This defines the mode, transport or tunnel. |
| Path MTU | This defines the path MTU (fragmentation). |

## 18.4 SECURITY POLICY

Another import aspect of IPSec is the **Security Policy (SP),** which defines the type of security applied to a packet when it is to be sent or when it has arrived. Before using the SAD, discussed in the previous section, a host must determine the predefined policy for the packet.

### 18.4.1 Security Policy Database

Each host that is using the IPSec protocol needs to keep a **Security Policy Database (SPD).** Again, there is a need for an inbound SPD and an outbound SPD. Each entry in the SPD can be accessed using a sextuple index: source address, destination address, name, protocol, source port, and destination port, as shown in Fig. 18.12.

| Index | Policy |
|---|---|
| < SA, DA, Name, P, SPort, DPort > | |
| < SA, DA, Name, P, SPort, DPort > | |
| < SA, DA, Name, P, SPort, DPort > | |
| < SA, DA, Name, P, SPort, DPort > | |

**Legend:**

SA: Source Address  SPort: Source Port
DA: Destination Address  DPort: Destination Port
P: Protocol

**Fig. 18.12** *SPD*

Source and destination addresses can be unicast, multicast, or wildcard addresses. The name usually defines a DNS entity. The protocol is either AH or ESP. The source and destination ports are the port addresses for the process running at the source and destination hosts.

***Outbound SPD***  When a packet is to be sent out, the outbound SPD is consulted. Figure 18.13 shows the processing of a packet by a sender.

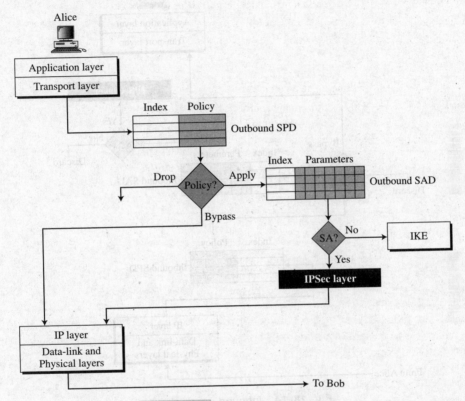

**Fig. 18.13**  *Outbound processing*

The input to the outbound SPD is the sextuple index; the output is one of the three following cases:

1.  **Drop.** This means that the packet defined by the index cannot be sent; it is dropped.
2.  **Bypass.** This means that there is no policy for the packet with this policy index; the packet is sent, bypassing the security header application.
3.  **Apply.** In this case, the security header is applied. Two situations may occur.
    a.  If an outbound SA is already established, the triple SA index is returned that selects the corresponding SA from the outbound SAD. The AH or ESP header is formed; encryption, authentication, or both are applied based on the SA selected. The packet is transmitted.
    b.  If an outbound SA is not established yet, the Internet Key Exchange (IKE) protocol (see the next section) is called to create an outbound and inbound SA for this traffic. The outbound SA is added to the outbound SAD by the source; the inbound SA is added to the inbound SAD by the destination.

***Inbound SPD*** When a packet arrives, the inbound SPD is consulted. Each entry in the inbound SPD is also accessed using the same sextuple index. Figure 18.14 shows the processing of a packet by a receiver.

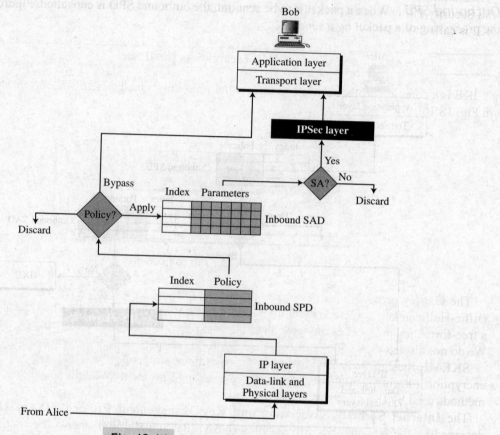

**Fig. 18.14** *Inbound processing*

The input to the inbound SPD is the sextuple index; the output is one of the three following cases:
1. **Discard.** This means that the packet defined by that policy must be dropped.
2. **Bypass.** This means that there is no policy for a packet with this policy index; the packet is processed, ignoring the information from AH or ESP header. The packet is delivered to the transport layer.
3. **Apply.** In this case, the security header must be processed. Two situations may occur:
   a. If an inbound SA is already established, the triple SA index is returned that selects the corresponding inbound SA from the inbound SAD. Decryption, authentication, or both are applied. If the packet passes the security criteria, the AH or ESP header is discarded and the packet is delivered to the transport layer.
   b. If an SA is not yet established, the packet must be discarded.

# 18.5   INTERNET KEY EXCHANGE (IKE)

The **Internet Key Exchange (IKE)** is a protocol designed to create both inbound and outbound Security Associations. As we discussed in the previous section, when a peer needs to send an IP packet, it consults the Security Policy Database (SPDB) to see if there is an SA for that type of traffic. If there is no SA, IKE is called to establish one.

---

**IKE creates SAs for IPSec.**

---

IKE is a complex protocol based on three other protocols: Oakley, SKEME, and ISAKMP, as shown in Fig. 18.15.

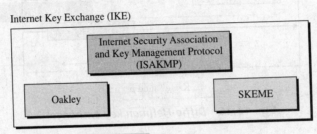

**Fig. 18.15**   *IKE components*

The **Oakley** protocol was developed by Hilarie Orman. It is a key creation protocol based on the Diffie-Hellman key-exchange method, but with some improvements as we shall see shortly. Oakley is a free-formatted protocol in the sense that it does not define the format of the message to be exchanged. We do not discuss the Oakley protocol directly in this chapter, but we show how IKE uses its ideas.

**SKEME,** designed by Hugo Krawcyzk, is another protocol for key exchange. It uses public-key encryption for entity authentication in a key-exchange protocol. We will see shortly that one of the methods used by IKE is based on SKEME.

The **Internet Security Association and Key Management Protocol (ISAKMP)** is a protocol designed by the National Security Agency (NSA) that actually implements the exchanges defined in IKE. It defines several packets, protocols, and parameters that allow the IKE exchanges to take place in standardized, formatted messages to create SAs. We will discuss ISAKMP in the next section as the carrier protocol that implements IKE.

In this section, we discuss IKE itself; the mechanism for creating SAs for IPSec.

## 18.5.1   Improved Diffie-Hellman Key Exchange

The key-exchange idea in IKE is based on the Diffie-Hellman protocol. This protocol provides a session key between two peers without the need for the existence of any previous secret. We have discussed Diffie-Hellman in Chapter 15; The concept is summarized in Fig. 18.16.

In the original Diffie-Hellman key exchange, two parties create a symmetric session key to exchange data without having to remember or store the key for future use. Before establishing a symmetric key, the two parties need to choose two numbers $p$ and $g$. The first number, $p$, is a large prime on the order of 300 decimal digits (1024 bits). The second number, $g$, is a generator in the group $<Z_p^*, \times>$. Alice chooses a large random number $i$ and calculates KE-I = $g^i \bmod p$. She sends KE-I to Bob. Bob chooses another large random number $r$ and calculates KE-R = $g^r$ mod $p$. He sends KE-R to Alice. We refer to KE-I and KE-R as Diffie-Hellman half-keys because each is a half-key generated by a peer. They need to be combined together to create the full key, which is K = $g^{ir}$ mod $p$. K is the symmetric key for the session.

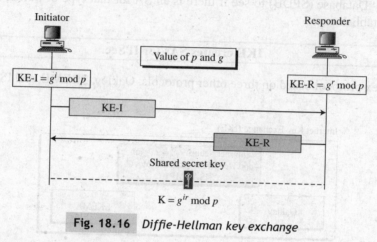

**Fig. 18.16** *Diffie-Hellman key exchange*

The Diffie-Hellman protocol has some weaknesses that need to be eliminated before it is suitable as an Internet key exchange.

**Clogging Attack**   The first issue with the Diffie-Hellman protocol is the **clogging attack** or *denial-of-service attack*. A malicious intruder can send many half-key ($g^x$ mod $q$) messages to Bob, pretending that they are from different sources. Bob then needs to calculate different responses ($g^y$ mod $q$) and at the same time calculate the full-key ($g^{xy}$ mod $q$). This keeps Bob so busy that he may stop responding to any other messages. He denies services to clients. This can happen because the Diffie-Hellman protocol is computationally intensive.

To prevent this clogging attack, we can add two extra messages to the protocol to force the two parties to send **cookies**. Figure 18.17 shows the refinement that can prevent a clogging attack. The cookie is the result of hashing a unique identifier of the peer (such as IP address, port number, and protocol), a secret random number known to the party that generates the cookie, and a timestamp.

The initiator sends its own cookie; the responder its own. Both cookies are repeated, unchanged, in every following message. The calculations of half-keys and the session key are postponed until the cookies are returned. If any of the peers is a hacker attempting a clogging attack, the cookies are not returned; the corresponding party does not spend the time and effort to calculate the half-key or the session key. For example, if the initiator is a hacker using a bogus IP address, the initiator does not receive the second message and cannot send the third message. The process is aborted.

---

**To protect against a clogging attack, IKE uses cookies.**

---

**Replay Attack**   Like other protocols we have seen so far, Diffie-Hellman is vulnerable to a **replay attack**; the information from one session can be replayed in a future session by a malicious intruder. To prevent this, we can add nonces to the third and fourth messages to preserve the freshness of the message.

**To protect against a replay attack, IKE uses nonces.**

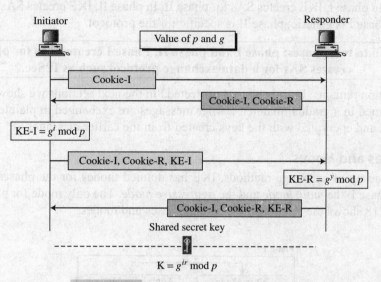

**Fig. 18.17** *Diffie-Hellman with cookies*

***Man-In-The-Middle Attack*** The third, and the most dangerous, attack on the Diffie-Hellman protocol is the man-in-the-middle attack, previously discussed in Chapter 15. Eve can come in the middle and create one key between Alice and herself and another key between Bob and herself. Thwarting this attack is not as simple as the other two. We need to authenticate each party. Alice and Bob need to be sure that the integrity of the messages is preserved and that both are authenticated to each other.

Authentication of the messages exchanged (message integrity) and the authentication of the parties involved (entity authentication) require that each party proves his/her claimed identity. To do this, each must prove that it possesses a secret.

**To protect against man-in-the-middle attack, IKE requires that each party shows that it possesses a secret.**

In IKE, the secret can be one of the following:
a. A preshared secret key
b. A preknown encryption/decryption public-key pair. An entity must show that a message encrypted with the announced public key can be decrypted with the corresponding private key.
c. A preknown digital signature public-key pair. An entity must show that it can sign a message with its private key which can be verified with its announced public key.

### 18.5.2 IKE Phases

IKE creates SAs for a message-exchange protocol such as IPSec. IKE, however, needs to exchange confidential and authenticated messages. What protocol provides SAs for IKE itself? The reader may realize that this requires a never-ending chain of SAs: IKE must create SAs for IPSec, protocol X must create SAs for IKE, protocol Y needs to create SAs for protocol X, and so on. To solve this dilemma and, at the same time, make IKE independent of the IPSec protocol, the designers of IKE divided IKE into two phases. In phase I, IKE creates SAs for phase II. In phase II, IKE creates SAs for IPSec or some other protocol. Phase I is generic; phase II is specific for the protocol.

---

**IKE is divided into two phases: phase I and phase II. Phase I creates SAs for phase II; phase II creates SAs for a data exchange protocol such as IPSec.**

---

Still, the question remains: How is phase I protected? In the next sections we show how phase I uses an SA that is formed in a gradual manner. Earlier messages are exchanged in plaintext; later messages are authenticated and encrypted with the keys created from the earlier messages.

### 18.5.3 Phases and Modes

To allow for a variety of exchange methods, IKE has defined modes for the phases. So far, there are two modes for phase I: the *main mode* and the *aggressive mode*. The only mode for phase II is the *quick mode*. Figure 18.18 shows the relationship between phases and modes.

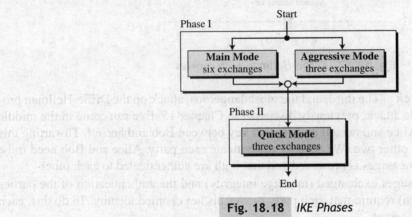

**Fig. 18.18** *IKE Phases*

Based on the nature of the pre-secret between the two parties, the phase I modes can use one of four different authentication methods: the preshared secret key method, the original public-key method, the revised public-key method, or the digital signature method, as shown in Fig. 18.19.

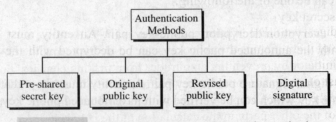

**Fig. 18.19** *Main-mode or aggressive-mode methods*

### 18.5.4 Phase I: Main Mode

In the **main mode,** the initiator and the responder exchange six messages. In the first two messages, they exchange cookies (to protect against a clogging attack) and negotiate the SA parameters. The initiator sends a series of proposals; the responder selects one of them. When the first two messages are exchanged, the initiator and the responder know the SA parameters and are confident that the other party exists (no clogging attack occurs).

In the third and fourth messages, the initiator and responder usually exchange their half-keys ($g^i$ and $g^r$ of the Diffie-Hellman method) and their nonces (for replay protection). In some methods other information is exchanged; that will be discussed later. Note that the half-keys and nonces are not sent with the first two messages because the two parties must first ensure that a clogging attack is not possible.

After exchanging the third and fourth messages, each party can calculate the common secret between them in addition to its individual hash digest. The common secret SKEYID (secret key ID) is dependent on the calculation method as shown below. In the equations, *prf* (pseudorandom function) is a keyed-hash function defined during the negotiation phase.

$$\text{SKEYID} = \textbf{\textit{prf}}\,(\text{preshared-key, N-I} \mid \text{N-R}) \qquad \text{(preshared-key method)}$$
$$\text{SKEYID} = \textbf{\textit{prf}}\,(\text{N-I} \mid \text{N-R}, g^{ir}) \qquad \text{(public-key method)}$$
$$\text{SKEYID} = \textbf{\textit{prf}}\,(\text{hash (N-I} \mid \text{N-R)}, \text{Cookie-I} \mid \text{Cookie-R}) \qquad \text{(digital signature)}$$

Other common secrets are calculated as follows:

$$\text{SKEYID\_d} = \textbf{\textit{prf}}\,(\text{SKEYID}, g^{ir} \mid \text{Cookie-I} \mid \text{Cookie-R} \mid 0)$$
$$\text{SKEYID\_a} = \textbf{\textit{prf}}\,(\text{SKEYID}, \text{SKEYID\_d} \mid g^{ir} \mid \text{Cookie-I} \mid \text{Cookie-R} \mid 1)$$
$$\text{SKEYID\_e} = \textbf{\textit{prf}}\,(\text{SKEYID}, \text{SKEYID\_a} \mid g^{ir} \mid \text{Cookie-I} \mid \text{Cookie-R} \mid 2)$$

SKEYID_d (derived key) is a key to create other keys. SKEYID_a is the authentication key and SKEYID_e is used for the encryption key; both are used during the negotiation phase. The first parameter (SKEYID) is calculated for each key-exchange method separately. The second parameter is a concatenation of various data. Note that the key for prf is always SKEYID.

The two parties also calculate two hash digests, HASH-I and HASH-R, which are used in three of the four methods in the main mode. The calculation is shown below:

$$\text{HASH-I} = \textbf{\textit{prf}}\,(\text{SKEYID}, \text{KE-I} \mid \text{KE-R} \mid \text{Cookie-I} \mid \text{Cookie-R} \mid \text{SA-I} \mid \text{ID-I})$$
$$\text{HASH-R} = \textbf{\textit{prf}}$$
$$(\text{SKEYID}, \text{KE-I} \mid \text{KE-R} \mid \text{Cookie-I} \mid \text{Cookie-R} \mid \text{SA-I} \mid \text{ID-R})$$

Note that the first digest uses ID-I, while the second uses ID-R. Both use SA-I, the entire SA data sent by the initiator. None of them include the proposal selected by the responder. The idea is to protect the proposal sent by the initiator by preventing an intruder from making changes. For example, an intruder might try to send a list of proposals more vulnerable to attack. Similarly, if the SA is not included, an intruder might change the selected proposal to one more favorable to himself. Note also a party does not need to know the ID of the other party in the calculation of the HASHs.

After calculating the keys and hashes, each party sends the hash to the other party to authenticate itself. The initiator sends HASH-I to the responder as proof that she is Alice. Only Alice knows the authentication secret and only she can calculate HASH-I. If the HASH-I then calculated by Bob matches the HASH-I sent by Alice, she is authenticated. In the same way, Bob can authenticate himself to Alice by sending HASH-R.

Note that there is a subtle point here. When Bob calculates HASH-I, he needs Alice's ID and vice versa. In some methods, the ID is sent by previous messages; in others it is sent with the hash, with both the hash and the ID encrypted by SKEYID_e.

## Preshared Secret-Key Method

In the preshared secret-key method, a symmetric key is used for authentication of the peers to each other. Figure 18.20 shows shared-key authentication in the main mode.

KE-I (KE-R): Initiator's (responder's) half-key
N-I (N-R): Initiator's (responder's) nonce
ID-I (ID-R): Initiator's (responder's) ID
HASH-I (HASH-R): Initiator's (responder's) hash

HDR: General header including cookies
🔒 Encrypted with SKEYID_e

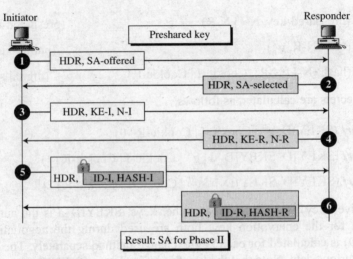

**Fig. 18.20** *Main mode, preshared secret-key method*

In the first two messages, the initiator and responder exchange cookies (inside the general header) and SA parameters. In the next two messages, they exchange the half-keys and the nonces (see Chapter 15). Now the two parties can create SKEYID and the two keyed hashes (HASH-I and HASH-R). In the fifth and sixth messages, the two -parties exchange the created hashes and their IDs. To protect the IDs and hashes, the last two messages are encrypted with SKEYID_e.

Note that the pre-shared key is the secret between Alice (initiator) and Bob (responder). Eve (intruder) does not have access to this key. Eve cannot create SKEYID and therefore cannot create either HASH-I or HASH-R. Note that the IDs need to be exchanged in messages 5 and 6 to allow the calculation of the hash.

There is one problem with this method. Bob cannot decrypt the message unless he knows the preshared key, which means he must know who Alice is (know her ID). But Alice's ID is encrypted in message 5. The designer of this method has argued that the ID in this case must be the IP address of each party. This is not an issue if Alice is on a stationary host (the IP address is fixed). However, if Alice is moving from one network to another, this is a problem.

***Original Public-Key Method*** In the original public-key method, the initiator and the responder prove their identities by showing that they possess a private key related to their announced public key. Figure 18.21 shows the exchange of messages using the original public-key method.

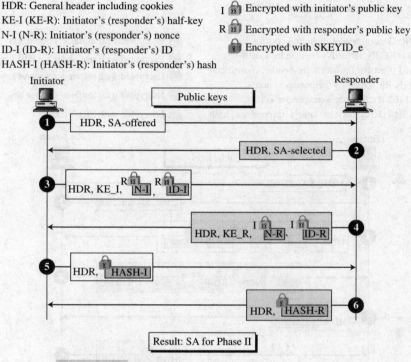

HDR: General header including cookies
KE-I (KE-R): Initiator's (responder's) half-key
N-I (N-R): Initiator's (responder's) nonce
ID-I (ID-R): Initiator's (responder's) ID
HASH-I (HASH-R): Initiator's (responder's) hash

I 🔒 Encrypted with initiator's public key
R 🔒 Encrypted with responder's public key
🔒 Encrypted with SKEYID_e

**Fig. 18.21** *Main mode, original public-key method*

The first two messages are the same as in the previous method. In the third message, the initiator sends its half-key, the nonce, and the ID. In the fourth message, the responder does likewise. However, the nonces and IDs are encrypted by the public key of the receiver and decrypted by the private key of the receiver. As can be seen from Fig. 18.21, the nonces and IDs are encrypted separately, because, as we will see later, they are encoded separately from separate payloads.

One difference between this method and the previous one is that the IDs are exchanged with the third and fourth messages instead of the fifth and sixth messages. The fifth and sixth messages just carry the HASHs.

The calculation of SKEYID in this method is based on a hash of the nonces and the symmetric key. The hash of the nonces is used as the key for the keyed-HMAC function. Note that here we use a double hash. Although SKEYID, and consequently, the hashes are not directly dependent on the secret that each party possesses, they are related indirectly. SKEYID depends on the nonces and the nonces can only be decrypted by the private key (secret) of the receiver. So if the calculated hashes match those received, it is proof that each party is who it claims to be.

**Revised Public-Key Method** The original public-key method has some drawbacks. First, two instances of public-key encryption/decryption place a heavy load on the initiator and responder. Second, the initiator cannot send its certificate encrypted by the public key of the responder, since anyone could do this with a false certificate. The method was revised so that the public key is used only to create a temporary secret key, as shown in Fig. 18.22.

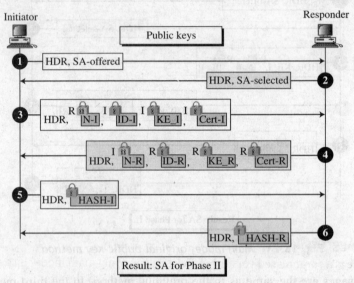

**Fig. 18.22** *Main mode, revised public-key method*

Note that two temporary secret keys are created from a hash of nonces and cookies. The initiator uses the public key of the responder to send its nonce. The responder decrypts the nonce and calculates the initiator's temporary secret key. After that the half-key, the ID, and the optional certificate can be decrypted. The two temporary secret keys, K-I and K-R, are calculated as

$$\text{K-I} = \textbf{\textit{prf}}\,(\text{N-I, Cookie-I}) \qquad \text{K-R} = \textbf{\textit{prf}}\,(\text{N-R, Cookie-R})$$

**Digital Signature Method** In this method, each party shows that it possesses the certified private key related to a digital signature. Figure 18.23 shows the exchanges in this method. It is similar to the preshared-key method except for the SKEYID calculation.

Note that in this method the sending of the certificates is optional. The certificate can be sent here because it can be encrypted with SKEYID_e, which does not depend on the signature key. In message 5, the initiator signs all the information exchanged in messages 1 to 4 with its signature key. The responder verifies the signature using the public key of the initiator, which authenticates the initiator. Likewise, in message 6, the responder signs all the information exchanged with its signature key. The initiator verifies the signature.

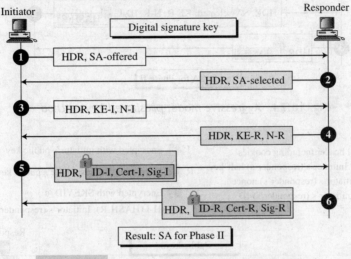

HDR: General header including cookies
Sig-I: Initiator's signature on messages 1–4
Sig-R: Initiator's signature on messages 1–5
Cert-I (Cert-R): Initiator's (responder's) certificate

N-I (N-R): Initiator's (responder's) nonce
KE-I (KE-R): Initiator's (responder's) half-key
ID-I (ID-R): Initiator's (responder's) ID
Encrypted with SKEYID_e

Initiator
Responder

Digital signature key

1    HDR, SA-offered

HDR, SA-selected    2

3    HDR, KE-I, N-I

HDR, KE-R, N-R    4

5    HDR,  ID-I, Cert-I, Sig-I

HDR,  ID-R, Cert-R, Sig-R    6

Result: SA for Phase II

**Fig. 18.23**  *Main mode, digital signature method*

## 18.5.5  Phase I: Aggressive Mode

Each **aggressive mode** is a compressed version of the corresponding main mode. Instead of six messages, only three are exchanged. Messages 1 and 3 are combined to make the first message. Messages 2, 4, and 6 are combined to make the second message. Message 5 is sent as the third message. The idea is the same.

### Preshared-Key Method

Figure 18.24 shows the preshared-key method in the aggressive mode. Note that after receiving the first message, the responder can calculate SKEYID and consequently, HASH-R. But the initiator cannot calculate SKEYID until it receives the second message. HASH-I in the third message can be encrypted.

### Original Public-Key Method    Figure 18.25 shows the exchange of messages using the original public-key method in the aggressive mode. Note that the responder can calculate the SKEYID and HASH-R after receiving the first message, but the initiator must wait until it receives the second message.

KE-I (IK-R): Initiator's (responder's) half-key
N-I (N-R): Initiator's (responder's) nonce
HASH-I (HASH-R): Initiator's (responder's) hash

HDR: General header including cookies
🔒 Encrypted with SKEYID_e
ID-I (ID-R): Initiator's (responder's) ID

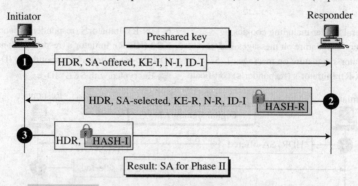

**Fig. 18.24** *Aggressive mode, preshared-key method*

HDR: General header including cookies
KE-I (KE-R): Initiator's (responder's) half-key
N-I (N-R): Initiator's (responder's) nonce
ID-I (ID-R): Initiator's (responder's) ID

I 🔒 Encrypted with initiator's public key
R 🔒 Encrypted with responder's public key
🔒 Encrypted with SKEYID_e
HASH-I (HASH-R): Initiator's (responder's) hash

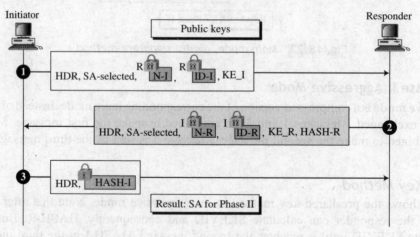

**Fig. 18.25** *Aggressive mode, original public-key method*

***Revised Public-Key Method*** Figure 18.26 shows the revised public-key method in the aggressive mode. The idea is the same as for the main mode, except that some messages are combined.

HDR: General header including cookies

KE-I (KE-R): Initiator's (responder's) half-key

Cert-I (Cert-R): Initiator's (responder's) certificate

N-I (N-R): Initiator's (responder's) nonce

ID-I (ID-R): Initiator's (responder's) ID

HASH-I (HASH-R): Initiator's (responder's) hash

I    Encrypted with initiator's public key

R    Encrypted with responder's public key

R    Encrypted with responder's secret key

I    Encrypted with initiator's secret key

     Encrypted with SKEYID_e

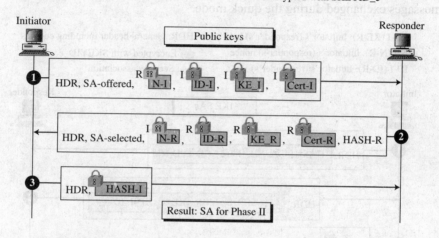

**Fig. 18.26** *Aggressive mode, revised public-key method*

**Digital Signature Method**    Figure 18.27 shows the digital signature method in the aggressive mode. The idea is the same as for the main mode, except that some messages are combined.

   Encrypted with SKEYID_e

Sig-I (Sig-R): Initiator's (responder's) signature

HDR: General header including cookies

Cert-I (Cert-R): Initiator's (responder's) certificate

N-I (N-R): Initiator's (responder's) nonce

KE-I (KE-R): Initiator's (responder's) half-key

ID-I (ID-R): Initiator's (responder's) ID

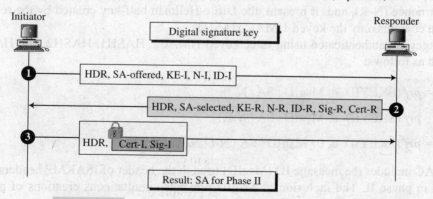

**Fig. 18.27** *Aggressive mode, digital signature method*

## 18.5.6 Phase II: Quick Mode

After SAs have been created in either the main mode or the aggressive mode, phase II can be started. There is only one mode defined for phase II so far, the *quick mode*. This mode is under the supervision of the IKE SAs created by phase I. However, each quick-mode method can follow any main or aggressive mode.

The quick mode uses IKE SAs to create IPSec SAs (or SAs for any other protocol). Figure 18.28 shows the messages exchanged during the quick mode.

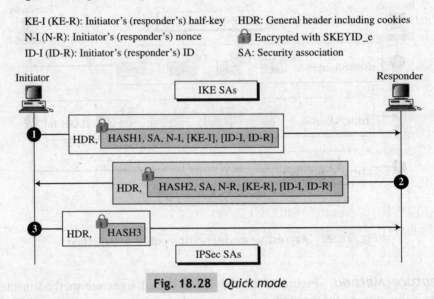

**Fig. 18.28**  *Quick mode*

In phase II, either party can be the initiator. That is, the initiator of phase II can be the initiator of phase I or the responder of phase I.

The initiator sends the first message, which includes the keyed-HMAC HASH1 (explained later), the entire SA created in phase I, a new nonce (N-I), an optional new Diffie-Hellman half-key (KE-I), and the optional IDs of both parties. The second message is similar, but carries the keyed-HMAC HASH2, the responder nonce (N-R), and, if present, the Diffie-Hellman half-key created by the responder. The third message contains only the keyed-HMAC HASH3.

The messages are authenticated using three keyed-HMACs: HASH1, HASH2, and HASH3. These are calculated as follows:

HASH1 = *prf* (SKEYID_d, MsgID | SA | N-I)

HASH2 = *prf* (SKEYID_d, MsgID | SA | N-R)

HASH3 = *prf* (SKEYID_d, 0 | MsgID | SA | N-I | N-R)

Each HMAC includes the message ID (MsgID) used in the header of ISAKMP headers. This allows multiplexing in phase II. The inclusion of MsgID prevents simultaneous creations of phase II from bumping into each other.

All three messages are encrypted for confidentiality using the SKEYID_e created during phase I.

**Perfect Forward Security (PFS)** After establishing an IKE SA and calculating SKEYID_d in phase I, all keys for the quick mode are derived from SKEYID_d. Since multiple phase IIs can be derived from a single phase I, phase II security is at risk if the intruder has access to SKEYID_d. To prevent this from happening, IKE allows **Perfect Forward Security (PFS)** as an option. In this option, an additional Diffie-Hellman half-key is exchanged and the resulting shared key ($g^{ir}$) is used in the calculation of key material (see the next section) for IPSec. PFS is effective if the Diffie-Hellman key is immediately deleted after the calculation of the key material for each quick mode.

**Key Materials** After the exchanges in phase II, an SA for IPSec is created including the key material, K, that can be used in IPSec. The value is derived as:

$$K = \textit{prf}\,(\text{SKEYID\_d, protocol} \mid \text{SPI} \mid \text{N-I} \mid \text{N-R}) \qquad \text{(without PFS)}$$
$$K = \textit{prf}\,(\text{SKEYID\_d}, g^{ir} \mid \text{protocol} \mid \text{SPI} \mid \text{N-I} \mid \text{N-R}) \qquad \text{(with PFS)}$$

If the length of K is too short for the particular cipher selected, a sequence of keys is created, each key is derived from the previous one, and the keys are concatenated to make a longer key. We show the case without PFS; we need to add $g^{ir}$ for the case with PFS.

The key material created is unidirectional; each party creates different key material because the SPI used in each direction is different.

$$K_1 = \textit{prf}\,(\text{SKEYID\_d, protocol} \mid \text{SPI} \mid \text{N-I} \mid \text{N-R})$$
$$K_2 = \textit{prf}\,(\text{SKEYID\_d}, K_1 \mid \text{protocol} \mid \text{SPI} \mid \text{N-I} \mid \text{N-R})$$
$$K_3 = \textit{prf}\,(\text{SKEYID\_d}, K_2 \mid \text{protocol} \mid \text{SPI} \mid \text{N-I} \mid \text{N-R})$$
$$\cdots$$
$$K = K_1 \mid K_2 \mid K_3 \mid \cdots$$

---

**The key material created after phase II is unidirectional; there is one key for each direction.**

---

### 18.5.7 SA Algorithms

Before leaving this section, let us give the algorithms that are negotiated during the first two IKE exchanges.

**Diffie-Hellman Groups** The first negotiation involves the Diffie-Hellman group used for exchanging half-keys. Five groups have been defined, as shown in Table 18.3.

**Table 18.3** *Diffie-Hellman groups*

| Value | Description |
|-------|-------------|
| 1 | Modular exponentiation group with a 768-bit modulus |
| 2 | Modular exponentiation group with a 1024-bit modulus |
| 3 | Elliptic curve group with a 155-bit field size |
| 4 | Elliptic curve group with a 185-bit field size |
| 5 | Modular exponentiation group with a 1680-bit modulus |

***Hash Algorithms*** The hash algorithms that are used for authentication are shown in Table 18.4.

**Table 18.4** *Hash algorithms*

| Value | Description |
|-------|-------------|
| 1 | MD5 |
| 2 | SHA |
| 3 | Tiger |
| 4 | SHA2-256 |
| 5 | SHA2-384 |
| 6 | SHA2-512 |

***Encryption Algorithms*** The encryption algorithms that are used for confidentiality are shown in Table 18.5. All of these are normally used in CBC mode.

**Table 18.5** *Encryption algorithms*

| Value | Description |
|-------|-------------|
| 1 | DES |
| 2 | IDEA |
| 3 | Blowfish |
| 4 | RC5 |
| 5 | 3DES |
| 6 | CAST |
| 7 | AES |

## 18.6 ISAKMP

The ISAKMP protocol is designed to carry messages for the IKE exchange.

### 18.6.1 General Header

The format of the general header is shown in Fig. 18.29.

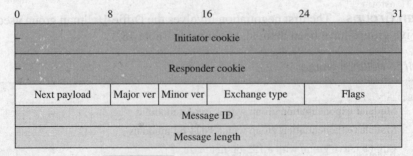

**Fig. 18.29** *ISAKMP general header*

❑ **Initiator cookie.** This 32-bit field defines the cookie of the entity that initiates the SA establishment, SA notification, or SA deletion.

- ❑ **Responder cookie.** This 32-bit field defines the cookie of the responding entity. The value of this field is 0 when the initiator sends the first message.
- ❑ **Next payload.** This 8-bit field defines the type of payload that immediately follows the header. We discuss the different types of payload in the next section.
- ❑ **Major version.** This 4-bit version defines the major version of the protocol. Currently, the value of this field is 1.
- ❑ **Minor version.** This 4-bit version defines the minor version of the protocol. Currently, the value of this field is 0.
- ❑ **Exchange type.** This 8-bit field defines the type of exchange that is being carried by the ISAKMP packets. We have discussed the different exchange types in the previous section.
- ❑ **Flags.** This is an 8-bit field in which each bit defines an option for the exchange. So far only the three least significant bits are defined. The encryption bit, when set to 1, specifies that the rest of the payload will be encrypted using the encryption key and the algorithm defined by SA. The commitment bit, when set to 1, specifies that encryption material is not received before the establishment of the SA. The authentication bit, when set to 1, specifies that the rest of the payload, though not encrypted, is authenticated for integrity.
- ❑ **Message ID.** This 32-bit field is the unique message identity that defines the protocol state. This field is used only during the second phase of negotiation and is set to 0 during the first phase.
- ❑ **Message length.** Because different payloads can be added to each packet, the length of a message can be different for each packet. This 32-bit field defines the length of the total message, including the header and all payloads.

## 18.6.2 Payloads

The payloads are actually designed to carry messages. Table 18.6 shows the types of payloads.

**Table 18.6** *Payloads*

| Types | Name | Brief Description |
|-------|------|-------------------|
| 0 | None | Used to show the end of the payloads . |
| 1 | SA | Used for starting the negotiation |
| 2 | Proposal | Contains information used during SA negotiation |
| 3 | Transform | Defines a security transform to create a secure channel |
| 4 | Key Exchange | Carries data used for generating keys |
| 5 | Identification | Carries the identification of communication peers |
| 6 | Certification | Carries a public-key certificate |
| 7 | Certification Request | Used to request a certificate from the other party |
| 8 | Hash | Carries data generated by a hash function |
| 9 | Signature | Carries data generated by a signature function |
| 10 | Nonce | Carries randomly generated data as a nonce |
| 11 | Notification | Carries error message or status associated with an SA |
| 12 | Delete | Carries one more SA that the sender has deleted |
| 13 | Vendor | Defines vendor-specification extensions |

Each payload has a generic header and some specific fields. The format of the generic header is shown in Fig. 18.30.

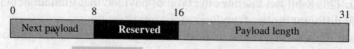

**Fig. 18.30** *Generic payload header*

❑ **Next payload.** This 8-bit field identifies the type of the next payload. When there is no next payload, the value of this field is 0. Note that there is no type field for the current payload. The type of the current payload is determined by the previous payload or the general header (if the payload is the first one).

❑ **Payload length.** This 16-bit field defines the length of the total payload (including the generic header) in bytes.

**SA Payload** The SA payload is used to negotiate security parameters. However, these parameters are not included in the SA payload; they are included in two other payloads (*proposal* and *transform*) that we will discuss later. An SA payload is followed by one or more *proposal payloads*, and each proposal payload is followed by one or more *transform payloads*. The SA payload just defines the *domain of interpretation* field and the *situation* field. Figure 18.31 shows the format of the SA payload.

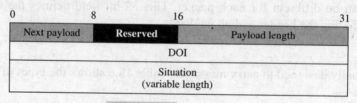

**Fig. 18.31** *SA payload*

The fields in the generic header have been discussed. The descriptions of the other fields follow:

❑ **Domain of interpretation (DOI).** This is a 32-bit field. For phase I, a value of 0 for this field defines a generic SA; a value of 1 defines IPSec.

❑ **Situation.** This is a variable-length field that defines the situation under which the negotiation takes place.

**Proposal Payload** The *proposal payload* initiates the mechanism of negotiation. Although by itself it does not propose any parameters, it does define the protocol identification and the SPI. The parameters for negotiation are sent in the transform payload that follows. Each proposal payload is followed by one or more transform payloads that give alternative sets of parameters. Figure 18.32 shows the format of the proposal payload.

| Next payload | Reserved | Payload length | |
|---|---|---|---|
| Proposal # | Protocol ID | SPI size | No. of transforms |
| SPI (variable length) | | | |

**Fig. 18.32** *Proposal payload*

The fields in the generic header have been discussed. The descriptions of the other fields follow:

❏ **Proposal #.** The initiator defines a number for the proposal so that the responder can refer to it. Note that an SA payload can include several proposal payloads. If all of the proposals belong to the same set of protocols, the proposal number must be the same for each protocol in the set. Otherwise, the proposals must have different numbers.

❏ **Protocol ID.** This 8-bit field defines the protocol for the negotiation. For example, IKE phase1 = 0, ESP = 1, AH = 2, etc.

❏ **SPI size.** This 8-bit field defines the size of the SPI in bytes.

❏ **Number of Transforms.** This 8-bit field defines the number of transform payloads that will follow this proposal payload.

❏ **SPI.** This variable-length field is the actual SPI. Note that if the SPI does not fill the 32-bit space, no padding is added.

**Transform Payload** The *transform payload* actually carries attributes of the SA negotiation. Figure 18.33 shows the format of the transform payload.

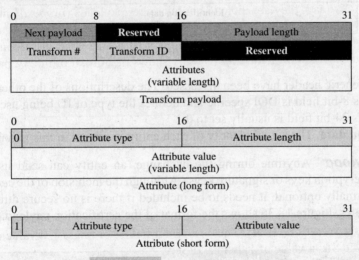

**Fig. 18.33** *Transform payload*

The fields in the generic header have been discussed. The descriptions of the other fields follow:

❏ **Transform #.** This 8-bit field defines the transform number. If there is more than one transform payload in a proposal payload, then each must have its own number.

❏ **Transform ID.** This 8-bit field defines the identity of the payload.

❏ **Attributes.** Each transform payload can carry several attributes. Each attribute itself can have three or two subfields (see Fig. 18.33). The *attribute type* subfield defines the type of attribute as defined in the DOI. The *attribute length* subfield, if present, defines the length of the attribute value. The *attribute value* field is two bytes in the short form or of variable-length in the long form.

**Key-Exchange Payload** The *key exchange payload* is used in those exchanges that need to send preliminary keys that are used for creating session keys. For example, it can be used to send a Diffie-Hellman half-key. Figure 18.34 shows the format of the key-exchange payload.

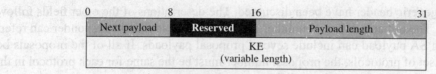

**Fig. 18.34** *Key-exchange payload*

The fields in the generic header have been discussed. The description of the KE field follows:
❑ **KE.** This variable-length field carries the data needed for creating the session key.

***Identification Payload*** The *identification payload* allows entities to send their identifications to each other. Figure 18.35 shows the format of the identification payload.

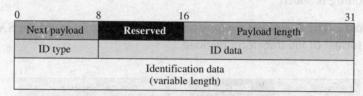

**Fig. 18.35** *Identification payload*

The fields in the generic header have been discussed. The descriptions of the other fields follow:
❑ **ID type.** This 8-bit field is DOI specific and defines the type of ID being used.
❑ **ID data.** This 24-bit field is usually set to 0.
❑ **Identification data.** The actual identity of each entity is carried in this variable-length field.

***Certification Payload*** Anytime during the exchange, an entity can send its certification (for public-encryption/decryption keys or signature keys). Although the inclusion of the *certification payload* in an exchange is normally optional, it needs to be included if there is no secure directory available to distribute the certificates. Figure 18.36 shows the format of the certification payload.

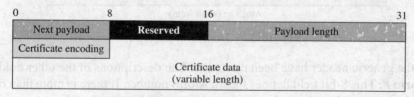

**Fig. 18.36** *Certification payload*

The fields in the generic header have been discussed. The descriptions of the other fields follow:
❑ **Certificate encoding.** This 8-bit field defines the encoding (type) of the certificate. Table 18.7 shows the types defined so far.
❑ **Certificate data.** This variable-length field carries the actual value of the certificate. Note that the previous field implicitly defines the size of this field.

**Table 18.7** *Certification types*

| Value | Type |
|-------|------|
| 0 | None |
| 1 | Wrapped X.509 Certificate |
| 2 | PGP Certificate |
| 3 | DNS Signed Key |
| 4 | X.509 Certificate—Signature |
| 5 | X.509 Certificate—Key Exchange |
| 6 | Kerberos Tokens |
| 7 | Certification Revocation List |
| 8 | Authority Revocation List |
| 9 | SPKI Certificate |
| 10 | X.509 Certificate—Attribute |

**Certificate Request Payload** Each entity can explicitly request a certificate from the other entity using the *certificate request payload*. Figure 18.37 shows the format of this payload.

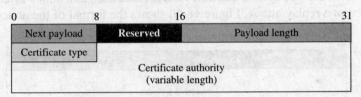

**Fig. 18.37** *Certification request payload*

The fields in the generic header have been discussed. The descriptions of the other fields follow:

❑ **Certificate type.** This 8-bit field defines the type of certificate as previously defined in the certificate payload.
❑ **Certificate authority.** This is a variable-length field that defines the authority for the type of certificate issued.

**Hash Payload** The *hash payload* contains data generated by the hash function as described in the IKE exchanges. The hash data guarantee the integrity of the message or part of the ISAKMP states. Figure 18.38 shows the format of the hash payload.

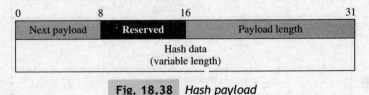

**Fig. 18.38** *Hash payload*

The fields in the generic header have been discussed. The description of the last field follows:

❏ **Hash data.** This variable-length field carries the hash data generated by applying the hash function to the message or part of the ISAKMP states.

**Signature Payload** The *signature payload* contains data generated by applying the digital signature procedure over some part of the message or ISAKMP state. Figure 18.39 shows the format of the signature payload.

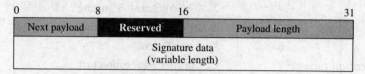

**Fig. 18.39** *Signature payload*

The fields in the generic header have been discussed. The description of the last field follows:

❏ **Signature.** This variable-length field carries the digest resulting from applying the signature over part of the message or ISAKMP state.

**Nonce Payload** The *nonce payload* contains random data used as a nonce to assure liveliness of the message and to prevent a replay attack. Figure 18.40 shows the format of the nonce payload.

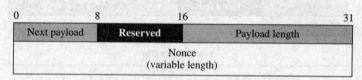

**Fig. 18.40** *Nonce payload*

The fields in the generic header have been discussed. The description of the last field follows:

❏ **Nonce.** This is a variable-length field carrying the value of the nonce.

**Notification Payload** During the negotiation process, sometimes a party needs to inform the other party of the status or errors. The *notification payload* is designed for these two purposes. Figure 18.41 shows the format of the notification payload.

```
0              8              16                          31
| Next payload |   Reserved   |       Payload length       |
|                    DOI (32 bits)                          |
| Protocol ID  |   SPI size   | Notification message type   |
|                        SPI                                |
|                  (variable length)                        |
|                 Notification data                         |
|                  (variable length)                        |
```

**Fig. 18.41** *Notification payload*

The fields in the generic header have been discussed. The descriptions of the other fields follow:

❑ **DOI.** This 32-bit field is the same as that defined for the Security Association payload.

❑ **Protocol ID.** This 8-bit field is the same as that defined for the proposal payload.

❑ **SPI size.** This 8-bit field is the same as that defined for the proposal payload.

❑ **Notification message type.** This 16-bit field specifies the status or the type of error that is to be reported. Table 18.8 gives a brief description of these types.

❑ **SPI.** This variable-length field is the same as that defined for the proposal payload.

❑ **Notification data.** This variable-length field can carry extra textual information about the status or errors. The types of errors are listed in Table 18.8. The values 31 to 8191 are for future use and the values 8192 to 16383 are for private use.

**Table 18.8** *Notification types*

| Value | Description | Value | Description |
|---|---|---|---|
| 1 | INVALID-PAYLOAD-TYPE | 16 | PAYLOAD-MALFORMED |
| 2 | DOI-NOT-SUPPORTED | 17 | INVALID-KEY-INFORMATION |
| 3 | SITUATION-NOT-SUPPORTED | 18 | INVALID-ID-INFORMATION |
| 4 | INVALID-COOKIE | 19 | INVALID-CERT-ENCODING |
| 5 | INVALID-MAJOR-VERSION | 20 | INVALID-CERTIFICATE |
| 6 | INVALID-MINOR-VERSION | 21 | CERT-TYPE-UNSUPPORTED |
| 7 | INVALID-EXCHANGE-TYPE | 22 | INVALID-CERT-AUTHORITY |
| 8 | INVALID-FLAGS | 23 | INVALID-HASH-INFORMATION |
| 9 | INVALID-MESSAGE-ID | 24 | AUTHENTICATION-FAILED |
| 10 | INVALID-PROTOCOL-ID | 25 | INVALID-SIGNATURE |
| 11 | INVALID-SPI | 26 | ADDRESS-NOTIFICATION |
| 12 | INVALID-TRANSFORM-ID | 27 | NOTIFY-SA-LIFETIME |
| 13 | ATTRIBUTE-NOT-SUPPORTED | 28 | CERTIFICATE-UNAVAILABLE |
| 14 | NO-PROPOSAL-CHOSEN | 29 | UNSUPPORTED EXCHANGE-TYPE |
| 15 | BAD-PROPOSAL-SYNTAX | 30 | UNEQUAL-PAYLOAD-LENGTHS |

Table 18.9 is a list of status notifications. Values from 16385 to 24575 and 40960 to 65535 are reserved for future use. Values from 32768 to 40959 are for private use.

**Table 18.9** *Status notification values*

| Value | Description |
|---|---|
| 16384 | CONNECTED |
| 24576-32767 | DOI-specific codes |

***Delete Payload***    The delete payload is used by an entity that has deleted one or more SAs and needs to inform the peer that these SAs are no longer supported. Figure 18.42 shows the format of the delete payload.

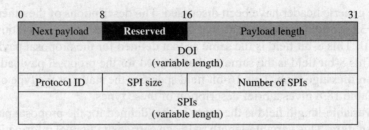

**Fig. 18.42** *Delete payload*

The fields in the generic header have been discussed. The descriptions of the other fields follow:

❑ **DOI.** This 32-bit field is the same as that defined for the Security Association payload.
❑ **Protocol ID.** This 8-bit field is the same as that defined for the proposal payload.
❑ **SPI size.** This 8-bit field is the same as that defined for the proposal payload.
❑ **Number of SPIs.** This 16-bit field defines the number of SPIs. One delete payload can report the deletion of several SAs.
❑ **SPIs.** This variable-length field defines the SPIs of the deleted SAs.

***Vendor Payload*** ISAKMP allows the exchange of information particular to a specific vendor. Figure 18.43 shows the format of the *vendor payload*.

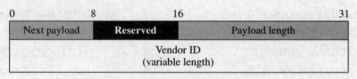

**Fig. 18.43** *Vendor payload*

The fields in the generic header have been discussed. The description of the last field follows:
❑ **Vendor ID.** This variable-length field defines the constant used by the vendor.

## 18.7                RECOMMENDED READING

The following books and websites give more details about subjects discussed in this chapter. The items enclosed in brackets refer to the reference list at the end of the book.

### Books
[DH03], [Fra01], [KPS02], [Res01], [Sta06], and [Rhe03] discuss IPSec thoroughly.

### WebSites
The following websites give more information about topics discussed in this chapter.
    http://www.ietf.org/rfc/rfc2401.txt
    http://www.unixwiz.net/techtips/iguide-ipsec.html
    http://rfc.net/rfc2411.html

## Key Terms

aggressive mode

Authentication Header (AH) Protocol

clogging attack

cookie

Encapsulating Security Payload (ESP)

Internet Key Exchange (IKE)

Internet Security Association and Key

Management Protocol (ISAKMP)

IP Security (IPSec)

main mode

Oakley

Perfect Forward Security (PFS)

replay attack

Security Association Database (SAD)

Security Association (SA)

Security Policy (SP)

Security Policy Database (SPD)

SKEME

transport mode

tunnel mode

## Summary

★ IP Security (IPSec) is a collection of protocols designed by the IETF (Internet Engineering Task Force) to provide security for a packet at the network level.

★ IPSec operates in transport or tunnel mode. In transport mode, IPSec protects information delivered from the transport layer to the network layer, but does not protect the IP header. In tunnel mode, IPSec protects the whole IP packet, including the original IP header.

★ IPSec defines two protocols: Authentication Header (AH) Protocol and Encapsulating Security Payload (ESP) Protocol to provide authentication and encryption or both for packets at the IP level. The Authentication Header (AH) Protocol authenticates the source host and ensures the integrity of the payload carried by the IP packet. Encapsulating Security Payload (ESP) provides source authentication, integrity, and privacy. ESP adds a header and trailer.

★ IPSec indirectly provides access control using a Security Association Database (SAD).

★ In IPSec, Security Policy (SP) defines what type of security must be applied to a packet at the sender or at the receiver. IPSec uses a set of SPs called Security Policy Database (SPD).

★ The Internet Key Exchange (IKE) is the protocol designed to create Security Associations, both inbound and outbound. IKE creates SAs for IPSec. IKE is a complex protocol based on three other protocols: Oakley, SKEME, and ISAKMP.

★ IKE is designed in two phases: phase I and phase II. Phase I creates SAs for phase II; phase II creates SAs for a data exchange protocol such as IPSec.

★ The ISAKMP protocol is designed to carry the message for IKE exchange.

## Practice Set

### Review Questions

**18.1** Distinguish between two modes of IPSec.

**18.2** Define AH and the security services it provides.

**18.3** Define ESP and the security services it provides.

**18.4** Define Security Association (SA) and explain its purpose.

**18.5** Define SAD and explain its relation to Security Association.

**18.6** Define Security Policy and explain its purpose with relation to IPSec.

**18.7** Define IKE and explain why it is needed in IPSec.

**18.8** List phases of IKE and the goal of each phase.

**18.9** Define ISAKMP and its relation to IKE.

**18.10** List ISAKMP payload types and the purpose of each type.

## Exercises

**18.11** A host receives an authenticated packet with the sequence number 181. The replay window spans from 200 to 263. What will the host do with the packet? What is the window span after this event?

**18.12** A host receives an authenticated packet with the sequence number 208. The replay window spans from 200 to 263. What will the host do with the packet? What is the window span after this event?

**18.13** A host receives an authenticated packet with the sequence number 331. The replay window spans from 200 to 263. What will the host do with the packet? What is the window span after this event?

**18.14** The diagram for calculation of SKEYID for the preshared-key method is shown in Fig. 18.44. Note that the key to the prf function in this case is a preshared key.

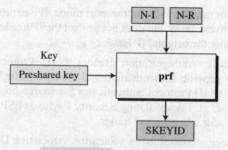

**Fig. 18.44** *Exercise 14*

    a. Draw a similar diagram of SKEYID for the public-key method.
    b. Draw a similar diagram of SKEYID for the digital signature method.

**18.15** Draw a diagram similar to Fig. 18.44 for the following; the key in each case is SKEYID.
    a. SKEYID_a
    b. SKEYID_d
    c. SKEYID_e

**18.16** Draw a diagram similar to Fig. 18.44 for the following, the key in each case is SKEYID.
    a. HASH-I
    b. HASH-R

**18.17** Draw a diagram similar to Fig. 18.44 for the following; the key in each case is SKEYID_d:
    a. HASH1
    b. HASH2
    c. HASH3

**18.18** Draw a diagram similar to Fig. 18.44 for the following; the key in each case is SKEYID_d:
    a. K for the case without PFS
    b. K for the case with PFS

**18.19** Repeat Exercise 19 for the case in which the length of K is too short.

**18.20** Draw a diagram and show actual ISAKMP packets that are exchanged between an initiator and a responder using the *preshared-key* method in the *main* mode (see Fig. 18.20). Use at least two proposal packets with at least two transform packets for each proposal.

**18.21** Repeat Exercise 20 using the *original public-key* method in the *main* mode (see Fig. 18.21).

**18.22** Repeat Exercise 20 using the *revised public-key* method in the *main* mode (see Fig. 18.22).

**18.23** Repeat Exercise 20 using the *digital signature* method in the *main* mode (see Fig. 18.23).

**18.24** Repeat Exercise 20 in the *aggressive* mode (see Fig. 18.24).

**18.25** Repeat Exercise 21 in the *aggressive* mode (see Fig. 18.25).

**18.26** Repeat Exercise 22 in the *aggressive* mode (see Fig. 18.26).

**18.27** Repeat Exercise 23 in the *aggressive* mode (see Fig. 18.27).

**18.28** Draw a diagram and show the actual ISAKMP packets that are exchanged between an initiator and a responder in the *quick* mode (see Fig. 18.28).

**18.29** Compare the preshared-key methods in the main mode and aggressive modes. How much compromise is made in the aggressive mode with respect to security? What is the gain with respect to efficiency?

**18.30** Compare the general public-key methods in the main and aggressive modes. How much compromise is made in the aggressive mode with respect to security? What is the gain with respect to efficiency?

**18.31** Compare the revised public-key methods in the main and aggressive modes. How much compromise is made in the aggressive mode with respect to security? What is the gain with respect to efficiency?

**18.32** Compare the digital signature method in the main and aggressive modes. How much compromise is made in aggressive mode with respect to security? What is the gain with respect to efficiency?

**18.33** In the main and aggressive mode, we assume that an intruder cannot calculate the SKEYID. Give the reasoning behind this assumption.

**18.34** In IKE phase I, the identity is usually defined as the IP address. In the preshared key method, the preshared key is also a function of the IP address. Show how this may create a vicious circle.

**18.35** Compare methods for the main mode and show which method exchanges protected IDs.

**18.36** Repeat Exercise 36 for aggressive methods.

**18.37** Show how IKE reacts to the replay attack in the main mode. That is, show how IKE responds to an attacker that tries to replay one or more messages in the main mode.

**18.38** Show how IKE reacts to the replay attack in the aggressive mode. That is, show how IKE responds to an attacker that tries to replay one or more messages in the aggressive mode.

**18.39** Show how IKE reacts to the replay attack in the quick mode. That is, show how IKE responds to an attacker that tries to replay one or more messages in the quick mode.

**18.40.** Show how IPSec reacts to a brute-force attack. That is, can an intruder do an exhaustive computer search to find the encryption key for IPSec?

# 19

# System Security

## Objectives

This chapter has several objectives:
- ☞ To present the importance of security at the system level
- ☞ To define and discuss the components of the systems involved and the level of security associated with each of them
- ☞ To provide a detailed overview of buffer overflows, and show how they may be exploited for writing malicious programs
- ☞ To describe commonly known malicious programs, like viruses, worms, trojans, logic bombs, spywares and adwares
- ☞ To explain the working principles and classifications of viruses and worms
- ☞ To discuss the UNIX password system and its security issues
- ☞ To present an overview of Information Detection Systems (IDS) and their types
- ☞ To discuss firewalls and their classifications

The development of computer networks has lead to a world full of connected computational resources. The ubiquitous nature of networks has provided human society with the capability of solving problems in a distributed but yet collective manner. However, the boon of communication is accompanied with the concern for security. For an end to end security, it is thus not only sufficient to secure the network, but also imperative to consider threats which may exist because of the loopholes existing in the computational systems. Building correct and fault-free systems is an extremely difficult task. With the complexity of modern computers and systems, a bugfree design is impossible. Designers try to ensure that the bugs do not hamper the normal functionality. Thus, although we know systems have bugs, they are mostly adequate for normal functions. However, security has more stringent requirements. A single bug may compromise all the security measures adopted, as a system is as strong as its weakest defence. In spite of the importance of security, it has remained an additional feature and an after thought. This approach makes the job of the security designers even more challenging. Along with the needed security, the designers are pressed with the additional challenge of maintaining transparency to the user and also not increasing the cost of the service significantly.

## 19.1             DESCRIPTION OF THE SYSTEM

A system is a vague entity that comprises the totality of the computing and the communications environment over which the developers have some control. A system boundary demarcates between the protected and the unprotected components of a system. It defines the interface between the system and the outside world. As long as the definition of the boundary is not changed, system security principles try to provide security of information within the system from threats that originate in the world outside the boundary.

The components inside the system can also be divided into two distinct categories.

*1. Security Relevant*    These components are crucial to the security. A malfunction or penetration in these components can lead to security violations. The Operating System (OS) and the computer hardware its examples.

*2. Others*    These are objects that the system controls and protects. Examples are programs (note not processes), data, terminals, modems, etc.

The line of demarcation between the security relevant components and others are called security perimeter.

A common misconception which must be avoided is that "encryption provides system security". Encryption, as we have seen in the previous discussions in the book, provides data-confidentiality. However, for system security it is needed to have trust in the security-related components inside the security perimeter. For example, the OS needs to be trusted. If the OS is found to be untrustworthy then the result of an encryption program which runs on the OS cannot also be relied upon. Hence, encryption alone cannot solve the problem, other principles and methods are necessary.

## 19.2            USERS, TRUST AND TRUSTED SYSTEMS

A user is a person whose information the system protects and whose access to information is controlled by the system. A user is in general trusted to keep his secret, often in the form of a password, confidential from other users who do not have access to the trusted user's documents. In spite of this, a user may be deceived to manipulate his data in a fashion which compromises the security of the system. In order to protect against such a threat, a trusted user should be warned when he accidentally gives away valuable information. However, if a user betrays this trust intentionally, then system security cannot handle such a scenario.

The system identifies a user through a unique identifier (ID), which is public information like name or account number. The identifier must be unique and unforgetable. The act of associating a user with a unique identifier is called authentication. The identification number is used by the system to associate a process (a running program) with a user. Trust in systems is built using the techniques of identification and authentication. Systems in a network authentication as other systems, or programs impersonating as other programs is a serious security threat. Trusted system enforces a given security policy based on this trust. Trusted systems classify programs based on the level of trust on them. Trusted programs are those upon which the security of the system relies. These programs are responsible for the security of the system. The outputs of these programs are verified and are believed to be correct even if they interact with untrusted programs. On the other hand, benign programs are believed to be benign and obtained generally from trusted vendors, like OS providers. They are believed to be harmless and are trustworthy as long as they do not come into play with untrusted programs. Untrusted programs are obtained from unknown or untrusted sources, like a downloaded file from an unknown web-page.

## 19.3      BUFFER OVERFLOW AND MALICIOUS SOFTWARE

Buffer overflow is a commonly known mistake that exist in some C implementations. These classes of bugs are extremely dangerous, as they write past the end of a buffer or array and hence corrupt the process stack. Often they change the return address of a process after a function call to a secret memory location where a malicious code is planted. This calls for the understanding of these kinds of errors to develop secure coding principles to lessen these security threats in systems.

A buffer, often visualized as an array is a contiguous space of related variables of the same data type. In C or C++ there are no automatic checks on the buffer, which means a user may write past a buffer. This phenomenon is known as **buffer overflow**. Arrays, like all variables in C, can be either static or dynamic. Static variables are allocated at load time on data segment. Dynamic variables are allocated at run time on the stack. We shall discuss on the overflow of dynamic buffers, commonly referred as stack-based buffer overflows.

For example, consider the following C code snippet as a simple example of buffer overflow.

```c
int main( ){
    int buffer[10];
    buffer[20]=5;
}
```

Compilers will compile the above program without any errors. This seemingly simple mistake can be used by the authors of malicious softwares to trigger their codes and thus compromise security. In order to understand the principle behind these attacks let us look at the organization of the process in memory.

A process, which is a program in execution, is divided into three regions: text, data and stack, as shown in Fig. 19.1. The text region is decided by the program and is made of binary instructions and read-only data. Any effort to write in this area leads to a segmentation fault. The initialized or uninitialized data region stores static variables. If the available memory is rendered unavailable, the process is blocked and rescheduled with a larger memory space between the text and stack segments.

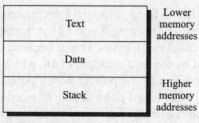

**Fig. 19.1** *Process memory regions*

A stack is a contiguous block of memory containing data, which grows from higher memory address to lower ones. A stack of object has the property of LIFO (Last In First Out), which means that the last object placed on the stack is the first object to be removed. Two of the most important stack operations are the PUSH and the POP. PUSH adds an element at the top of the stack, while POP removes the last element from the stack. This removes the last element from the stack. High level languages use stacks to implement procedure or function calls. After the call of a function, the program flow is changed towards the function being called. But after the function finishes its task, the control returns to the instruction immediately after the call instruction. The parameters of the function call, the return address and the local variables used in the function are dynamically located in the stack. A register called the *stack pointer (sp)* points to the top of the stack. The bottom of the stack is a fixed address, while the *sp* is updated by the kernel at run time to accommodate for extra space required by the local variables of the function. In general architectures like Intel, SPARC and MIPS processors, the stack grows down, that is from higher memory address to lower memory addresses. The stack pointer is thus decremented to allocate the extra space. The reduction of the *sp* to allocate the extra space depends on the *gcc* compiler, which converts the code to assembly instructions. In versions like 3.3.5, for every byte of variable the *sp* is decremented by 4 bytes. Thus, if a character array of size 5 is declared in C, the *sp* shall be decremented by 8 bytes. On the other hand for a 4.1.2 version, the *sp* is decremented in multiples of 16. Thus, for the same array the *sp* will be reduced by 16. In the gcc 3.3.5, the *sp* is decremented for each local variable separately, for version 4.1.2 the sum total of all the bytes required by the local variables is considered and the *sp* is decremented by the next multiple of 16. Further, the stack is required to be aligned on a 4 byte boundary. On modern processors like Intel Core 2 Duo, the stack is typically aligned to 16 bytes. To ensure proper alignment of the stack, every function must be generated such that it keeps the stack alignment. Thus, calling a function compiled with a higher preferred stack boundary from a function compiled with a lower stack boundary will most likely misalign the stack. The extra alignment does consume extra stack space.

Consider the following C code:

```
void function(int a, int b, int c) {
  char buffer1[5];
  char buffer2[10];
}

void main() {
  function(1,2,3);
}
```

On call of this function, the sp has to be appropriately decremented. In case of a *gcc* 3.3.5 the *sp* is reduced by 20 bytes, buffer1 and buffer2 needing 8 and 12 bytes, respectively. However, in case of *gcc* 4.1.2 compiler, the *sp* gets decremented by 16 bytes. This is because collectively the space needed is for 15 bytes and the *sp* is decremented by the next multiple of 16, which is 16 itself.

Further to the stack pointer, there is a frame pointer which points to a fixed location within a stack frame. It is often referred to as the local based pointer. Due to words being constantly pushed onto and popped out from the stack, the relative offsets of the local variables from the stack pointer change. Thus, it becomes inconvenient and cumbersome to access local variables with respect to the stack pointers. Hence, many compilers use a second register called the frame pointer for accessing local variables and parameters as the distance between them and the frame pointer is a constant and does not change with words get into and out from the stack. Remember, the parameters have positive offset while the local variables have negative offset with respect to the frame pointer. On Intel machines the stack pointer is being denoted by ESP and the frame pointer is being denoted by EBP.

The first thing a procedure does when called, is save the current frame pointer in the stack, so that it can be retrieved on the procedure exit. Then the stack pointer is saved as the current frame pointer. Subsequently, the stack pointer is decremented to allocate space for the local variables. This code is called the procedure prolog. When the procedure is exited, then the stack is cleaned: this is called the procedure epilog. The Intel ENTER and LEAVE instructions are provided to perform these two procedures, prolog and epilog efficiently.

We shall consider the following example to understand these stacking activities. A knowledge of assemble language and the *gdb* debugger is helpful but not strictly required. The programs which are mentioned in the following text are compiled on Red Hat Linux operating system using 4.1.2 *gcc* compiler on an Intel Core 2 Duo Machine.

---

**Example 19.1**

```
void function(int a, int b, int c) {
     char buffer1[5];
     char buffer2[10];
}
     void main() {
     function(1,2,3);
}
```

When the above code, named *ex1.c* is compiled using *gcc* compiler with the -S switch, the assemble code *ex1.s* is generated. The corresponding command is:

```
gcc -S -o ex1.s ex1.c
```

---

The corresponding assembly code to call the function is described next. The parameters immediate values 1, 2 and 3 are saved in the stack. In the assembly code, $ means immediate value and (%esp) indicates the address value of the register stack pointer, esp. The number before the parenthesis indicates the offset. Since the stack is filled from higher memory address to lower memory address, first 3 is pushed, then 2 and finally 1.

```
movl    $3, 8(%esp)
movl    $2, 4(%esp)
movl    $1, (%esp)
call    function
```

The instruction call will push the instruction pointer into the stack. The saved ip is the return address (RET) to which the program counter jumps back after the call is executed.

The function upon its execution does the following operations:

```
pushl   %ebp
movl    %esp, %ebp
subl    $16, %esp
```

Thus, the frame pointer, *ebp* is pushed into the stack. This is the old frame pointer which has to be retrieved when the function completes its task. The current stack pointer is saved in the register frame pointer, which is the updated value of *ebp*. The stack pointer is then decremented by 16 bytes to allocate for the space required for the character buffer of size 13 (remember the space required is collectively decided).

Thus, the size of the stack looks like as shown in the Fig. 19.2:

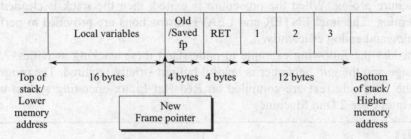

**Fig. 19.2** *Arrangement of the stack*

With this background we shall consider another example to understand the threat of buffer overflows to the security of a code. The purpose of the example is to appreciate the fact that buffer overflows can change the return address stored during the function call. In this example, this shall lead to a segmentation fault as data is accessed outside the process address space. But if carefully controlled can be changed to the address of a malicious code, thus compromising the security of the system.

**Example 19.2** Consider the following program, named ex2.c, which shows an instance of buffer overflow.

```
#include <stdio.h>
#include <stdlib.h>
void function(char *str) {
  char buffer[16];
  strcpy(buffer,str);
}
void main() {
  char large_string[256];
  int i;
  for( i = 0; i < 255; i++)
  large_string[i] = 'A';
  function(large_string);
}
```

This code shows an example of over-writing on a 16-byte character array named buffer. The main function passes as argument a large string of size 256 bytes and filled with the ascii value of the letter 'A', that is the integer value 65. Thus the strcpy function creates an overflow attempting to write 256 bytes onto an array of size 16 bytes. The program compiles successfully and thus hides the fact that there is a buffer overflow.

The corresponding assembly code for the program is as shown below:

```
        .file   "ex2.c"
        .text
.globl function
        .type   function, @function
function:
    pushl   %ebp
    movl    %esp, %ebp
    subl    $24, %esp
```

```
—      movl    8(%ebp), %eax
       movl    %eax, 4(%esp)
       leal    -16(%ebp), %eax
       movl    %eax, (%esp)
       call    strcpy
       leave
       ret
       .size   function, .-function
.globl main
       .type   main, @function
main:
       leal    4(%esp), %ecx
       andl    $-16, %esp
       pushl   -4(%ecx)

       pushl   %ebp
       movl    %esp, %ebp
       pushl   %ecx
       subl    $276, %esp
       movl    $0, -8(%ebp)
       jmp     .L4
.L5:
       movl    -8(%ebp), %eax
       movb    $65, -264(%ebp,%eax)
       addl    $1, -8(%ebp)
.L4:
       cmpl    $254, -8(%ebp)
       jle     .L5
       leal    -264(%ebp), %eax
       movl    %eax, (%esp)
       call    function
       addl    $276, %esp
       popl    %ecx
       popl    %ebp
       leal    -4(%ecx), %esp
       ret
       .size   main, .-main
       .ident  "GCC: (GNU) 4.1.2 20070925 (Red Hat 4.1.2-33)"
       .section    .note.GNU-stack,"",@progbits
```

The stack is updated by the main function as shown in Fig. 19.3.

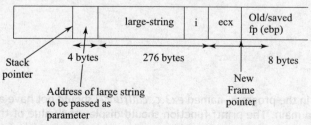

**Fig. 19.3** *Stack's configuration by the main function*

The main passes the character string large_string to the function. The function calls the *strcpy( )* function to overwrite the string buffer which is of size only 16 bytes. This causes an overflow in the buffer, and the ascii value of the letter 'A' is written onto the buffer, across the saved frame pointer, the return address and *str. The return address is thus overwritten by the value 0x41414141 (41 is the hexadecimal value of 65, which is the ascii value of 'A'). This being an illegal address, outside the process address space leads to a segmentation fault. The state of the stack after the function call is shown in Fig. 19.4.

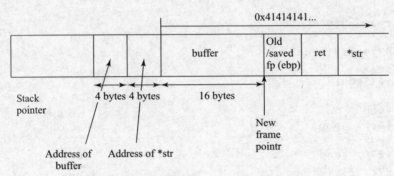

**Fig. 19.4**  *Stack's configuration by the function*

This example shows that the seemingly innocent buffer overflow can lead to a change of the return address. Although in this case, it is an illegal address and the program runs to give a segmentation fault, but the fact to be learnt is that overflow can change the flow of a program. In the next example, we shall consider an example where the change of the return address by the called function leads to a wrong or faulty output of a program 19.3

**Example 19.3**
```
#include <stdio.h>

void callfunc()
{
int buf[3];
int *ret;
ret = buf + 5;
*ret = *ret + 7;
}
void main( )
{
   int b;
   b = 0;
   callfunc();
   b = 1;
   printf("%d\n", b);
}
```
It may be noted that in the program, named *ex3.c*, *callfunc()* should not have any effect on the output of the printf function in main. The printf function should display the value of the local variable *b* as 1. However, the *callfunc()* changes the return address and makes the control of the program to skip the assignment of *x*=1. Thus the program prints 0, while it should print 1.

The called function, *callfunc*( ) changes the return address so that the assignment *x*=1 is skipped. In order to understand the corresponding code, let us study the contents of the stack in the following Fig. 19.5.

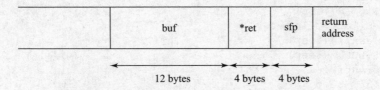

**Fig. 19.5** *The status of the stack after callfunc( )*

The stack is decremented by 16 bytes to allocate space for the pointer *ret and the buf array, which is made of 3 integers and thus requiring 12 bytes. Thus the distance between the address to buf and the return address is 20 bytes, and thus ret is set to buf + 5 (5 integer address means 20 bytes). The assembly code provided next explains the stack operation in more details.

```
        .file    "ex3.c"
        .text
.globl callfunc
        .type    callfunc, @function
callfunc:
        pushl   %ebp
        movl    %esp, %ebp
        subl    $16, %esp
        leal    -16(%ebp), %eax
        addl    $20, %eax
        movl    %eax, -4(%ebp)
        movl    -4(%ebp), %eax
        movl    (%eax), %eax
        leal    7(%eax), %edx
        movl    -4(%ebp), %eax
        movl    %edx, (%eax)
        leave
        ret
        .size   callfunc, .-callfunc
        .section        .rodata
.LC0:
        .string         "%d\n"
        .text
.globl main
        .type   main, @function
main:
        leal    4(%esp), %ecx
        andl    $-16, %esp
        pushl   -4(%ecx)
        pushl   %ebp
        movl    %esp, %ebp
```

```
        pushl  %ecx
        subl   $36, %esp
        movl   $0, -8(%ebp)
        call   callfunc
        movl   $1, -8(%ebp)
        movl   -8(%ebp), %eax
        movl   %eax, 4(%esp)
        movl   $.LC0, (%esp)
        call   printf
        addl   $36, %esp
        popl   %ecx
        popl   %ebp
        leal   -4(%ecx), %esp
        ret
        .size  main, .-main
        .ident "GCC: (GNU) 4.1.2 20070925 (Red Hat 4.1.2-33)"
        .section    .note.GNU-stack,"",@progbits
```

Next lets explain why the return address is incremented by 7. We need to skip the assignment $x=1$ and go to the next line. The address values are obtained using the gdb tool, the output of which is provided next. We Observe the assignment $x=1$ marked in bold face. It is evident from the output of the *gdb* tool, that the return address needs to be increased by 7, the difference between the memory locations 0x080483ff and 0x08048406.

```
$ gcc ex3.c -o ex3
$ gdb ex3
GNU gdb Red Hat Linux (6.6-35.fc8rh)
Copyright (C) 2006 Free Software Foundation, Inc.
GDB is free software, covered by the GNU General Public License, and you are
welcome to change it and/or distribute copies of it under certain conditions.
Type "show copying" to see the conditions.
There is absolutely no warranty for GDB. Type "show warranty" for details.
This GDB was configured as "i386-redhat-linux-gnu"...
(no debugging symbols found)
Using host libthread_db library "/lib/libthread_db.so.1".
(gdb) disassemble main
Dump of assembler code for function main:
0x080483e2 <main+0>: lea 0x4(%esp),%ecx
0x080483e6 <main+4>: and $0xfffffff0,%esp
0x080483e9 <main+7>: pushl 0xfffffffc(%ecx)
0x080483ec <main+10>: push %ebp
0x080483ed <main+11>: mov %esp,%ebp
0x080483ef <main+13>: push %ecx
0x080483f0 <main+14>: sub $0x24,%esp
0x080483f3 <main+17>: movl $0x0,0xfffffff8(%ebp)
0x080483fa <main+24>: call 0x80483c4 <callfunc>
0x080483ff <main+29>: movl $0x1,0xfffffff8(%ebp)
0x08048406 <main+36>: mov 0xfffffff8(%ebp),%eax
0x08048409 <main+39>: mov %eax,0x4(%esp)
```

```
0x0804840d <main+43>: movl $0x8048500,(%esp)
0x08048414 <main+50>: call 0x80482dc <printf@plt>
0x08048419 <main+55>: add $0x24,%esp
0x0804841c <main+58>: pop %ecx
0x0804841d <main+59>: pop %ebp
0x0804841e <main+60>: lea 0xfffffffc(%ecx),%esp
0x08048421 <main+63>: ret
End of assembler dump.
```

This ability to overflow the buffer and change the return address provides the attacker the power to plant malicious programs and execute them on a function call. The attacker copies a large string into a buffer without doing any bound check. The return address is thus overwritten with the address where the malicious code is located. Typically, the exploit for the stack overflow writes or corrupts an environment variable. The environment variable is filled with the return address pointing to the location of the malicious program. When the actual program comes into execution and uses the environment variable and copies into any string, the malicious code comes into play. These kinds of attacks are known as *stack smashing attacks*.

Modern compilers take strategy to prevent these kinds of stack overflow attacks. As the correct computation of the return address is needed for the attack, the compilers tries to prevent them using stack misalignment. Modern compilers emit extra code to check for buffer overflows, such as stack smashing attacks. This is done by adding a guard variable to functions with vulnerable objects. This includes functions that call *alloca*, and functions with buffers larger than 8 bytes. The guards are initialized when a function is entered and then check when the function exits. If a guard check fails, an error message is printed and the program exits. In Ubuntu 6.10 and later versions this option is enabled by default for C, and C++.

However, in spite of these protections stack smashing remains a threat for softwares and needs to be carefully tackled. In the next section, we elaborate on some commonly known types of malicious programs.

## 19.4                                  MALICIOUS PROGRAMS

*Malicious programs*, as already clarified, are those programs which try to subvert the expected operation of secured and benign codes. As mentioned in the previous section, buffer overflow attacks give the adversary the power to change the return address. Typically, the changed return address points back to the buffer itself, where a malicious exploit is written. The exploit could be a program to run a shell in the victim computer. The ability to open up a shell in a target computer, gives in turn the ability to the attacker to run various types of harmful programs. The two most commonly known categories of malicious programs are *worms* and *viruses*. Although often worms are also referred to as *viruses*, it would be appropriate to mention at this point the difference between these two types.

**Worms**    These are programs that can run independently. It can propagate a full working version of itself to other machines. The term tries to draw an analogy of these programs with that of parasites which live inside a host and uses its resources for its existence. The concept of a worm program that spreads itself among machines was first mentioned in the classic science fiction, named '*The Shockwave Rider*' by John Brunner in 1975. Thereafter researchers at Xerox PARC reported their experiments on the worm programs in an article in the Communications of the ACM.

Interestingly, the initial worm programs were designed to do "good" work in a distributive way, and not break systems. However as of now, worms are used only as a special category of harmful programs.

**Viruses**   These programs on the other hand, cannot run independently. It requires the host program to run and activate them. These are analogous to biological viruses, which are not alive themselves, but invade and corrupt host cells. The first time when the word *VIRUS* was used to indicate a program that infects a computer was by David Gerrold in a science fiction, named "*When Harlie Was One*". The first formal usage of the term was made by Fred Cohen around 1983. He defined computer virus to be a program that can infect other programs by modifying them to include a copy of itself.

Some other types of malicious programs are *logic bombs*, *Trojans*, *spywares* and *adwares*.

**Logic Bombs**   A *logic bomb* is a malicious program which has typically two parts: payload and the trigger. The payload typically is a malicious piece of code, and the trigger is usually a Boolean logic that triggers the malicious code when the condition is satisfied. The trigger is usually developed using local conditions like date.

Logic bombs are inserted stealthily into a big program. They often have an objective of causing financial harm. Thus, the logic bomb creates violation of security when some external events occur.

Historically, there are several examples of such codes. Recently, a person fired from his job, implanted a logic bomb in the system such that it will be fired on a particular date after he left the company. The logic bomb would delete all the files in the system. The man was ultimately detained in jail for several years for this misdoing. Such examples of logic bombs which fires on a particular time or date, say April 1, 2010 is known as *time bombs*.

Once, a program was posted in the USENET news network to make system administration easy. In the program which was to be compiled and run with root privilege, dangerously there were lines to change to the root directory and remove all files.

**Trojans**   *Trojans* are malicious programs that perform some harmless activities in addition to some malicious activities. A *Trojan horse* is a program with some known or documented effect and some undocumented or unexpected effects.

A classic example is password grabbing programs. A fake login prompt asks the user to enter the password. The program then obtains the password and displays an error message showing incorrect password. Then the actual login prompt is displayed, thus making the user believe that he typed in the password incorrectly. Now he enters the system with correct password, but meanwhile he has given away his password.

A propagating Trojan horse or a replicating Trojan horse is an example of Trojan horse which can create a copy of itself. One of the earliest examples, called the *animal*, was an example of a Trojan which would create an extra copy of itself.

**Spyware**   *Spyware* is software that is used to collect information from a computer and transmit it to another computer. The information which the spyware exports to the another system could be of the same type as done by viruses, but the essential difference is that spywares do not replicate. They are also different from Trojans, in the fact that the spywares do not deceive the user but does its malice passively. Spywares often get downloaded when we are viewing some webpage, the phenomenon being called **drive by download**.

Examples of information gathered include the following:

1. **Passwords:** A key logger is often used to retrieve the information typed in as password by the user during login. A use of a virtual key board can often be a way to subvert actions of these key loggers which uses the key strokes to ascertain the content of the typed message.
2. **Credit card numbers and bank secrets:** These are special subjects of spywares for their financial benefits.
3. **Software license keys:** They can be used for piracy of softwares.

**Adwares** *Adwares* have much similarity with spywares. They are also not self replicating like the spywares. Their objective is more from the marketing perspective. Examples of them could include the advertisements popping up unintentionally depending on the content or website we are viewing. Their purpose is to increase the sale of some products. They can also transmit information which may be useful from the marketing point of view.

In the next few sections, we try to provide an overview on the working principles of the more important malicious programs, namely *worms* and *viruses*.

## 19.5                       WORMS

The worm programs exposed the security flaws of the standard functions provided by UNIX. We shall discuss some problems specific to some UNIX utilities. A family of routines in the standard C library takes inputs to buffers without checking for bounds. Examples include *gets, scanf, fscanf,* sscanf and other such routines. They may thus be used to overrun buffers unless the user explicitly takes care of the number of characters. Careless usage of the routines like *sprintf* and usage of *strcat* and *strcpy* instead of *strncat* and *strncpy* may also overflow buffers. The problem with these codes is they are functionally correct and seemingly harmless. However, the usage of such codes in networking or trusted programs can cause exploits to work by carefully doctoring inputs.

In order to circumvent this issue patches were developed. The first measure adopted was to replace all such codes by bounded versions. These versions accept values for bounds on their buffer arguments. Next, all servers and trusted applications should be checked for usage of these bounded versions of codes. For example, consider the fingerd program which runs as a daemon to service remote requests using the finger protocol, an utility which allows users to obtain information about other users. The fingerd servers used the gets call, and thus patches had to be developed for these programs. These revised versions of programs do not make use of the original gets commands and were devoid of function calls which fill buffers without checking for bounds.

The other way of running a worm is by targeting the sendmail program. The sendmail program is used to route mail in a heterogeneous network. When the sendmail program operates as a daemon process, the program "listens" on a TCP port 25 in order to deliver mails using *Simple Message Transfer Protocol* (SMTP). The worm worked by exploiting the debugging option in the program. The worm would specify the debug command to sendmail and then specify a set of commands instead of a user address as the recipient of a message. Normally, this is not allowed but it is kept to allow easy testing of the complicated sendmail program. New versions of this program have been released where the debug option has been disabled. Or, it requests the user to enter the root password in order to avail of the debug option.

The worms also attempt to determine the passwords which the users provide. The Unix passwords previously were stored as plaintext in a "password file". The system protected the passwords by controlling the access, such that the passwords were visible only to system administrators and privileged users. However, due to unintentional errors or wrong programming, this practice can be dangerous. There is an instance which occurred in the early 1960s, when two system administrators at MIT were editing the password file and the daily message that gets printed on every ones terminal during login. However due to a software error, both the files got swapped and for a time the password file was printed on every terminal when it was logged in.

In order to avoid such problems, UNIX does not keep actual passwords anywhere on the system. Instead, UNIX uses a program called *crypt*( ) to encrypt a block of 0 bits with the user password. The result of the encryption is stored in the */etc/passwd file*. When a user tries to login, the password is not decrypted (it was actually never encrypted). Instead the login program takes a block of zeros and compares the newly transformed block with the block stored in */etc/passwd file*. If there is a match the user is allowed in by the system.

The algorithm that *crypt*( ) uses is based on the *Data Encryption Standard* (DES), developed by *National Institute of Standards and Technology* (NIST). The *crypt*( ) functions takes the user password as the encryption key and uses it to encrypt a 64 bit block of 0's. The resulting 64 bit ciphertext is then encrypted again with the password, the process being repeated 25 times. The final 64 bits are unpacked into a string of 11 printable characters that are stored in the */etc/passwd file*. The ability of DES function to resist against cryptanalysis, has lead to the fact that the only way of breaking the UNIX password security is to do a brute force search or a dictionary attack.

A dictionary attack is launched by the adversary by recording possible passwords chosen from say English and numbers in a file. Then they are encrypted by the UNIX crypt function and verified with the */etc/passwd* file for any matches.

At the time of design of DES, the security of 56 bits brute force search was considered to be high. However, in today's world with the progress of VLSI designs and parallel processors systems have been developed which can quite efficiently do such a search. The recent DES cracker named *COPACOBANA* was built in 2006 by teams from Universities of Bochum and Kiel. COPACOBANA consists of 120 Field-programmable gate arrays (FPGAs) of type XILINX Spartan3-1000 running in parallel. The cost of the machine is approximately $10,000, which is a reduction by a factor of 25 over previous such machines. Since 2007, SciEngines GmbH, a spin-off company of the two project partners of COPACOBANA has enhanced and developed successors of COPACOBANA. In 2008, their *COPACOBANA RIVYERA* reduced the time to break DES to less than one day, using 128 Spartan-3 5000's.

In order to reduce such attacks, an approach was taken long back, which was to shadow the passwords. The hashed passwords (they are not really encrypted) are stored in a file, which is visible to only the system administrator, and a privileged call performs encryptions and comparisons with an appropriate delay. Additionally, often a threshold is set, which exceeded an alarm is raised by the system.

In addition the password is often "salted" to ensure that the result of the DES encryption gets changed. The DES salt is a 12 bit number, between 0 and 4095, which slightly changes the result of the DES function. When the password is changed with the */bin/passwd program*, a salt is selected depending on the time of the day. The salt is converted into a two-character string and is stored in the */etc/passwd file* along with the encrypted password. The purpose of the salt is thus that the same password can be stored in 4096 ways in the */etc/passwd* file and thus increase the complexity of a dictionary attack 4096 times.

Worms can be classified by the primary method they use for transport. They can be divided into the following types:

1. **IM worms:** Worms using instant messaging is called IM worms.
2. **email worms:** Worms using email as a means of spreading are called email worms.

## 19.6            VIRUSES

The number of computer viruses is on the rise. Literature says that a computer connected to the Internet may experience an attack every 39 seconds. The art of using new vulnerabilities in systems and using them for building viruses has evolved. As told above, viruses are malicious programs that can copy itself and infect a computer without permission or knowledge of the user. A computer virus has three parts:

*1. Infection Mechanism*    This part involves how a virus spreads by modifying other code to contain a copy of the virus. The exact means through which the virus spreads is commonly known as the infection vector of the virus.

*2. Payload*    This part details what the virus does, besides spreading. The payload may create accidental or intentional damage. Accidental damage may result from unknown systems, bugs in the virus code etc.

*3. Trigger*    The payload is triggered on some conditions.

The parts 'payload' and 'trigger' are optional according to the definition of a virus. By definition, a virus has to infect. *A logic bomb* is a term attributed to a program, which has the trigger and the payload, but is devoid of the infection step.

A pseudocode for the virus is as shown below:

```
infect( );
if trigger( )
  then payload( );
```

The virus by definition targets a locally accessible target code, which includes codes in shared network. The virus does not select the same target code always, but rather varies its target as infecting the same code is useless. However, it should be kept in mind that being able to detect whether a code is infected or not, means that the virus can also be detected by an anti virus. Thus this has to be done cleverly.

In next section we will discuss detail classifications of the virus based on the target of the virus and the method adopted by the virus.

### 19.6.1    Classification by the Target

The important classes of virus depending on the type of the target code are the boot sector virus, the executable file infectors and the data file infectors, also called macro virus.

*Boot Sector Virus*

The basic boot sequence has two important steps after power on:

*1. Primary Boot*    The ROM based instructions first run, and then after a self test identifies the boot device. The boot block is then read, and the control is transferred to the loaded code.

**2. Secondary Boot**  The code loaded during the primary boot loads a program that understands the boot device's file system structure. This is called the *secondary boot* and the operating system kernel is loaded during this step.

A boot sector virus, or Boot Sector Infector (BSI) is a virus that infects by copying itself into the master boot block. The content of the former boot block is copied else where in the disk. Thus, the virus after completing the infection and other tasks can complete the booting process.

The advantage of a boot sector virus is that it launches before any anti-virus starts or the operating system is loaded. However BSI's are now rare. Machines are not booted with boot floppies, and operating systems prevent writing to the disk's boot block.

Examples of boot virus were *Michelangelo* and *Stone*.

## 19.6.2  Executable File Infectors

A file infector is a virus which infects files which the operating system considers to be executables. Binary executables are the commonest targets of these viruses. The viruses can be placed at the beginning, end, over-written or inserted into a file.

Viruses which places its codes at the beginning of a target executable code is often called Prepending virus. Older file formats like .COM, MS-DOS when executed, the entire file gets loaded and the execution starts from the beginning of the loaded file. Thus the virus gets control first when the infected file is run. An example of a .COM prepending virus is the *Hungarian virus Polimer.512* A, which is 512 bytes long and prepends itself at the beginning of the executable.

In contrast, there are some viruses which append itself at the end of the target file. This is even easier than the prepending virus. These viruses are called *appending virus*. Many executable files have a header which points to the start location of a file. The virus can change this start location to point to the virus code and then jump to the original start location when it has completed its work. An example of this virus is *Vienna*.

## 19.6.3  Overwriting Virus

*Overwriting* viruses, as the name suggests, overwrites the target files with their own copy. This avoids change in the size of the file size, which occurs in the prepending or the appending virus discussed above. This is advantageous for the virus as a change in size of a file may be used to identify a virus. However, blind overwriting can also be detected easily by the anti-virus. The virus can thus adopt several techniques:

❏ The virus can overwrite sections of repeated values in the program's data. After finishing its activity the virus can restore the repeated values.

❏ The virus can save the original content of the file which it is overwriting, similar to the boot sector virus. Viruses can take advantage of the fact that the operating system allocates more data than required for a file. This extra space can be used stealthily by the virus to evade detection.

❏ Due to alignment to the page boundary, parts of executable files are padded. The unused space can be used by the virus to be silently present in the target code.

❏ A virus can also apply compression methods to create space for itself. But enough space needs to be created for itself and also the decompression program. The decompression program is used by the virus after finishing its activity to restore the original code.

### 19.6.4  Companion Virus

Some types of viruses do not modify the infected code. A **companion virus** is one that installs itself such that it is executed before the target code. It takes advantage of the process by which the operating system or shell searches for executable files. One approach used in MS-DOS is to give the virus the same name as the target, but change the extension from .EXE to .COM. In MS-DOS if an executable named foo is searched, the files looked after consecutively are foo.com, foo.exe and foo.bat. This technique was used by the Globe virus around 1992. The victim trying to execute a file, generally types without the extension. In such a case the operating systems give priority to the .COM extension over the .EXE extension, thus triggering the malicious program.

Yet another important class of functions is known as the *Macro Virus*, which takes advantage of the "macros" embedded in some editing applications, like word processors. Macros are short snippets of codes written in a language which is interpreted by the application. The language is equipped enough to write a virus much easily compared to that using a low level language. An example of such a virus was the *Concept virus*, which targeted the set of macros which are used by all edited documents in Microsoft Word. For example, the *FileSaveAs* macro applies to all documents which we edit in word. The effect of the macro virus was that it takes an uninfected virus and as the user uses the *FileSaveAs* menu, the file gets infected as the macro virus gets triggered.

Next we consider classifications of virus based on the way the virus program conceals or hides itself from an anti-virus program. The types of virus classified based on the concealment strategy can be: *Encryption*, *Oligomorphism*, *Polymorphism* and *Metamorphism*. We briefly describe these types one by one.

### 19.6.5  Encryption

The virus body if not encrypted, is trivial to detect and analyze. However, if the virus body, consisting of the infection, trigger and payload, is encrypted then it becomes difficult to be detected. To execute the virus, the encrypted body thus needs to be decrypted. Hence encrypted virus has a dedicated decryptor loop, which decrypts the virus body and transfer the control to it. This loop is typically much smaller in size compared to the body, and thus provides a smaller profile to the antivirus.

For encryption of the body generally the following methods are adopted. In general, the encryptions used are more of obfuscation techniques rather than strong cryptographic mechanisms.

1. **Simple Transformations**   The transformations in the virus body could be a sequence of simple logical and arithmetical operations. They could include logical not, arithmetic shift, rotations, incrementations and decrementations. Note that these operations are key-less transformations.

2. **Key Mixing**   A static or variable key is mixed with the body using some reversible transformations, like xoring or addition. The key could either be a static key for the entire body or it could vary along with the decryption. The body could be divided into some components, and the key for the $i^{th}$ component could be derived from the key of the previous component by adding with the content of the $i^{th}$ component of the body.

3. **Substitution Cipher**   Look up tables could also be used to achieve the encryption. The $i^{th}$ component of the virus body could be looked into fixed tables and transformed accordingly.

4. **Strong Encryption**   With the development of cryptographic libraries like openssl, virus bodies can also decrypt using these function calls without much overhead.

The problem with these encryption schemes is that the encrypted output remains the same. This increases the possibility of being detected by anti-virus routines. Hence, a natural way out is to use varying keys, but then the decryptor loop needs to be updated with the changed key.

### 19.6.6 Oligomorphism

When the virus uses a varying key, the virus body gets changed with every encryption. However, the decryptor loop does not change for most of the part. This again gives an avenue to the anti-virus routines to spot the virus.

A scheme which is used by virus programs is that instead of one decryptor loop, a pool of decryptor loops are used. The virus selects one of these decryptor loops. Thus, the entire virus changes and hence become harder to detect. But the increase in difficulty is only marginal as the detecting software now needs to check for the variants of the decryptor loop. For example, the virus Memorial has 96 decryptors.

### 19.6.7 Polymorphism

A polymorphic virus is almost the same as the oligomorphic virus. But in these viruses, the total number of decryptor loops are extremely large. For example, a virus called *Tremor* has almost six billion possible decryptor loops.

The virus changes its decryptor loop by using a mutation engine, which changes the decryptor loop every encryption. The mutation engine randomly (or pseudo-randomly) selects a trick from a repository of possible transformations to change the loop.

Various methods used for code obfuscation and by compilers for optimizing codes. Some of the methods which are used for writing virus are *Instruction equivalence*, *Instruction sequence equivalence*, *Instruction reordering, register renaming, concurrency, writing convoluted programs, inlining and outlining of function calls*. Next we briefly explain these techniques:

***Instruction Equivalence*** This method takes advantage of the fact that often many instructions are provided which can be used to the same effect. Like the instructions, clear r1 (clear the register r1) is the same as xor r1 r1 (perform a xor between the contents stored in register r1 with itself and store the result, which is zero, back to register r1.

***Instruction Sequence Equivalence*** While in Instruction equivalence, two instructions are equivalent, in Instruction sequence equivalence, it is the sequence of instructions which are the same. Thus an assignment $x=1$, can be stated equivalently as the sequence of instructions: $x=10$, $x=x-9$. Note that this technique can be adopted both for assembly level programming as well as for high level languages.

***Instruction Reordering*** A sequence of instructions may have dependencies among themselves. Using the independence among some instructions, they can be performed in different orders. These techniques are well studied for instruction level parallelism. Register renaming is a minor method which indicates change of the names of the registers that are used in the instructions. It is an extremely simple technique but may confuse anti virus routines.

## Concurrency

The original code can be separated into multiple threads of execution. This method can greatly complicate automatic analysis by the anti virus. For example, a sequence of operations, $a$=func1( ), $b$=func2( ) and $c$=$a$+$b$ can be implemented using two threads. One of the thread computes $a$, while the other evaluates $b$. Finally, the sum $c$ is determined. Hence we have,

```
       start thread T
       a=func1( );
       wait for signal
       c=a + b;
    T:
       b=func2( );
       send signal;
       exit thread T;
```

This procedure naturally takes advantage of the scope of concurrency in the program.

***Inlining and Outlining of Functions*** Code inlining is the procedure to replace subroutine calls with subroutine codes. It is normally used to avoid function call overheads. Outlining is the reverse operations. Writing convoluted codes or spaghetti codes is also a technique used for varying the decryptor loop body of the virus.

### 19.6.8 Metamorphism

These viruses do not use decryption but changes the entire body of the virus using the techniques used by polymorphic viruses for their decryptor loop. Thus, they are often described as "Metamorphics are body polymorphics". Thus the mutation engine of a metamorphic virus needs to change from infection to infection.

Win32/Apparition virus carries its source and drops it whenever it can find a compiler installed on the machine. This is a real threat for Linux based systems, which has C compilers placed in a typical installation of the operating system. The virus inserts junk code into and removes itself from the source, and then recompiles itself. Thus, each new generation of the virus is completely different and thus makes detection a difficult problem.

In December 1998, Vecna, a noted (notorious?) Virus writer, created the Win95/Regswap virus. Regswap achieved metamorphosis via register usage exchange. Any part of the virus body will use different registers but the same code.

For example consider the following code:

```
5A                   pop edx
BF04000000           mov edi, 0004h
8BF5                 mov esi, ebp
B80C000000           mov eax, 000ch
81C288000000         add edx, 008h
8B1A                 mov ebx, [edx]
899C8618110000       mov [esi+eax*4+00001118], ebx
```

A new generation of the above code with some register exchanges and renaming are as follows:

```
58                pop eax
BB04000000        mov ebx, 0004h
8BD5              mov edx, ebp
BF0C000000        mov edi, 000ch
81C088000000      add eax, 008h
8B30              mov esi, [edx]
89B4BA18110000    mov [esi+eax*4+00001118], esi
```

The similarity in the code generation may be observed from the above two generations. The similarities may be used for detection of the virus. This may involve string matching techniques, to obtain the wild string which will help to identify the virus body.

More recent viruses like Win95/Zperm family, which appears in 2000, inserts random jump instructions into a code. The *jmps* will be inserted to point to the next instruction of the virus. The mutation of the virus involves removal and addition of jump and garbage instructions. A code with $n$ instructions can be rearranged in at least $n!$ (read $n$ factorial) ways, with the inserted jmp instructions helping in the reordering of the instructions. Most polymorphic viruses decrypt themselves to a single constant body in the memory. However, metamorphic viruses do not. Thus the detection of such viruses needs to be algorithmic, even in the memory. String matching methods do not work as the virus body is nowhere constant.

In case of polymorphic viruses, there is a snap shot of the complete decrypted virus body. Anti-virus programs use generic decryption engines based on code emulation to observe this snap-shot. However, in case of metamorphic viruses this particular moment does not exist.

The development of metamorphic viruses has given developers of viruses lots of power. Development of suitable anti-virus techniques is an increasingly growing challenge.

## 19.7 INTRUSION DETECTION SYSTEMS (IDS)

Intrusion Detection is the process of monitoring the events occurring in a computer system or network. Signs of violations of computer security policies, acceptable use policies, or standard security practices are analyzed. *Intrusion Prevention* is the process of detecting the signs of intrusion and attempting to stop the intrusive efforts. Collectively the system is known as Intrusion Detection and Privacy systems (IDPS). IDSPs have become a necessary addition to the security infrastructure of nearly every organization.

Intruders can be broadly divided into three different types:

1. **Masquerador** They are typically outsiders from the trusted users and are not authorized to use the computer systems. These intruders penetrate the system protection by way of legitimate user accounts.
2. **Misfeasor** They are typically insiders and legitimate users who accesses resources that they are not authorized to use. Or, they may be authorized but misuses her privileges.
3. **Clandestine users** They can be both insiders and outsiders. These type of intruders gain supervisory access to the system.

### 19.7.1 Types of IDS Technologies

An Intrusion Detection system (IDS) is software that automates the intrusion detection process, while the Intrusion Prevention System (IPS) is software with all the properties of IDS, with the additional feature that it stops the intrusions.

The types of IDPS technologies are differentiated primarily by the types of events that they monitor and the ways by which the features are achieved. Broadly there are four types of IDPS technologies:

1. **Network-based**   These monitor the network traffic for a segment of the network. It also analyzes the network and application protocol activity to identify suspicious activity.
2. **Wireless**   These IDS monitor wireless network traffic. Its analysis is to identify suspicious activities involving the wireless protocols.
3. **Network Behaviour Analysis**   The network traffic is again analyzed to identify threats that create unusual traffic flows, Distributed Denial of Service (DDoS) attacks, malwares and policy violations.
4. **Host-based**   These IDS monitors the host and the events that occur within the host.

### 19.7.2   Usage of IDS

Apart from identifying suspicious incidents, there are some other usages of IDSs also:

1. **Identifying Security Policy Problems**   An IDPS can provide some amount of quality control for security policy implementations. This can include duplicating firewalls and also raising alerts when it sees that the network traffic is not blocked by firewall because of configuration errors.
2. **Documenting the existing threat to an organization**   They maintain logs about the threats that they detect.
3. **Deterring individuals from violating security policies**   The fact that the users are monitored by IDPS, makes them less likely to commit violations.
4. **Preventive actions of the IDPS**   The IDPS uses several response techniques to prevent the attempts to perform security attacks on the systems. Some of the ways of how this can be achieved are by terminating the network connection or user sessions that are being used in the attack, block access to the target from the offending accounts or IPs. The preventive step could be a drastic measure like blocking all accesses to the target host.

Other important functions of the IPS involve the following:

5. **The IDPS change the security environment**   The IDPS changes security environment to stop an attack. This could include reconfiguration of the network firewalls, application of patches onto the host computers which are suspected to have vulnerabilities.
6. **The IDPS can change the content of the attack**   The IDPS often acts like a proxy which does normalization. That means they unpackage the payloads of the request, remove the headers. This step nullifies certain attacks. They often remove malicious attachments from incoming files and pass the cleaned email to the recipient.

### 19.7.3   False Positives and Negatives

The IDPS technology adopts statistical methods to comprehend the threats to the system. Thus, this has an accompanying attribute of false positives and negatives. They arise because of the fact that the IDPS cannot provide complete and accurate detection. The false alarms are defined as follows:

1. **False Positive**   When the IDPS incorrectly identifies a benign (harmless) activity as malicious, a false positive is said to have occurred.
2. **False Negative**   When the IDPS fails to identify a malicious activity, a false negative is said to have occurred.

It is not possible to eliminate both false positives and negatives, as reducing one of the errors has a consequence of increasing the other. It is intuitive that organizations prefer to reduce the false negatives at the cost of an increased false positive. Thus more malicious events are detected. However, extra work needs to be done to be sure (or surer) that they are really malicious. Altering the configurations of an IDPS to improve the detection accuracies is technically known as tuning of the IDPS.

The malicious activities adopt several evasive techniques to bypass the IDPS. For example, the attack can encompass changing the encoding of characters, hoping that while the target will be able to understand the encoding, the IDPS would not. Thus the IDPS needs to take measures to compensate these evasive techniques. The thumb rule is that if the IDPS is capable to see the activity the same way as the target, then most of the evasive techniques will fail.

### 19.7.4 Intrusion Detection Techniques

Next we highlight the common detection methodologies of the IDPS technology. The classes of detection methodologies are: signature-based, anomaly-based and stateful protocol analysis. Most of the IDPS uses a combination of these techniques to reduce the error of its detections.

*1. Signature Based Detection*   A signature is a pattern that corresponds to a known threat. **Signature based detection** is the process of comparing the signature, which signifies a known threat against the events that are observed. Examples of signatures could be a telnet attempt with root as the username. Or, an email with a subject name as "Free xyz" or an attachment, "picture.jpg" are other examples of signatures of malicious events.

Signature based detection schemes are simple methods which use string matching as the underlying technique. The current packet or log entry is matched to a list of signatures. Although simple and effective against known threats, signature based schemes have several disadvantages:

1.  They are ineffective against unknown threats: Simply modifying the subject name to "Free xyzw" will change the signature and go undetected.
2.  They cannot pair a request with the corresponding response, like knowing that a request to a web server for a particular page generated a response status code of 403.
3.  They cannot detect attacks that comprise multiple events if none of the events alone contains an indication of an attack. This limitation is because of the inherent incapability of this method to remember previous requests when processing the current one.

*2. Anomaly-Based Detection*   **Anomaly based detection** is the process of comparing definitions of activities which are supposed to be normal against observed events to identify deviations. An IDPS which uses anomaly based detection techniques has profiles that represent the normal behaviors of users, hosts, network connections, or applications. For example, a normal profile could include the fact that web activity is the most commonly done activity during day hours.

The major benefit of anomaly detection is that they can be very effective in detecting previously unknown threats. For example, the power consumption of a computer may increase drastically compared to normal characteristic due to an infection from a malware. An initial profile is generated over a period of time, this period being called a training period. Profiles can be either static or dynamic. Static profiles are not changed for a long period of time, unless the IDPS is specifically directed to obtain a new profile. A dynamic profile on the other hand, constantly gets updated with additional events. Because of the inherent dynamic behavior of networks and systems, static profiles are not suitable as they get out-dated soon. Dynamic profiles do not suffer from this deficiency. But they suffer from the fact that the attackers can adopt evasive techniques to fool such an IDPS. For example, the attacker can slowly increase its activity. The IDPS may think that the rate of change is quite less and the small increase in activity may get included in the present profile. The malicious programs then further increase its activity and thus incrementally evade the IDPS.

Another problem with IDPS technology implemented with anomaly detection methods have the problem of false positives. They often treat benign activities as malicious events. For example, a system administrator's may include backup of large files. Such large file transfers may not be specified during the training period and thus this perfectly benign activity may raise an alarm. It is often quite difficult to decide whether a raised alarm is false, due to the complexity and the number of events that have resulted in the alarm.

**3. Stateful Protocol Analysis** This is the process of comparing predetermined profiles of generally accepted definitions of benign protocol activity for each protocol state against observed events to identify deviations. Unlike anomaly based detection, which uses host or network specific profiles, stateful protocol analysis relies on vendor-developed universal profiles that specify how protocols should work. The "stateful" in this protocol analysis means that the IDPS is capable of checking networks, applications and application protocols that have the notion of state in them. For example, the FTP (File Transfer Protocol) session can be visualized to consist of two states: unauthenticated and authenticated. While the authenticated state can consist of several operations, there are few "benign" operations in the unauthenticated state, viz. providing user names and passwords and seeing help manuals. Thus, the IDPS considers operations benign or malicious depending on the present state of the protocol.

Stateful protocol analysis can identify unexpected sequences of commands. Such suspicious sequences could be repeated issues of same commands or issuing of a command without first issuing a command upon which it is dependent on.

The primary drawback of these analysis methods is that they are extremely resource intensive. This is because of the complexity involved in tracking the transitions of states for several sessions. Another serious problem is that these methods do not capture attacks that do not violate the characteristics of generally accepted protocol behavior. These may be several benign requests to create a denial of service attack.

## 19.8 FIREWALLS: DEFINITIONS, CONSTRUCTION AND WORKING PRINCIPLES

A **firewall** is a single point of defense between two networks. It is an extremely important field of study with the tremendous growth of industry in the recent days. Access to internet is a great source of information and fast transaction, which is necessary for the steep competition faced in the modern industrial era. However, internet access comes with a cautionary note. Not only does it bring information from the outside world to the insiders of a company, but it has the eerie fact of opening the inside information to the external world. Thus understanding and design of proper firewalls is extremely important.

A **firewall** can be simply a router that is used to filter the packets or a complex multi-computer, multi-router solution that performs filtering of packets along with application level proxy services. A firewall is essentially a router or a group of routers and computers to enforce access control between two networks. A firewall can be through of as a pair of mechanisms: allow, which permits traffic and deny, which blocks traffic. There are some firewalls which emphasize on blocking traffic, while others emphasize on permitting traffic.

A standard corporate network topology has a hierarchy, often referred to as the security perimeters. Broadly the external perimeter of network and the internal network perimeter are separated by a DMZ (Demilitarized Zone). When information moves from the Internet to the internal world, integrity of data is a greater concern than the confidentiality of data. Suitable guards are enforced between the Internet and the DMZ and between the DMZ and the internal network to ensure that messages which can cause servers to function incorrectly or crash are not accepted. However when information travels from the internal network to the external world, both integrity and confidentiality are concerns. Guards placed have to check further that no confidential information is leaked and the data is not altered (or spoofed) while traveling from the internal computers to the Internet. If such changes are found in the packets being transmitted either while traveling into or out of the internal network, it is assumed that the network is attacked. Thus the job of the guards is reduced to allow or deny access to the external network of internal systems selectively. These guards are technically known as **firewalls** and are hence essential for the integrity and confidentiality of the information present in the internal network.

The first generation of firewall architectures were essentially packet filters and appeared first around 1985 and came out of *Cisco's IOS* software division. However the first paper describing the principles of packet filters was published in 1988 by Jeff Mogul from *Digital Equipment Corporation*. Since then there has been evolutions of the firewall industry. After packet filters, circuit level firewalls, application layer firewalls, dynamic firewalls etc were developed. Most firewalls technologies provide different capabilities of auditing communication events. The firewalls record the causes which lead to the firing of auditing events. With the evolution of the firewalls, they inspect additional network packet information, use more sophisticated inspection algorithms, maintain more state information, and inspect the network packets at more network layers. In the next sections we present an overview on the firewall architectures.

## 19.8.1 Packet Filters

A *packet filter* is one of the foremost firewall technologies that analyze network traffic at the transport protocol layer. Each IP network packet is examined to see if it matches one of a set of rules which defines the nature of allowable data flow. These rules specify the allowable data flow and also the direction of data flow, i.e. internal to external network or vice-versa.

Following factors allow or deny the data flow through the packet filters:
1. The physical network interface (network adaptor) that the packet arrives on.
2. The address the data is coming from.
3. The address the data is going to.
4. The type of transport layer, TCP, UDP.
5. The transport layer source port.
6. The transport layer destination port.

Packet filters generally do not understand the application layer protocols used in the communication packets. The rules are instead kept in the TCP/IP kernel and applied to any packet. The actions taken may be either deny or permit the packet. For a network packet to be routed to its destination, it has to match with a permit list rule maintained in the kernel. If a packet matches with a deny rule, then it is dropped. However, if a packet does not match with either an allow rule or a deny rule, then also it is dropped. There are however some packet filters which allow packets, if it does not match with a deny rule.

Commands in packet filters check the source and destination port numbers on the TCP and UDP transport layer protocols. The combinations of ports and protocols which are to be allowed are mentioned in the allow list.

Because packet filters work in the network layer, they are unable to process protocols with state information. The packet filters do not also inspect the application layer data in the packets. This makes these filters the least secured. However they are the fastest firewall technologies and often a part of the IP routers. The packet filters often do network address translation so that the topology of the network and the addressing scheme of the network is hidden to untrusted or external network.

The advantages of the packet firewalls are summarized below:

## Advantages

1. Packet filters are faster than other techniques.
2. Less complicated, in the sense that a single rule controls deny or allow of packets.
3. They do not require client computers to be configured specially.
4. They shield the internal IP address from the external world.

## Disadvantages

1. Packet filters do not understand application layer protocols and hence cannot restrict access to ftp services, such and PUT and GET commands.
2. They are stateless, and hence not suitable for application layer protocols.
3. Packet filters have almost no audit event generation and alerting mechanisms.

Next we present an example of a packet filter. This example is written specifically for *ipfwadm*, which is an example of a cheap packet filtering tools. It is a kernel based tool on Linux. The principles (and even much of the syntax) can be applied for other kernel interfaces for packet filtering on open source Unix systems.

There are four basic categories covered by the *ipfwadm* rules:

-A

Packet Accounting

-I

Input firewall

-O

Output firewall

-F

Forwarding firewall

*ipfwadm* also has masquerading (-M) capabilities. For more information on the switches and options, see the *ipfwadm* manual page.

Imagine that the organization uses a private network 192.168.1.0. The Internet Service Provider has assigned the address 201.123.102.32 as the gateway and 201.123.102.33 as the mail server. The policies of the organization are as follows:

❏ To allow all outgoing TCP connections
❏ To allow incoming SMTP and DNS to external mail server
❏ To block all other traffic

The following block of commands can be placed in a system boot file (perhaps *rc.local* on Unix systems).

ipfwadm -F –f
ipfwadm -F -p deny
ipfwadm -F -i m -b -P tcp -S 0.0.0.0/0 1024:65535 -D 201.123.102.33 25
ipfwadm -F -i m -b -P tcp -S 0.0.0.0/0 1024:65535 -D 201.123.102.33 53
ipfwadm -F -i m -b -P udp -S 0.0.0.0/0 1024:65535 -D 201.123.102.33 53
ipfwadm -F -a m -S 192.168.1.0/24 -D 0.0.0.0/0 -W eth0
/sbin/route add -host 201.123.102.33 gw 192.168.1.2

The lines can be explained as follows: the first line flushes (-f) all forwarding (-F) rules. The second line sets the default policy (-p) to deny, while the line three to five are input rules (-i) in the following format:

ipfwadm -F (forward) -i (input) m (masq.) -b (bi-directional) –P (protocol)[protocol]-S (source) [subnet/mask] [originating ports]-D (destination)[subnet/mask][port]

The sixth line appends (-a) a rule that permits all internal IP addresses output to all external addresses on all protocols, all ports. The seventh line adds a route so that the traffic going to 201.123.102.33 will be directed to the internal address 192.168.1.2.

In the next section we present the working principle of circuit level firewalls, which are second generation firewalls.

## 19.8.2 Circuit Level Firewalls

*Circuit-level firewalls* are similar in operation to packet-filtering firewalls, but they operate at the transport and session layers of the OSI model. The biggest difference between a packet-filtering firewall and a circuit-level firewall is that a circuit-level firewall validates TCP and UDP sessions before opening a connection, or circuit, through the firewall. When the session is established, the firewall maintains a table of valid connections and lets data pass through when session information matches an entry in the table. The table entry is removed, and the circuit is closed when the session is terminated.

To validate a session, these kinds of firewall thus examine each connection set up to ensure that it follows a legitimate handshake for the transport layer protocol. TCP is a widely used protocol in the transport layer which uses handshake. The firewall maintains a virtual circuit table, which stores the connection details, namely the session state and the sequencing information, of the successful connections. When a connection is set up, the circuit level firewall typically stores the following:

1. A unique session identifier for the connection.
2. The state of the connection, namely handshake, established, or closing.
3. The sequencing information.
4. The source IP address, from where the data has arrived.
5. The destination IP address, where the data is to be delivered.
6. The physical network interface through which the data arrives.
7. The physical network interface, through which the packet goes out.

The circuit level firewall checks the header information contained in the network packet to see whether it has the necessary permissions to be transmitted. These firewalls have a limited understanding of the protocols used in network packets. They can only detect one transport layer protocol, TCP. Like packet filters, the rule sets are kept in the TCP kernel.

These firewalls perform a minimal security check compared to the application layer firewalls. Only those network connections that are associated with existing ones are allowed. But once a connection is allowed, all packets associated with the connection are allowed without further security checks. The method is hence fast and performs a limited amount of state checking, but is less secured. However, they perform limited checks to detect whether the packet data has been modified or spoofed. They check that the data contained in the transport protocol header complies with the definition of the corresponding protocol. Like packet filters, these firewalls also perform network address translation to hide the internal addresses from the external world.

We summarize the advantages and disadvantages of the circuit level firewalls:

### Advantages
1. They are faster than application layer firewalls.
2. They are more secured than packet filter firewalls.
3. They maintain limited state information of the protocols.
4. They protect against spoofing of packets.
5. They shield internal IP addresses from external networks by network address translation.

### Disadvantages
1. They cannot restrict access to protocol subsets other than TCP.
2. They have limited audit event generation capabilities.
3. They cannot perform security checks on higher level protocols.

## 19.8.3  Application Layer Firewalls

An **application layer firewall** is a third generation firewall technology that evaluates network packets for valid data at the application layer before allowing a connection. It examines the data in all network packets at the application layer and maintains a complete list of connection states and sequencing information. Further, other security items that appear only in the application layer protocols, like user passwords and service requests are validated.

Application layer firewalls use special purpose programs, called proxy services to manage data transfer through a firewall for a specific service such as *ftp* or *http*. Proxy services are thus dedicated to a particular protocol and provide increased security checks, access controls and generate appropriate audit records.

Proxy services do not allow direct connection between the real service and the user. They sit transparently between the user and the real server and handles and inspects every communication between them. A proxy service has two components that are typically implemented as a single executable: *proxy server* and *proxy client*.

When a real client wants to communicate to an external service in the internet, like *ftp* or *telnet*, the request is directed to the proxy server, because the user's default gateway is set to the proxy server. The proxy server then evaluates the request and decides to deny or allow it, depending on a set of rules that are managed for the network service. Proxy servers are aware of the protocols, and thus allow only complying packets with the protocol definitions. They also perform auditing, user authentication and caching, services which were not performed by the packet filters or the circuit level firewalls.

On the other hand, once the packet from the real client is allowed by the proxy server the packet is forwarded to a proxy client who contacts the actual server providing the service. The proxy client subsequently relays back the information sent by the actual server to the proxy server, who decides whether to send the information to the actual client. Thus the proxy service is transparent to a user, who believes that he is communicating directly with the service in the internet. However, the proxy services are implemented on the top of the firewall host's network stack and operate only in the application layer of the operating system. Hence each packet must pass through the low-level protocols in the kernel before being passed to the top of the stack to the application layer for a thorough analysis by the proxy services. Then the packet must travel back down the stack and then be distributed by the low level protocols in the kernel. Hence the application layer protocols are very slow.

The advantages and disadvantages of the application layer protocols are summarized below:

## Advantages

1. They enforce and understand high level protocols, like HTTP and FTP.
2. They maintain information about the communication passing through the firewall server: partial communication derived state information, full application derived state information, partial session information.
3. They can be used to deny access to certain network services, while allowing others.
4. They are capable of processing and manipulating packet data.
5. They do not allow direct communication between external servers and internal systems, thus shielding internal IP addresses from the outside network.
6. They are transparent between the user and the external network.
7. They provide features like HTTP object caching, URL filtering, and user authentication.
8. They are good at generating auditing records, allowing administrators to monitor threats to the firewall.

## Disadvantages

1. They require replacing the native network stack on the firewall server.
2. They do not allow network servers to run on the firewall servers, as the proxy servers use the same port to listen.
3. They are slow and thus lead to degradation in performance.
4. They are not scalable, as each new network service adds onto the number of proxy services required.
5. Proxy services require modifications to client procedures.
6. They rely on operating system support and thus are vulnerable to bugs in the system. Thus bugs in NDIS, TCP/IP, WinSock, Win32 or the standard C library can cause security concerns in the security provided by the application layer firewalls.

**Dynamic packet filter** firewalls are a fourth generation firewalls that allow modifications of the security rules on the fly. This technology is most suitable for providing limited support for the UDP transport protocol. This firewall associates all UDP packets that cross from the internal network to the external network or vice-versa, with a virtual connection. If a response packet is generated and sent back to the original requester, then a virtual connection is established and the packet is allowed to pass the firewall server. The information corresponding to a virtual connection is remembered for a small unit of time. If no response packet is received within this time frame then the virtual connection is invalidated. The response packet that is allowed back must contain a destination address that matches the original source address, a transport layer destination port that matches the original source port, and the same transport layer protocol type. This feature is useful for allowing application layer protocols like Domain Name System (DNS). An internal DNS server must request other DNS servers on the Internet to obtain address information for unknown hosts. These connections may be made by TCP or UDP virtual connections.

Thus to summarize application layer firewalls are the most secured among the firewall technologies.

They are more secure than the dynamic firewalls, which are more secure than the circuit level firewalls, which are in turn more secure than the packet level filters. However performance wise, the application layer filters are slowest. A point to be noted is that the circuit level firewalls are often faster than the packet level filters, as they do not perform extensive security checks, other than whether a network packet is associated with a valid connection in contrast to packet filters which have a large set of allow and deny rules.

An IDS (Intrusion Detection System) may only detect and warn about security violations. A firewall, on the other hand, may not notify a security violation but may simply block the attack or action violating the security policy of the firewall.

In practice, it is good to have both an IDS and a firewall, because the IDS warns us and a firewall blocks attacks on the systems security. Some firewall and IDS are combined into one security program, like Norton Internet Security.

## 19.9                         RECOMMENDED READING

1. "*Building a Secure Computer System*", Morrie Gasser.
2. "*Smashing the Stack for Fun and Profit*", Aleph One.
3. "*Computer Viruses and Malware*", John Aycock, Springer.
4. "*Guide to Intrusion Detection and Prevention Systems (IDPS)*", Recommendation of National Institute of Standards and Technology.
5. "*Evolution of Firewall Industry*", http://www.cisco.com/univercd/cc/td/doc/product/iaabu/centri4/user/scf4ch3.htm, CISCO documentation
6. Internet Firewalls: Frequently Asked Questions, Matt Curtin, Marcus Ranum and Paul Robertson, http://www.faqs.org/faqs/firewalls-faq/

## *Key Terms*

| | |
|---|---|
| Systems | Virus |
| Trust | Worm |
| Buffer overflow | Payload |
| Stack | Trigger |
| Malicious software | Intrusion Detection |
| Firewalls | |

## *Practice Set*

### Review Questions

**19.1**   Define system and the components of system. Reflect on the statement "encryption provides system security".

**19.2**   What is the importance of trust in context to system security?

**19.3**   Explain how malicious programs exploit the principle of stack overflow for attacking systems.

**19.4**   How do modern compilers protect operating systems from using stack overflow?

**19.5**   What is the difference between worms and viruses?

**19.6**   Describe the components of a virus code. Explain the purpose of the components of the virus. How does the virus protect itself from being detected by anti-virus softwares.

**19.7** What are the types of analysis adopted by Intrusion Detection and Protection systems (IDPS)? What are the types of IDPS?

**19.8** Compare the various generation of firewalls. Comment on the security achieved and the ease of implementation of the various generations of firewalls.

**19.9** Explain a logic bomb and a time bomb.

**19.10** What is the difference between spywares and viruses?

**19.11** Defferentiate between Signature based IDPS and Anomaly based IDPS.

**19.12** Defferentiate between Stateful IDPS and Anomaly based IDPS.

**19.13** How can Anomaly based detection schemes be used to detect unknown threats? What is the pitfall of such a mechanism?

**19.14** What are false positives and negatives in context to an IDPS? What should be the approach of the system designer to reduce both the errors?

**19.15** Justify metamorphics are body polymorphics in context to computer viruses.

**19.16** Differentiate between oligomorphism and polymorphism in context to computer viruses.

**19.17** Explain the common types of viruses based on their target.

**19.18** Explain the common types of viruses based on their concealing techniques.

**19.19** What are the various funtionalities of IDS in system security?

**19.20** What is the difference between a firewall and IDS?

## Exercises

**19.21** In the book, we have seen examples of "faults" created in the execution of a C program, due to a function call from itself. So, in a way the malicious function is called by the victim program. Can we create a similar scenario, when a program runs independent of the malicious code? If yes, create some simple programs to demonstrate such instances.

**19.22** Explain what is meant by the terms 'shadowing' and 'salting' in context to the Unix password system. Explain their purposes to increase the security of the Unix system.

**19.23** An anti-virus program is to be developed for scanning files for virus infections. The algorithm used in the detecting software is based on scanning the file for signatures. Implement the program by following steps.

Consider that the virus signatures belong to the set: '01', '010','101', '1110', '0101', '11111', '01010' and '11001'. Now write a program in C which scans a given binary file and looks for the above sequences. Note that your program should report "Virus found", if any of the above sequence is detected and terminate. Otherwise it should resume the search from the next character in the file.

[Hint: An efficient way of implementing the program is by conceptualizing the detector as a finite automaton. Construct the automaton as a tree like structure, called "Trie".]

**19.24** In an Intrusion Detection Scheme, false positives and negatives are an integral part. Justify whether you will go for a scheme with high false positive but less false negative or the other way round.

**19.25** What is the difference between stateful and stateless Intrusion Detection schemes? Comment on their levels of security in detecting intrusions.

**19.26** The unix utility *ipfwadm* can be used for controlling all incoming, outgoing and forwarding of packets. Install ipfwadm from *ftp://ftp.xos.nl/pub/linux/ipfwadm/*. Use the utility to create a firewall with the following capabilities:

a. deny all incoming, outgoing and forwarding of packets.

b. Flush the rules, and start from the beginning. Log and track any packets which are coming through the external perimeter (could be the gateway) and pretending to be arriving from an internal ip (spoofing)

c. Configure such that any packets which have actually been originated from internal network, but masquerading as coming from the ip of the external perimeter, should be denied.

d. All other outgoing packets should be allowed (that is those packets which have originated from the ip of the external perimeter and are being sent through that should be allowed).

e. Configure such that masquerading is prevented from a particular ip in your network.

Note that you should install and run a ipfwadm binary as root.

# Appendix

# A

# ASCII

The **American Standard Code for Information Interchange (ASCII)** is a 7-bit code that was designed to provide codes for 128 symbols, as shown in Table A.1.

**Table A.1** *ASCII Codes*

| Hex | Char | Hex | Char | Hex | Char | Hex | Char | Hex | Char | Hex | Char |
|-----|------|-----|------|-----|------|-----|------|-----|------|-----|------|
| 00 | null | 18 | CAN | 30 | 0 | 48 | H | 60 | ` | 78 | x |
| 01 | SOH | 19 | EM | 31 | 1 | 49 | I | 61 | a | 79 | y |
| 02 | STX | 1A | SUB | 32 | 2 | 4A | J | 62 | b | 7A | z |
| 03 | ETX | 1B | ESC | 33 | 3 | 4B | K | 63 | c | 7B | { |
| 04 | EOT | 1C | FS | 34 | 4 | 4C | L | 64 | d | 7C | \| |
| 05 | ENQ | 1D | GS | 35 | 5 | 4D | M | 65 | e | 7D | } |
| 06 | ACK | 1E | RS | 36 | 6 | 4E | N | 66 | f | 7E | ~ |
| 07 | BEL | 1F | US | 37 | 7 | 4F | O | 67 | g | 7F | DEL |
| 08 | BS | 20 | SP | 38 | 8 | 50 | P | 68 | h | | |
| 09 | HT | 21 | ! | 39 | 9 | 51 | Q | 69 | i | | |
| 0A | LF | 22 | " | 3A | : | 52 | R | 6A | j | | |
| 0B | VT | 23 | # | 3B | ; | 53 | S | 6B | k | | |
| 0C | FF | 24 | $ | 3C | < | 54 | T | 6C | l | | |
| 0D | CR | 25 | % | 3D | = | 55 | U | 6D | m | | |
| 0E | SO | 26 | & | 3E | > | 56 | V | 6E | n | | |
| 0F | SI | 27 | ' | 3F | ? | 57 | W | 6F | o | | |
| 10 | DLE | 28 | ( | 40 | @ | 58 | X | 70 | p | | |
| 11 | DC1 | 29 | ) | 41 | A | 59 | Y | 71 | q | | |
| 12 | DC2 | 2A | * | 42 | B | 5A | Z | 72 | r | | |
| 13 | DC3 | 2B | + | 43 | C | 5B | [ | 73 | s | | |
| 14 | DC4 | 2C | , | 44 | D | 5C | \ | 74 | t | | |
| 15 | NAK | 2D | − | 45 | E | 5D | ] | 75 | u | | |
| 16 | SYN | 2E | . | 46 | F | 5E | ^ | 76 | v | | |
| 17 | ETB | 2F | / | 47 | G | 5F | _ | 77 | w | | |

# Appendix

# B

# Standards and Standard Organizations

Standards are essential in creating and maintaining an open and competitive market for equipment manufacturers and in guaranteeing national and international interoperability of technology. Standards provide guidelines to manufacturers, vendors, government agencies, and other service providers to ensure the kind of interconnectivity necessary in today's marketplace and in international communications.

## B.1                                      INTERNET STANDARDS

An **Internet standard** is a thoroughly tested specification that is useful to and adhered to by those who work with the Internet. It is a formalized regulation that must be followed. There is a strict procedure by which a specification attains Internet standard status. A specification begins as an Internet draft. An **Internet draft** is a working document (a work in progress) with no official status and a six-month lifetime. Upon recommendation from the Internet authorities, a draft may be published as a **Request for Comment (RFC).** Each RFC is edited, assigned a number, and made available to all interested parties. RFCs go through maturity levels and are categorized according to their requirement level.

### B.1.1  Maturity Levels

An RFC, during its lifetime, falls into one of six **maturity levels:** proposed standard, draft standard, Internet standard, historic, experimental, and informational, as shown in Fig. B.1.

***Proposed Standard***   A proposed standard is a specification that is stable, well understood, and of sufficient interest to the Internet community. At this level, the specification is usually tested and implemented by several different groups.

***Draft Standard***   A proposed standard is elevated to draft standard status after at least two successful independent and interoperable implementations. Barring difficulties, a draft standard, with modifications if specific problems are encountered, normally becomes an Internet standard.

***Internet Standard***   A draft standard reaches Internet standard status after demonstrations of successful implementation.

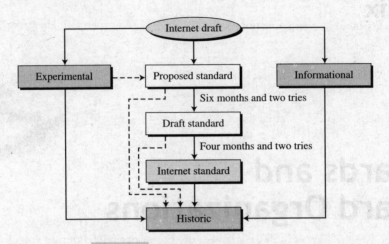

**Fig. B.1** *Maturity levels of an RFC*

**Historic** The historic RFCs are significant from a historical perspective. They either have been superseded by later specifications or have never passed the necessary maturity levels to become an Internet standard.

**Experimental** An RFC classified as experimental describes work related to an experimental situation that does not affect the operation of the Internet. Such an RFC should not be implemented in any functional Internet service.

**Informational** An RFC classified as informational contains general, historical, or tutorial information related to the Internet. It is usually written by someone in a non-Internet organization, such as a vendor.

## B.1.2 Requirement Levels

RFCs are classified into five **requirement levels:** required, recommended, elective, limited use, and not recommended, as shown in Fig. B.2.

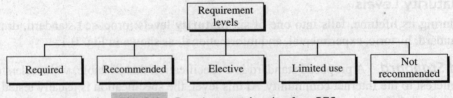

**Fig. B.2** *Requirement levels of an RFC*

**Required** An RFC is labeled *required* if it must be implemented by all Internet systems to achieve minimum conformance.

**Recommended** An RFC labeled *recommended* is not required for minimum conformance; it is recommended because of its usefulness.

***Elective***   An RFC labeled *elective* is not required and not recommended. However, a system can use it for its own benefit.

***Limited Use***   An RFC labeled *limited use* should be used only in limited situations. Most of the experimental RFCs fall under this category.

***Not Recommended***   An RFC labeled *not recommended* is inappropriate for general use. Normally a historic (obsolete) RFC may fall under this category.

---

**RFCs can be found at www.faqs.org/rfcs**

---

## B.1.3   Internet Administration

The Internet, with its roots primarily in the research domain, has evolved and gained a broader user base with significant commercial activity. Various groups that coordinate Internet issues have guided this growth and development. Figure B.3 shows the general organization of Internet administration.

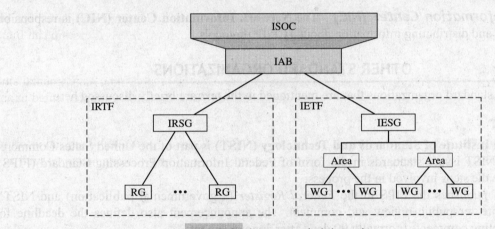

**Fig. B.3**   *Internet administration*

***Internet Society (ISOC)***   The **Internet Society (ISOC)** is an international, nonprofit organization formed in 1992 to provide support for the Internet standards process. ISOC accomplishes this through maintaining and supporting other Internet administrative bodies such as IAB, IETF, IRTF, and ICANN (see the following sections). ISOC also promotes research and other scholarly activities relating to the Internet.

***Internet Architecture Board (IAB)***   The **Internet Architecture Board (IAB)** is the technical advisor to ISOC. The main purposes of the IAB are to oversee the continuing development of the TCP/IP Protocol Suite and to serve in a technical advisory capacity to research members of the Internet community. The IAB accomplishes this through its two primary components, the Internet Engineering Task Force (IETF) and the Internet Research Task Force (IRTF). Another responsibility of the IAB is the editorial management of the RFCs, described earlier in this appendix. The IAB is also the external liaison between the Internet administration and other standard organizations and forums.

*Internet Engineering Task Force (IETF)*  The **Internet Engineering Task Force (IETF)** is a forum of working groups managed by the Internet Engineering Steering Group (IESG). IETF is responsible for identifying operational problems and proposing solutions to these problems. IETF also develops and reviews specifications intended as Internet standards. The working groups are collected into areas, and each area concentrates on a specific topic. Currently nine areas have been defined: applications, Internet protocols, routing, operations, user services, network management, transport, Internet protocol next generation (IPng), and security.

*Internet Research Task Force (IRTF)*  The **Internet Research Task Force (IRTF)** is a forum of working groups managed by the Internet Research Steering Group (IRSG). IRTF focuses on long-term research topics related to Internet protocols, applications, architecture, and technology.

*Internet Corporation for Assigned Names and Numbers (ICANN)*  The **Internet Corporation for Assigned Names and Numbers (ICANN),** a private nonprofit corporation managed by an international board, is responsible for the management of Internet domain names and addresses.

*Network Information Center (NIC)*  The **Network Information Center (NIC)** is responsible for collecting and distributing information about TCP/IP protocols.

## B.2              OTHER STANDARD ORGANIZATIONS

Several other standard organizations that are mentioned in the text are briefly discussed here.

### B.2.1   NIST

The **National Institute of Standards and Technology (NIST)** is part of the United States Commerce Department. NIST issues standards in the form of Federal Information Processing Standard (FIPS). Following are the steps involved in the process:
1. NIST publishes the FIPS in the *Federal Register* (a governmental publication) and NIST's website for public review and comment. The announcement also defines the deadline for accepting comments (normally 90 days after announcement).
2. After the deadline, an expert group in NIST reviews the comments and makes any necessary modifications.
3. The recommended FIPS is sent to the secretary of commerce for approval.
4. The approval of the FIPS is published in the *Federal Register* and NIST's website.

### B.2.2   ISO

The **International Organization for Standardization** (ISO) is a multinational body whose membership is drawn mainly from the standards creation committees of various governments throughout the world. The ISO is active in developing cooperation in the realms of scientific, technological, and economic activity.

### B.2.3   ITU-T

**International Telecommunication Union—Telecommunication Standards Sector** (ITU-T) is part of its International -Telecommunication Union (ITU). The sector is devoted to the research and establishment of standards for telecommunications in general and for phone and data systems in particular.

## B.2.4 ANSI

The **American National Standards Institute (ANSI)** is a completely private, nonprofit corporation not affiliated with the U.S. federal government. However, all ANSI activities are undertaken with the welfare of the United States and its citizens being of primary importance.

## B.2.5 IEEE

The **Institute of Electrical and Electronics Engineers (IEEE)** is the largest professional engineering society in the world. International in scope, it aims to advance theory, creativity, and product quality in the fields of electrical engineering, electronics, and radio as well as in all related branches of engineering. As one of its goals, the IEEE oversees the development and adoption of international standards for computing and communications.

## B.2.6 EIA

Aligned with ANSI, the **Electronic Industries Association (EIA)** is a nonprofit organization devoted to the promotion of electronics manufacturing concerns. Its activities include public awareness education and lobbying efforts in addition to standards development. In the field of information technology, the EIA has made significant contributions by developing standards for data communication.

# Appendix

# C

# TCP/IP Protocol Suite

The networking model used in the Internet today is the **Transmission Control Protocol/Internetworking Protocol (TCP/IP)** or **TCP/IP Protocol Suite.** The suite is made of five layers—*application, transport, network, data link,* and *physical*—as shown in Fig. C.1.

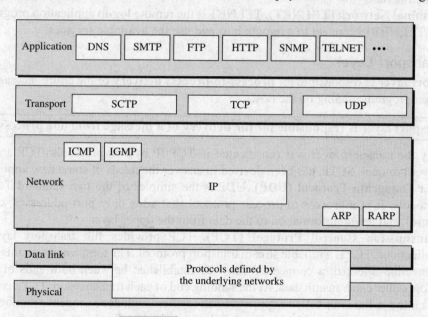

**Fig. C.1** *TCP/IP protocol suite*

TCP/IP is a hierarchical protocol made up of interactive modules, each of which provides a specific functionality. The term *hierarchical* means that each upper-layer protocol uses the services of one or more lower-layer protocols.

## C.1                                     LAYERS IN THE TCP/IP

In this section we briefly describe the functions of each layer in the TCP/IP protocol suite.

## C.1.1 Application Layer

The **application layer** enables the user, whether human or software, to access the network. It provides user interfaces and support for services such as file transfer, electronic mail, and remote logging.

---
**The application layer is responsible for providing services to the user.**

---

- ❑ **Domain Name System (DNS).** DNS is an application program that gives services to other application programs. It finds the logical (network-layer) address when given the specific (application-layer) address.
- ❑ **Simple Mail Transfer Protocol (SMTP).** SMTP is the protocol used for electronic mail. Electronic mail is discussed in Chapter 16.
- ❑ **File Transfer Protocol (FTP).** FTP is the file transfer protocol in the Internet. It is used to transfer large files from one computer to another.
- ❑ **Hypertext Transfer Protocol (HTTP).** HTTP is the protocol that is normally used to access the World Wide Web (WWW).
- ❑ **Simple Network Management Protocol (SNMP).** SNMP is the official management protocol in the Internet.
- ❑ **Terminal Network (TELNET).** TELNET is the remote log-in application program. A user can use TELNET to connect to a remote host and use the available services.

## C.1.2 Transport Layer

The **transport layer** is responsible for **process-to-process delivery** of the entire message. A process is an application program running on the host.

---
**The transport layer is responsible for the delivery of a message from one process to another.**

---

Traditionally the transport layer was represented in TCP/IP by two protocols: TCP and UDP. A new transport layer protocol, SCTP, has been devised to answer the needs of some new applications.

- ❑ **User Datagram Protocol (UDP).** UDP is the simpler of the two standard TCP/IP transport protocols. It is a process-to-process protocol that adds only port addresses, checksum error control, and length information to the data from the upper layer.
- ❑ **Transmission Control Protocol (TCP).** TCP provides full transport layer services to applications. TCP is a reliable stream transport protocol. The term *stream,* in this context, means connection-oriented: a connection must be established between both ends of a transmission before either can transmit data. At the sending end of each transmission, TCP divides a stream of data into smaller units called *segments.* Each segment includes a sequence number for reordering after receipt, together with an acknowledgment number for the segments received. Segments are carried across the Internet inside of IP datagrams. At the receiving end, TCP collects each datagram as it comes in and reorders the transmission based on sequence numbers.
- ❑ **Stream Control Transmission Protocol (SCTP).** SCTP provides support for new applications such as IP telephony. It is a transport layer protocol that combines the good features of UDP and TCP.

## C.1.3 Network Layer

The **network layer** is responsible for the source-to-destination delivery of a packet, possibly across multiple physical networks (links). The network layer ensures that each packet gets from its point of origin to its final destination. Some responsibilities of the network layer include logical addressing and routing.

---

**The network layer is responsible for the delivery of individual packets from the source host to the destination host.**

---

- ❑ **Internet Protocol (IP).** IP is the transmission mechanism used by the TCP/IP protocols. It is an unreliable and connectionless protocol—a best-effort delivery service. The term *best-effort* means that IP provides no error checking or tracking. IP assumes the unreliability of the underlying layers and does its best to get a transmission through to its destination, but with no guarantees. IP transports data in packets called *datagrams,* each of which is transported separately. Datagrams can travel along different routes and can arrive out of sequence or be duplicated. IP does not keep track of the routes and has no facility for reordering datagrams once they arrive at their destination. The limited functionality of IP should not be considered a weakness, however. IP provides bare-bones transmission functions that free the user to add only those facilities necessary for a given application and thereby allows for maximum efficiency.

- ❑ **Address Resolution Protocol (ARP).** ARP is used to associate an IP address with the physical address. On a typical physical network, each device on the network is identified by a physical or station address usually imprinted on the network interface card (NIC). ARP is used to find the physical address of the node when its Internet address is known.

- ❑ **Reverse Address Resolution Protocol (RARP).** RARP allows a host to discover its Internet address when it knows only its physical address. It is used when a computer is connected to the network for the first time or when a diskless computer is booted.

- ❑ **Internet Control Message Protocol (ICMP).** ICMP is a mechanism used by hosts and other intermediate devices to send notification of datagram problems back to the sender. ICMP sends query and error reporting messages.

- ❑ **Internet Group Message Protocol (IGMP).** IGMP is used to facilitate the simultaneous transmission of a message to a group of recipients.

## C.1.4 Data Link Layer

The **data link layer** transforms the physical layer, a raw transmission facility, to a reliable link. It makes the physical layer appear error-free to the upper layer (network layer). Some responsibilities of the data link layer include framing, physical addressing, flow control, error control, and access control.

---

**The data link layer is responsible for moving frames from one hop (node) to the next.**

---

## C.1.5 Physical Layer

The **physical layer** coordinates the functions required to carry a bit stream over a physical medium. The physical layer is concerned with physical characteristics of interfaces and transmission media, representation of bits, data rate, synchronization of bits, and physical topology.

---

**The physical layer is responsible for movements of individual bits from one hop (node) to the next.**

---

## C.2 ADDRESSING

Four different levels of addresses are used in the Internet using the TCP/IP protocols: **specific address, port address, logical address,** and **physical address,** as shown in Fig. C.2.

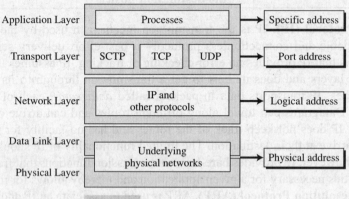

**Fig. C.2**  *Addresses in TCP/IP*

### C.2.1 Specific Address

Communication at the application layer is done using specific addresses: addresses belonging to specific application layer protocols. For example, one uses an e-mail address to send an e-mail.

### C.2.2 Port Address

Today, computers are devices that can run multiple processes at the same time. The end objective of Internet communication is a process communicating with another process. For example, computer A can communicate with computer C using TELNET. At the same time, computer A communicates with computer B using File Transfer Protocol (FTP). For these processes to occur simultaneously, there must be a method to label different processes. In other words, the processes need addresses. In TCP/IP architecture, the label assigned to a process is called a port address. A port address in TCP/IP is 16 bits long.

### C.2.3 Logical Address

Logical addresses are necessary for universal communication services that are independent of underlying physical networks. A universal addressing system in which each host can be identified uniquely, regardless of the underlying physical network, is needed. The logical addresses are designed for this purpose. A logical address (IP address) in the Internet is currently a 32-bit address that can uniquely define a host connected to the Internet. No two publicly addressed and visible hosts on the Internet can have the same IP address.

### C.2.4 Physical Address

The **physical address,** also known as the link address, is the address of a node as defined by its physical network. It is included in the frame used by the data link layer. It is the lowest-level address. The physical addresses have authority over the physical network. The size and format of these addresses vary depending on the network.

# Appendix

# D

# Elementary Probability

**P**robability theory plays a very important role in cryptography because it provides the best way to quantify uncertainty, and the field of cryptography is full of uncertainty. This appendix reviews basic concepts of probability theory that are needed to understand some topics discussed in this book.

## D.1                                                    INTRODUCTION

We begin with some definitions, axioms, and properties.

### D.1.1   Definitions

***Random Experiment***   An **experiment** can be defined as any process that changes an input to an output. A **random experiment** is an experiment in which the same input can result in two different outputs. In other words, the output cannot be uniquely defined from knowledge of the input. For example, when we toss a fair coin two times, the input (the coin) is the same, but the output (heads or tails) can be different.

***Outcomes***   Each output of a random experiment is called an **outcome.** For example, when a six-sided die is rolled, the possible outcomes are 1, 2, 3, 4, 5, and 6.

***Sample Space***   A **sample space, S,** is a set of all possible outcomes of a random experiment. When a coin is tossed, the space has only two elements, $S = \{heads, tails\}$. When a die is rolled, the sample space has six elements, $S = \{1, 2, 3, 4, 5, 6\}$. A sample space is sometimes referred to as a probability space, a random space, or a universe.

***Events***   When a random experiment is performed, we are interested in a subset of the sample space, not necessarily a single outcome. For example, when a die is rolled, we may be interested in getting a 2, an even number, or a number less than 4. Each of these possible outcomes can be thought of as an **event.** An event, A, is a subset of the sample space. The previous mentioned events can be defined as follows:
   a.   Getting a 2 (simple outcome): $A_1 = \{2\}$
   b.   Getting an even number: $A_2 = \{2, 4, 6\}$
   c.   Getting a number less than 4: $A_3 = \{1, 2, 3\}$

## D.1.2   Probability Assignment

The main idea in probability theory is the idea of an event. But what is the probability of a given event? This has been debated for centuries. Recently, mathematicians have come to an agreement that we can assign probabilities to events using three methods: classical, statistical, and computational.

***Classical Probability Assignment***   In **classical probability assignment,** the probability of an event A is a number interpreted as $P(A) = n_A/n$, where $n$ is the total number of possible outcomes and $n_A$ is the number of possible outcomes related to event A. This definition is useful only if each outcome is equally probable.

> **Example D.1**   We toss a fair coin. What is the probability that the outcome will be heads?

***Solution***   The total number of possible outcomes is 2 (heads or tails). The number of possible outcomes related to this event is 1 (only heads). Therefore, we have $P(\text{heads}) = n_{\text{heads}}/n = 1/2$.

> **Example D.2**   We roll a fair die. What is the probability of getting a 5?

***Solution***   The total number of possible outcomes is 6, $S = \{1, 2, 3, 4, 5, 6\}$. The number of possible outcomes related to this event is 1 (only 5). Therefore, we have $P(5) = n_5/n = 1/6$.

***Statistical Probability Assignment***   In **statistical probability assignment,** an experiment is performed $n$ times under equal conditions. If event A occurs $m$ times when $n$ is reasonably large, the probability of an event A is a number interpreted as $P(A) = m/n$. This definition is useful when the events are not equally likely.

> **Example D.3**   We toss a nonfair coin 10,000 times and get heads 2600 times and tails 7400 times. Therefore, $P(\text{heads}) = 2600/10,000 = 0.26$ and $P(\text{tails}) = 7400/10,000 = 0.74$.

***Computational Probability Assignment***   In **computational probability assignment,** an event is assigned a probability based on the probabilities of other events, using the axioms and properties discussed in the next section.

## D.1.3   Axioms

Probability axioms cannot be proved, but they are assumed when using probability theory. The following three axioms are fundamental to probability theory.

- ❏ **Axiom 1.** The probability of an event is a nonnegative value: $P(A) \geq 0$.
- ❏ **Axiom 2.** The probability of the random space is 1: $P(S) = 1$. In other words, one of the possible outcomes will definitely occur.
- ❏ **Axiom 3.** If $A_1, A_2, A_3, \ldots$ are pairwise disjoint events, then
$$P(A_1 \text{ or } A_2 \text{ or } A_3 \text{ or } \ldots) = P(A_1) + P(A_2) + P(A_3) + \cdots$$
  Events $A_1, A_2, A_3, \ldots$ are pairwise disjoint events if the occurrence of one does not change the probability of the occurrence of the others.

## D.1.4   Properties

Accepting the above axioms, a list of properties can be proven. Following are the minimum properties required to understand the related topics in this book (we leave the proofs to the books on probability):

❏  The probability of an event is always between 0 and 1: $0 \le P(A) \le 1$.
❏  The probability of no outcome is 0: $P(\overline{\mathrm{S}}) = 0$. In other words, if we roll a die, the probability that none of the numbers will show is 0 (impossible event).
❏  If $A$ is the complement of A, then $P(\overline{\mathrm{A}}) = 1 - P(A)$. For example, if the probability of getting a 2 in rolling a die is 1/6, the probability of not getting a 2 is $(1 - 1/6)$.
❏  If $A$ is a subset of $B$, then $P(A) \le P(B)$. For example, when we roll a die, P(2 or 3) is less than P(2 or 3 or 4).
❏  If events A, B, C, … are independent, then
$$P(A \text{ and } B \text{ and } C \text{ and } \dots) = P(A) \times P(B) \times P(C) \times \cdots$$

## D.1.5  Conditional Probability

The occurrence of an event A may convey some information about the occurrence of another event B. The **conditional probability** of an event B, given that event A has occurred, is shown as P(B | A). It can be proved that
$$P(B \mid A) = P(A \text{ and } B) / P(A)$$
Note that if A and B are independent events, then P(B | A) = P(B).

**Example D.4**   A fair die has been rolled. If we are told that the outcome is an even number, what is the probability that it is 4?

**Solution**   P(4 | even) = P(4 and even)/P(even). Because there is only one way to get 4, and the number is also even, P(4 and even) = 1/6. P(even) = P(2 or 4 or 6) = 3/6. Therefore,

$$P(4 \mid \text{even}) = (1/6)/(3/6) = 1/3$$

Note that the conditional probability of P(4 | even) is larger than P(4).

## D.2                                      RANDOM VARIABLES

A variable can assume different values. Variables whose values depend on the outcomes of a random experiment are called **random variables.**

### D.2.1  Continuous Random Variables

The random variables that can take an unaccountably infinite number of values are referred to as **continuous random variables.** We are not usually interested in this type of random variables in cryptography.

### D.2.2  Discrete Random Variables

In cryptography, we are interested in random experiments with a countable number of outcomes (such as rolling a die). The random variables associated with this type of experiment are referred to as **discrete random variables.** A discrete random variable is a mapping from the set of countable outcomes to the set of real values. For example, we can map the outcomes of flipping a coin {heads, tails} to the set {0, 1}.

# Appendix

# E

# Birthday Problems

irthday problems were introduced in Chapter 11. In this appendix, general solutions to four birthday problems are given using the probability discussed in Appendix D. The following relations from mathematics are used to simplify the solutions:

$$1 - x \approx e^{-x} \qquad \text{//Taylor's series when } x \text{ is small}$$
$$1 + 2 + \cdots + (k - 1) = k(k - 1)/2$$
$$k(k - 1) \approx k^2$$

## E.1                               FOUR PROBLEMS

We present solutions to four problems discussed in Chapter 11.

### E.1.1   First Problem

We have a sample set of $k$ values, in which each sample can take only one of the $N$ equally probable values. What is the minimum size of the sample set, $k$, such that, with probability $P \geq 1/2$, at least one of the samples is equal to a predetermined value?

To solve the problem, we first find the probability P that at least one sample is equal to the predetermined value. We then set the probability to 1/2 to find the minimum size of the sample.

***Probability***    We follow four steps to find the probability P:

1. If $P_{sel}$ is the probability that a selected sample is equal to the predefined value, then $P_{sel} = 1/N$ because the sample can equally likely be any of the $N$ values.

2. If $Q_{sel}$ is the probability that a selected sample is not equal to the predefined value, then $Q_{sel} = 1 - P_{sel} = (1 - 1/N)$.

3. If each sample is independent (a fair assumption), and Q is the probability that no sample is equal to the predefined value, then $Q = Q_{sel}^{k} = (1 - 1/N)^{k}$.

4. Finally, if P is the probability that at least one sample is equal to the predetermined value, then $P = 1 - Q$ or $P = 1 - (1 - 1/N)^{k}$.

***Sample Size***    Now we find the minimum size of the sample with $P \geq 1/2$ to be $k \geq \ln2 \times N$ as shown below:

$$P = 1 - (1 - 1/N)^k \geq 1/2 \quad \rightarrow (1 - 1/N)^k \leq 1/2$$
$$(1 - 1/N)^k \leq 1/2 \qquad \rightarrow (e^{-k/N}) \leq 1/2 \text{ Using the approximation } 1 - x \approx e^{-x} \text{ with } x = 1/N$$
$$(e^{-k/N}) \leq 1/2 \rightarrow e^{k/N} \geq 2 \rightarrow k/N \geq \ln 2 \rightarrow k \geq \ln 2 \times N$$

---

### First Problem

**Probability: $P = 1 - (1 - 1/N)^k$**       **Sample size: $k \geq \ln 2 \times N$**

---

## E.1.2  Second Problem

The second problem is the same as the first except that the predefined value is one of the samples. This means that we can use the result of the second problem if we replace $k$ with $k - 1$ because after selecting one sample from the sample set only $k - 1$ samples are left. Therefore, $P = 1 - (1 - 1/N)^{k-1}$ and $k \geq \ln 2 \times N + 1$.

---

### Second Problem

**Probability: $P = 1 - (1 - 1/N)^k - 1$**       **Sample size: $k \geq \ln 2 \times N + 1$**

---

## E.1.3  Third Problem

In the third problem, we need to find the minimum size, $k$, of the sample set, such that, with probability $P \geq 1/2$, at least two of the samples have the same values. To solve the problem, we first find the corresponding probability P. We then set the probability to 1/2 to find the minimum size of the sample.

***Probability***   We use a different strategy here:

1.  We assign probabilities to samples one at a time. Assume that $P_i$ is the probability that the sample $i$ has a same value as one of the previous samples and $Q_i$ is the probability that the sample $i$ has a value different from all previous samples.
    a.  Because there is no sample before the first sample, $P_1 = 0$ and $Q_1 = 1 - 0 = 1$.
    b.  Because there is one sample before the second sample and the first sample can have one of the $N$ values, $P_2 = 1/N$ and $Q_2 = (1 - 1/N)$.
    c.  Because there are two samples before the third sample and each of the two samples can have one of the $N$ values, $P_3 = 2/N$ and $Q_1 = (1 - 2/N)$.
    d.  Continuing with the same logic, $P_k = (k - 1)/N$ and $Q_k = (1 - (k - 1)/N)$.
2.  Assuming that all samples are independent, the probability Q that all samples have different values is

$$Q = Q_1 \times Q_2 \times Q_3 \times \cdots \times Q_k = 1 \times (1 - 1/N) \times (1 - 2/N) \times \cdots \times (1 - (k-1)/N)$$
$$Q = (e^{-1/N}) \times (e^{-2/N}) \times \cdots \times (e^{-(k-1)/N}) \text{ Using the approximation } 1 - x \approx e^{-x} \text{ with } x = i/N$$
$$Q = e^{-k(k-1)/2N} \qquad\qquad\quad \text{Using the relation } 1 + 2 + \cdots + (k - 1) = k(k - 1)/2$$
$$Q = e^{-k^2/2N} \text{ Using the approximation } k(k - 1) \approx k^2$$

3.  Finally, if P is the probability that at least two samples have the same values, then we have
    $P = 1 - Q$ or $P = 1 - e^{-k^2/2N}$.

**Sample Size**    Now we find the minimum size of the sample with $P \geq 1/2$ to be $k \geq (2 \times \ln 2)^{1/2} \times N^{1/2}$ or $k \geq 1.18 \times N^{1/2}$ as shown below:

$$P = 1 - e^{-k^2/2N} \geq 1/2 \rightarrow e^{-k^2/2N} \leq 1/2$$
$$e^{-k^2/2N} \leq 1/2 \rightarrow e^{k^2/2N} \geq 2 \rightarrow k^2/2N \geq \ln 2 \rightarrow k \geq (2 \times \ln 2)^{1/2} \times N^{1/2}$$

---

**Third Problem**
**Probability: $P = 1 - e^{-k^2/2N}$    Sample size: $k \geq (2 \times \ln 2)^{1/2} \times N^{1/2}$**

---

## E.1.4   Fourth Problem

In the fourth problem, we have two samples of equal size, $k$. We need to find the minimum value of $k$, such that, with probability $P \geq 1/2$, at least one of the samples in the first set has the same value as a sample in the second set. To solve the problem, we first find the corresponding probability P. We then set the probability to 1/2 to find the minimum size of the sample.

**Probability**    We solve this using a strategy similar to the one we used for the first problem:

1.  According to the first problem, the probability that all samples in the first set have values different from the value of the first sample in the second set is $Q_1 = (1 - 1/N)^k$.
2.  The probability that all samples in the first set have values different from the first and second samples in the second set is $Q_2 = (1 - 1/N)^k \times (1 - 1/N)^k$.
3.  We can extend the logic to say that the probability that all samples in the first set have values different from any sample in the second set is

$$Q_k = (1 - 1/N)^k \times (1 - 1/N)^k \times \cdots \times (1 - 1/N)^k \rightarrow Q_k = (1 - 1/N)^{k^2}$$
$$Q_k = (1 - 1/N)^{k^2} \rightarrow Q_k = e^{-k^2/N} \quad \text{Using the approximation } 1 - x \approx e^{-x} \text{ with } x = 1/N$$

4.  Finally, if P is the probability that at least one sample from the first set has the same value as one of the samples in the second set, then $P = 1 - Q_k$ or $P = 1 - e^{-k^2/N}$.

**Sample Size**    Now we find the minimum common size of the samples as shown below:

$$P = 1 - e^{-k^2/N} \geq 1/2 \rightarrow e^{-k^2/N} \leq 1/2 \rightarrow e^{k^2/N} \leq 2$$
$$e^{-k^2/N} \leq 1/2 \rightarrow e^{k^2/N} \geq 2 \rightarrow k^2/N \geq \ln 2 \rightarrow k \geq (\ln 2)^{1/2} \times N^{1/2}$$

---

**Fourth Problem**
**Probability: $P = 1 - e^{-k^2/N}$    Sample size: $k \geq (\ln 2)^{1/2} \times N^{1/2}$**

---

# E.2 SUMMARY

Table E.1 gives the expressions for the probability (P) and the sample size ($k$) for each of the four problems.

**Table E.1**   *Summarized solutions to four birthday problems*

| Problem | Probability | General value for $k$ | Value of $k$ with $P \geq 1/2$ |
|---|---|---|---|
| 1 | $P \approx 1 - e^{-k/N}$ | $k \approx \ln[1/(1-P)] \times N$ | $k \approx 0.69 \times N$ |
| 2 | $P \approx 1 - e^{-(k-1)/N}$ | $k \approx \ln[1/(1-P)] \times N + 1$ | $k \approx 0.69 \times N + 1$ |
| 3 | $P \approx 1 - e^{-k^2/2N}$ | $k \approx [2 \ln (1/(1-P))]^{1/2} \times N^{1/2}$ | $k \approx 1.18 \times N^{1/2}$ |
| 4 | $P \approx 1 - e^{-k^2/N}$ | $k \approx [\ln (1/(1-P))]^{1/2} \times N^{1/2}$ | $k \approx 0.83 \times N^{1/2}$ |

# Appendix

# F

# Information Theory

In this appendix, we discuss several concepts from *information theory* that are related to topics discussed in this book.

## F.1        MEASURING INFORMATION

How can we measure the information in an event? How much information does an event carry? Let us answer these questions through examples.

> **Example F.1**   Imagine a person sitting in a room. Looking out the window, she can clearly see that the sun is shining. If at this moment she receives a call (an event) from a neighbor saying, "It is now daytime," does this message contain any information? It does not. She is already certain that it is daytime. The message does not remove any uncertainty in her mind.

> **Example F.2**   Imagine a person has bought a lottery ticket. If a friend calls to tell her that she has won first prize, does this message (event) contain any information? It does. The message contains a lot of information, because the probability of winning first prize is very small. The receiver of the message is totally surprised.

The above two examples show that there is a relationship between the usefulness of an event and the expectation of the receiver. If the receiver is surprised when the event happens, the message contains a lot of information; otherwise, it does not. In other words, the information content of a message is inversely related to the probability of the occurrence of that message. If the event is very probable, it does not contain any information (Example F.1); if it is very improbable, it contains a lot of information (Example F.2).

## F.2        ENTROPY

Assume that S is a finite probability sample space (See Appendix D). The entropy or uncertainty of S is defined as

$$H(\mathbf{S}) = \Sigma \ \mathbf{P}(s) \times [\log_2 1/\mathbf{P}(s)] \ \textbf{bits}$$

where $s \in \mathbf{S}$ is the possible outcome of the experiment. Note that if $\mathrm{P}(s) = 0$, then we let the corresponding term, $\mathrm{P}(s) \times [\log_2 1/\mathrm{P}(s)]$, be 0 to avoid dividing by 0.

---

**Example F.3**   Assume that we toss a fair coin. The outcomes are heads and tails, each with a probability of 1/2. This means

$$H(S) = P(heads) \times [\log_2 1/(P(heads))] + P(tails) \times [\log_2 1/(P(tails))]$$

$$H(S) = (1/2) \times [\log_2 1/(1/2)] + (1/2) \times [\log_2 1/(1/2)] = 1 \text{ bit}$$

This example shows that the result of flipping a fair coin gives us 1 bit of information (uncertainty). In each flipping, we don't know what the outcome will be; the two possibilities are equally likely.

---

**Example F.4**   Assume that we toss a nonfair coin. The outcomes are heads and tails, with P(heads) = 3/4 and P(tails) = 1/4. This means

$$H(S) = (3/4) \times [\log_2 1/(3/4)] + (1/4) \times [\log_2 1/(1/4)] \approx 0.8 \text{ bit}$$

This example shows that the result of flipping a nonfair coin gives us only 0.8 bit of information (uncertainty). The amount of information here is less than the amount of information in Example F.3, because we are expecting to get heads most of the time; we are surprised only when we get tails.

---

**Example F.5**   Now assume that we toss a totally nonfair coin, in which the outcome is always heads, P(heads) = 1 and P(tails) = 0. The entropy in this case is

$$H(S) = (1) \times [\log_2 1/(1)] + (0) \times [\log_2 1/(0)] = (1) \times (0) + (0) = 0$$

There is no information (uncertainty) in this experiment. We know that the outcome will always be heads; the entropy is 0.

---

## F.2.1   Maximum Entropy

It can be proven that for a particular probability sample space with $n$ possible outcomes, maximum entropy can be achieved only if all the probabilities are the same (all outcomes are equally likely). In this case, the maximum entropy is

$$\mathbf{H_{max}(S) = \log_2 n \text{ bits}}$$

In other words, the entropy of every probability sample space has an upper limit defined by this formula.

---

**Example F.6**   Assume that we roll a six-sided fair die. The entropy of the experiment is

$$H(S) = \log_2 6 \approx 2.58 \text{ bits}$$

---

## F.2.2   Minimum Entropy

It can be proven that for a particular probability sample space with $n$ possible outcomes, minimum entropy is obtained when only one of the outcomes occurs all the time. In this case, the minimum entropy is

$$\mathbf{H_{min}(S) = 0 \text{ bits}}$$

In other words, the entropy of every probability sample space has a lower limit defined by the above formula.

---

**The entropy of a probability sample space is between 0 bits and $\log_2 n$ bits, where $n$ is the number of possible outcomes.**

---

## F.2.3  Interpretation of Entropy

Entropy can be thought of as the number of bits needed to represent each outcome of a probability sample space when the outcomes are equally probable. For example, when a probability sample space has eight possible outcomes, each outcome can be represented as three bits (000 to 111). When we receive the result of the experiment, we can say that we have received 3 bits of information. The entropy of this probability sample space is also 3 bits ($\log_2 8 = 3$).

## F.2.4  Joint Entropy

When we have two probability sample spaces, $S_1$ and $S_2$, we can define the joint entropy $H(S_1, S_2)$ as

$$H(S_1, S_2) = \Sigma\Sigma \, P\,(x, y) \times [\log_2 1/P\,(x, y)] \text{ bits}$$

## F.2.5  Conditional Entropy

We often need to know the uncertainty in the probability sample space $S_1$, given the uncertainty in probability sample space $S_2$. This is referred to as conditional entropy $H(S_1 \mid S_2)$. It can be proven that

$$H(S_1 \mid S_2) = H(S_1, S_2) - H(S_2) \text{ bits}$$

## F.2.6  Other Relations

There are some other entropy relations that we mention here without proof:

---

1. $H(S_1, S_2) = H(S_2 \mid S_1) + H(S_1) = H(S_1 \mid S_2) + H(S_2)$
2. $H(S_1, S_2) \leq H(S_1) + H(S_2)$
3. $H(S_1 \mid S_2) \leq H(S_1)$
4. $H(S_1, S_2, S_3) = H(S_1 \mid S_2, S_3) + H(S_1, S_3)$

---

In the second and third relation, the equality holds if $S_1$ and $S_2$ are independent.

---

**Example F.7**  In cryptography, if we let **P** be the plaintext probability sample space, let **C** be the ciphertext probability sample space, and let **K** be the key sample space, then **H (K | C)** can be interpreted as a ciphertext attack in which knowledge of C can lead to knowledge of K.

---

**Example F.8**  In cryptography, given the plaintext and key, a deterministic encryption algorithm creates a unique ciphertext, which means **H(C | K, P) = 0**. Also given the ciphertext and the key, the decryption algorithm creates a unique plaintext, which means **H(P | K, C) = 0**. If given the ciphertext and the plaintext, the key is also determined uniquely, then **H(K | P, C) = 0**.

---

## F.2.7  Perfect Secrecy

In cryptography, if P, K, and C are probability sample spaces of plaintext, ciphertext, and the key, respectively, then we have $H(P \mid C) \leq H(P)$. This can be interpreted as saying that the uncertainty of P given C is less than or equal to the uncertainty of P. In most cryptosystems, the relation $H(P \mid C) < H(P)$ holds, which means that the interception of the ciphertext reduces the knowledge required to find the plaintext. A cryptosystem provides **perfect secrecy** if the relation $H(P \mid C) = H(P)$ holds, which means the uncertainty about the plaintext given the ciphertext is the same as the uncertainty about the plaintext.

In other words, Eve gains no information by intercepting the ciphertext; she still needs to guess the value of the plaintext by examining all possibilities.

---

**A cryptosystem provides perfect secrecy if H(P | C) = H(P).**

---

**Example F.9** In previous chapters, we claimed that the *one -time pad* cipher provides prefect secrecy. Let us prove this fact using the previous relations about entropies. Assume that the alphabet is made of only 0 and 1. If the length of the message is *L*, it can be proved that the key and the ciphertext each are made of $2^L$ symbols, in which each symbol is equally probable. Hence $H(K) = H(C) = \log_2 2^L = L$. Using the relations obtained in Example F.8 and the fact that $H(P, K) = H(P) + H(K)$ because P and K are independent, we have

H(P, K, C) = H(C | P, K) + H(P, K) = H(P, K) =  H(P) + H(K)

H(P, K, C) = H(K | P, C) + H(P, C) = H(P, C) = H(P | C) + H(C)

This implies H(P | C) = H(P)

---

**Example F.10** Shannon showed that in a cryptosystem, if (1) the keys in the key sample space occur with equal probability and (2) for each plaintext and each ciphertext, there is a unique key, then the cryptosystem provides perfect secrecy. The proof uses the fact that, in this case, the key, plaintext, and ciphertext probability sample spaces are of the same size.

## F.3 ENTROPY OF A LANGUAGE

It is interesting to relate the concept of entropy to natural languages such as English. In this section, we highlight some points related to entropy.

### F.3.1 Entropy of an Arbitrary Language

Assume that a language uses *N* letters and that all the letters have equal likelihood of occurring. We can say that the entropy of this language is $H_L = \log_2 N$. For example, if we use the twenty-six uppercase letters (A to Z) to send our message, the entropy, or the information contained in each letter, is $H_L = \log_2 26 \approx 4.7$ bits. In other words, receiving a letter in this language is equal to receiving 4.7 bits. This means that we can encode the letters in this language using 5-bit words; instead of sending a letter, we can send one 5-bit word.

### F.3.2 Entropy of the English Language

The entropy of the English language is much less than 4.7 bits (if we use only uppercase letters), for two reasons. First, the letters are not equally likely to occur. Chapter 3 shows the frequencies of letters occurring in the English language. The letter E is much more likely to occur than the letter Z. Second, the existence of digrams and trigrams reduces the amount of information in the received text. If we receive the letter Q, it is very likely that the next letter is U. Also, if we receive the five consecutive letters SELLI, it is very likely that the next two letters are NG. These two facts reduce the entropy of the English language, as Shannon has cleverly calculated, to the average value of 1.50.

## F.3.3 Redundancy

The redundancy of a language has been defined as

$$R = 1 - H_L/(\log_2 N)$$

In the case of the English language using only uppercase letters R = 1 − 1.50/4.7 = 0.68. In other words, there is a 70 percent redundancy in an English message. A compression algorithm can compress an English text up to 70 percent without losing the contents.

## F.3.4 Unicity Distance

Another definition by Shannon is the **unicity distance.** The unicity distance is the minimum length of the ciphertext, $n_0$, required for Eve to uniquely determine the key (given enough time) and eventually calculates the plaintext. The unicity distance is defined as

$$n_0 = H(K)/[R \times H(P)]$$

**Example F.11**  The substitution cipher uses a key domain of 26! keys and the alphabet of 26 characters. Using the redundancy of 0.70 for the English language, the unicity distance is

$$n_0 = (\log_2 26!)/(0.70 \times \log_2 26) \approx 27$$

This means that a ciphertext of at least 27 characters is needed for Eve to uniquely find the plaintext.

**Example F.12**  The shift cipher uses a key domain of 26 keys and the alphabet of 26 characters. Using the redundancy of 0.70 for the English language, the unicity distance is

$$n_0 = (\log_2 26)/(0.70 \times \log_2 26) \approx 1.5$$

This means that a ciphertext of at least 2 characters is needed for Eve to uniquely find the plaintext. Of course, this is a very rough estimate. In an actual situation, Eve needs more characters to break the code.

# Appendix

# G

# List of Irreducible and Primitive Polynomials

Recall from Chapter 4 that an *irreducible polynomial* in $\mathbf{GF}(2^n)$ is a polynomial with degree $n$ that cannot be factored into a polynomial with degree of less than $n$. Also recall from Chapter 5 that a *primitive polynomial* is an irreducible polynomial that divides $x^e + 1$, where $e$ is the least integer in the form $e = 2^k - 1$ and $k \geq 2$. This means that a primitive polynomial is necessarily an irreducible polynomial, but an irreducible polynomial is not necessarily a primitive polynomial. Table G.1 shows the irreducible and primitive polynomials for degrees 1 to 8. Those in parentheses are only irreducible but not primitive.

**Table G.1** *Irreducible and primitive polynomials.*

| n | Polynomials (in hexadecimal format) | | | | | | | | | |
|---|---|---|---|---|---|---|---|---|---|---|
| 1 | 3 | 2 | | | | | | | | |
| 2 | 7 | | | | | | | | | |
| 3 | B | D | | | | | | | | |
| 4 | 13 | 19 | (1F) | | | | | | | |
| 5 | 25 | 29 | 2F | 37 | 3B | 3D | | | | |
| 6 | 43 | (45) | 49 | 57 | 5B | 61 | 6D | 73 | | |
| 7 | 83 | 87 | 91 | 9D | A7 | AB | B9 | BF | C1 | CB |
|   | D3 | D4 | E5 | EF | F1 | F7 | FD | | | |
| 8 | (11B) | 11D | 12B | 12D | (139) | (13F) | 14D | 15F | 163 | 165 |
|   | 169 | 171 | (177) | (17B) | 187 | (18B) | (19F) | (1A3) | 1A9 | (1B1) |
|   | (1BD) | 1CF | (1D7) | (1DB) | 1E7 | (1F3) | 1F5 | (1F9) | | |

To find the polynomial represented by the hexadecimal number in the table, first write the number in binary and then convert it to the polynomial.

**Example G.1**  Find the first primitive polynomial of degree 7.

**Solution**  The first entry for degree 7 is 83 in hexadecimal, which is both an irreducible and primitive polynomial. The integer 83 in hexadecimal is equivalent to 1000 0011 in binary. The corresponding polynomial is $x^7 + x + 1$.

**Example G.2**  Find the first irreducible polynomial of degree 6, which is not a primitive polynomial.

**Solution**  The first nonprimitive polynomial of degree 6 is (45) in hexadecimal. The integer 45 in hexadecimal is equivalent to 100 0101 in binary (note that we must keep only 7 bits). The corresponding polynomial is $x^6 + x^2 + 1$.

**Example G.3**  Find the second irreducible polynomial of degree 8, which is not a primitive polynomial.

**Solution**  The second nonprimitive polynomial of degree 8 is (139) in hexadecimal. The integer 139 in hexadecimal is equivalent to 1 0011 1001 in binary (note that we must keep only 9 bits). The corresponding polynomial is $x^8 + x^5 + x^4 + x^3 + 1$.

# Appendix

# H

# Primes Less Than 10,000

This appendix lists the primes less than 10,000. In each table, each number in the first column is the number of primes in the corresponding range for that row.

**Table H.1** *List of primes in the range 1-1000*

| | |
|---|---|
| 25 | 2 3 5 7 11 13 17 19 23 29 31 37 41 43 47 53 59 61 67 71 73 79 83 89 97 |
| 21 | 101 103 107 109 113 127 131 137 139 149 151 157 163 167 173 179 181 191 193 197 199 |
| 16 | 211 223 227 229 233 239 241 251 257 263 269 271 277 281 283 293 |
| 16 | 307 311 313 317 331 337 347 349 353 359 367 373 379 383 389 397 |
| 17 | 401 409 419 421 431 433 439 443 449 457 461 463 467 479 487 491 499 |
| 14 | 503 509 521 523 541 547 557 563 569 571 577 587 593 599 |
| 16 | 601 607 613 617 619 631 641 643 647 653 659 661 673 677 683 691 |
| 14 | 701 709 719 727 733 739 743 751 757 761 769 773 787 797 |
| 15 | 809 811 821 823 827 829 839 853 857 859 863 877 881 883 887 |
| 14 | 907 911 919 929 937 941 947 953 967 971 977 983 991 997 |

The total number of primes in the range 1–1000 is 168.

**Table H.2** *List of primes in the range 1001-2000*

| | |
|---|---|
| 16 | 1009 1013 1019 1021 1031 1033 1039 1049 1051 1061 1063 1069 1087 1091 1093 1097 |
| 12 | 1103 1109 1117 1123 1129 1151 1153 1163 1171 1181 1187 1193 |
| 15 | 1201 1213 1217 1223 1229 1231 1237 1249 1259 1277 1279 1283 1289 1291 1297 |
| 11 | 1301 1303 1307 1319 1321 1327 1361 1367 1373 1381 1399 |
| 17 | 1409 1423 1427 1429 1433 1439 1447 1451 1453 1459 1471 1481 1483 1487 1489 1493 1499 |
| 12 | 1511 1523 1531 1543 1549 1553 1559 1567 1571 1579 1583 1597 |
| 15 | 1601 1607 1609 1613 1619 1621 1627 1637 1657 1663 1667 1669 1693 1697 1699 |
| 12 | 1709 1721 1723 1733 1741 1747 1753 1759 1777 1783 1787 1789 |
| 12 | 1801 1811 1823 1831 1847 1861 1867 1871 1873 1877 1879 1889 |
| 13 | 1901 1907 1913 1931 1933 1949 1951 1973 1979 1987 1993 1997 1999 |

The total number of primes in the range 1001–2000 is 134.

**Table H.3** *List of primes in the range 2001-3000*

| | |
|---|---|
| 14 | 2003 2011 2017 2027 2029 2039 2053 2063 2069 2081 2083 2087 2089 2099 |
| 10 | 2111 2113 2129 2131 2137 2141 2143 2153 2161 2179 |
| 15 | 2203 2207 2213 2221 2237 2239 2243 2251 2267 2269 2273 2281 2287 2293 2297 |
| 15 | 2309 2311 2333 2339 2341 2347 2351 2357 2371 2377 2381 2383 2389 2393 2399 |
| 10 | 2411 2417 2423 2437 2441 2447 2459 2467 2473 2477 |
| 11 | 2503 2521 2531 2539 2543 2549 2551 2557 2579 2591 2593 |
| 15 | 2609 2617 2621 2633 2647 2657 2659 2663 2671 2677 2683 2687 2689 2693 2699 |
| 14 | 2707 2711 2713 2719 2729 2731 2741 2749 2753 2767 2777 2789 2791 2797 |
| 12 | 2801 2803 2819 2833 2837 2843 2851 2857 2861 2879 2887 2897 |
| 11 | 2903 2909 2917 2927 2939 2953 2957 2963 2969 2971 2999 |

The total number of primes in the range 2001−3000 is 127.

**Table H.4** *List of primes in the range 3001-4000*

| | |
|---|---|
| 12 | 3001 3011 3019 3023 3037 3041 3049 3061 3067 3079 3083 3089 |
| 10 | 3109 3119 3121 3137 3163 3167 3169 3181 3187 3191 |
| 11 | 3203 3209 3217 3221 3229 3251 3253 3257 3259 3271 3299 |
| 15 | 3301 3307 3313 3319 3323 3329 3331 3343 3347 3359 3361 3371 3373 3389 3391 |
| 11 | 3407 3413 3433 3449 3457 3461 3463 3467 3469 3491 3499 |
| 14 | 3511 3517 3527 3529 3533 3539 3541 3547 3557 3559 3571 3581 3583 3593 |
| 13 | 3607 3613 3617 3623 3631 3637 3643 3659 3671 3673 3677 3691 3697 |
| 12 | 3701 3709 3719 3727 3733 3739 3761 3767 3769 3779 3793 3797 |
| 11 | 3803 3821 3823 3833 3847 3851 3853 3863 3877 3881 3889 |
| 11 | 3907 3911 3917 3919 3923 3929 3931 3943 3947 3967 3989 |

The total number of primes in the range 3001−4000 is 120.

**Table H.5** *List of primes in the range 4001-5000*

| | |
|---|---|
| 15 | 4001 4003 4007 4013 4019 4021 4027 4049 4051 4057 4073 4079 4091 4093 4099 |
| 9 | 4111 4127 4129 4133 4139 4153 4157 4159 4177 |
| 16 | 4201 4211 4217 4219 4229 4231 4241 4243 4253 4259 4261 4271 4273 4283 4289 4297 |
| 9 | 4327 4337 4339 4349 4357 4363 4373 4391 4397 |
| 11 | 4409 4421 4423 4441 4447 4451 4457 4463 4481 4483 4493 |
| 12 | 4507 4513 4517 4519 4523 4547 4549 4561 4567 4583 4591 4597 |
| 12 | 4603 4621 4637 4639 4643 4649 4651 4657 4663 4673 4679 4691 |
| 12 | 4703 4721 4723 4729 4733 4751 4759 4783 4787 4789 4793 4799 |
| 8 | 4801 4813 4817 4831 4861 4871 4877 4889 |
| 15 | 4903 4909 4919 4931 4933 4937 4943 4951 4957 4967 4969 4973 4987 4993 4999 |

The total number of primes in the range 4001−5000 is 119.

**Table H.6**   *List of primes in the range 5001-6000*

| | |
|---|---|
| 12 | 5003 5009 5011 5021 5023 5039 5051 5059 5077 5081 5087 5099 |
| 11 | 5101 5107 5113 5119 5147 5153 5167 5171 5179 5189 5197 |
| 10 | 5209 5227 5231 5233 5237 5261 5273 5279 5281 5297 |
| 10 | 5303 5309 5323 5333 5347 5351 5381 5387 5393 5399 |
| 13 | 5407 5413 5417 5419 5431 5437 5441 5443 5449 5471 5477 5479 5483 |
| 13 | 5501 5503 5507 5519 5521 5527 5531 5557 5563 5569 5573 5581 5591 |
| 12 | 5623 5639 5641 5647 5651 5653 5657 5659 5669 5683 5689 5693 |
| 10 | 5701 5711 5717 5737 5741 5743 5749 5779 5783 5791 |
| 16 | 5801 5807 5813 5821 5827 5839 5843 5849 5851 5857 5861 5867 5869 5879 5881 5897 |
| 7 | 5903 5923 5927 5939 5953 5981 5987 |

**The total number of primes in the range 5001–6000 is 114.**

**Table H.7**   *List of primes in the range 6001-7000*

| | |
|---|---|
| 12 | 6007 6011 6029 6037 6043 6047 6053 6067 6073 6079 6089 6091 |
| 11 | 6101 6113 6121 6131 6133 6143 6151 6163 6173 6197 6199 |
| 13 | 6203 6211 6217 6221 6229 6247 6257 6263 6269 6271 6277 6287 6299 |
| 15 | 6301 6311 6317 6323 6329 6337 6343 6353 6359 6361 6367 6373 6379 6389 6397 |
| 8 | 6421 6427 6449 6451 6469 6473 6481 6491 |
| 11 | 6521 6529 6547 6551 6553 6563 6569 6571 6577 6581 6599 |
| 10 | 6607 6619 6637 6653 6659 6661 6673 6679 6689 6691 |
| 12 | 6701 6703 6709 6719 6733 6737 6761 6763 6779 6781 6791 6793 |
| 12 | 6803 6823 6827 6829 6833 6841 6857 6863 6869 6871 6883 6899 |
| 13 | 6907 6911 6917 6947 6949 6959 6961 6967 6971 6977 6983 6991 6997 |

**The total number of primes in the range 6001–7000 is 117.**

**Table H.8**   *List of primes in the range 7001-8000*

| | |
|---|---|
| 9 | 7001 7013 7019 7027 7039 7043 7057 7069 7079 |
| 10 | 7103 7109 7121 7127 7129 7151 7159 7177 7187 7193 |
| 11 | 7207 7211 7213 7219 7229 7237 7243 7247 7253 7283 7297 |
| 9 | 7307 7309 7321 7331 7333 7349 7351 7369 7393 |
| 11 | 7411 7417 7433 7451 7457 7459 7477 7481 7487 7489 7499 |
| 15 | 7507 7517 7523 7529 7537 7541 7547 7549 7559 7561 7573 7577 7583 7589 7591 |
| 12 | 7603 7607 7621 7639 7643 7649 7669 7673 7681 7687 7691 7699 |
| 10 | 7703 7717 7723 7727 7741 7753 7757 7759 7789 7793 |
| 10 | 7817 7823 7829 7841 7853 7867 7873 7877 7879 7883 |
| 10 | 7901 7907 7919 7927 7933 7937 7949 7951 7963 7993 |

**The total number of primes in the range 7001–8000 is 107.**

**Table H.9** *List of primes in the range 8001-9000*

| | |
|---|---|
| 11 | 8009 8011 8017 8039 8053 8059 8069 8081 8087 8089 8093 |
| 10 | 8101 8111 8117 8123 8147 8161 8167 8171 8179 8191 |
| 14 | 8209 8219 8221 8231 8233 8237 8243 8263 8269 8273 8287 8291 8293 8297 |
| 9 | 8311 8317 8329 8353 8363 8369 8377 8387 8389 |
| 8 | 8419 8423 8429 8431 8443 8447 8461 8467 |
| 12 | 8501 8513 8521 8527 8537 8539 8543 8563 8573 8581 8597 8599 |
| 13 | 8609 8623 8627 8629 8641 8647 8663 8669 8677 8681 8689 8693 8699 |
| 11 | 8707 8713 8719 8731 8737 8741 8747 8753 8761 8779 8783 |
| 13 | 8803 8807 8819 8821 8831 8837 8839 8849 8861 8863 8867 8887 8893 |
| 9 | 8923 8929 8933 8941 8951 8963 8969 8971 8999 |

The total number of primes in the range 8001–9000 is 110.

**Table H.10** *List of primes in the range 9001-10,000*

| | |
|---|---|
| 11 | 9001 9007 9011 9013 9029 9041 9043 9049 9059 9067 9091 |
| 12 | 9103 9109 9127 9133 9137 9151 9157 9161 9173 9181 9187 9199 |
| 11 | 9203 9209 9221 9227 9239 9241 9257 9277 9281 9283 9293 |
| 11 | 9311 9319 9323 9337 9341 9343 9349 9371 9377 9391 9397 |
| 15 | 9403 9413 9419 9421 9431 9433 9437 9439 9461 9463 9467 9473 9479 9491 9497 |
| 7 | 9511 9521 9533 9539 9547 9551 9587 |
| 13 | 9601 9613 9619 9623 9629 9631 9643 9649 9661 9677 9679 9689 9697 |
| 11 | 9719 9721 9733 9739 9743 9749 9767 9769 9781 9787 9791 |
| 12 | 9803 9811 9817 9829 9833 9839 9851 9857 9859 9871 9883 9887 |
| 9 | 9901 9907 9923 9929 9931 9941 9949 9967 9973 |

The total number of primes in the range 9001–10,000 is 112.

# Appendix

# Prime Factors of Integers Less Than 1000

This appendix provides aid in finding prime factors of integers less than 1000. Tables I.1 and I.2 give the least prime factors. These tables do not include even integers (whose least prime factors are obviously 2) and integers with 5 as the rightmost digit (with a prime factors 5). Note that if no least factor is given for an integer, the integer itself is a prime (its least factor is itself).

To find all factors of an integer less than 1000, first find the least factor, divide the number by this factor, and search the table again to find the second factor, and so on.

---

**Example I.1**   To find all factors of 693, we use the following steps:
1. The least factor of 693 is 3; 693/3 = 231.
2. The least factor of 231 is 3; 231/3 = 77.
3. The least factor of 77 is 7; 77/7 = 11.
4. The integer 11 is itself a prime. Therefore, $693 = 3^2 \times 7 \times 11$.

---

**Example I.2**   To find all factors of 722, we use the following steps:
1. The number is even, so the least factor is obviously 2; 722/2 = 361.
2. The least factor of 361 is 19; 361/19 = 19.
3. The integer 19 is itself a prime. Therefore, $722 = 2 \times 19^2$.

---

**Example I.3**   To find all factors of 745, we use the following steps:
1. The number is divisible to 5, so the least factor is obviously 5; 745/5 = 149.
2. The integer 149 is itself a prime. Therefore, $745 = 5 \times 149$.

**Table I.1** *Least factor of integers in the range 1–500 (L. F. means least factor)*

| Integer | L. F. | Integer | L. F. | Integer | L. F. | Integer | L. F. | Integer | L. F. |
|---|---|---|---|---|---|---|---|---|---|
| 1 | – | 101 | – | 201 | 3 | 301 | 7 | 401 | – |
| 3 | – | 103 | – | 203 | 7 | 303 | 3 | 403 | 13 |
| 7 | – | 107 | – | 207 | 3 | 307 | – | 407 | 11 |
| 9 | 3 | 109 | – | 209 | 11 | 309 | 3 | 409 | – |
| 11 | – | 111 | 3 | 211 | – | 311 | – | 411 | 3 |
| 13 | – | 113 | – | 213 | 3 | 313 | – | 413 | 7 |
| 17 | – | 117 | 3 | 217 | 7 | 317 | – | 417 | 3 |
| 19 | – | 119 | 7 | 219 | 3 | 319 | 11 | 419 | – |
| 21 | 3 | 121 | 11 | 221 | 13 | 321 | 3 | 421 | – |
| 23 | – | 123 | 3 | 223 | – | 323 | 17 | 423 | 3 |
| 27 | 3 | 127 | – | 227 | – | 327 | 3 | 427 | 7 |
| 29 | – | 129 | 3 | 229 | – | 329 | 7 | 429 | 3 |
| 31 | 3 | 131 | – | 231 | 3 | 331 | – | 431 | – |
| 33 | – | 133 | 7 | 233 | – | 333 | 3 | 433 | – |
| 37 | – | 137 | – | 237 | 3 | 337 | – | 437 | 19 |
| 39 | 3 | 139 | – | 239 | – | 339 | 3 | 439 | – |
| 41 | – | 141 | 3 | 241 | – | 341 | 11 | 441 | 3 |
| 43 | – | 143 | 11 | 243 | 3 | 343 | 7 | 443 | – |
| 47 | – | 147 | 3 | 247 | 13 | 347 | – | 447 | 3 |
| 49 | 7 | 149 | – | 249 | 3 | 349 | – | 449 | – |
| 51 | 3 | 151 | – | 251 | – | 351 | 3 | 451 | 11 |
| 53 | – | 153 | 3 | 253 | 11 | 353 | – | 453 | 3 |
| 57 | 3 | 157 | – | 257 | – | 357 | 3 | 457 | – |
| 59 | – | 159 | 3 | 259 | 7 | 359 | – | 459 | 3 |
| 61 | – | 161 | 7 | 261 | 3 | 361 | 19 | 461 | – |
| 63 | 3 | 163 | – | 263 | – | 363 | 3 | 463 | – |
| 67 | – | 167 | 11 | 267 | 3 | 367 | – | 467 | – |
| 69 | 3 | 169 | 13 | 269 | – | 369 | 3 | 469 | 7 |
| 71 | – | 171 | 3 | 271 | – | 371 | 7 | 471 | 3 |
| 73 | – | 173 | – | 273 | 3 | 373 | – | 473 | 11 |
| 77 | 7 | 177 | 3 | 277 | – | 377 | 13 | 477 | 3 |
| 79 | – | 179 | – | 279 | 3 | 379 | – | 479 | – |
| 81 | 3 | 181 | – | 281 | – | 381 | 7 | 481 | 13 |
| 83 | – | 183 | 3 | 283 | – | 383 | – | 483 | 3 |
| 87 | 3 | 187 | 11 | 287 | 7 | 387 | – | 487 | – |
| 89 | – | 189 | 3 | 289 | 17 | 389 | 7 | 489 | 13 |
| 91 | 7 | 191 | – | 291 | 3 | 391 | 17 | 491 | – |
| 93 | 3 | 193 | – | 293 | – | 393 | 3 | 493 | 17 |
| 97 | – | 197 | – | 297 | 3 | 397 | – | 497 | 7 |
| 99 | 3 | 199 | – | 299 | 13 | 399 | 3 | 499 | – |

**Table I.2** *Least factor of integer in the range 501–1000 (L. F. means least factor)*

| Integer | L. F. | Integer | L. F. | Integer | L. F. | Integer | L. F. | Integer | L. F. |
|---------|-------|---------|-------|---------|-------|---------|-------|---------|-------|
| 501 | 3 | 601 | – | 701 | – | 801 | 3 | 901 | 17 |
| 503 | – | 603 | 3 | 703 | 19 | 803 | 11 | 903 | 3 |
| 507 | – | 607 | – | 707 | 7 | 807 | 3 | 907 | – |
| 509 | 3 | 609 | 3 | 709 | – | 809 | – | 909 | 3 |
| 511 | 7 | 611 | 13 | 711 | 3 | 811 | – | 911 | – |
| 513 | 3 | 613 | – | 713 | 13 | 813 | 3 | 913 | 11 |
| 517 | 11 | 617 | – | 717 | 3 | 817 | 19 | 917 | 7 |
| 519 | 3 | 619 | – | 719 | – | 819 | 3 | 919 | – |
| 521 | – | 621 | 3 | 721 | 7 | 821 | – | 921 | 3 |
| 523 | – | 623 | 7 | 723 | 3 | 823 | – | 923 | 13 |
| 527 | 17 | 627 | 3 | 727 | – | 827 | – | 927 | 3 |
| 529 | 23 | 629 | 17 | 729 | 3 | 829 | – | 929 | – |
| 531 | 3 | 631 | – | 731 | 17 | 831 | 3 | 931 | 7 |
| 533 | 13 | 633 | 3 | 733 | – | 833 | 7 | 933 | 3 |
| 537 | 3 | 637 | 7 | 737 | 11 | 837 | 3 | 937 | – |
| 539 | 7 | 639 | 3 | 739 | – | 839 | – | 939 | 3 |
| 541 | – | 641 | – | 741 | 3 | 841 | 29 | 941 | – |
| 543 | 3 | 643 | – | 743 | – | 843 | 3 | 943 | 23 |
| 547 | – | 647 | – | 747 | 3 | 847 | 7 | 947 | – |
| 549 | 3 | 649 | 11 | 749 | 7 | 849 | 3 | 949 | 13 |
| 551 | 19 | 651 | 3 | 751 | – | 851 | 23 | 951 | 3 |
| 553 | 7 | 653 | – | 753 | 3 | 853 | – | 953 | – |
| 557 | – | 657 | 3 | 757 | – | 857 | – | 957 | 3 |
| 559 | 13 | 659 | – | 759 | 3 | 859 | – | 959 | 7 |
| 561 | 3 | 661 | – | 761 | – | 861 | 3 | 961 | 3 |
| 563 | – | 663 | 3 | 763 | 7 | 863 | – | 963 | 13 |
| 567 | 3 | 667 | 23 | 767 | 13 | 867 | 3 | 967 | – |
| 569 | – | 669 | 3 | 769 | – | 869 | 11 | 969 | 3 |
| 571 | – | 671 | 11 | 771 | 3 | 871 | 13 | 971 | – |
| 573 | 3 | 673 | – | 773 | – | 873 | 3 | 973 | 7 |
| 557 | – | 677 | – | 777 | 3 | 877 | – | 977 | – |
| 579 | 3 | 679 | 7 | 779 | 19 | 879 | 3 | 979 | 11 |
| 581 | 7 | 681 | 3 | 781 | 11 | 881 | – | 981 | 3 |
| 583 | 11 | 683 | – | 783 | 3 | 883 | – | 983 | – |
| 587 | – | 687 | 3 | 787 | – | 887 | – | 987 | 3 |
| 589 | 19 | 689 | 13 | 789 | 3 | 889 | 7 | 989 | 23 |
| 591 | 3 | 691 | – | 791 | 7 | 891 | 3 | 991 | – |
| 593 | – | 693 | 17 | 793 | 3 | 893 | 19 | 993 | 3 |
| 597 | 3 | 697 | – | 797 | – | 897 | 3 | 997 | – |
| 599 | – | 699 | 3 | 799 | 17 | 899 | 29 | 999 | 3 |

# Appendix

# J

# List of First Primitive Roots for Primes Less Than 1000

Table J.1 shows the first primitive roots modulo a prime for primes less than 1000.

### Table J.1

| Prime | Root | Prime | Root | Prime | Root | Prime | Root | Prime | Root | Prime | Root | Prime | Root |
|-------|------|-------|------|-------|------|-------|------|-------|------|-------|------|-------|------|
| 2 | 1 | 103 | 5 | 241 | 7 | 401 | 3 | 571 | 3 | 739 | 3 | 919 | 7 |
| 3 | 2 | 107 | 2 | 251 | 6 | 409 | 21 | 577 | 5 | 743 | 5 | 929 | 3 |
| 5 | 2 | 109 | 6 | 257 | 3 | 419 | 2 | 587 | 2 | 751 | 3 | 937 | 5 |
| 7 | 3 | 113 | 2 | 263 | 5 | 421 | 2 | 593 | 3 | 757 | 2 | 941 | 2 |
| 11 | 2 | 127 | 3 | 269 | 2 | 431 | 7 | 599 | 7 | 761 | 6 | 947 | 2 |
| 13 | 2 | 131 | 2 | 271 | 6 | 433 | 5 | 601 | 7 | 769 | 11 | 953 | 3 |
| 17 | 3 | 137 | 3 | 277 | 5 | 439 | 15 | 607 | 3 | 773 | 2 | 967 | 5 |
| 19 | 2 | 139 | 2 | 281 | 3 | 443 | 2 | 613 | 2 | 787 | 2 | 971 | 2 |
| 23 | 5 | 149 | 2 | 283 | 3 | 449 | 3 | 617 | 3 | 797 | 2 | 977 | 3 |
| 29 | 2 | 151 | 6 | 293 | 2 | 457 | 13 | 619 | 2 | 809 | 3 | 983 | 5 |
| 31 | 3 | 157 | 5 | 307 | 5 | 461 | 2 | 631 | 3 | 811 | 3 | 991 | 6 |
| 37 | 2 | 163 | 2 | 311 | 17 | 463 | 3 | 641 | 3 | 821 | 2 | 997 | 7 |
| 41 | 6 | 167 | 5 | 313 | 10 | 467 | 2 | 643 | 11 | 823 | 3 | | |
| 43 | 3 | 173 | 2 | 317 | 2 | 479 | 13 | 647 | 5 | 827 | 2 | | |
| 47 | 5 | 179 | 2 | 331 | 3 | 487 | 3 | 653 | 2 | 829 | 2 | | |
| 53 | 2 | 181 | 2 | 337 | 10 | 491 | 2 | 659 | 2 | 839 | 11 | | |
| 59 | 2 | 191 | 19 | 347 | 2 | 499 | 7 | 671 | 2 | 853 | 2 | | |
| 61 | 2 | 193 | 5 | 349 | 2 | 503 | 5 | 673 | 5 | 857 | 3 | | |
| 67 | 2 | 197 | 2 | 353 | 2 | 509 | 2 | 677 | 2 | 859 | 2 | | |
| 71 | 2 | 199 | 3 | 359 | 7 | 521 | 3 | 683 | 5 | 863 | 5 | | |
| 73 | 5 | 211 | 2 | 367 | 6 | 523 | 2 | 691 | 3 | 877 | 2 | | |
| 79 | 3 | 223 | 3 | 373 | 2 | 541 | 2 | 701 | 2 | 881 | 3 | | |
| 83 | 2 | 227 | 2 | 379 | 2 | 547 | 2 | 709 | 2 | 883 | 2 | | |
| 89 | 2 | 229 | 6 | 383 | 5 | 557 | 2 | 719 | 11 | 887 | 5 | | |
| 97 | 5 | 233 | 3 | 389 | 2 | 563 | 2 | 727 | 5 | 907 | 2 | | |
| 101 | 2 | 239 | 7 | 397 | 5 | 569 | 3 | 733 | 6 | 911 | 17 | | |

# Appendix

# K

# Random Number Generator

Cryptography and randomness are closely related. In Appendix F, *Information Theory*, we mentioned that perfect secrecy can be achieved if the key of the encipherment algorithm is truly a random number. There are two approaches to generating a long stream of random bits: using a natural random process, such as flipping a coin many times and interpreting heads and tails as 0-bits and 1-bits, or using a deterministic process with feedback. The first approach is called a **true random number generator (TRNG)**; the second is called a **pseudorandom number generator (PRNG)**. Figure K.1 shows these two approaches.

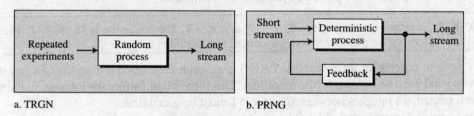

a. TRGN            b. PRNG

**Fig. K.1** *TRNG and PRNG*

## K.1                   TRNG

Although flipping a fair coin continuously creates a perfect stream of bits, it is not practical. There are many natural sources that can produce true random numbers, such as sampling thermal noise produced in an electric resistor or measuring the response time of a mechanical or electrical process. These natural resources have been used in the past, and some of them have been commercialized. However, there are several drawbacks to this approach. The process is normally slow, and the same random stream cannot be repeated if needed.

## K.2                   PRNG

A reasonably random stream of bits can be achieved using a deterministic process with a short random stream as the input (seed). A pseudorandom number generator uses this approach. The generated number is not truly random because the process that creates it is deterministic. PRNGs can be divided into two broad categories: congruential generators and generators using cryptographic ciphers. We discuss some generators in each category.

## K.2.1 Congruential Generators

Several methods use some congruential relations.

### Linear Congruential Generator

In computer science, the most common technique for generating pseudorandom numbers is the linear congruential method, introduced by Lehmer. As Fig. K.2 shows, this method recursively creates a sequence of pseudorandom numbers using a linear congruence equation of the form $x_{i+1} = (ax_i + b)$ mod $n$, where $x_0$, called the seed, is a number between 0 and $n - 1$.

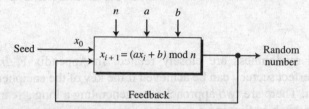

**Fig. K.2** *Linear congruential pseudorandom number generator*

The sequence is periodic, where the period depends one how carefully the coefficients, $a$ and $b$, are selected. The ideal is to make the period as large as the modulus $n$.

---

**Example K.1** Assume that $a = 4$, $b = 5$, $n = 17$, and $x_0 = 7$. The sequence is 16, 1, 9, 7, 16, 1, 9, 7, ..., which is definitely a poor pseudorandom sequence; the period is only 4.

---

*Criteria* Several criteria for an acceptable PRNG have been developed during the last few decades:
1. The period must be equal to $n$ (the modulus). This means that, before the integers in the sequence are repeated, all integers between 0 and $n - 1$ must be generated.
2. The sequence in each period must be random.
3. The generating process must be efficient. Most computers today are efficient when arithmetic is done using 32-bit words.

*Recommendation* Based on the previous criteria, the following are recommended for selecting the coefficients of the congruence equation and the value of the modulus.
1. A good choice for the modulus, $n$, is the largest prime number close to the size of a word in the computer being used. The recommendation is to use the thirty-first Mersenne prime as the modulus: $n = M_{31} = 2^{31} - 1$.
2. To create a period as long as the modulus, the value of the first coefficient, $a$, should be a primitive root of the prime modulus. Although the integer 7 is a primitive root of $M_{31}$, it is recommended to use $7^k$, where $k$ is an integer coprime with $(M_{31} - 1)$. Some recommended values for $k$ are 5 and 13. This means that $(a = 7^5)$ or $(a = 7^{13})$.
3. For the second recommendation to be effective, the value of the second coefficient, $b$, should be zero.

---

**Linear Congruential Generator:**

$$x_{i+1} = ax_i \bmod n, \text{ where } n = 2^{31} - 1 \text{ and } a = 7^5 \text{ or } a = 7^{13}$$

---

**Security**    A sequence generated by a linear congruential equation shows reasonable randomness if the previous recommendations are followed. The sequence is useful in some applications where only randomness is required (such as simulation); it is useless in cryptography where both randomness and secrecy are desired. Because $n$ is public, the sequence can be attacked by Eve using one of the two strategies:

a.   If Eve knows the value of the seed $(x_0)$ and the coefficient $a$, she can easily regenerate the whole sequence.

b.   If Eve does not know the value of $x_0$ and $a$, she can intercept the first two integers and use the following two equations to find $x_0$ and $a$:

$$x_1 = ax_0 \bmod n \qquad x_2 = ax_1 \bmod n$$

**Quadratic Residue Generator**    To make the pseudorandom sequence less predictable, a quadratic residue generator has been introduced (see Chapter 9), $x_{i+1} = x_i^2 \bmod n$, where $x_0$, called the seed, is a number between 0 and $n - 1$.

## Blum Blum Shub Generator

A simple but efficient method for generating a pseudorandom number generator is called **Blum Blum Shub (BBC)** after the names of its three inventors. BBC uses quadratic residue congruence, but it is a pseudorandom bit generator instead of a pseudorandom number generator; it generates a sequence of bits (0 or 1). Figure K.3 shows the idea of this generator.

The following shows the steps:

1.   Find two large primes numbers $p$ and $q$ in the form $4k + 3$, where $k$ is an integer (both $p$ and $q$ are congruent to 3 modulo 4).

2.   Select the modulus $n = p \times q$.

3.   Choose a random integer $r$ which is coprime to $n$.

4.   Calculate the seed as $x_0 = r^2 \bmod n$.

5.   Generate the sequence as $x_{i+1} = x_i^2 \bmod n$.

6.   Extract the least significant bit of the generated random integer as the random bit.

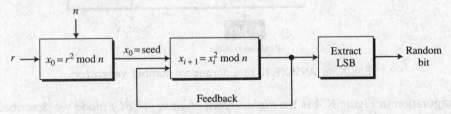

**Fig. K.3**    *Blum Blum Shub (BBC) pseudorandom number generator*

**Security**    It can be proven that if $p$ and $q$ are known, the $i$th bit in the sequence can be found as the least significant bit of

$$x_i = x_0^{2^i \bmod [(p-1)(q-1)]} \bmod n$$

This means that if Eve knows the value of $p$ and $q$, she can find the value of the $i$th bit by trying possible values of $x_0$ (the value of $n$ is usually public). This means that the complexity of this generator is the same as the factorization of $n$. If $n$ is large enough, the sequence is secure (unpredictable). It has been proved that with a very large $n$, Eve cannot guess the value of the next bit in the sequence even if she knows the values of all previous bits. The probability of each bit being 0 or 1 is very close to 50 percent.

---

**The security of BBC depends on the difficulty of factoring $n$.**

---

## K.2.2 Cryptosystem-Based Generators

A cryptosystem such as an encryption cipher or a hash function can also be use to generate a random stream of bits. We briefly mention two systems that use encryption algorithms.

### ANSI X9.17 PRNG

ANSI X9.17 defines a cryptographically strong pseudorandom number generator. The generator uses three 3DES with two keys (encryption-decryption-encryption). Figure K.4 shows the design. Note that the first pseudorandom number uses a 64-bit seed as the initial vector (IV); the rest of the pseudorandom numbers use the seed shown as the *next IV*. The same 112-bit secret key ($K_1$ and $K_2$ in 3DES), are used for all three 3DES ciphers.

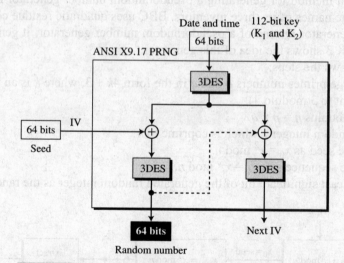

**Fig. K.4** *ANSI X9.17 pseudorandom number generator*

The configuration in Figure K.4 is the *cipher-block chaining (CBC)* mode we described in Fig. 8.3 in Chapter 8. X9.17 uses two stages of the block chaining. The plaintext for each stage comes from the output of the first 3DES, which uses the 64-bit date and time as the plaintext. The ciphertext created from the second 3DES is the random number; the ciphertext created from the third 3DES is the next IV for the next random number.

The strength of X9.17 can be due to the following facts:
1. The key is 112 ($2 \times 56$) bits.
2. The date-and-time input of 64 provides a good timestamp preventing replay attack.

3. The system provides an excellent confusion-diffusion effect with six encryptions and three decryptions.

## PGP PRNG

PGP uses the same idea as X9.17 with several changes. First, PGP PRNG uses seven stages instead of two. Second, the cipher is either IDEA or CAST-128 (not discussed in this book). Third, the key is normally 128 bits. PGP PRNG creates three 64-bit random numbers: the first is used as the IV secret (for communication using PGP, not for PRNG), the second and the third are concatenated to create a 128-bit secret key (for communication using PGP). Figure K.5 shows a rough design of PGP PRNG. The strength of PGP PRNG is in its key size and in the fact that the original IV (seed) and the 128-bit secret key can be generated from a 24-byte true random variable.

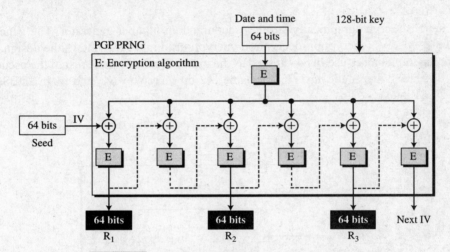

**Fig. K.5** *PGP pseudorandom number generator*

# Appendix

# L

# Complexity

In computer science, we normally talk about the complexity of an algorithm and the complexity of a problem. In this appendix, we give a brief review of these two issues as they are related to cryptography.

## L.1         COMPLEXITY OF AN ALGORITHM

In cryptography, we need a tool to analyze the computational complexity of an algorithm. We need an encryption (or decryption) algorithm to have a low level of complexity (efficient); we need an algorithm used by a cryptanalyst (to break the code) to have a high level of complexity (inefficient). In other words, we want to do encryption and decryption in a short span of time, but we want the intruder to have to run her computers forever if she tries to break the code.

The *complexity of an algorithm* is normally based on two types of resources. The **space complexity** of an algorithm refers to the amount of memory needed to store the algorithm (program) and the data. The **time complexity** of an algorithm refers to the amount of time needed to run the algorithm (program) and to get the result.

### L.1.1   Bit-Operation Complexity

In the rest of this appendix, we deal only with time complexity, which is of more concern, more common, and easier to measure. The time complexity of an algorithm depends on the particular computer on which the algorithm is to be run. To make the complexity independent from the corresponding computer, the **bit-operation complexity,** $f(n_b)$, is defined, which counts the number of bit operations the computer needs to perform to create the output from an $n_b$-bit input. A bit operation is the time required for a computer to add, subtract, multiply, or divide two single bits or to shift one single bit.

---

**Example L.1**   What is the bit-operation complexity of a function that adds two integers?

---

**Solution**   The complexity of the operation is $f(n_b) = n_b$, where $n_b$ is the number of bits needed to represent the larger integer. If the value of the larger integer is $N$, $n_b = \log_2 N$.

---

**Example L.2**   What is the bit-operation complexity of a function that multiplies two integers.

---

**Solution**   Although today there are faster algorithms available to multiply two integers, traditionally the number of bit operations is assumed to be $n_b^2$, where $n_b$ is the number of bits needed to represent the larger integer. The complexity is therefore $f(n_b) = n_b^2$.

**Example L.3**   What is the bit-operation complexity of a function that adds two integers, each having $d$ decimal digits.

***Solution***   The maximum value of a number of $d$ decimal digits is $N = 10^d - 1$ or $N \approx 10^d$. The number of bits in the input is $n_b = \log_2 N = \log_2 10^d = d \times \log_2 10$. The complexity is then $f(n_b) = d \times \log_2 10$. For example, if $d = 300$ digits, $f(n_b) = 300 \log_2 10 \approx 997$ bit operations.

**Example L.4**   What is the bit-operation complexity of a function that calculates $B = A^C$ (if $A < C$)?

***Solution***   Assume that the number of bits in $C$ is $n_b$ ($C = 2^{n_b}$ or $n_b = \log_2 C$). The conventional exponentiation method uses $C$ multiplications. Each multiplication operation needs $n_b^2$ bit operations (using a conventional multiplication algorithm). The complexity is therefore $f(n_b) = C \times = 2^{n_b} \times n_b^2$. For example, if $C$ is in the range of $2^{1024}$ ($n_b = 1024$), the conventional exponential method gives us

$$f(n_b) = 2^{1024} \times 1024^2 = 2^{1024} \times (2^{10})^2 = 2^{1044}$$

This means that if the computer can do $2^{20}$ (almost one million) bit operations per second, it takes $2^{1044} / 2^{20} = 2^{1024}$ seconds (forever) to perform this operation.

**Example L.5**   What is the bit-operation complexity of a function that calculates $B = A^C$ (if $A < C$) using the fast exponential algorithm (square-and-multiply method) discussed in Chapter 9?

***Solution***   We showed in Chapter 9 that the fast exponential algorithm uses a maximum of $2n_b$ multiplications, where $n_b$ is number of bits in the binary representation of $C$. Each multiplication operation needs bit operations. The complexity is therefore $f(n_b) = 2n_b \times n_b^2 = 2n_b^3$. For example, if $C$ is in the range of $2^{1024}$ ($n_b = 1024$), the fast exponential algorithm gives us

$$f(n_b) = 2 \times 1024^3 = 2^1 \times (2^{10})^3 = 2^{31}$$

This means that if the computer can do $2^{20}$ (almost one million) bit operations per second, it takes $2^{31}/2^{20} = 2^{11}$ seconds (almost 34 minutes) to perform this operation. Today computers can do this operation much faster.

***Asymptotic Complexity***   The whole purpose of complexity is to measure the behavior of algorithms when $n_b$, the number of bits in the input, is very large. For example, assume that the following shows the complexity of two algorithms:

$$f_1(n_b) = 5 \times 2^{n_b} + 5n_b \quad \text{and} \quad f_2(n_b) = 2^{n_b} + 4$$

When $n_b$ is small, these two algorithms behave differently; when $n_b$ is large (around 1000), the two algorithm behave almost the same. The reason is that terms 5, $5n_b$, and 4 are so small compared with the term $2^{n_b}$ that they can be totally ignored. We can say, for large $n_b$, $f_1(n_b) = f_2(n_b) = 2^{n_b}$. In other words, we are interested in $f(n_b)$, when $n_b$ approaches a very large number such as infinity.

### Big-O Notation

Using asymptotic complexity, we can define a standard scale of complexity with discrete values and assign complexity to algorithms using one of these values. One of the common standards is called Big-O notation, In this standard, $f(n_b) = O(g(n_b))$, where $g(n_b)$ is a function of $n_b$ derived from $f(n_b)$, using the following three theorems:

❑ **First Theorem.** If we can find a constant K such that $f(n_b) < K \times g(n_b)$, then we have $f(n_b) = O(g(n_b))$. This theorem can be easily implemented using the following two simple rules:

a. Set all coefficients of $n_b$ in $f(n_b)$ to 1.

b. Keep the largest term in $f(n_b)$ as $g(n_b)$, and discard the others. Terms are ranked from lowest to highest, as shown below:

$$(1), (\log n_b), (n_b), (n_b \log n_b), (n_b \log n_b \log \log n_b), (n_b^2), (n_b^3), \ldots, (n_b^k), (2^{m_b}), (n_b!)$$

❑ **Second Theorem.** If $f_1(n_b) = O(g_1(n_b))$ and $f_2(n_b) = O(g_2(n_b))$, then
$$f_1(n_b) + f_2(n_b) = O(g_1(n_b) + g_2(n_b)).$$

❑ **Third Theorem.** If $f_1(n_b) = O(g_1(n_b))$ and $f_2(n_b) = O(g_2(n_b))$, then
$$f_1(n_b) \times f_2(n_b) = O(g_1(n_b) \times g_2(n_b)).$$

**Example L.6**   Find the Big-O notation for $f(n_b) = n_b^5 + 3n_b^2 + 7$.

**Solution**   Note that $f(n_b) = n_b^5 + 3n_b^2 + 7$. Applying the first rule of the first theorem gives $g(n_b) = n_b^5 + n_b^2 + 1$. Applying the second rule gives us $g(n_b) = n_b^5$. The Big-O notation is $O()$.

**Example L.7**   Find the Big-O notation for $f(n_b) = (2^{n_b} + n_b^5) + (n_b \log_2 n_b)$.

**Solution**   We have $f_1(n_b) = (2^{n_b} + n_b^5)$ and $f_2(n_b) = (n_b \log_2 n_b)$. Therefore, $g_1(n_b) = 2^{n_b}$ and $g_2(n_b) = n_b \log_2 n_b$. Applying the second theorem, we have $g(n_b) = 2^{n_b} + n_b \log_2 n_b$. Applying the first theorem again, we get $g(n_b) = 2^{n_b}$. The Big-O notation is $O(2^{n_b})$.

**Example L.8**   Find the Big-O notation for $f(n_b) = n_b!$ ($n_b$ factorial).

**Solution**   We know that $n_b! = n_b \times (n_b - 1) \times \cdots \times 2 \times 1$. Each term has the maximum complexity of $O(n_b)$. According to the third theorem, the total complexity is $n_b$ times of $O(n_b)$ or $O(n_b^{n_b})$.

**Complexity Hierarchy**   The previous discussion allows us to rank algorithms based on their bit-operation complexity. Table L.1 gives common levels of hierarchy used in literature.

**Table L.1**   *Complexity hierarchy and Big-O notations*

| Hierarchy | Big-O Notation |
|---|---|
| Constant | $O(1)$ |
| Logarithmic | $O(\log n_b)$ |
| Polynomial | $O(n_b^c)$, where c is a constant |
| Subexponential | $O(2^{p(\log n_b)})$, where $p$ is a polynomial in $\log n_b$ |
| Exponential | $O(2^{n_b})$ |
| Superexponential | $O(n_b^{n_b})$ or $O(2^{2^{n_b}})$ |

An algorithm with *constant*, *logarithmic*, and *polynomial* complexity is considered feasible for any size of $n_b$. An algorithm with *exponential* and *superexponential* complexity is considered infeasible if $n_b$ is very large. An algorithm with *subexponential* complexity (such as $O(2^{(\log n_b)2})$) is feasible if $n_b$ is not very large.

---

**Example L.9**    As shown in Example L.4, the complexity of conventional exponentiation is $f(n_b) = 2^{n_b} \times n_b^2$. The Big-O notation for this algorithm is $O(2^{n_b} \times n_b^2)$, which is even more than exponential. This algorithm is infeasible if $n_b$ is very large.

---

**Example L.10**    As shown in Example L.5, the complexity of the fast exponential algorithm is $f(n_b) = 2n_b^3$. The Big-O notation for this algorithm is $O(n_b^3)$, which is polynomial. This algorithm is feasible; it is used in the RSA cryptosystem.

---

**Example L.11**    Assume that a cryptosystem has a key length of $n_b$ bits. To do a brute-force attack on this system, the adversary needs to check $2^{n_b}$ different keys. This means that the algorithm needs to go through $2^{n_b}$ steps. If $N$ is the number of bit operations to do each step, the complexity of the algorithm is definitely $f(n_b) = N \times 2^{n_b}$. Even if $N$ is a constant, the complexity of this algorithm is exponential, $O(2^{nb})$. Therefore, for a large $n_b$, the attack is infeasible. In Chapter 6, we showed that DES with the 56-bit key is vulnerable to brute-force attack, but 3DES, with the 112-bit is not. In Chapter 7, we also showed that AES, with 128-bit key is immune to this attack.

---

## L.2    COMPLEXITY OF A PROBLEM

Complexity theory also discusses the *complexity of a problem* before writing an algorithm for it. To define the complexity of a problem, one uses a **Turing machine** (devised by Alan Turing), a machine with an infinite amount of memory. Modern computers are realistic manifestations of the theoretical Turing machines. Two versions of theoretical Turing machines are used to evaluate the complexity of problems: deterministic and nondeterministic. A nondeterministic machine can solve harder problems by first guessing the solution and then checking its guess.

### L.2.1  Two Broad Categories

Complexity theory divides all problems into two broad categories: **undecidable problems** and **decidable problems.**

*Undecidable Problems*    An *undecidable problem* is a problem for which there is no algorithm that can solve it. Alan Turing proved that the famous *halting problem* is undecidable. The halting problem can be simply stated as follows: "Given an input and a Turing machine, there is no algorithm to determine if the machine will eventually halt." There are several problems in mathematics and computer science that are undecidable.

*Decidable Problems*    A problem is *decidable* if an algorithm can be written to solve it. The corresponding algorithm, however, may or may not be feasible. If a problem can be solved using an algorithm of polynomial complexity or less, it is called a *tractable* problem. If a problem can be solved using an algorithm of exponential complexity, it is called intractable.

*P, NP, and coNP*  Complexity theory divides tractable problems into three (possibly overlapping) classes, **P, NP,** and **coNP.** As shown in Figure L.1, NP and coNP classes overlap and the P class is in the cross section of these classes. Problems in class P (P stands for *polynomial*) can be solved by a deterministic Turing machine in polynomial time. Problems in class NP (NP stands for *nondeterministic polynomial*) can be solved by a nondeterministic Turing machine in polynomial time. Problems in class coNP (coNP stands for *complementary nondeterministic polynomial*) are those problems whose complements can be solved by a nondeterministic Turing machine. For example, a problem that decides if an integer can be factored into two primes is the complementary of the problem that can decide if a number is a prime. In other words, "can be factored" is equivalent of "is not a prime."

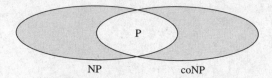

**Fig. L.1**  *Classes P, NP, and coNP*

## L.3  PROBABILISTIC ALGORITHMS

If a problem is intractable, we may be able to find a probabilistic algorithm for it. Although probabilistic algorithms do not guarantee that the solution is error-free, the probability of error can be made very small by repeating the algorithm using several different parameters. A probabilistic algorithm can be divided into two categories: *Monte Carlo* and *Las Vegas*.

### L.3.1  Monte Carlo Algorithms

A *Monte Carlo* algorithm is a yes/no decision algorithm: the output of the algorithm is either *yes* or *no*. A *yes-biased Monte Carlo* algorithm gives a yes-result with probability 1 (no mistake); it gives a no-result with probability $e$ (possible mistake). A *no-biased Monte Carlo* algorithm gives a no-result with probability 1 (no mistake); it gives a yes-result with probability $e$ (possible mistake). We saw in Chapter 9 that a Monte Carlo yes-biased algorithm for primality can test to see if an integer is prime. If the algorithm returns "prime," we are sure that the integer is prime; if it returns "composite," the number can be prime with a small probability.

### L.3.2  Las Vegas Algorithms

A *Las Vegas* algorithm is an algorithm that either succeeds or fails. If it succeeds, it always returns a correct answer. It it fails, there is no answer.

# Appendix

# M

# ZIP

P GP (Chapter 16) uses the ZIP data compression technique. ZIP, created by Jean-lup Gailey, Mark Adler, and Richard Wales, is based on an algorithm, called LZ77 (Lempel-Ziv 77), devised by Jacop Ziv and Abraham Lempel. In this appendix, we briefly discuss LZ77 as the basis for ZIP.

## M.1                                              LZ77 ENCODING

**LZ77** encoding is an example of **dictionary-based encoding.** The idea is to create a dictionary (table) of strings used during the communication session. If both the sender and the receiver have a copy of the dictionary, then already-encountered strings can be replaced by their indices in the dictionary to reduce the amount of information transmitted.

Although the idea appears simple, several difficulties surface in the implementation. First, how can a dictionary be created for each session? It cannot be universal due to its length. Second, how can the receiver acquire the dictionary made by the sender? If you send the dictionary, you are sending extra data, which defeats the whole purpose of compression.

A practical algorithm that uses the idea of adaptive dictionary-based encoding is the LZ77 algorithm. We introduce the basic idea of this algorithm with an example but do not delve into the details of different versions and implementations. In our example, assume that the following string is to be sent. We have chosen this specific string to simplify the discussion.

BAABABBBAABBBBAA

Using our simple version of the LZ77 algorithm, the process is divided into two phases: compressing the string and decompressing the string.

### M.1.1  Compression

In this phase, there are two concurrent events: building an indexed dictionary and compressing a string of symbols. The algorithm extracts from the remaining noncompressed string the smallest substring that cannot be found in the dictionary. It then stores a copy of this substring in the dictionary, (as a new entry) and assigns it an index value. Compression occurs when the substring, except for the last character, is replaced with the index found in the dictionary. The process then inserts the index and the last character of the substring into the compressed string. For example, if the substring is ABBB, you search for ABB in the dictionary. You find that the index for ABB is 4; the compressed substring is therefore 4B. Figure M.1 shows the process for our sample string.

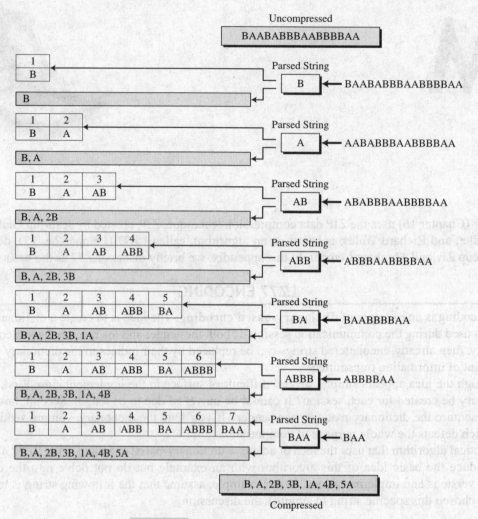

**Fig. M.1** *Example of LZ77 encoding*

Let us go through a few steps in Figure M.1:

❑ **Step 1.** The process extracts from the original string the smallest substring that is not in the dictionary. Because the dictionary is empty, the smallest character is one character (the first character, B). The process stores a copy of it as the first entry in the dictionary. Its index is 1. No part of this substring can be replaced with an index from the dictionary (it is only one character). The process inserts B in the compressed string. So far, the compressed string has only one character: B. The remaining noncompressed string is the original string without the first character.

❑ **Step 2.** The process extracts from the remaining string the next smallest substring that is not in the dictionary. This substring is the character A, which is not in the dictionary. The process stores a copy of it as the second entry in the dictionary. No part of this substring can be replaced with an index from the dictionary (it is only one character). The process inserts A in the compressed string. So far, the compressed string has two characters: B and A (we have placed commas between the substrings in the compressed string to show the separation).

❑ **Step 3.** The process extracts from the remaining string the next smallest substring that is not in the dictionary. This situation differs from the two previous steps. The next character (A) is in the dictionary, so the process extracts two characters (AB) that are not in the dictionary. The process stores a copy of AB as the third entry in the dictionary. The process now finds the index of an entry in the dictionary that is the substring without the last character (AB without the last character is A). The index for A is 2, so the process replaces A with 2 and inserts 2B in the compressed string.

❑ **Step 4**. Next the process extracts the substring ABB (because A and AB are already in the dictionary). A copy of ABB is stored in the dictionary with an index of 4. The process finds the index of the substring without the last character (AB), which is 3. The combination 3B is inserted into the compressed string. You may have noticed that in the three previous steps, we have not actually achieved any compression because we have replaced one character by one (A by A in the first step and B by B in the second step) and two characters by two (AB by 2B in the third step). But in this step, we have actually reduced the number of characters (ABB becomes 3B). If the original string has many repetitions (which is true in most cases), we can greatly reduce the number of characters.

Each of the remaining steps is similar to one of the preceding four steps, and we let the reader follow through. Note that the dictionary is used by the sender to find the indices. It is not sent to the receiver; the receiver must create the dictionary for herself, as we will see in the next section.

## M.1.2 Decompression

Decompression is the inverse of the compression process. The process extracts the substrings from the compressed string and tries to replace the indices with the corresponding entries in the dictionary, which is empty at first and built up gradually. The whole idea is that when an index is received, there is already an entry in the dictionary corresponding to that index. Figure M.2 shows the decompression process.

Let us go through a few steps in Figure M.2:

❑ **Step 1.** The first substring of the compressed string is examined. It is B without an index. Because the substring is not in the dictionary, it is added to the dictionary. The substring (B) is inserted into the decompressed string.

❑ **Step 2.** The second substring (A) is examined; the situation is similar to step 1. Now the decompressed string has two characters (BA), and the dictionary has two entries.

❑ **Step 3.** The third substring (2B) is examined. The process searches the dictionary and replaces the index 2 with the substring A. The new substring (AB) is added to the decompressed string, and AB is added to the dictionary.

❑ **Step 4.** The fourth substring (3B) is examined. The process searches the dictionary and replaces the index 3 with the substring AB. The substring ABB is now added to the decompressed string, and ABB is added to the dictionary.

We leave the exploration of the last three steps as an exercise. As you have noticed, we used a number such as 1 or 2 for the index. In reality, the index is a binary pattern (possibly variable in length) for better efficiency.

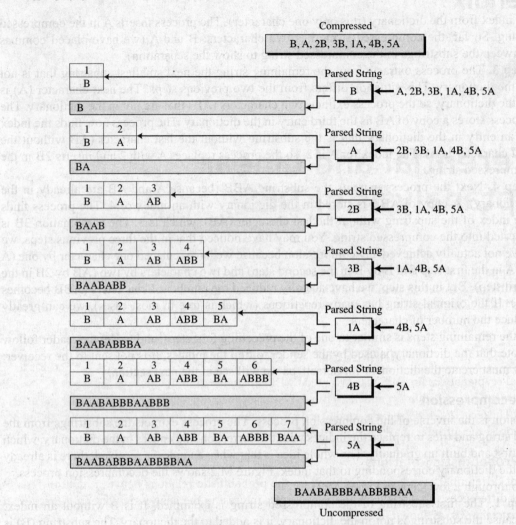

**Fig. M.2** Example of LZ77 decoding

# Appendix

# N

# Differential and Linear Cryptanalysis of DES

I
n this appendix, we briefly discuss two issues related to the DES cipher discussed in Chapter 6: differential and linear cryptanalysis. Thorough coverage of these two issues is beyond the scope of this book. This appendix is designed to give the general picture and a motivation for interested readers.

## N.1 DIFFERENTIAL CRYPTANALYSIS

Differential cryptanalysis for DES was invented by Biham and Shamir. In this cryptanalysis, the intruder concentrates on *chosen-plaintext* attacks. The analysis uses the propagation of input differences through the cipher. The term *difference* here is used to refer to the exclusive-or of two different inputs (plaintexts). In other words, the intruder analyzes how $P \oplus P'$ is propagated through rounds.

### N.1.1 Probabilistic Relations

The idea of differential cryptanalysis is based on the probabilistic relations between input differences and output differences. Two relations are of particular interest in the analysis: *differential profiles* and *round characteristics,* as shown in Fig. N.1.

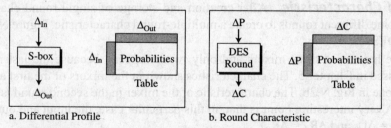

a. Differential Profile        b. Round Characteristic

**Fig. N.1** *Differential profile and round characteristic for DES*

***Differential Profile*** A differential profile (or XOR profile) shows the probabilistic relation between the input differences and output differences of an S-box. We discussed this profile for a simple S-box in Chapter 5 (see Table 5.5). Similar profiles can be created for each of the eight S-boxes in DES.

**Round Characteristic** A round characteristic is similar to a differential profile, but calculated for the whole round. The characteristic shows the probability that one input difference would create one output difference. Note that the characteristic is the same for each round because any relation that involves differences is independent of the round key. Figure N.2 shows four different round characteristics.

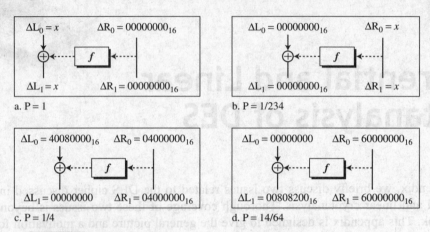

**Fig. N.2** *Some round characteristics for differential cryptanalysis*

Although we can have many characteristics for a round, Fig. N.2 shows only four of them. In each characteristic, we have divided the input differences and the output differences into the left and right sections. Each left or right difference is made of 32 bits or eight hexadecimal digits. All of these characteristics can be proved using a program that finds the input/output relation in a round of DES. Fig. N.2a shows that the input difference of $(x, 00000000_{16})$ produces the output difference of $(x, 00000000_{16})$ with probability 1. Figure N.2b shows the same characteristic as Fig. N.2a except that the left and right inputs and outputs are swapped; the probability will change tremendously. Figure N.2c shows that input difference of $(40080000_{16}, 04000000_{16})$ produces the output difference $(00000000_{16}, 04000000_{16})$ with probability 1/4. Finally, Fig. N.2d shows that the input difference $(00000000_{16}, 60000000_{16})$ produces the output difference $(00808200_{16}, 6000000_{16})$ with probability 14/64.

**A Three-Round Characteristic** After creation and storage of single-round characteristics, the analyzer can combine different rounds to create a multiple-round characteristic. Figure N.3 shows a case of a three-round DES.

In Fig. N.3, we have used three mixers and only two swappers, because the last round needs no swapper, as discussed in Chapter 5. The characteristics shown in the mixers of the first and third rounds is the same as the one in Fig. N.2b. The characteristic of the mixer in the second round is the same as the one in Fig. N.2a. A very interesting point is that, in this particular case, the input and output differences are the same ($\Delta L_3 = \Delta L_0$ and $\Delta R_3 = \Delta R_0$).

**A Sixteen-Round Characteristic** Many different characteristics can be compiled for a sixteen-round cipher. Figure N.4 shows an example. In this figure, a complete DES cipher is made of eight two-round sections. Each section uses the characteristics *a* and *b* in Fig. N.2. It is clear that if the last round lacks the swapper, the input $(x, 0)$ creates the output $(0, x)$ with probability $(1/234)^8$.

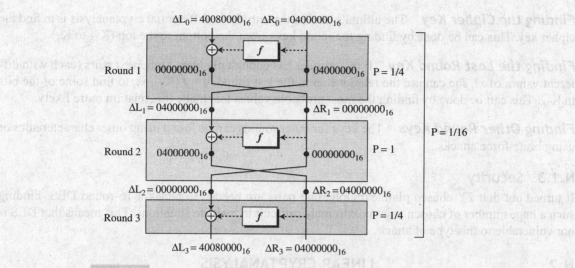

**Fig. N.3** *A three-round characteristic for differential cryptanalysis*

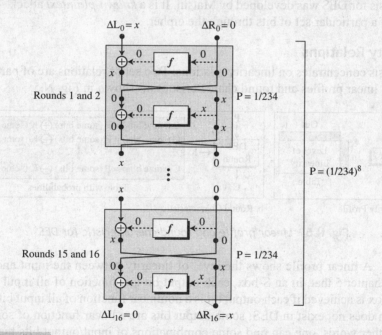

**Fig. N.4** *A sixteen-round characteristic for differential cryptanalysis*

## N.1.2 Attack

For the sake of example, let us assume that Eve uses the characteristic of Fig. N.4 to attack a sixteen-round DES. Eve somehow lures Alice to encrypt a lot of plaintexts in the form $(x, 0)$, in which the left half is $x$ (different values) and the right half is 0. Eve then keeps all ciphertexts received from Alice in the form $(0, x)$. Note that 0 here means $00000000_{16}$.

***Finding the Cipher Key*** The ultimate goal of the intruder in differential cryptanalysis is to find the cipher key. This can be done by finding the round keys from the bottom to the top ($K_{16}$ to $K_1$).

***Finding the Last Round Key*** If the intruder has enough plaintext/ciphertext pairs (each with different values of $x$), she can use the relationship in the last round, $0 = f(K_{16}, x)$, to find some of the bits in $K_{16}$. This can be done by finding the most probable values that make this relation more likely.

***Finding Other Round Keys*** The keys for other rounds can be found using other characteristics or using brute-force attacks.

### N.1.3 Security

It turned out that $2^{47}$ chosen plaintext/ciphertext pairs are needed to attack a 16-round DES. Finding such a huge number of chosen pairs is extremely difficult in real-life situations. This means that DES is not vulnerable to this type of attack.

## N.2                   LINEAR CRYPTANALYSIS

Linear cryptanalysis for DES was developed by Matsui. It is a *known-plaintext* attack. The analysis uses the propagation of a particular set of bits through the cipher.

### N.2.1 Linearity Relations

Linear cryptanalysis concentrates on linearity relations. Two set of relations are of particular interest in this cryptanalysis: linear profiles and round characteristics, as shown in Fig. N.5.

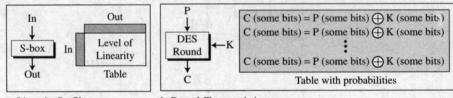

a. Linearity Profile            b. Round Characteristic

**Fig. N.5** *Linear profile and round characteristic for DES*

***Linear Profile*** A linear profile shows the level of linearity between the input and output of an S-box. We saw in Chapter 5 that, in an S-box, each output bit is a function of all input bits. The desired property in an S-box is achieved if each output bit is a nonlinear function of all input bits. Unfortunately, this ideal situation does not exist in DES; some output bits are a linear function of some combinations of input bits. In other words, one can find some combinations of input/output bits that can be mapped to each other with a linear function. The linear profile shows the level of linearity (or nonlinearity) between an input and an output. The cryptanalysis can create eight different tables, one for each S-box, in which the first column shows the possible combination of six-bit inputs, $00_{16}$ to $3F_{16}$, and the first row shows the possible combinations of four-bit outputs, $0_{16}$ to $F_{16}$. The entries shows the level of linearity (or nonlinearity, based on the design). We cannot delve into the details of how we measure the level of linearity, but the entries with a high-level of linearity are interesting to the cryptanalysis.

***Round Characteristic*** A round characteristic in linear cryptanalysis shows the combination of input bits, round key bits, and output bits that show a linear relation. Figure N.6 shows two different round characteristics. The notation used for each case defines the bits that must be exclusive-ored together. For example, O(7, 8, 24, 29) means the exclusive-or of 7th, 8th, 24th, and 29th bits coming out of the function; K(22) means the 22nd bit in the round key; I(15) means the 15th bit going into the function.

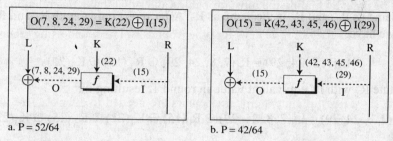

a. P = 52/64          b. P = 42/64

**Fig. N.6** *Some round characteristics for linear cryptanalysis*

The following shows the relations for part a and b in Fig. N.6 using individual bits.

**Part a:** $O(7) \oplus O(8) \oplus O(24) \oplus O(29) = I(15) \oplus K(22)$

**Part b:** $F(15) = I(29) \oplus K(42) \oplus K(43) \oplus K(45) \oplus K(46)$

***A Three-Round Characteristic*** After creation and storage of single-round characteristics, the analyzer can combine different rounds to create a multiple-round characteristic. Figure N.7 shows a case of a three-round DES in which rounds 1 and 3 use the same characteristic as shown in Fig. N.6a, but round 2 uses an arbitrary characteristic.

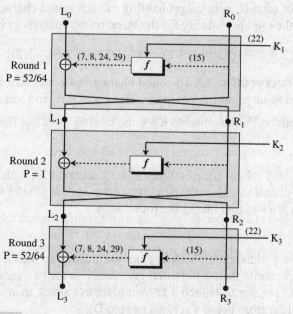

**Fig. N.7** *A three-round characteristic for linear cryptanalysis*

The goal of linear cryptanalysis is to find a linear relation between some bits in the plaintext, the ciphertext, and the key. Let us see if we can establish such relation for a 3-round DES depicted in .

**Round 1:** $R_1(7, 8, 24, 29) = L_0(7, 8, 24, 29) \oplus R_0(15) \oplus K_1(22)$
**Round 3:** $L_3(7, 8, 24, 29) = L_2(7, 8, 24, 29) \oplus R_2(15) \oplus K_3(22)$

But $L_2$ is the same as $R_1$, and $R_2$ is the same as $R_3$. After replacing $L_2$ with $R_1$ and $R_2$ with $R_3$ in the second relation, we have:

$$L_3(7, 8, 24, 29) = R_1(7, 8, 24, 29) \oplus R_3(15) \oplus K_3(22)$$

We can substitute $R_1$ with its equivalent value in round 1, resulting in:

$$L_3(7, 8, 24, 29) = L_0(7, 8, 24, 29) \oplus R_0(15) \oplus K_1(22) \oplus R_3(15) \oplus K_3(22)$$

This is a relationship between input and output bits for the whole three rounds after being reordered:

$$L_3(7, 8, 24, 29) \oplus R_3(15) = L_0(7, 8, 24, 29) \oplus R_0(15) \oplus K_1(22) \oplus K_3(22)$$

In other words, we have

$$C(7, 8, 15, 24, 29) = P(7, 8, 15, 24, 29) \oplus K_1(22) \oplus K_3(22)$$

**Probability** One interesting question is how to find the probability of a three-round (or $n$-round) DES. Matsui proved that the probability in this case is

$$P = 1/2 + 2^{n-1} \prod (p_i - 1/2)$$

in which $n$ is the number of rounds, $p_i$ is the probability of each round characteristic, and P is the total probability. For example, the total probability for the three-round analysis in is

$$P = 1/2 + 2^{3-1} [(52/64 - 1/2) \times (1 - 1/2) \times (52/64 - 1/2)] \approx 0.695$$

**A Sixteen-Round Characteristic** A 16-round characteristic can also be compiled to provide a linear relationship between some plaintext bits, some ciphertext bits, and some bits in the round keys.

$$C(\text{some bits}) = P(\text{some bits}) \oplus K_1(\text{some bits}) \oplus \cdots \oplus K_{16}(\text{some bits})$$

## N.2.2 Attack
After finding and storing many relationship between some plaintext bits, ciphertext bits, and round-key bits. Eve can access some plaintext/ciphertext pairs (known-plaintext attack) and use the corresponding bits in the stored characteristics to find bits in the round keys.

## N.2.3 Security
It turned out that $2^{43}$ known plaintext/ciphertext pairs are needed to attack a 16-round DES. Linear cryptanalysis looks more probable than differential cryptanalysis for two reasons. First, the number of steps is smaller. Second it is easier to launch a known plaintext attack than a chosen-plaintext attack. However, the attack is still far from being a serious treat to DES.

# Appendix

# O

# Simplified DES (S-DES)

**S**implified DES (S-DES), developed by Professor Edward Schaefer of Santa Clara University, is an educational tool designed to help students learn the structure of DES using cipher blocks and keys with a small number of bits. Readers may choose to study this appendix before reading Chapter 6.

## O.1                                                                S-DES STRUCTURE

S-DES is a block cipher, as shown in Fig. O.1.

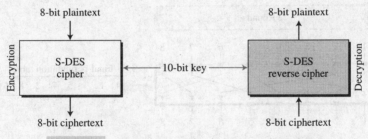

**Fig. O.1** *Encryption and decryption with S-DES*

At the encryption site, S-DES takes an 8-bit plaintext and creates an 8-bit ciphertext; at the decryption site, S-DES takes an 8-bit ciphertext and creates an 8-bit plaintext. The same 10-bit cipher key is used for both encryption and decryption.

Let us concentrate on encryption; later we will discuss decryption. The encryption process consists of two permutations (P-boxes), which we call initial and final permutations (also called IP and $IP^{-1}$), and two Feistel rounds. Each round uses a different 8-bit round key generated from the cipher key according to a predefined algorithm described later in this appendix. Figure O.2 shows the elements of the S-DES cipher at the encryption site.

### O.1.1   Initial and Final Permutations

Figure O.3 shows the initial and final permutations (P-boxes). Each of these permutations takes an 8-bit input and permutes it according to a predefined rule. These permutations are straight permutations that are the inverses of each other as discussed in Chapter 5. These two permutations have no cryptographic significance in S-DES. They are included in S-DES to make it compatible with DES.

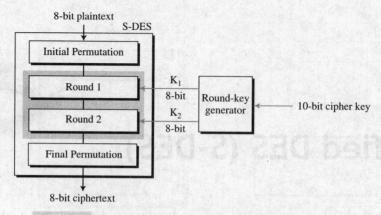

**Fig. O.2** *General structure of S-DES encryption cipher*

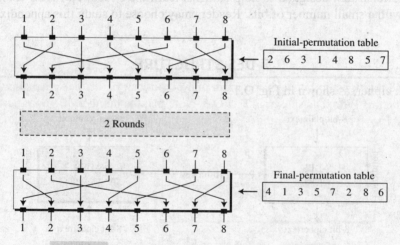

**Fig. O.3** *Initial and final permutations (IP and IP$^{-1}$)*

## O.1.2 Rounds

S-DES uses two rounds. Each round of S-DES is a Feistel cipher, as shown in Fig. O.4.

The round takes $L_{I-1}$ and $R_{I-1}$ from the previous round (or the initial permutation box) and creates $L_I$ and $R_I$, which go to the next round (or the final permutation box). As we discussed in Chapter 5, we can assume that each round has two cipher elements, a mixer and a swapper. Each of these elements is invertible. The swapper is obviously invertible. It swaps the left half of the text with the right half. The mixer is invertible because of the XOR operation. All noninvertible elements are collected inside the function, shown as $f(R_{I-1}, K_I)$.

**S-DES Function** The heart of S-DES is the S-DES function. The S-DES function applies an 8-bit key to the rightmost 4 bits ($R_{I-1}$) to produce a 4-bit output. This function is made up of four sections: an expansion P-box, a whitener (which adds key), a group of S-boxes, and a straight P-box as shown in Fig. O.4.

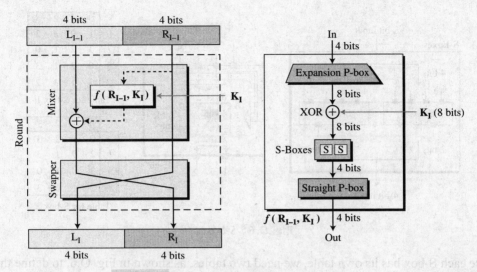

**Fig. O.4** *A round in S-DES (encryption site)*

**Expansion P-box** $R_{I-1}$ is a 4-bit input and $K_I$ is an 8-bit key, so we first need to expand $R_{I-1}$ to 8 bits. Although the relationship between the input and output can be defined mathematically, S-DES uses a table to define this P-box, as shown in Fig. O.5. Note that the number of output ports is 8, but the value range is only 1 to 4. Some of the inputs go to more than one output.

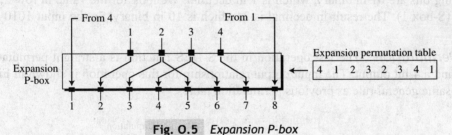

**Fig. O.5** *Expansion P-box*

**Whitener (XOR)** After the expansion permutation, S-DES uses the XOR operation on the expanded right section and the round key. Note that the round key is used only in this operation.

### S-Boxes

The S-boxes do the real mixing (confusion). S-DES uses two S-boxes, each with a 4-bit input and a 2-bit output. See Fig. O.6.

The 8-bit data from the second operation is divided into two 4-bit chunks, and each chunk is fed into a box. The result of each box is a 2-bit chunk; when these are combined, the result is a 4-bit text. The substitution in each box follows a predetermined rule based on a $4 \times 4$ table. The combination of bits 1 and 4 of the input defines one of four rows; the combination of bits 2 and 3 defines one of the four columns, as shown in Fig. 15.8.

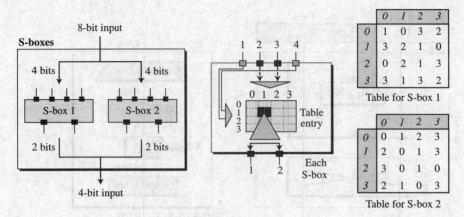

**Fig. O.6** *S-boxes*

Because each S-box has its own table, we need two tables, as shown in Fig. O.6, to define the output of these boxes. The values of the inputs (row number and column number) and the values of the outputs are given as decimal numbers to save space. These need to be changed to binary.

**Example O.1**   The input to S-box 1 is $1010_2$. What is the output?

**Solution**   If we write the first and the fourth bits together, we get 10 in binary, which is 2 in decimal. The remaining bits are 01 in binary, which is 1 in decimal. We look for the value in row 2, column 1, in Fig. O.6 (S-box 1). The result in decimal is 2, which is 10 in binary. So the input $1010_2$ yields the output $10_2$.

**Straight Permutation**   The last operation in the S-DES function is a straight permutation with a 4-bit input and a 4-bit output. The input/output relationship for this operation is shown in Fig. O.7 and follows the same general rule as previous permutation tables.

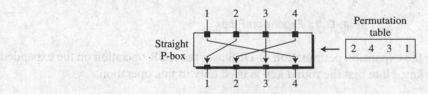

**Fig. O.7** *Straight P-Box*

### O.1.3   Key Generation

The *round-key generator* creates two 8-bit keys out of a 10-bit cipher key.

**Straight Permutation**   The first process is a straight permutation. It permutes the 10 bits in the key according to a predefined table, as shown in Fig. O.8.

**Shift Left**   After the straight permutation, the key is divided into two 5-bit parts. Each part is shifted left (circular shift) $r$ bits, where $r$ is the round number (1 or 2). The two parts are then combined to form a 10-bit unit. See Chapter 5 for a discussion of shift operation.

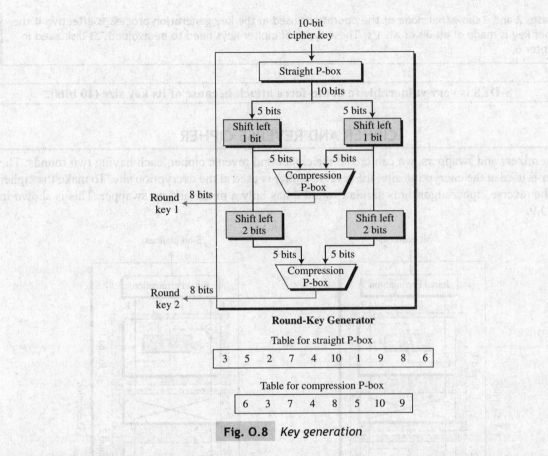

**Round-Key Generator**

Table for straight P-box

| 3 | 5 | 2 | 7 | 4 | 10 | 1 | 9 | 8 | 6 |
|---|---|---|---|---|----|---|---|---|---|

Table for compression P-box

| 6 | 3 | 7 | 4 | 8 | 5 | 10 | 9 |
|---|---|---|---|---|---|----|---|

**Fig. O.8**   *Key generation*

**Compression Permutation**   The compression permutation (P-box) changes the 10 bits to 8 bits, which are used as a key for a round. The compression permutation table is also shown in Fig. O.8.

**Example O.2**   Table O.1 shows three cases of key generation.

**Table O.1**

| Steps | Case 1 | | Case 2 | | Case 3 | |
|---|---|---|---|---|---|---|
| Cipher Key | **1011100110** | | **0000000000** | | **1111111111** | |
| After permutation | 1100101110 | | 0000000000 | | 1111111111 | |
| After splitting | L: 11001 | R: 01110 | L: 00000 | R: 00000 | L: 11111 | R: 11111 |
| **Round 1:** | | | | | | |
| Shifted keys: | L: 10011 | R: 11100 | L: 00000 | R: 00000 | L: 11111 | R: 11111 |
| Combined key: | 1001111100 | | 0000000000 | | 1111111111 | |
| Round Key 1: | **10111100** | | **00000000** | | **11111111** | |
| **Round 2:** | | | | | | |
| Shifted keys: | L: 01110 | R: 10011 | L: 00000 | R: 00000 | L: 11111 | R: 11111 |
| Combined key: | 0111010011 | | 0000000000 | | 1111111111 | |
| Round Key 2: | **11010011** | | **00000000** | | **11111111** | |

Cases 2 and 3 show that none of the operations used in the key generation process is effective if the cipher key is made of all 0's or all 1's. These types of cipher keys need to be avoided, as discussed in Chapter 6.

**S-DES is very vulnerable to brute-force attack because of its key size (10 bits).**

## O.2        CIPHER AND REVERSE CIPHER

Using mixers and swappers, we can create the cipher and reverse cipher, each having two rounds. The cipher is used at the encryption site; the reverse cipher is used at the decryption site. To make the cipher and the reverse cipher algorithms similar, round 2 has only a mixer and no swapper. This is shown in Fig. O.9.

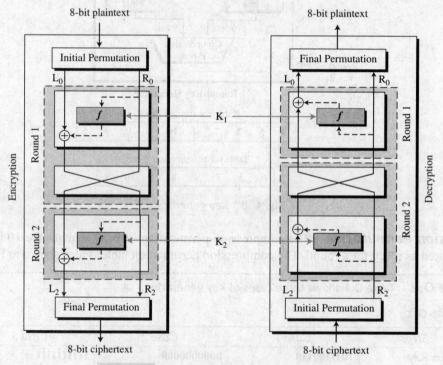

**Fig. O.9** *S-DES cipher and reverse cipher*

Although the rounds are not aligned, the elements (mixer or swapper) are aligned. We proved in Chapter 5 that a mixer is a self-invertible; so is a swapper. The final and initial permutations are also inverses of each other. The left section of the plaintext at the encryption site, $L_0$, is enciphered as $L_2$; $L_2$ at the decryption site is deciphered as $L_0$. The situation is the same with the right section.

A very important point we need to remember about the ciphers is that the round keys ($K_1$ and $K_2$) should be applied in the reverse order. At the encryption site, round 1 uses $K_1$ and round 2 uses $K_2$; at the decryption site, round 1 uses $K_2$ and round 2 uses $K_1$.

---

**There is no swapper in the second round.**

---

**Example O.3**   We choose a random plaintext block and a random key, and determine what the ciphertext block would be:

Plaintext: 11110010      Key: 1011100110      Ciphertext: 11101011

Let us show the result of each round and the text created before and after the rounds. Table O.2 first shows the result of steps before starting the round. The plaintext goes through the initial permutation to create completely different 8 bits. After this step, the text is split into two

**Table O.2**

| Initial Processing | Plaintext: **11110010** | Cipher key: **1011100110** |
|---|---|---|
| | After IP: 10111001 | |
| | $L_0$: 1011          $R_0$: 1001 | |
| Round 1 | $L_1$: 1001          $R_1$: 0111 | Round key: 10111100 |
| Round 2 | $L_2$: 1011          $R_2$: 0111 | Round key: 11010011 |
| Final Processing | Before IP$^{-1}$: 10110111 | |
| | Ciphertext: **11101011** | |

halves, $L_0$ and $R_0$. The table shows the results of two rounds that involve mixing and swapping (except for the second round). The results of the last rounds ($L_2$ and $R_2$) are combined. Finally the text goes through final permutation to create the ciphertext.

Some points are worth mentioning here. First, the right section out of each round is the same as the left section out of the next round. The reason is that the right section goes through the mixer without change, but the swapper moves it to the left section. For example, $R_1$ passes through the mixer of the second round without change, but then it becomes $L_2$ because of the swapper. The interesting point is that we do not have a swapper at the last round. That is why $R_1$ becomes $R_2$ instead of becoming $L_2$.

---

**Because of its small number of rounds, S-DES is more vulnerable to cryptanalysis than DES.**

---

# Appendix

# P

# Simplified AES (S-AES)

**S**implified AES (S-AES), developed by Professor Edward Schaefer of Santa Clara University, is an educational tool designed to help students learn the structure of AES using smaller blocks and keys. Readers may choose to study this appendix before reading Chapter 7.

## P.1 S-AES STRUCTURE

S-AES is a block cipher, as shown in Fig. P.1.

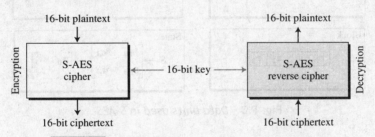

**Fig. P.1** *Encryption and decryption with S-AES*

At the encryption site, S-AES takes a 16-bit plaintext and creates a 16-bit ciphertext; at the decryption site, S-AES takes a 16-bit ciphertext and creates a 16-bit plaintext. The same 16-bit cipher key is used for both encryption and decryption.

### P.1.1 Rounds

S-AES is a non-Feistel cipher that encrypts and decrypts a data block of 16 bits. It uses one pre-round transformation and two rounds. The cipher key is also 16 bits. Figure P.2 shows the general design for the encryption algorithm (called the cipher); the decryption algorithm (called the inverse cipher) is similar, but the round keys are applied in the reverse order.

In Fig. P.2, the round keys, which are created by the key-expansion algorithm, are always 16 bits, the same size as the plaintext or ciphertext block. In S-AES, there are three round keys, $K_0$, $K_1$, and $K_2$.

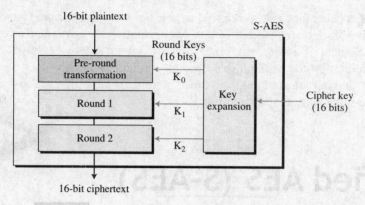

**Fig. P.2** *General design of S-AES encryption cipher*

## P.1.2 Data Units

S-AES uses five units of measurement to refer to data: bits, nibbles, words, blocks, and states, as shown in Fig. P.3.

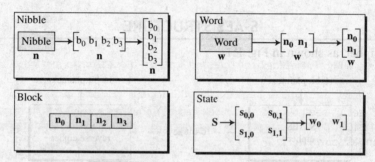

**Fig. P.3** *Data units used in S-AES*

**Bit** In S-AES, a *bit* is a binary digit with a value of 0 or 1. We use a lowercase letter b to refer to a bit.

**Nibble** A **nibble** is a group of 4 bits that can be treated as a single entity, a row matrix of 4 bits, or a column matrix of 4 bits. When treated as a row matrix, the bits are inserted into the matrix from left to right; when treated as a column matrix, the bits are inserted into the matrix from top to bottom. We use a lowercase bold letter **n** to refer to a nibble. Note that a nibble is actually a single hexadecimal digit.

**Word** A *word* is a group of 8 bits that can be treated as a single entity, a row matrix of two nibbles, or a column matrix of 2 nibbles. When it is treated as a row matrix, the nibbles are inserted into the matrix from left to right; when it is considered as a column matrix, the nibbles are inserted into the matrix from top to bottom. We use the lowercase bold letter **w** to refer to a word.

**Block** S-AES encrypts and decrypts data blocks. A *block* in S-AES is a group of 16 bits. However, a block can be represented as a row matrix of 4 nibbles.

**State** In S-AES, a data block is also referred to as a *state*. We use an uppercase bold letter **S** to refer to a state. States, like blocks, are made of 16 bits, but normally they are treated as matrices of 4 nibbles. In this case, each element of a state is referred to as $s_{r,c}$, where $r$ (0 to 1) defines the row and the $c$ (0 to 1) defines the column. At the beginning of the cipher, nibbles in a data block are inserted into a state column by column, and in each column, from top to bottom. At the end of the cipher, nibbles in the state are extracted in the same way, as shown in Fig. P.4.

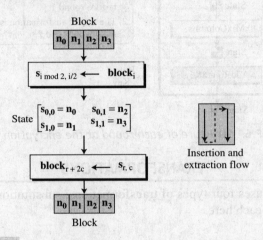

**Fig. P.4** *Block-to-state and state-to-block transformation*

**Example P.1** Let us see how a 16-bit block can be shown as a 2 × 2 matrix. Assume that the text block is 1011 0111 1001 0110. We first show the block as 4 nibbles. The state matrix is then filled up, column by column, as shown in Fig. P.5.

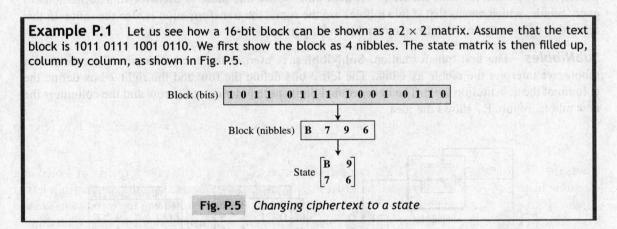

**Fig. P.5** *Changing ciphertext to a state*

## P.1.3 Structure of Each Round

Figure P.6 shows that each transformation takes a state and creates another state to be used for the next transformation or the next round. The pre-round section uses only one transformation (AddRoundKey); the last round uses only three transformations, (MixColumns transformation is missing).

At the decryption site, the inverse transformations are used: InvSubNibbles, InvShiftRows, InvMixColumns, and AddRoundKey (this one is self-invertible).

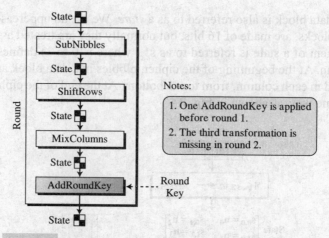

**Fig. P.6**  *Structure of each round at the encryption site*

# P.2                                    TRANSFORMATIONS

To provide security, S-AES uses four types of transformations: substitution, permutation, mixing, and key-adding. We will discuss each here.

## P.2.1   Substitution

Substitution is done for each nibble (4-bit data unit). Only one table is used for transformations of every nibble, which means that if two nibbles are the same, the transformation is also the same. In this appendix, transformation is defined by a table lookup process.

**SubNibbles**   The first transformation, **SubNibbles,** is used at the encryption site. To substitute a nibble, we interpret the nibble as 4 bits. The left 2 bits define the row and the right 2 bits define the column of the substitution table. The hexadecimal digit at the junction of the row and the column is the new nibble. Figure P.7 shows the idea.

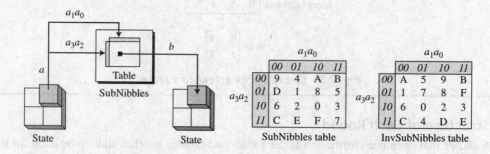

**Fig. P.7**  *SubNibbles transformations*

In the SubNibbles transformation, the state is treated as a $2 \times 2$ matrix of nibbles. Transformation is done one nibble at a time. The contents of each nibble is changed, but the arrangement of the nibbles in the matrix remains the same. In the process, each nibble is transformed independently: There are four distinct nibble-to-nibble transformations.

---

**SubNibbles involves four independent nibble-to-nibble transformations.**

---

Figure P.7 also shows the substitution table (S-box) for the SubNibbles transformation. The transformation definitely provides confusion effect. For example, two nibbles, $A_{16}$ and $B_{16}$, which differ only in one bit (the rightmost bit), are transformed to $0_{16}$ and $3_{16}$, which differ in two bits.

***InvSubNibbles*** InvSubNibbles is the inverse of SubNibbles. The inverse transformation is also shown in Fig. P.7. We can easily check that the two transformations are inverses of each other.

**Example P.2** Figure P.8 shows how a state is transformed using the SubNibbles transformation. The figure also shows that the InvSubNibbles transformation creates the original state. Note that if the two nibbles have the same values, their transformation are also the same. The reason is that every nibble uses the same table.

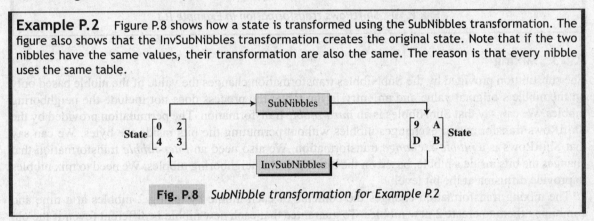

**Fig. P.8** *SubNibble transformation for Example P.2*

## P.2.2 Permutation

Another transformation found in a round is shifting, which permutes the nibbles. Shifting transformation in S-AES is done at the nibble level; the order of the bits in the nibble is not changed.

***ShiftRows*** In the encryption, the transformation is called *ShiftRows* and the shifting is to the left. The number of shifts depends on the row number (0, 1) of the state matrix. This means row 0 is not shifted at all and row 1 is shifted 1 nibble. Figure P.9 shows the shifting transformation. Note that the ShiftRows transformation operates one row at a time.

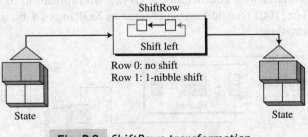

**Fig. P.9** *ShiftRows transformation*

***InvShiftRows*** In the decryption, the transformation is called *InvShiftRows* and the shifting is to the right. The number of shifts is the same as the number of the row (0, 1) in the state matrix.

**The ShiftRows and InvShiftRows transformations are inverses of each other.**

**Example P.3** Figure P.10 shows how a state is transformed using ShiftRows. The figure also shows that the InvShiftRows transformation creates the original state.

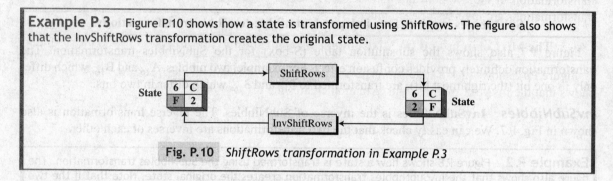

**Fig. P.10** *ShiftRows transformation in Example P.3*

## P.2.3 Mixing

The substitution provided by the SubNibbles transformation changes the value of the nibble based only on the nibble's original value and an entry in the table; the process does not include the neighboring nibbles. We can say that SubNibbles is an *intra-nibble* transformation. The permutation provided by the ShiftRows transformation exchanges nibbles without permuting the bits inside the bytes. We can say that ShiftRows is a *nibble-exchange* transformation. We also need an *inter-nibble* transformation that changes the bits inside a nibble, based on the bits inside the neighboring nibbles. We need to mix nibbles to provide diffusion at the bit level.

The mixing transformation changes the contents of each nibble by taking 2 nibbles at a time and combining them to create 2 new nibbles. To guarantee that each new nibble is different (even if the old nibbles are the same), the combination process first multiplies each nibble with a different constant and then mixes them. The mixing can be provided by matrix multiplication. As we discussed in Chapter 2, when we multiply a square matrix by a column matrix, the result is a new column matrix. Each element in the new matrix depends on the two elements of the old matrix after they are multiplied by row values in the constant matrix.

**MixColumns** The *MixColumns* transformation operates at the column level; it transforms each column of the state into a new column. The transformation is actually the matrix multiplication of a state column by a constant square matrix. The nibbles in the state column and constants matrix are interpreted as 4-bit words (or polynomials) with coefficients in GF(2). Multiplication of bytes is done in GF($2^4$) with modulus ($x^4 + x + 1$) or (10011). Addition is the same as XORing of 4-bit words. Figure P.11 shows the MixColumns transformation.

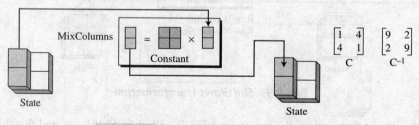

**Fig. P.11** *MixColumns transformation*

***InvMixColumns*** The *InvMixColumns* transformation is basically the same as the MixColumns transformation. If the two constant matrices are inverses of each other, it is easy to prove that the two transformations are inverses of each other.

---

**The MixColumns and InvMixColumns transformations are inverses of each other.**

---

Figure P.12 shows how a state is transformed using the MixColumns transformation. The figure also shows that the InvMixColumns transformation creates the original one.

**Fig. P.12** *The MixColumns transformation in Example 7.5*

Note that equal bytes in the old state, are not equal any more in the new state. For example, the two bytes F in the second row are changed to 4 and A.

## P.2.4 Key Adding

Probably the most important transformation is the one that includes the cipher key. All previous transformations use known algorithms that are invertible. If the cipher key is not added to the state at each round, it is very easy for the adversary to find the plaintext, given the ciphertext. The cipher key is the only secret between Alice and Bob in this case.

S-AES uses a process called key expansion (discussed later in this appendix) that creates three round keys from the cipher key. Each round key is 16 bits long—it is treated as two 8-bit words. For the purpose of adding the key to the state, each word is considered as a column matrix.

***AddRoundKey*** *AddRoundKey* also proceeds one column at a time. It is similar to MixColumns in this respect. MixColumns multiplies a constant square matrix by each state column; AddRoundKey adds a round key word with each state column matrix. The operations in MixColumns are matrix multiplication; the operations in AddRoundKey are matrix addition. The addition is performed in the $GF(2^4)$ field. Because addition and subtraction in this field are the same, the AddRoundKey transformation is the inverse of itself. Figure P.13 shows the AddRoundKey transformation.

---

**The AddRoundKey transformation is the inverse of itself.**

---

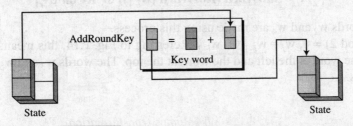

**Fig. P.13** *AddRoundKey transformation*

## P.3                                       KEY EXPANSION

The *key expansion* routine creates three 16-bit round keys from one single 16-bit cipher key. The first round key is used for pre-round transformation (AddRoundKey); the remaining round keys are used for the last transformation (AddRoundKey) at the end of round 1 and round 2.

The key-expansion routine creates round keys word by word, where a word is an array of 2 nibbles. The routine creates 6 words, which are called $w_0$, $w_1$, $w_2$, ..., $w_5$.

### P.3.1   Creation of Words in S-AES

Figure P.14 shows how 6 words are made from the original key.

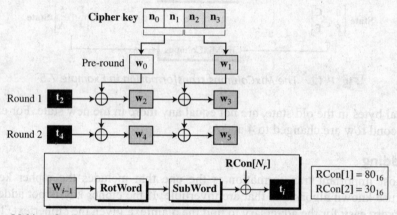

Making of $t_i$ (temporary) words $i = 2N_r$, where $N_r$ is the round number

**Fig. P.14**   *Creation of words in S-AES*

The process is as follows:

1.    The first two words ($w_0$, $w_1$) are made from the cipher key. The cipher key is thought of as an array of 4 nibbles ($n_0$ to $n_3$). The first 2 nibbles ($n_0$ to $n_1$) become $w_0$; the next 2 nibbles ($n_2$ to $n_3$) become $w_1$. In other words, the concatenation of the words in this group replicates the cipher key.

2.    The rest of the words ($w_i$ for $i = 2$ to 5) are made as follows:

    a.    If ($i \bmod 2$) = 0, $w_i = t_i \oplus w_{i-2}$. Here $t_i$, a temporary word, is the result of applying two routines, SubWord and RotWord, on $w_{i-1}$ and XORing the result with a round constant, RC[$N_r$], where $N_r$ is the round number. In other words, we have

$$t_i = \text{SubWord (RotWord } (w_{i-1})) \oplus \text{RCon } [N_r]$$

        The words $w_2$ and $w_4$ are made using this process.

    b.    If ($i \bmod 2$) $\neq$ 0, $w_i = w_{i-1} \oplus w_{i-2}$. Referring to Fig. P.14, this means each word is made from the word at the left and the word at the top. The words $w_3$ and $w_5$ are made using this process.

***RotWord***   The *RotWord* (rotate word) routine is similar to the ShiftRows transformation, but it is applied to only one row. The routine takes a word as an array of 2 nibbles and shifts each nibble to the left with wrapping. In S-AES, this is actually swapping the 2 nibbles in the word.

***SubWord***   The *SubWord* (substitute word) routine is similar to the SubNibble transformation, but it is applied only to 2 nibbles. The routine takes each nibble in the word and substitutes another nibble for it using the SubNibble table in Fig. P.7.

***Round Constants***   Each round constant, RC, is a 2-nibble value in which the rightmost nibble is always zero. Figure P.14 also shows the value of RCs.

---

**Example P.4**   Table P.1 shows how the keys for each round are calculated assuming that the 16-bit cipher key agreed upon by Alice and Bob is $2475_{16}$.

**Table P.1**   *Key expansion example*

| Round | Values of $t$'s | First word in the round | Second word in the round | Round Key |
|-------|-----------------|-------------------------|--------------------------|-----------|
| *0* | | $w_0 = 24$ | $w_1 = 75$ | $K_0 = 2475$ |
| *1* | $t_2 = 95$ | $w_2 = 95 \oplus 24 = B1$ | $w_3 = B1 \oplus 75 = C4$ | $K_0 = B1C4$ |
| *2* | $t_4 = EC$ | $w_4 = B1 \oplus EC = 5D$ | $w_5 = 5D \oplus C4 = 99$ | $K_2 = 5D99$ |

In each round, the calculation of the second word is very simple. For the calculation of the first word we need to first calculate the value of the temporary word ($t_i$), as shown below:

**RotWord** (75) = 57    → **SubWord** (57) = 15    → $t_2 = 15 \oplus \mathbf{RC[1]} = 15 \oplus 80 = 95$

**RotWord** (C4) = 4C    → **SubWord** (4C) = DC    → $t_4 = DC \oplus \mathbf{RC[2]} = DC \oplus 30 = EC$

---

## P.4                           CIPHERS

Now let us see how S-AES uses the four types of transformations for encryption and decryption. The encryption algorithm is referred to as the *cipher* and the decryption algorithm as the *inverse cipher*.

S-AES is a non-Feistel cipher, which means that each transformation or group of transformations must be invertible. In addition, the cipher and the inverse cipher must use these operations in such a way that they cancel each other. The round keys must also be used in the reverse order. To comply with this requirement, the transformations occur in a different order in the cipher and the reverse cipher, as shown in Fig. P.15.

First, the order of SubNibbles and ShiftRows is changed in the reverse cipher. Second, the order of MixColumns and AddRoundKey is changed in the reverse cipher. This difference in ordering is needed to make each transformation in the cipher aligned with its inverse in the reverse cipher. Consequently, the decryption algorithm as a whole is the inverse of the encryption algorithm. Note that the round keys are used in the reverse order.

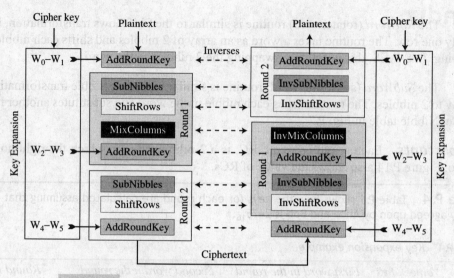

**Fig. P.15**  *Cipher and inverse cipher of the original design*

**Example P.5**  We choose a random plaintext block, the cipher key used in Example P.4, and determine what the ciphertext block would be:

Plaintext: $1A23_{16}$ Key: $2475_{16}$ Ciphertext: $3AD2_{16}$

Figure P.16 shows the value of states in each round. We are using the round keys generated in Example P.4.

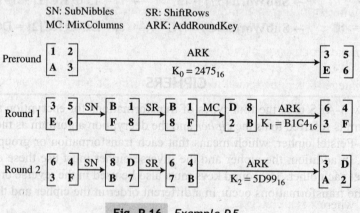

**Fig. P.16**  *Example P.5*

# Appendix

# Q

# Some Proofs

This appendix presents some proofs for theorems used in Chapters 2 and 9. The proofs are mostly short and informal so that they will be useful for students in a cryptography course. The reader interested in more details can consult books on number theory.

## Q.1  CHAPTER 2

This section presents some proofs for theorems on divisibility, Euclidean algorithms, and congruence.

### Q.1.1  Divisibility

Following are proofs for several theorems on divisibility.

### Theorem Q.1:  Division Relation (Algorithm)

For integer $a$ and $b$ with $b > 0$, there exist integers $q$ and $r$ such that $a = q \times b + r$.

> **Proof:**
> Consider an arithmetic progression in the form:
> $$\ldots, -3 \times b, -2 \times b, -1 \times b, 0 \times b, 1 \times b, 2 \times b, 3 \times b, \ldots$$
> It is obvious that integer $a$ is either equal to one of the terms or between two consecutive terms. In other words, $a = q \times b + r$, where $q \times b$ is a term in the above progression and $r$ is the offset from the term.

### Theorem Q.2

If $a \mid 1$, then $a = \pm 1$.

> **Proof:**
> $a \mid 1 \rightarrow 1 = x \times a$, where $x$ is an integer.
> This means: ($x = 1$ and $a = 1$) or ($x = -1$ and $a = -1$).
> Therefore: $a = \pm 1$.

### Theorem Q.3

If $a \mid b$ and $b \mid a$, then $a = \pm b$.

*Proof:*

$a \mid b \rightarrow b = x \times a$, where $x$ is an integer.

$b \mid a \rightarrow a = y \times b$, where $y$ is an integer.

We have $a = y \times (x \times a) = (y \times x) \times a. \rightarrow y \times x = 1$.

This means: $(x = 1$ and $y = 1)$ or $(x = -1$ and $y = -1)$.

Therefore: $a = y \times b \rightarrow a = \pm b$.

## Theorem Q.4

If $a \mid b$ and $b \mid c$, then $a \mid c$.

*Proof:*

$a \mid b \rightarrow b = x \times a$, where $x$ is an integer.

$b \mid c \rightarrow c = y \times b$, where $y$ is an integer.

We have $c = y \times (x \times a) = (y \times x) \times a$.

Therefore, $a \mid c$.

## Theorem Q.5

If $a \mid b$ and $a \mid c$, then $a \mid (b + c)$.

*Proof:*

$a \mid b \rightarrow b = x \times a$, where $x$ is an integer.

$a \mid c \rightarrow c = y \times a$, where $y$ is an integer.

We have $b + c = (x + y) \times a$.

Therefore, $a \mid (b + c)$.

## Theorem Q.6

If $a \mid b$ and $a \mid c$, then $a \mid (m \times b + n \times c)$, where $m$ and $n$ are arbitrary integers.

*Proof:*

$a \mid b \rightarrow b = x \times a$, where $x$ is an integer.

$a \mid c \rightarrow c = y \times a$, where $y$ is an integer.

We have $m \times b + n \times c = m \times (x \times a) + n \times (y \times a) = (m \times x + n \times y) \times a$.

Therefore, $a \mid (m \times b + n \times c)$.

### Q.1.2   Euclidean Algorithms

We used Euclidean and extended Euclidean algorithms in Chapter 2. Following are proofs of two theorems related to these algorithms.

## Theorem Q.7

If $a = b \times q + r$ ($r$ is the remainder of dividing $a$ by $b$), then gcd $(a, b) =$ gcd $(b, r)$.

*Proof:*

Assume that $E$ is the set of all common divisors of $a$ and $b$. Every element of $E$ divides $a$ and $b$; therefore, it divides $r = a - b \times q$. This means that $E$ is the set of all common divisors of $a$, $b$, and $r$. Assume that $F$ is the set of all common divisors of $b$ and $r$. Every element of $F$ divides $b$ and $r$; therefore, it divides $a = b \times q + r$. This means that $F$ is the set of all common divisors of $a$, $b$, and $r$. This means that $E = F \rightarrow a$, $b$, and $r$ have the same set of common divisors. Therefore, gcd $(a, b) =$ gcd $(b, r)$.

As we saw in Chapter 2, this theorem is the basis of the Euclidean algorithm to find the greatest common divisor of two integers.

## Theorem Q.8

If $a$ and $b$ are integers, not both of which zero, then there exist integers $x$ and $y$ such that gcd $(a, b) = x \times a + y \times b$.

**Proof:**
Assume that D is the set of all values of $(x \times a + y \times b)$, with $d$ the smallest nonzero value.
We can write $a = q \times d + r \rightarrow r = a - q \times d = (1 - q \times x)\, a + (-q \times y)\, b$, where $0 \leq r < d$.
This implies that $r$ is a member of D. But because $r < d$, then $r = 0$ or $d \mid a$.
With a similar argument, we can show that $d \mid b$.
Therefore, $d$ is the common divisor of $a$ and $b$.
Any other divisor of $a$ and $b$ divides $d = x \times a + y \times b$. Therefore, $d$ must be the gcd $(a, b)$.

As we saw in Chapter 2, this theorem is the basis of the extended Euclidean algorithm.

## Q.1.3   Congruence

Following are proofs of some theorems about congruence used in Chapter 2.

## Theorem Q.9

If $a$, $b$, and $n$ are integers with $n > 0$, then $a \equiv b \pmod{n}$ if and only if there exists an integer $q$ such that $a = q \times n + b$.

**Proof:**
If $a \equiv b \pmod{n}$, then $n \mid (a - b)$, which means there is an integer $q$ such that $a - b = q \times n$.
Therefore, we have $a = q \times n + b$.
If there is an integer $q$ such that $a = q \times n + b$, then $a - b = q \times n$, which means $n \mid (a - b)$.
Therefore, we have $a \equiv b \pmod{n}$.

## Theorem Q.10

If $a$, $b$, $c$, and $n$ are integers with $n > 0$, such that $a \equiv b \pmod{n}$, then

   a.   $a + c \equiv b + c \pmod{n}$.
   b.   $a - c \equiv b - c \pmod{n}$.
   c.   $a \times c \equiv b \times c \pmod{n}$.

**Proof:** Note that $a \equiv b \pmod{n} \rightarrow n \mid (a - b)$.
   a.   $(a + c) - (b + c) = a - b$. Because $n \mid (a - b)$, $n \mid (a + c) - (b + c)$.
        Therefore, $a + c \equiv b + c \pmod{n}$.
   b.   $(a - c) - (b - c) = a - b$. Because $n \mid (a - b)$, $n \mid (a - c) - (b - c)$.
        Therefore, $a - c \equiv b - c \pmod{n}$.
   c.   $(a \times c) - (b \times c) = (a - b) \times c$. Because $n \mid (a - b)$, $n \mid (a - b) \times c$.
        Therefore, $a \times c \equiv b \times c \pmod{n}$.

## Theorem Q.11

If $a$, $b$, $c$, $d$, and $n$ are integers with $n > 0$, such that $a \equiv b \pmod{n}$ and $c \equiv d \pmod{n}$, then
   a.   $a + c \equiv b + d \pmod{n}$.

   b.   $a - c \equiv b - d \pmod{n}$.

   c.   $a \times c \equiv b \times d \pmod{n}$.

**Proof:** Note that $a \equiv b \pmod{n} \rightarrow (a - b) = k \times n; c \equiv d \pmod{n} \rightarrow (c - d) = l \times n$

   a.   $(a + c) - (b + d) = (a - b) + (c - d) = k \times n + l \times n = (k + l) \times n$.

       Therefore, $a + c \equiv b + d \pmod{n}$.

   b.   $(a - c) - (b - d) = (a - b) - (c - d) = k \times n - l \times n = (k - l) \times n$.

       Therefore, $a - c \equiv b - d \pmod{n}$.

   c.   $a \times c - b \times d = c \times (a - b) + b \times (c - d) = (c \times k + b \times l) \times n$.

       Therefore, $a \times c \equiv b \times d \pmod{n}$.

## Q.2                                     CHAPTER 9

This section presents some proofs of the theorems used in Chapter 9. We leave the discussion of the lengthy proofs, such as the proof of Chinese remainder theorem, to books in number theory.

### Q.2.1   Primes

We prove just one theorem about primes.

### Theorem Q.12

If $n$ is a composite, then there is a prime divisor $p$ such that $p \leq \sqrt{n}$.

**Proof:**

Because $n$ is a composite, $n = a \times b$.

If $p$ is the smallest prime divisor of $n$, then $p \leq a$ and $p \leq b$.

Therefore, $p^2 \leq a \times b$ or $p^2 \leq n \rightarrow p \leq \sqrt{n}$

This theorem is used in the sieve of Eratosthenes to find all prime factors of $n$.

### Q.2.2   Euler's Phi-Function

Following are three proofs related to the Euler's phi-function.

### Theorem Q.13

If $p$ is a prime, then $\phi(p) = p - 1$

**Proof:**

Because $p$ is a prime, all integers less than $p$, except $p$ itself, are relatively prime to $p$.

Therefore, $\phi(p) = p - 1$.

This theorem is part of the Euler's phi-function.

### Theorem Q.14

If $p$ is a prime and $e$ is a positive integer, then $\phi(p^e) = p^e - p^{e-1}$.

**Proof:**

The integers that are not relatively prime to $p^e$ are $(1 \times p), (2 \times p), \ldots, (p^{e-1} \times p)$. All of these integers have the common divisor $p$ with $p^e$. The total number of these integers is $p^{e-1}$. The rest of the integers are relatively prime with $p^e$.

Therefore, $\phi(p^e) = p^e - p^{e-1}$

This theorem is another part of Euler's phi-function.

## Theorem Q.15

If $n$ is a composite with prime factorization of $\prod p_i^{ei}$, then $\phi(n) = \prod (p_i^{ei} - p_i^{ei-1})$

### Proof:
The proof is based on the fact that the $\phi(n)$ is a *multiplicative function* in which $\phi(m \times n) = \phi(m) \times \phi(n)$ if $m$ and $n$ are relatively prime. Because the terms in the prime factorization of $n$ are relatively prime, $\phi(\prod p_i^{ei}) = \prod \phi(p_i^{ei})$.
   Therefore, $\phi(n) = \prod (p_i^{ei} - p_i^{ei-1})$.

This theorem is the generalization of Euler's phi-function.

## Q.2.3   Fermat's Little Theorem

Following are proofs of two theorems related to Fermat's little theorem.

## Theorem Q.16

If $p$ is a prime and $a$ is a positive integer relatively prime to $p$, then $a^{p-1} \equiv 1 \pmod{p}$.

### Proof:
It can be proven that the residues of the terms $a, 2a, \ldots, (p-1)a$ modulo $p$ are $1, 2, \ldots, (p-1)$, but not necessarily in the same order.
The result of $a \times 2a \times \cdots (p-1)a$ is $[(p-1)]!\, a^{p-1}$.
The result of $1 \times 2 \times \cdots \times (p-1)$ is $[(p-1)]!$
This means $[(p-1)]!\, a^{p-1} \equiv [(p-1)]! \pmod{p}$
Therefore, $a^{p-1} \equiv 1 \pmod{p}$, when we divide both sides by $[(p-1)]!$

This theorem is the first version of Fermat's little theorem.

## Theorem Q.17

If $p$ is a prime and $a$ is a positive integer, then $a^p \equiv a \pmod{p}$.

### Proof:
If $a$ and $p$ are coprime, we multiply both sides of the congruence using the result of the previous theorem to get $a^p \equiv a \pmod{p}$.
If $p \mid a$, then $a^p \equiv a \equiv 0 \pmod{p}$.

This theorem is the second version of Fermat's little theorem.

## Q.2.4   Euler's Theorem

Following is a proof of one theorem related to the first version of Euler's theorem. We proved the second version in Chapter 9.

## Theorem Q.18

If $n$ and $a$ are coprime, then $a^{\phi(n)} \equiv 1 \pmod{n}$.

*Proof:*

Assume that the elements in $Z_n^*$ are $r_1, r_2, \ldots, r_{\phi(n)}$.

We create another set $ar_1, ar_2, \ldots, ar_{\phi(n)}$ by multiplying each element in $Z_n^*$ by $a$. It can be proven that each element in this new set is congruent to an element in $Z_n^*$ (not necessarily in the same order).

Thus, $ar_1 \times ar_2 \times \cdots \times ar_{\phi(n)} \equiv r_1 \times r_2 \times \cdots \times r_{\phi(n)} \pmod{n}$

We have $a^{\phi(n)}[r_1 \times r_2 \times \cdots \times r_{\phi(n)}] \equiv r_1 \times r_2 \times \cdots \times r_{\phi(n)} \pmod{n}$

Therefore, $a^{\phi(n)} \equiv 1 \pmod{n}$.

## Fundamental Theorem of Arithmetic

Following is a partial proof of the Fundamental Theorem of Arithmetic.

### Theorem Q.19

Any positive integer $n$ greater than 1 can be written as the product of prime.

*Proof:*

We use induction. The base case is $n = 2$, which is a prime. For the general case, assume that all positive integers less than $n$ can be written as the product of primes, we prove that $n$ can also be written as the product of primes.

We can have two cases: $n$ is a prime or $n$ is a composite.

1. If $n$ is prime, it can be written as the product of one prime, itself.
2. If $n$ is a composite, then we can write $n = a \times b$. Because $a$ and $b$ are both less than $n$, each can be written as the product of primes according to the assumption. Therefore, $n$ can be written as the product of primes.

This theorem is a partial proof of the Fundamental Theorem of Arithmetic. To completely prove this theorem, we need to show the product is unique. But we leave this part to books on number theory.

# Appendix

# R

# Secured Electronic
# Transaction (SET)

## R.1    INTRODUCTION TO SECURED ELECTRONIC TRANSACTIONS

Electronic transaction is a part and parcel of our daily life. Every time we do a transaction online a huge amount of information is exchanged over the network. These data must be protected from an eavesdropper, in order to protect the privacy of the customer and prevent malicious activities, which can lead to the loss and theft of the customer's money. It is hence imperative that any good electronic commerce system should guarantee authenticity, integrity, privacy and data protection. To elaborate, these criteria ensures that the legal users should not be impersonated, money orders and payment values should be tamper-proof, details of a transaction should be secret and valuable data should be protected.

The credit card companies, namely MasterCard and Visa called for the establishment of standards for electronic transaction in 1996. Several companies participated in this process of standardization and what emerged is called SET, or **Secure Electronic Transaction**. The SET protocol is fairly complex. For example, the SSL protocol certifies the legality of the card holder and the merchant site, and also specifies how payment requests are to be made. Thus it encompasses the existing credit card system and allows users to perform secured transactions over public channels.

## R.2    SECURE ELECTRONIC TRANSACTION (SET) PROTOCOL

As more and more companies are opting Internet as a medium for electronic commerce, trust and security requirements are increasing. The important security requirements for a successful e-commerce transaction are presented in Table R.1.

**Table R.1**  *Important Security Requirements*

| Requirement | Description |
|---|---|
| Privacy | Information shared among the communicating parties must be known only to them. All others must be kept out of the loop. |
| Authentication | Both the communicating parties must be in a position to establish and prove their identities. |
| Integrity | The message that is transmitted by the sender should not be tampered. If tampered, the receiver must be in a position to identify the same and discard the message. |
| Non-Repudiation | Both the communicating parties must have the facility to legally prove that messages have been sent and received. |

These security requirements are achieved using a combination of symmetric and asymmetric algorithms, which we have studied in the previous chapters. These algorithms are applied through some protocols, which are described next.

## R.2.1 Transaction Security Protocols

To successfully implement an e-commerce transaction, two acceptable protocols that are deployed are:
- **(a)** **Secure-Socket Layer (SSL) protocol**
- **(b)** **Secure Electronic Transaction (SET) protocol**

### SSL Protocol

Netscape Inc. originally created the **Secure Sockets Layer** (SSL) **protocol**. On account of its popularity and acceptance, it is now implemented in all web browsers.

SSL has two main objectives:
1. To ensure confidentiality, by encrypting the data that moves between the communicating parties (client and the server).
2. To provide authentication of the session partners, using RSA algorithm.

The SSL protocol consists of two protocols:
1. **The SSL Handshake protocol**, in which the communicating parties (client and the server) authenticate themselves and negotiate an encryption key. One point to note here is that the SSL there is significant additional overhead in starting up an SSL session.
2. **The SSL Record protocol**, in which the session data is exchanged between the communicating parties (client and the server) in an encrypted fashion.

The ten steps in a SSL transaction are:
1. The client first sends a request by introducing itself.
2. The server acknowledges.
3. The server sends its certificate to the client.
4. The client checks if the certificate was issued by a *Certificate Authority* (CA) it trusts.
5. The client then compares the information in the certificate with the information it just received concerning the site.
6. The client then tells the server what encryption algorithms are to be used.
7. The client then generates a session key using the agreed cipher.
8. The client then encrypts the session key using the server's public key and sends it to the server.
9. The server receives the encrypted session key and decrypts it with its private key.
10. The client and the server then use the session key for the rest of the transaction.

Although SSL protocol has been implemented in all browsers, there are two main risks associated with SSL.
- a. The cardholder is NOT protected from the merchant. If the merchant is dishonest and charge more, users stand to lose.
- b. Similarly, the merchant is also NOT protected from dishonest customers who supply an invalid credit card number.

In a nutshell,
- ❑ SSL is a secure message protocol, not a payment protocol
- ❑ SSL requires the vendor to have a certificate
- ❑ SSL protocol does not provide facilities for non-repudiation.

SSL was followed by *Transport Layer Security* (TLS), which is an Internet Engineering Task Force (IETF) version of SSL. TLS functions very similar to SSL but they do not interoperate.

IBM later developed a standard called *Internet Keyed Payment Protocol* (iKP), which led to the development of Secure Electronic Transaction Protocol (SET).

To carry out transactions successfully and without compromising security and trust, business communities, financial institutions and companies offering technological solutions wanted a protocol that works very similar to the way how a credit card transactions work.

Visa and MasterCard, leading credit card companies in the world formed a consortium with computer vendors such as IBM and developed an open protocol which emerged as a standard in ensuring security, authenticity, privacy and trust in electronic transactions.

## Set Business Requirements
The main business requirements for SET are

1. Provide security, authenticity, privacy, integrity and trust with regard to payment and ordering information
2. Provide authentication that a cardholder is a legitimate user of a credit card account
3. Provide authentication that a merchant can accept credit card transactions.
4. To formulate a protocol that facilitates and encourages interoperability among software and network providers and which does not depend on the transport security mechanism.

## Participants of the SET System
The main participants of the SET system and their details are presented in Table R.2.

**Table R.2  *Main Participants of the SET System***

| Participant | Details |
|---|---|
| Cardholder | Refers to the person who holds the card and who makes the purchases on the Internet. |
| Merchant | A person or organization that has goods or services to sell to the cardholder. |
| Issuer | Refers to the financial institutions that provide the cardholder with the credit card and are responsible for the payment. |
| Acquirer | Refers to organizations that provide verbal or telephonic card authorization for merchants. Merchants pay a small fee to the acquirer for their services. |
| Acquirer Payment Gateway | Acts as an interface between SET and the computer networks of banks. To put it simpler terms, the acquirer payment gateway acts as a proxy for the bank's network functions. |
| Certifying Authority (CA) | Refers to the organization that provides public key certification. One of the best-known Certifying Authority (CA) is *Verisign* which offers several classes of certificates.<br><br>Class 1 certificate is of the lowest level which binds e-mail address and associated public keys. Class 4 certificates are the highest level certificates that apply to servers and their organizations. |

## How SET Works?
The following is a simplified version of how SET works.

Before SET can work, there is a preliminary step which has to completed.

*Preliminary Step:* Both cardholders and merchants must register with the CA (certifying authority).

## Actual Steps in SET
Step 1: Customer browses website of the merchant, decides what to purchase and adds them to the shopping cart.

Step 2: Customer then communicates with the merchant and payment gateway in a single message. The message has two parts:

Part a: *Purchase Order* for use by the merchant.

Part b: *Card Information* for use by the merchant's bank.

Step 3: Merchant forwards the card information (part b) to their bank.

Step 4: Merchant's bank contacts the issuer and checks with the issuer for payment authorization.

Step 5: Issuer authorizes the purchase and sends authorization to Merchant's bank.

Step 6: Merchant's bank sends a copy of the authorization to merchant.

Step 7: Merchant completes the order and sends confirmation to the customer.

Step 8: Merchant captures the transaction from their bank.

Step 9: Issuer prints the credit card invoice to customer.

## Encryption Process in SET

Algorithm used: 1024 bit RSA algorithm for asymmetric encryption process

56 bit DES algorithm for symmetric encryption process

SHA-1 for computing the message digest.

The sequence of steps the sender S adopts in encryption process is as follows:

Step 1: The sender S subjects the message through a hash algorithm. SET uses *Secure Hash Algorithm* (SHA-1) for this. The output of the hash algorithm is the message digest.

Step 2: Sender S then encrypts the message digest using his RSA private key. The output of this step is the Digital Signature.

Step 3: Sender S then creates a key for the symmetric encryption.

Step 4: Sender S takes the message, digital signature obtained in step 2 and his digital certificate and encrypts all of them using the symmetric key encryption method of *Data Encryption Standard* (DES). The result of step 4 is the encrypted message.

Step 5: Sender S then picks the public key of the recipient R. Encrypts the symmetric key of step 3. The output is called as *digital envelope*.

The encrypted message obtained from step 4 and the digital envelope obtained from step 5 is sent to the receiver R.

## Decryption Process in SET

Algorithm used: 1024 bit RSA algorithm for asymmetric encryption process

56 bit DES algorithm for symmetric encryption process

SHA-1 for computing the message digest.

The sequence of steps the receiver R adopts in decryption process is as follows:

Step 1: Receiver R decrypts the digital envelope using his RSA private key to obtain the DES symmetric key.

Step 2: Using the DES symmetric key obtained from step 1, the receiver decrypts the encrypted message to obtain the plain text message, digital signature and the digital certificate of the sender S.

Step 3: Receiver R then extracts the RSA public key of the sender S from the digital certificate.

Step 4: Using the RSA public key of the sender S, the encrypted message digest obtained from step 3 is decrypted to get the message digest.

Step 5: Receiver R then subjects the message again through the hash function SHA-1. A message digest is thus obtained. This computed message digest is then compared with the message digest obtained from step 4. If both of them are the same, the authenticity of the sender S is guaranteed.

Figure R.1 shows the encryption and decryption process.

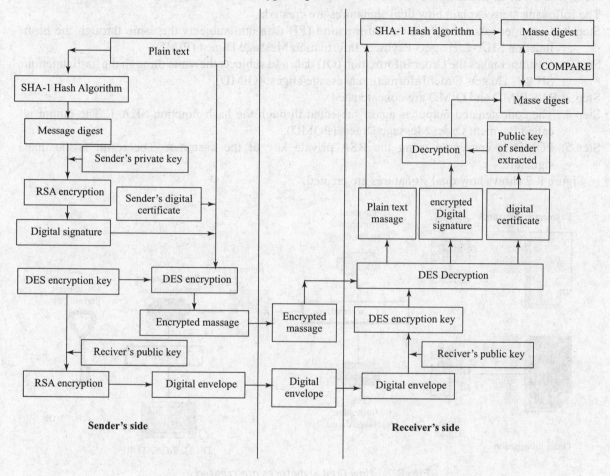

**Fig. R.1**  *Encryption and decryption process*

## R.2.2   Dual Signatures

As mentioned earlier, in SET, the customer communicates with the merchant and the payment gateway through a single message. The message has two parts, a purchase order part for use by the merchant and a card information part for use by the merchant's bank.

The customer has to ensure that

1.   the merchant shall not view see the payment instruction.
2.   the acquirer shall not view the order instruction.

It is also necessary to link the order and payment so that the customer can prove that the payment is for the particular order and not for other orders.

This is achieved by a new concept introduced in SET named as **dual signature**.

## How are Dual Signatures Created?

The following steps explain how dual signatures are created:

Step 1: Customer takes the Payment Information (PI) data and subjects the same through the hash function SHA-1. He gets Payment Information Message Digest (PIMD).

Step 2: Customer takes the Order Information (OI) data and subjects the same through the hash function SHA-1. He gets Order Information Message Digest (OIMD).

Step 3: Both PIMD and OIMD are concatenated.

Step 4: The concatenated output is again subjected through the hash function SHA-1. The output is called Payment Order Message Digest (POMD).

Step 5: POMD is encrypted using the RSA private key of the customer. The result is the dual signature.

Figure R.2 shows how dual signatures are created.

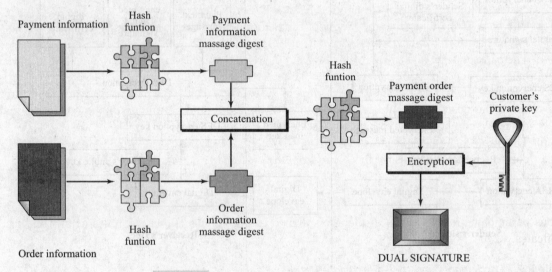

**Fig. R.2** *How Dual Signatures are created*

## How does a Dual Signature Help the Bank?

Here also, there are two steps, encryption process and decryption process.

### Encryption Process

Algorithms used: 1024 bit RSA algorithm for asymmetric encryption process.

56 bit DES algorithm for symmetric encryption process.

SHA-1 for computing the message digest.

The sequence of steps the customer C adopts after the dual signature has been created:

Step 1: The customer C creates a key for the DES symmetric encryption.

Step 2: The customer C then uses the DES encryption method to encrypt the Payment Instruction (PI) message, the dual signature, his certificate and the Order Information Message Digest (OIMD). The result is the encrypted message.

Step 3: The customer C then picks the RSA public key of the bank B. Encrypts the DES symmetric key of step 1. The output is called as digital envelope.

The encrypted message obtained from step 2 and the digital envelope obtained from step 3 is sent to the bank B.

## Decryption Process

Algorithms used:    1024 bit RSA algorithm for asymmetric encryption process.

                       56 bit DES algorithm for symmetric encryption process.

                       SHA-1 for computing the message digest.

The sequence of steps the bank B adopts after it has received the encrypted message and the digital envelope are:

Step 1:  The bank B uses its RSA private key to decrypt the digital envelope to obtain the DES symmetric key.

Step 2:  The bank B then uses the DES symmetric key to decrypts the first portion of the encrypted message to obtain the Payment Instruction (PI) message, the dual signature, certificate of the customer and the Order Information Message Digest (OIMD).

Step 3:  The bank B then subjects the Payment Instruction (PI) to the hash function SHA-1 to get the Payment Information Message Digest (PIMD).

Step 4:  The bank concatenates the PIMD value and the OIMD and subjects the result again through the hash function SHA-1. The result is the Payment Order Message Digest (POMD).

Step 5:  The bank then decrypts the second portion of the encrypted message which is the **dual signature** using the customer's public key (obtained from the digital certificate of the customer) and obtains a copy of the Payment Order Message Digest (POMD).

Step 6:  The value of POMD obtained from steps 4 and 5 are compared. If they are same, then it is confirmed that the message has come from the customer.

## Certificates of Various Participants

Certificates play a critical role in SET for trust is always built on certificates. Since there are various participants in SET, each of them has their own certificates. Table R.3 gives details on these certificates.

**Table R.3**  *Participants and their Certificate Details*

| Participant | Certificate Details |
|---|---|
| Cardholder certificate | Used to verify that the cardholder is a genuine person. These are digitally signed by a financial institution and the certificate does not contain the account number and expiration date of the card |
| Merchant certificate | These are digitally signed by the merchant's financial institution and provide assurance that the merchant has a valid agreement with an acquirer.<br>In SET, the merchant needs two public key pairs, one for digital signatures and one for encrypting key exchanges. It will therefore need two certificates for each payment card brand that it accepts. |
| Payment Gateway Certificate | Payment gateway obtains its certificates from their acquirers for the systems that process authorization. |

## Hierarchy of Trust in Set Certificates

As you might have noticed, all the participants of SET needs to have a certificate for operating.

Certificates are created by Certifying Authorities (CA) and there is a hierarchy of trust among the SET certificate authorities.

Figure R.3 shows the hierarchy of trust among SET CA.

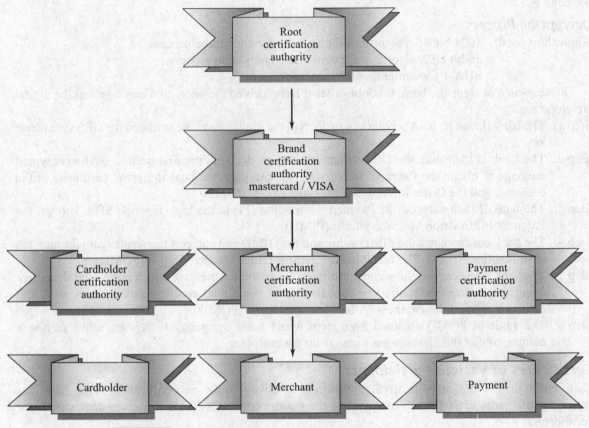

**Fig. R.3** *Hierarchy of trust among SET Certification Authorities*

**Limitations of SET** Despite being very secure, SET has not been a success in e-commerce environments. The reasons attributed are the following:

1. The overheads associated with SET are heavy. For a simple purchase transaction:
   a. Four messages are exchanged between the merchant and customer,
   b. Two messages are exchanged between the merchant and payment gateway,
   c. 6 digital signatures are computed,
   d. There are 9 RSA encryption/decryption cycles,
   e. There are 4 DES encryption/decryption cycles and
   f. Four certificate verifications
2. It has been argued by merchants that they have to expend lot of money in order to process SET transactions. From consumer's point of view, they have to install appropriate software.
3. Inter-operability problem has not been solved.
4. With SET, while the payment information is secure, order information is not secure.

# Glossary

## A

**A5/1** A member of the A5 family of stream ciphers used in the Global System for Mobile Communication (GSM).

**abelian group** A commutative group.

**access control** A security service that protects against unauthorized access to data. Also a security mechanism that verifies a user's right to access the data.

**active attack** An attack that may change the data or harm the system.

**additive cipher** The simplest monoalphabetic cipher in which each character is encrypted by adding its value with a key.

**additive inverse** In modular arithmetic, $a$ and $b$ are additive inverses of each other if $(b + a)$ $mod \ n = 0$.

**AddRoundKey** In AES, an operation that adds a round key word with each state column matrix.

**Advanced Encryption Standard (AES)** A non-Feistel symmetric-key block cipher published by the NIST.

**affine cipher** A cipher that combines the additive and multiplicative ciphers.

**aggressive mode** In IKE, a mode that is a compressed version of the corresponding main mode using three message exchange instead of six.

**Alert Protocol** In SSL and TLS, a protocol for reporting errors and abnormal conditions.

**algebraic structure** A structure consists of a set of elements and operations that are defined for the sets. Groups, rings, and fields are examples of algebraic structures.

**anonymous Diffie-Hellman** In SSL and TLS, the original Diffie-Hellman protocol.

**associativity** In an algebraic structure, if $a$, $b$, and $c$ are elements of the underlying set and • denotes one of the operations, the associative property guarantees that $(a \bullet b) \bullet c = a \bullet (b \bullet c)$.

**asymmetric-key cryptosystem** A cryptosystem that uses two different keys for encryption and decryption: a public key for encryption and a private key for decryption.

**asymmetric-key encipherment** An encipherment using an asymmetric-key cryptosystem.

**authentication**   A security service that checks the identity of the party at the other end of the line.

**authentication exchange**   A security mechanism in which two entities exchange a set of messages to prove their identity to each other.

**Authentication Header (AH)**   A protocol in IPSec that provides message integrity and authentication.

**authentication server (AS)**   The server that plays the role of the KDC in the Kerberos protocol.

**autokey cipher**   A stream cipher in which each subkey in the stream is the same as the previous plaintext character. The first subkey is the secret between two parties.

**availability**   This component of information security requires that the information created and stored by an organization to be available to authorized entities.

**avalanche effect**   A desired characteristic in a cipher in which a small change in the plaintext or key results in a large change in the ciphertext.

## B

**binary operation**   An operation that takes two inputs and creates one output.

**biometrics**   The measurement of physiological or behavioral features that identify a person.

**birthday problem**   A classical problem concerning the probability that $n$ people have distinct birthdays where $n \leq 365$.

**bit**   A binary digit with a value of 0 or 1.

**bit-oriented cipher**   A cipher in which the symbols in the plaintext, the ciphertext, and the key are bits.

**blind signatures**   A patented scheme developed by David Chaum that allows a document to get signed without revealing the contents of the document to the signer.

**block**   A group of bits treated as one unit.

**block cipher**   A type of cipher in which blocks of plaintext are encrypted one at a time using the same cipher key.

**broadcast attack**   A type of attack on RSA that can be launched if one entity sends the same small message to a group of recipients with the same low encryption exponent.

**brute-force attack**   A type of attack in which the attacker tries to use all possible keys to find the cipher key.

**bucket brigade attack**   See *man-in-the-middle attack*.

**byte**   A group of eight bits. An octet.

## C

**Caesar cipher**   An additive cipher with a fixed-value key used by Julius Caesar.

**CBC-MAC**   See *CMAC*.

**certification authority (CA)**   An organization that binds a public key to an entity and issues a certificate.

**challenge-response authentication**   An authentication method in which the claimant proves that she *knows* a secret without sending it.

**ChangeCipherSpec Protocol**   In SSL and TLS, the protocol that allows the movement from the pending state to the active state.

**characteristic polynomial**   In an LFSR, the polynomial representing the feedback function.

**character-oriented cipher**   A cipher in which the symbols in the plaintext, the ciphertext, and the key are characters.

**Chinese remainder theorem (CRT)**   A theorem that proves that there exists a unique solution for a set of congruent equations with one variable if the moduli are relatively prime.

**chosen-ciphertext attack**   A type of attack in which the adversary chooses a set of ciphertexts and somehow finds the corresponding plaintexts. She then analyzes the ciphertext/plaintexts pairs to find the cipher key.

**chosen-message attack**   An attack in which the attacker somehow makes Alice sign one or more messages. The attacker later creates another message, with the content she wants, and forges Alice's signature on it.

**chosen-plaintext attack**   A type of attack in which the adversary chooses a set of plaintexts and somehow finds the corresponding ciphertexts. She then analyzes the plaintext/ciphertext pairs to find the cipher key.

**cipher**   A decryption and/or encryption algorithm.

**cipher feedback (CFB) mode**   A mode of operation in which each $r$-bit block is exclusive-ored with an $r$-bit key, which is part of an encrypted register.

**cipher block chaining (CBC) mode**   A mode of operation similar to ECB, but each block is first exclusive-ored with the previous ciphertext.

**cipher suite**   In SSL and TLS, the combination of key exchange, hash, and encryption algorithms.

**ciphertext**   The message after being encrypted.

**ciphertext-only attack**   A type of attack in which the intruder has only the intercepted ciphertext to analyze.

**circular shift operation**   An operation in modern block ciphers that removes $k$ bits from one end and inserts them at the other end.

**claimant**   In entity authentication, the entity whose identity needs to be proved.

**clogging attack**   In the Diffie-Hellman method, a type of attack in which an intruder can send many half-keys to one of the parties, pretending that they are from different sources. The attack may eventually result in denial of service.

**closure**   In an algebraic structure, if $a$ and $b$ are elements of the underlying set and $\bullet$ denotes one of the operations, the closure property guarantees that $c = a \bullet b$ is also a member of the set.

**CMAC**   A standard MAC defined by NIST (FIPS 113) as the Data Authentication Algorithm. The method is similar to the cipher block chaining (CBC) mode.

**coefficient**   In a polynomial, the constant value in each term.

**collision resistance**   A property of a cryptographic hash function that ensures that the intruder cannot find two messages that hash to the same digest.

**column matrix**   A matrix with only one column.

**combine operation**   An operation in some block ciphers that concatenates two equal-length blocks to create a new block.

**common modulus attack**   A type of attack on RSA that can be launched if a community uses a common modulus.

**commutative group**   A group in which the binary operation satisfies the commutative property.

**commutativity**   In an algebraic structure, if $a$ an $b$ are elements of the underlying set and $\bullet$ denotes one of the operations, the commutative property guarantees that $a \bullet b = b \bullet a$.

**composite**   A positive integer with more than two divisors.

**composition**   Composition of two functions $f$ and $g$ is defined as $g(f(x))$, which means that first the function $f$ is applied to the domain $x$, and then the function $g$ is applied to the range of $f$.

**compression function**   A function that creates a fixed-size digest out of a variable-size message.

**compression P-box**   A P-box with $n$ inputs and $m$ outputs, where $n > m$.

**confidentiality**   A security goal that defines procedures to hide information from an unauthorized entity.

**confusion**   A desired property of a block cipher introduced by Shannon that hides the relationship between the ciphertext and the key. This will frustrate the adversary who tries to use the ciphertext to find the key.

**congruence**   If $n$ is a positive integer, two integers $a$ and $b$ are said to be congruent modulo $n$, $a \equiv b$ (mod $n$), if $a - b = kn$, for some integer $k$.

**congruence operator**   The operator ($\equiv$) used in a congruence relation.

**connection**   In SSL and TLS, the process that allows two entities to exchange two random numbers and create the keys and parameters needed for communication.

**cookie**   A text that holds some information about the receiver and must be returned to the sender untouched.

**Coppersmith theorem attack**   A type of attack on RSA that can be launched if the value of the encryption exponent is small.

**coprime**   See *relatively prime*.

**counter (CTR) mode**   A mode of operation in which there is no feedback. It is similar to OFB, but a counter is used instead of a shift register.

**cryptanalysis**   The science and art of breaking codes.

**cryptographic hash function**   A function that creates a much shorter output from an input. To be useful, the function must be resistant to image, preimage, and collision attacks.

**Cryptographic Message Syntax (CMS)**   The syntax used in S/MIME that defines the exact encoding scheme for each content type.

**cryptography**   The science and art of transforming messages to make them secure and immune to attacks.

**cyclic subgroup**   A subgroup that can be generated using the power of an element in the group.

**cycling attack** A type of attack on RSA that uses the fact that the ciphertext is a permutation of the plaintext; continuous encryption of the ciphertext will eventually result in the plaintext.

## D

**data confidentiality** A security service designed to protect data from disclosure attacks, snooping, and traffic analysis.

**Data Encryption Standard (DES)** A symmetric-key block cipher using rounds of Feistel ciphers and standardized by NIST.

**data expansion function** In TLS, a function that uses a predefined HMAC to expand a secret into a longer one.

**data integrity** A security service designed to protect data from modification, insertion, deletion, and replaying. Also, a security mechanism that appends a short checkvalue to the data that has been created by a specific process from the data itself. The checkvalue can be use to protect the integrity of data.

**Davies-Meyer scheme** A hash function scheme basically the same as the Rabin scheme except that it uses forward feed to protect against meet-in-the-middle attack.

**deciphering** See *decryption*.

**decoding** This term has many definitions. In this text, one of the meanings is to transform an $n$-bit integer into a $2^n$-bit string with only a single 1. The position of the single 1 is the value of the integer.

**decryption** De-scrambling of the ciphertext to create the original plaintext.

**decryption algorithm** An algorithm used for decryption.

**denial of service** The only attack on the availability goal that may slow down or interrupt the system.

**determinant** A scalar value defined for a square matrix. A matrix is reversible if its determinant is nonzero.

**dictionary attack** An attack in which the intruder is interested in finding one password regardless of the user ID.

**differential cryptanalysis** A type of *chosen-plaintext* attack introduced by Biham and Shamir that uses the differential profile of S-boxes to attack a product cipher.

**Diffie-Hellman protocol** A protocol for creating a session key without using a KDC.

**diffusion** A desired property of a block cipher introduced by Shannon that hides the relationship between the ciphertext and the plaintext. This will frustrate the adversary who uses ciphertext statistics to find the plaintext.

**digital signature** A security mechanism in which the sender can electronically sign the message and the receiver can verify the message to prove that the message is indeed signed by the sender.

**Digital Signature Algorithm (DSA)** The digital signature algorithm used by the Digital Signature Standard (DSS).

**digital signature scheme** A method of systematic creation of a secure digital signature.

**Digital Signature Standard (DSS)** The digital signature standard adopted by NIST under FIPS 186.

**digram** A two-letter string.

**discrete logarithm**   The integer $d$ is called the discrete logarithm of $a$ to the base $r$ if $r^d \equiv a \pmod{n}$, where $r$ is a primitive root of $n$, and $a$ and $n$ are relatively prime.

**distributivity**   In an algebraic structure with two operations $\square$ and $\bullet$, distributivity of h over $\bullet$ means that for all $a$, $b$, and $c$ elements of the underlying set, we have $a \square (b \bullet c) = (a \square b) \bullet (a \square c)$ and $(a \bullet b) \square c = (a \square c) \bullet (b \square c)$.

**divisibility**   If $a$ and $b$ are integers and $a \neq 0$, we say that $a$ divides $b$ if there is an integer $k$ such that $b = k \times a$.

**divisibility test**   The most elementary deterministic method for a primality test in which the number is declared a prime if all numbers less than $\sqrt{n}$ cannot divide it.

**double DES (2DES)**   A cipher that uses two instances of DES ciphers for encryption and two instances of reverse ciphers for decryption.

**double transposition cipher**   A transposition cipher in which the same encryption or decryption algorithm is repeated with two keys or the same key.

## E

**electronic cookbook (ECB) mode**   A mode of operation in which each block is encrypted independently with the same cipher key.

**electronic mail (e-mail)**   An electronic version of a postal mail system.

**ElGamal cryptosystem**   An asymmetric-key cryptosystem, devised by ElGamal, which is based on the discrete logarithm problem.

**ElGamal signature scheme**   The digital signature scheme derived from the ElGamal cryptosystem using the same keys.

**elliptic curves**   Cubic equations in two variables of the following form: $y^2 + b_1xy + b_2y = x^3 + a_1x^2 + a_2x + a_3$.

**elliptic curves cryptosystem**   An asymmetric-key cryptosystem based on elliptic curves.

**elliptic curves logarithm problem**   Given two points, $e_1$ and $e_2$, on an elliptic curve, this problem must find the multiplier $r$ such that $e_2 = r \times e_1$.

**elliptic curves digital signature scheme (ECDSA)**   A digital signature algorithm based on DSA but using elliptic curves.

**Encapsulating Security Payload (ESP)**   A protocol in IPSec that provides source authentication, integrity, and privacy.

**encipherment**   See *encryption*.

**encoding**   The term has many definitions. In this text, one of the meanings is to transform a $2^n$-bit string with only a single 1 to an $n$-bit integer. The position of the single 1 defines the value of the integer.

**encryption**   Producing ciphertext from plaintext using a cryptosystem.

**Enigma machine**   A machine based on the principle of rotor ciphers. It was used by the German army during World War II.

**entity authentication**   A technique designed to let one party prove the identity of another party. The entity whose identity needs to be proved is called the claimant; the party that tries to prove the identity of the claimant is called the verifier.

**ephemeral Diffie-Hellman**   A version of the Diffie-Hellman key exchange protocol in which each party sends a Diffie-Hellman key signed by its private key.

**Euclidean algorithm**   An algorithm to find the greatest common divisor of two positive integers.

**Euler's phi-function**   A function that finds the number of integers that are both smaller than $n$ and relatively prime to $n$.

**Euler's theorem**   A generalization of Fermat's little theorem in which the modulus is an integer.

**existence of identity**   In an algebraic structure, if $a$ is an element of the underlying set and • defines one of the operations, this property guarantees that there exists an element $e$, called the identity element, such that $a • e = e • a = a$.

**existence of inverse**   In an algebraic structure, if $a$ is an element of the underlying set and • defines one of the operations, this property guarantees that there exists an element $a'$, called the inverse element, such that $a • a' = a' • a = e$, where $e$ is the identity element.

**existential forgery**   A type of signature forgery in which the forger may be able to create a valid message-signature pair, but not one that she can really use.

**expansion P-box**   A P-box with $n$ inputs and $m$ outputs where $m > n$.

**extended Euclidean algorithm**   An algorithm that, given two integers $a$ and $b$, can find the values of two variables, $s$ and $t$, that satisfy the equation $s \times a + t \times b = \gcd(a, b)$. The algorithm can also find the multiplicative inverse of an integer in modular arithmetic.

## F

**factorization**   Finding all prime factors of an integer.

**false acceptance rate (FAR)**   The parameter measuring how often the system recognizes a person who should not be recognized.

**false rejection rate (FRR)**   The parameter measuring how often the system fails to recognize a person who should be recognized.

**Federal Information Processing Standard (FIPS)**   A U.S. document specifying a data-processing standard.

**feedback function**   The function used in a feedback shift register. The input to the function is all cell values; the output is the value fed to the first cell.

**feedback shift register (FSR)**   A shift register with a feedback function.

**Feige-Fiat-Shamir protocol**   A zero-knowledge authentication method similar to Fiat-Shamir protocol but using a vector of private keys.

**Feistel cipher**   A class of product ciphers consisting of both invertible and noninvertible components. A Feistel cipher combines all noninvertible elements in a unit (called a mixer in this text) and uses the same unit in the encryption and decryption algorithms.

**Fermat factorization method**   A factorization method in which an integer $n$ is divided into two positive integers $a$ and $b$ so that $n = a \times b$.

**Fermat number**   A set of integers in the form $F_n = 2^{2^n} + 1$, where $n$ is an integer.

**Fermat primality test method**   A primality test based on Fermat's little theorem.

**Fermat prime**   A *Fermat number* that is a prime.

**Fermat's little theorem**   In the first version, if $p$ is a prime and $a$ is an integer such that $p$ does not divide $a$, then $a^{p-1} = 1 \bmod p$. In the second version, if $p$ is a prime and $a$ is an integer, then $a^p = a \bmod p$.

**Fiat-Shamir protocol**   A zero-knowledge authentication method devised by Fiat and Shamir.

**field**   An algebraic structure with two operations in which the second operation satisfies all five properties defined for the first operation except that the identity element of the first operation has no inverse with respect to the second operation.

**finite field**   A field with a finite number of elements.

**finite group**   A group with a finite number of elements.

**fixed Diffie-Hellman**   In SSL or TLS, a version of the Diffie-Hellman protocol in which each entity can create a fixed half-key and send the half-keys embedded in a certificate.

**fixed-password**   A password that is used repeatedly for every access.

**function**   A mapping that associates one element in set A, called the domain, to one element in set B, called the range.

## G

**Galois field**   See *finite field*.

**greatest common divisor (gcd)**   The largest possible integer that can divide two integers $a$ and $b$.

**group**   An algebraic structure with only one binary operation that satisfies four properties: closure, associativity, existence of identity, and existence of inverse.

**Guillou-Quisquater protocol**   An extension of the Fiat-Shamir protocol in which a fewer number of rounds can be used to prove the identity of the claimant.

## H

**Handshake Protocol**   In SSL and TLS, the protocol that uses messages to negotiate the cipher suite, to authenticate the server to the client and the client to the server, and to exchange information for building the cryptographic secrets.

**hashed message authentication**   Authentication using a message digest.

**hashed message authentication code (HMAC)**   A standard issued by NIST (FIPS 198) for a nested MAC.

**hashing**   A cryptographic technique in which a fixed-length message digest is created from a variable-length message.

**HAVAL**   A variable-length hashing algorithm with a message digest of size 128, 160, 192, 224, and 256. The block size is 1024 bits.

**Hill cipher**   A polyalphabetic cipher in which the plaintext is divided into equal-size blocks. The blocks are encrypted one at a time in such a way that each character in the block contributes to the encryption of other characters in the block.

**Hypertext Transfer Protocol (HTTP)**   An application-layer service for retrieving a Web document.

## I

**infinite group**   A group with an infinite number of elements.

**initial vector (IV)**   A block used by some mode of operations to initialize the first iteration.

**input pad (ipad)**   The first padding used in the HMAC algorithm.

**integrity**   See *data integrity.*

**International Telecommunication Union-Telecommunication Standardization Sector (ITU–T)**   An international standards group responsible for communication standard.

**Internet Engineering Task Force (IETF)**   A group working on the design and development of the TCP/IP protocol suite and the Internet.

**Internet Key Exchange (IKE)**   A protocol designed to create security associations in IPSec.

**Internet Security Association and Key Management Protocol (ISAKMP)**   A protocol designed by the NSA that implements the exchanges defined in IKE.

**inverse cipher**   The decryption algorithm.

**invertible function**   A function that associates each element in the range with exactly one element in the domain.

**InvMixColumns**   In AES, the inverse of the MixColumns operation used in the reverse cipher.

**InvShiftRows**   In AES, the inverse of ShiftRows operation used in the reverse cipher.

**InvSubBytes**   In AES, the inverse of SubBytes operation used in the reverse cipher.

**Internet Protocol Security (IPSec)**   A collection of protocols designed by the IETF to provide security for a packet at the network level.

**irreducible polynomial**   A polynomial of degree $n$ with no divisor polynomial of degree less than $n$. An irreducible polynomial cannot be factored into a polynomial with degree of less than $n$.

**iterated cryptographic hash function**   A hashing function in which a function with fixed-size input is created and is used a necessary number of times.

## K

**Kasiski test**   A test to find the key length in a polyalphabetic cipher.

**Kerberos**   An authentication protocol, and at the same time a KDC, developed at MIT as part of Project Athena.

**Kerckhoff's principle**   A principle in cryptography that one should always assume that the adversary knows the encryption/decryption algorithm. Therefore, the cipher's resistance to attacks must be based only on the secrecy of the key.

**key**   A set of values that the cipher, as an algorithm, operates on.

**key complement**   A string made by inverting each bit in the key.

**key-distribution center (KDC)**   A trusted third party that establishes a shared secret key between two parties.

**key domain**   The possible set of keys for a cipher.

**key expansion**   In a round cipher, the process of creating round keys from the cipher key.

**key generator**   The algorithm that creates round keys from a cipher key.

**key-only attack**   An attack on a digital signature in which the attacker has access only to the public key.

**key material**   In SSL and TLS, a variable-length string from which the necessary keys and parameters for communication are extracted.

**key ring**   A set of public or private keys used in PGP.

**key schedule**   See *key expansion*.

**knapsack cryptosystem**   The first idea of public-key cryptography, devised by Merkle and Hellman using a knapsack of integers.

**known-message attack**   An attack on a digital signature in which the attacker has access to one or more message-signature pairs.

**known-plaintext attack**   An attack in which the attacker uses a set of known plaintexts and their corresponding ciphertexts to find the cipher key.

## L

**least residue**   The remainder in modular arithmetic.

**linear congruence**   In this text, an equation of the form $ax \equiv b \pmod{n}$.

**linear cryptanalysis**   A known-plaintext attack, presented by Mitsuru Matsui, that uses a linear approximation to analyze a block cipher.

**linear feedback shift register (LFSR)**   A feedback shift register in which the feedback function is linear.

**linear Diophantine equations**   An equation of two variables of the form $ax + by = c$.

**linear S-box**   An S-box in which each output is a linear function of inputs.

**low-private-exponent attack**   In RSA, an attack that can be launched if the private exponent is small.

## M

**main mode**   In IKE, any mode that uses a six-message exchange.

**man-in-the-middle attack**   An attack on the Diffie-Hellman protocol in which the attacker fools two parties involved in the protocol by creating two session keys: one between the first party and the attacker, the other between the attacker and the second party.

**masquerading**   A type of attack on integrity of information in which the attacker impersonates somebody else. Spoofing.

**master secret**   In SSL, a 48-byte secret created from the *pre-master secret*.

**matrix**   A rectangular array of $l \times m$ elements, in which $l$ is the number of rows and $m$ is the number of columns.

**Matyas-Meyer-Oseas scheme**   A dual version of the Davies-Meyer scheme in which the message block is used as the key to the cryptosystem.

**meet-in-the-middle attack**   In double encipherment, an attack that tries to find a plaintext and a ciphertext such that the encryption of the first and the decryption of the second are the same.

**Merkle-Damgard scheme**   An iterated hash function that is collision resistant if the compression function is collision resistant.

**Mersenne number**   A set of integers in the form $M_p = 2^p - 1$, where $p$ is a prime.

**Mersenne prime**   A *Mersenne number* that is a prime.

**message access agent (MAA)**   A client program that pulls stored messages from a server.

**message authentication**   Proving the authenticity of a sender in a connectionless communication.

**message authentication code (MAC)**   An MDC that includes a secret between two parties.

**message digest**   The fixed-length string created from applying a hash function to a message.

**Message Digest (MD)**   A set of several hash algorithms designed by Ron Rivest and referred to as MD2, MD4, and MD5.

**message digest domain**   The set of possible results of a cryptographic hash function.

**message transfer agent (MTA)**   An e-mail component that transfers messages across the Internet.

**Miller-Rabin primality test**   A combination of the *Fermat test* and the *square root test* to find a strong pseudoprime.

**MixColumns**   In AES, an operation that transforms each column of the state to a new column.

**mixer**   In a Feistel cipher, a self-convertible component made of the nonconvertible function and an exclusive-or operation.

**MixRows**   In Whirlpool, an operation similar to MixColumns in AES except that rows, instead of columns, are mixed.

**Miyaguchi-Preneel scheme**   An extended version of Matyas-Meyer-Oseas. in which the plaintext, the cipher key, and the ciphertext are all exclusive-ored together to create the new digest.

**modes of operation**   A set of modes devised to encipher text of any size employing block ciphers of fixed sizes.

**modern block cipher**   A symmetric-key cipher in which each $n$-bit block of plaintext is encrypted to an $n$-bit block of ciphertext using the same key.

**modern stream cipher**   A symmetric-key cipher in which encryption and decryption are done $r$ bits at a time using a stream of keys.

**modification**   A type of attack on the integrity of information in which the attacker delays, deletes, or changes information to make it beneficial to herself.

**modification detection**   A message digest that can prove the integrity of the message.

**modular arithmetic**   A type of arithmetic in which, when dividing an integer by another, only one of the outputs, the remainder $r$, is used and the quotient is dropped.

**modulo operator (mod)**   The operator used in modular arithmetic to create the remainder.

**modulus**   The divisor in modular arithmetic.

**monoalphabetic cipher**   A substitution cipher in which a symbol in the plaintext is always changed to the same symbol in the ciphertext, regardless of its position in the text.

**monoalphabetic substitution cipher**   A cipher in which the key is a mapping between each plaintext character and the corresponding ciphertext character.

**multiplicative cipher**   A cipher in which the encryption algorithm specifies multiplication of the plaintext by the key and the decryption algorithm specifies division of the ciphertext by the key.

**multiplicative inverse**   In modular arithmetic, $a$ and $b$ are multiplicative inverses of each other if $(a \times b) \bmod n = 1$.

**Multipurpose Internet Mail Extension (MIME)**   A protocol that allows non-ASCII data to be sent through e-mail.

## N

**National Institute of Standards and Technology (NIST)**   An agency in the U.S. government that develops standards and technology.

**National Security Agency (NSA)**   A U.S. intelligence-gathering security agency.

**Needham-Schroeder protocol**   A key-exchange protocol using a KDC that uses multiple challenge-response interactions between parties.

**nested MAC**   A two-step MAC.

**New European Schemes for Signatures, Integrity, and Encryption (NESSIE)**   The European research project to identify secure cryptographic algorithms.

**nonce**   A random number that can be used only once.

**non-Feistel cipher**   A product cipher that uses only invertible components.

**nonlinear feedback shift register (NLFSR)**   A feedback shift register in which the feedback function is nonlinear.

**nonlinear S-box**   An S-box in which there is at least one output that is not a linear function of the inputs.

**nonrepudiation**   A security service that protects against repudiation attack by either the sender or the receiver of the data.

**nonsingular elliptic curve**   An elliptic curve in which the equation $x^3 + ax + b = 0$ has three distinct roots.

**nonsynchronous stream cipher**   A stream cipher in which each key in the key stream depends on a previous plaintext or ciphertext.

**notarization**   A security mechanism that selects a third trusted party to control the communication between two entities.

## O

**Oakley**   A key-exchange protocol developed by Hilarie Orman; it is an improved Diffie-Hellman method.

**one-time pad**   A cipher invented by Vernam in which the key is a random sequence of symbols having the same length as the plaintext.

**one-time password**   A password that is used only once.

**one-way function (OWF)**   A function that can be easily calculated, but the calculation of the inverse is infeasible.

**optimal asymmetric encryption padding (OAEP)**   A method proposed by the RSA group and some vendors that applies a sophisticated procedure to pad a message for encryption using RSA.

**order of a group**   The number of elements in the group.

**order of an element**   In a group, the smallest positive integer $n$ such that $a^n = e$.

**Otway-Rees protocol**   A key-exchange protocol similar to the Needham-Schroeder protocol, but more sophisticated.

**output feedback (OFB) mode**   A mode of operation similar to CFB but the shift register is updated by the previous $r$-bit key.

**output pad (opad)**   The second padding used in the HMAC algorithm.

## P

**passive attack**   A type of attack in which the attacker's goal is to obtain information; the attack does not modify data or harm the system.

**password-based authentication**   The simplest and oldest method of entity authentication, in which a password is used to identify the claimant.

**pattern attack**   An attack on a transposition cipher that uses the repeated pattern created in the ciphertext.

**P-box**   A component in a modern block cipher that transposes bits.

**Perfect Forward Security (PFS)**   The property of a cryptosystem in which the disclosure of a long-term secret does not compromise the security of the future communication.

**permutation group**   A group in which the set is all permutations of the elements, and the operation is composition.

**pigeonhole principle**   The principle that if $n$ pigeonholes are occupied by $n + 1$ pigeons, then at least one pigeonhole is occupied by two pigeons.

**plaintext**   The message before encryption or after decryption.

**Playfair cipher**   A polyalphabetic cipher in which the secret key is made of 25 alphabet letters arranged in a $5 \times 5$ matrix.

**Polard $p$–$1$ factorization method**   A method developed by John M. Pollard that finds a prime factor $p$ of a number based on the condition that $p - 1$ has no factor larger than a predefined value B, called the bound.

**Polard *rho* factorization method**   A method developed by John M. Pollard that finds a prime factor $p$ of a number in which the values output by the algorithm are repeated, creating a shape similar to the Greek letter rho ($\rho$).

**polyalphabetic cipher**   A cipher in which each occurrence of a character may have a different substitute.

**polynomial**   An expression of the form $a_n x^n + a_{n-1} x^{n-1} + \cdots + a_0 x^0$, where $a_i x^i$ is called the $i$th term and $a_i$ is called coefficient of the $i$th term.

**possible w**⟨...⟩ ⟨...⟩t of 48 keys in DES, where each key creates only four distinct round keys.

**power atta**⟨...⟩ ⟨...⟩ attack similar to the timing attack that measures the power consumed during decryption.

**preimage** ⟨...⟩ ⟨...⟩ desired property of a cryptographic hash function in which, given h and $y = h(M)$, it ⟨...⟩ ⟨...⟩ely difficult for the adversary to find any message, $M'$, such that $y = h(M')$.

**pre-master** ⟨...⟩ ⟨...⟩L, a secret exchanged between the client and server before calculation of the master secre⟨...⟩

**Pretty Goo**⟨...⟩ ⟨...⟩P) A protocol invented by Phil Zimmermann to provide e-mail with privacy, integrity, an⟨...⟩ ⟨...⟩n.

**primality t**⟨...⟩ ⟨...⟩nistic or probabilistic algorithm that determines whether a positive integer is a prime.

**prime** A p⟨...⟩ ⟨...⟩that is exactly divisible by only two integers, 1 and itself.

**primitive** ⟨...⟩ ⟨...⟩n irreducible polynomial that divides $x^e + 1$, where $e$ is the least integer in the form $e =$ ⟨...⟩

**primitive** ⟨...⟩ ⟨...⟩oup $\mathbf{G} = <\mathbf{Z}_n^*, \times>$, when the order of an element is the same as $\phi(n)$, that element is c⟨...⟩ ⟨...⟩tive root of the group.

**private key** ⟨...⟩ ⟨...⟩netric-key cryptosystem, the key used for decryption. In a digital signature, the key is us⟨...⟩

**product cip**⟨...⟩ ⟨...⟩lex cipher, introduced by Shannon, that combines substitution, permutation, and other co⟨...⟩ ⟨...⟩rovide confusion and diffusion effects.

**pseudoprim**⟨...⟩ ⟨...⟩that passes several primality test, but it is not guaranteed to be a prime.

**pseudorand**⟨...⟩ ⟨...⟩(**PRF**) In TLS, a function that combines two data-expansion functions, one using MD5 an⟨...⟩ ⟨...⟩sing SHA-1.

**public key** ⟨...⟩ ⟨...⟩etric-key cryptosystem, the key used for encryption. In digital signature, the key is used⟨...⟩ ⟨...⟩.

**public-key** ⟨...⟩ ⟨...⟩(**PKI**) A model for creating and distributing certificates based on X.509.

## Q

**quadratic** ⟨...⟩ ⟨...⟩ congruence equation of the form $ax^2 + bx + c = 0 \pmod{n}$.

**quadratic** ⟨...⟩ ⟨...⟩R) Coefficient $a$ in the equation $x^2 = a \pmod{p}$, where the equation has no solution.

**quadratic** ⟨...⟩ ⟨...⟩Coefficient $a$ in the equation $x^2 = a \pmod{p}$, where the equation has two solutions.

**quoted-pr**⟨...⟩ ⟨...⟩ding scheme used when the data consist mostly of ASCII characters with a small non⟨...⟩ ⟨...⟩ character is ASCII, it is sent as is. If a character is not ASCII, it is sent as three chara⟨...⟩ ⟨...⟩racter is the equals sign (=). The next two characters are the hexadecimal representati⟨...⟩

# R

**Rabin cryptosystem**   A variation of the RSA cryptosystem, devised by M. Rabin, in which the value of $e$ and $d$ are fixed to 2.

**Rabin scheme**   An iterated hash function scheme proposed by Rabin baed on the Merkle-Damgard scheme.

**RACE Integrity Primitives Evaluation Message Digest (RIPMED)**   A cryptographic hash algorithm designed by RACE with several versions.

**Radix 64 encoding**   An encoding system in which binary data are divided into 24-bit blocks. Each block is then divided into four 6-bit section. Each 6-bit section is then interpreted as one printable character.

**Random Oracle Model**   An ideal mathematical model, introduced by Bellare and Rogaway for a hash function.

**RC4**   A byte-oriented stream cipher designed by Ronald Rivest.

**Record Protocol**   In SSL and TLS, the protocol that carries messages from the upper layer.

**related message attack**   An attack on RSA, discovered by Franklin Reiter, in which two related ciphertexts are used to find two related plaintexts when the public exponent is low.

**relatively prime**   Two integers are relatively prime if their greatest common divisor is 1.

**replay attack**   See *replaying*.

**replaying**   A type of attack on information integrity in which the attacker intercepts the message and resends it again.

**repudiation**   A type of attack on information integrity that can be launched by one of the two parties in the communication: the sender or the receiver.

**residue**   Remainder.

**residue class**   A set of least residues.

**revealed private exponent attack**   An attack on RSA, in which the attacker uses a probabilistic algorithm to factor $n$ and find the value of $p$ and $q$ if she knows the value of $d$.

**Rijndael**   The modern block cipher designed by Belgian researchers Joan Daemen and Vincent Rijment, and selected as the Advanced Encryption Standard (AES) by NIST.

**ring**   An algebraic structure with two operations. The first operation must satisfy all five properties required for an abelian group. The second operation must satisfy only the first two. In addition, the second operation must be distributed over the first.

**rotor cipher**   A monoalphabetic substitution that changes the mapping (key) between the plaintext and the ciphertext characters for each plaintext character.

**RotWord**   In AES, an operation similar to the ShiftRows operation applied to only one row of a word in the key-expansion process.

**round**   Each iterated section in an iterative block cipher.

**round-keys generation**   In a modern block cipher, the process that creates round keys from the cipher key.

**routing control**  A security mechanism that continuously changes different available routes between the sender and the receiver to prevent the opponent from eavesdropping on a particular route.

**row matrix**  A matrix with only one row.

**RSA cryptosystem**  The most common public-key algorithm, devised by Rivest, Shamir, and Adleman.

**RSA signature scheme**  A digital signature scheme that is based on the RSA cryptosystem, but changes the roles of the private and public keys, the sender uses her own private key to sign the document, and the receiver uses the sender's public key to verify it.

## S

**salting**  A method of improving password-based authentication in which a random string, called the salt, is concatenated to the password.

**S-box**  A component in a block cipher that substitutes the bits in the input with new bits in the output.

**Schnorr signature scheme**  A digital signature scheme based on the ElGamal digital signature scheme but with a reduced signature size.

**second preimage resistance**  A desired property in a cryptographic hash function in which given $M$ and $h(M)$ the intruder cannot find another message $M'$ such that $h(M') = h(M)$.

**Secure Hash Algorithm (SHA)**  A series of hash function standards developed by NIST and published as FIPS 180. It is mostly based on MD5.

**Secure Key Exchange Mechanism (SKEME)**  A protocol designed by Hugo Krawcyzk for key exchange that uses public-key encryption for entity authentication.

**Secure Sockets Layer (SSL)**  A protocol designed to provide security and compression services to data generated from the application layer.

**Secure/Multipurpose Internet Mail Extension (S/MIME)**  An enhancement to MIME designed to provide security for the electronic mail.

**Security Association (SA)**  In IPSec, a logical relationship between two hosts.

**Security Association Database (SAD)**  A two-dimensional table with each row defining a single security association (SA).

**security attacks**  Attacks threatening the security goals of a system.

**security goals**  The three goals of information security: confidentiality, integrity, and availability.

**security mechanisms**  Eight mechanism recommended by ITU-T to provide security services: encipherment, data integrity, digital signature, authentication exchange, traffic padding, routing control, notarization, and access control.

**Security Policy (SP)**  In IPSec, a set of predefined security requirements applied to a packet when it is to be sent or when it has arrived.

**Security Policy Database (SPD)**  A database of security policies (SPs).

**security services**  Five services related to security goals and attacks: data confidentiality, data integrity, authentication, nonrepudiation, and access control.

**seed**  An initial value used in a pseudorandom number generator or used to load the cells in a shift register.

**selective forgery**   A type of forgery in which the forger may be able to forge sender's signature on a message with the content selectively chosen by the forger.

**semi-weak keys**   A set of six key in DES where each key creates only two different round keys and each of them is repeated eight times.

**session**   In SSL, an association between a client and a server. After a session is established, the two parties have common information such as the session identifier, the certificate authenticating each of them (if necessary), the compression method (if needed), the cipher suite, and a master secret that is used to create keys for message authentication encryption.

**session key**   A secret one-time key between two parties.

**set of integers (Z)**   The set of all integral numbers from negative infinity to positive infinity.

**set of residues (Z$_n$)**   The set of positive integers modulo $n$.

**SHA-1**   An SHA with a block of 512 bits and a digest of 160 bits.

**SHA-224**   An SHA with a block of 512 bits and a digest of 224 bits.

**SHA-256**   An SHA with a block of 512 bits and a digest of 256 bits.

**SHA-384**   An SHA with a block of 1024 bits and a digest of 384 bits.

**SHA-512**   An SHA with a block of 1024 bits and a digest of 512 bits.

**shared secret key**   The key used in asymmetric-key cryptography.

**shift cipher**   A type of additive cipher in which the key defines shifting of characters toward the end of the alphabet.

**ShiftColumns**   In Whirlpool, an operation similar to the *ShiftRows* transformation in AES, except that the columns, instead of rows, are shifted.

**shift register**   A sequence of cells where each cell holds a single bit. Shifting the values of bits can create a random-looking sequence of bits.

**ShiftRows**   In AES, a transformation that shifts bytes.

**short-message attack**   An attack on RSA, in which the attacker knows the set of possible plaintexts and encrypts them to find a ciphertext equivalent to the one intercepted.

**short-pad attack**   An attack on RSA, discovered by Coppersmith, in which the intruder can find the plaintext if she has two instances of the corresponding ciphertexts, each created with a different short padding.

**sieve of Eratosthenes**   A method devised by the Greek mathematician Eratosthenes to find all primes less than $n$.

**signing algorithm**   In a signature scheme, the process used by the sender.

**singular elliptic curve**   An elliptic curve in which the equation $x^3 + ax + b = 0$ does not have three distinct roots.

**snooping**   Unauthorized access to confidential information. An attack on the confidentiality goal in information security.

**something inherent**   A characteristic of the claimant, such as conventional signatures, fingerprints, voice, facial characteristics, retinal pattern, and handwriting, used for entity authentication.

**something known**   A secret known only by the claimant that can be checked by the verifier in entity authentication.

**something possessed**   Something belonging to the claimant that can prove the claimant's identity, such as a passport, a driver's license, an identification card, a credit card, or a smart card.

**split operation**   An operation in a block cipher that splits a block in the middle, creating two equal-length blocks.

**spoofing**   See *masquerading*.

**square-and-multiply algorithm**   A fast exponentiation method in which two operations, squaring and multiplying, are used instead of only multiplying operation.

**square matrix**   A matrix with the same number of rows and columns.

**square root primality test method**   A method of primality testing based on the fact that the square root of a positive integer modulo $n$ is only +1 or −1.

**state**   In AES, a unit of data in intermediate stages consists of a matrix of 16 bytes. In S-AES a unit of data consists of 4 nibbles.

**station-to-station protocol**   A method of creating a session key based on the Diffie-Hellman protocol that uses public-key certificates to prevent man-in-the-middle attacks.

**statistical attack**

**steganography**   A security technique in which a message is concealed by covering it with something else.

**straight P-Boxes**   A P-box with $n$ inputs and $n$ outputs.

**stream cipher**   A type of cipher in which encryption and decryption are done one symbol (such as a character or a bit) at a time.

**SubBytes**   In AES, a transformation that uses a table to substitute bytes.

**subgroup**   A subset **H** of a group **G** is a subgroup of **G** if **H** itself is a group with respect to the operation on **G**.

**substitution cipher**   A cipher that replaces one symbol with another.

**SubWord**   In AES, a routine similar to the SubBytes transformation, but applied only to one row.

**superincreasing tuple**   A tuple in which each element is greater than or equal to the sum of all previous elements.

**symmetric-key cryptosystem**   A cryptosystem in which a single secret key is used for both encryption and decryption.

**symmetric-key encipherment**   An encipherment using a symmetric-key cryptosystem.

**synchronous stream cipher**   A stream cipher in which the key stream is independent of the plaintext or ciphertext stream.

# T

**ticket**   An encrypted message intended for entity B, but sent to entity A for delivery.

**ticket-granting server (TGS)**   In Kerberos, the server that creates tickets for the real server.

**time-stamped signatures** A digital signature with a timestamp to preven  replayed by an adversary.

**timing attack** An attack on RSA based on the fast exponential algorithm.  the fact that the timing required to do each iteration is longer if the corresponding bit is

**traffic analysis** A type of attack on confidentiality in which the attacker ob  formation by monitoring online traffic.

**traffic padding** A security mechanism in which some bogus data are inse  data traffic to thwart traffic-analysis attack.

**Transport Layer Security (TLS)** An IETF version of the SSL protocol.

**transport mode** A mode in IPSec that protects what is delivered from  layer to the network layer.

**transposition cipher** A cipher that transposes symbols in the plaintext to  iphertext.

**trapdoor** A feature of an algorithm that allows an intruder to bypass the  she knows that feature.

**trapdoor one-way function (TOWF)** A one-way function that can re  one knows the trapdoor.

**trial division factorization method** The simplest and least efficient algori  the factors of a positive integer in which all positive integers, starting with 2, are tried to find  des $n$.

**trigram** A three-letter string.

**triple DES (3DES)** A cipher that uses three instances of DES ciphers for enc  e instances of reverse DES ciphers for decryption.

**triple DES with three keys** A triple DES implementation where there a  $K_1$, $K_2$, and $K_3$.

**triple DES with two keys** A triple DES implementation where there are  keys: $K_1$ and $K_2$. The first and the third stages use $K_1$; the second stage uses $K_2$.

**tunnel mode** A mode in IPSec that protects the entire IP packet. It takes a  ncluding the header, applies IPSec security methods to the entire packet, and then adds a

## U

**unconcealed message attack** An attack on RSA, based on the permuta  hip between plaintext and ciphertext; an unconcealed message is a message that encrypts

**undeniable signatures** A signature scheme invented by Chaum and  with three components: a signing algorithm, a verification protocol, and a disavowal pr

**user agent (UA)** A component in an e-mail system that prepares the messa  nvelope.

## V

**verifying algorithm** The algorithm that verifies the validity of a digital si  receiver site.

**Vigenere cipher** A polyalphabetic cipher designed by Blaise de Vigenere  ey stream is a repetition of an initial secret key stream.

**Vigenere tableau**   A table used to encrypt and decrypt in the Vigenere cipher.

## W

**weak keys**   A set of four keys in DES where each key, after dropping parity bits, consists either of all 0s, all 1s, or half 0s and half 1s.

**web of trust**   In PGP, the key rings shared by a group of people.

**Whirlpool**   A cryptosystem based on altered AES.

**Whirlpool hash function**   An iterated cryptographic hash function, based on the Miyaguchi-Preneel scheme, designed by Vincent Rijmen and Paulo S. L. M. Barreto, and endorsed by NESSIE. It is based on the Whirlpool cryptosystem.

**word**   In AES, a group of 32 bits that can be treated as a single entity, a row matrix of four bytes, or a column matrix of four bytes.

## X

**X.509**   A recommendation devised by ITU and accepted by the Internet that defines certificates in a structured way.

## Z

**zero-knowledge authentication**   An entity authentication method in which the claimant does not reveal anything that might endanger the confidentiality of the secret. The claimant proves to the verifier that she knows a secret, without revealing it.

# References

[Bar02]    Barr, T. *Invitation to Cryptology*. Upper Saddle River, NJ: Prentice Hall, 2002.

[Bis03]    Bishop, D. *Cryptography with Java Applets*. Sudbury, MA: Jones and Bartlett, 2003.

[Bis05]    Bishop, M. *Computer Security*. Reading, MA: Addison-Wesley, 2005.

[Bla03]    Blahut, U. *Algebraic Codes for Data Transmission*. Cambridge: Cambridge University Press, 2003.

[BW00]     Brassoud, D., and Wagon, S. *Computational Number Theory*. Emerville, CA: Key College, 2000.

[Cou99]    Coutinho, S. *The Mathematics of Ciphers*. Natick, MA: A. K. Peters, 1999.

[DF04]     Dummit, D., and Foote, R. *Abstract Algebra*. Hoboken, NJ: John Wiley & Sons, 2004.

[DH03]     Doraswamy, H., and Harkins, D. *IPSec*. Upper Saddle River, NJ: Prentice Hall, 2003.

[Dur05]    Durbin, J. *Modern Algebra*. Hoboken, NJ: John Wiley & Sons, 2005.

[Eng99]    Enge, A. *Elliptic Curves and Their Applications to Cryptography*. Norwell, MA: Kluver Academic, 1999.

[For06]    Forouzan, B. *TCP/IP Protocol Suite*. New York: McGraw-Hill, 2006.

[For07]    Forouzan, B. *Data Communication and Networking*. New York: McGraw-Hill, 2007.

[Fra01]    Frankkel, S. *Demystifying the IPSec Puzzle*. Norwood, MA: Artech House, 2001.

[Gar01]    Garret, P. *Making, Breaking Codes*. Upper Saddle River, NJ: Prentice Hall, 2001.

[Kah96]    Kahn, D. *The Codebreakers*: *The Story of Secret Writing*. New York: Scribner, 1996.

[KPS02]    Kaufman, C., Perlman, R., and Speciner, M. *Network Security*. Upper Saddle River, NJ: Prentice Hall, 2001.

[LEF04]    Larson, R., Edwards, B., and Falvo, D. *Elementary Linear Algebra*. Boston: Houghton Mifflin, 2004.

[Mao04]    Mao, W. *Modern Cryptography*. Upper Saddle River, NJ: Prentice Hall, 2004.

[MOV97]    Menezes, A., Oorschot, P., and Vanstone, S. *Handbook of Applied Cryptograpy*. New York: CRC Press, 1997.

[PHS03]    Pieprzyk, J., Hardjono, T., and Seberry, J. *Fundamentals of Computer Security*. Berlin: Springer, 2003.

[Res01]    Rescorla, E. *SSL and TLS*. Reading, MA: Addison-Wesley, 2001.

[Rhe03]    Rhee, M. *Internet Security*. Hoboken, NJ: John Wiley & Sons, 2003.

[Ros06]    Rosen, K. *Elementary Number Theory*. Reading, MA: Addison-Wesley, 2006.

[Sal03]    Solomon, D. *Data Privacy and Security*. Berlin: Springer, 2003.

[Sch99]    Schneier, B. *Applied Cryptography*. Reading, MA: Addison-Wesley, 1996.

[Sta06]    Stallings, W. *Cryptography and Network Security*. Upper Saddle River, NJ: Prentice Hall, 2006.

[Sti06]    Stinson, D. *Cryptography: Theory and Practice*. New York: Chapman & Hall/CRC, 2006.

[Tho00]    Thomas, S. *SSL and TLS Essentials*. New York: John Wiley & Sons, 2000.

[TW06]    Trappe, W., and Washington, L. *Introduction to Cryptography and Coding Theory*. Upper Saddle River, NJ: Prentice Hall, 2006.

[Vau06]    Vaudenay, S. *A Classical Introduction to Cryptography*. New York: Springer, 2006.

# Index

# Acronyms

| | |
|---|---|
| **2DES** | double DES |
| **3DES** | triple DES |
| **AES** | Advanced Encryption Standard |
| **AH** | Authentication Header |
| **AS** | authentication server |
| **CA** | certification authority |
| **CBC** | cipher-block chaining |
| **CFB** | cipher feedback |
| **CMAC** | cipher-based message authentication code |
| **CMS** | Cryptographic Message Syntax |
| **CRT** | Chinese remainder theorem |
| **CTR** | counter |
| **DES** | Data Encryption Standard |
| **DSA** | Digital Signature Algorithm |
| **DSS** | Digital Signature Standard |
| **ECB** | electronic codebook |
| **ECDSA** | elliptic curve digital signature algorithm |
| **ESP** | Encapsulating Security Payload |
| **FAR** | false acceptance rate |
| **FCC** | Federal Communications Commission |
| **FIPS** | Federal Information Processing Standard |
| **FRR** | false rejection rate |
| **FSR** | feedback shift register gcd greatest common divisor |
| **GMS** | Global System for Mobile Communication |
| **HMAC** | hashed message authentication code |
| **HTTP** | Hypertext Transfer Protocol |
| **IAB** | Internet Architecture Board |
| **IANA** | Internet Assigned Numbers Authority |
| **ICANN** | Internet Corporation for Assigned Names and Numbers |
| **IEEE** | Institute of Electrical and Electronics Engineers |
| **IEGS** | Internet Engineering Steering Group |
| **IETF** | Internet Engineering Task Force |
| **IKE** | Internet Key Exchange |
| **IP** | Internet Protocol |
| **ipad** | input pad |
| **IPSec** | IP Security |
| **ISAKMP** | Internet Security Association and Key Management Protocol |
| **ISO** | International Organization for Standardization |
| **ISOC** | Internet Society |
| **ITU** | International Telecommunication Union |

| | | | |
|---|---|---|---|
| **ITU-T** | International Telecommunication Union–Telecommunication Standardization Sector | **RACE** | Research in Advanced Communications for Europe |
| **IV** | initial vector | **RC** | round constant |
| **KDC** | key-distribution center | **RC4** | Ron's Code 4 |
| **LFSR** | linear feedback shift register | **RFC** | Request for Comment |
| **MAA** | message access agent | **RIPMED** | RACE Integrity Primitives Evaluation Message Digest |
| **MAC** | media access control | **RNG** | random number generator |
| **MAC** | message authentication code | **RSA** | Rivest, Shamir, Adelman |
| **MD** | Message Digest | **SA** | Security Association |
| **MIC** | message integrity code | **SAD** | Security Association Database |
| **MIME** | Multipurpose Internet Mail Extension | **SCTP** | Stream Control Transmission Protocol |
| **MTA** | message transfer agent | **SET** | Secured Electronic Transaction |
| **MTU** | Maximum Transmission Unit | **SHA** | Secure Hash Algorithm |
| **NESSIE** | New European Schemes for Signature, Integrity, and Encryption | **SKEME** | Secure Key Exchange Mechanism |
| | | **SHS** | Secure Hash Standard |
| **NIST** | National Institute of Standards and Technology | **S/MIME** | Secure/Multipurpose Internet Mail Extension |
| **NLFSR** | nonlinear feedback shift register | **SP** | Security Policy |
| **NSA** | National Security Agency | **SPD** | Security Policy Database |
| **OAEP** | optimal asymmetric encryption padding | **SSL** | Secure Sockets Layer |
| | | **TCP** | Transmission Control Protocol |
| **OFB** | output feedback opad output pad | **TCP/IP** | Transmission Control Protocol/Internet Protocol |
| **OWF** | one-way function | **TELNET** | TERMINAL NETWORK |
| **PFS** | Perfect Forward Security | **TGS** | ticket-granting server |
| **PGP** | Pretty Good Privacy | **TLS** | Transport Layer Security |
| **PKI** | public-key infrastructure | **TOWF** | trapdoor one-way function |
| **PRF** | pseudorandom function | **UA** | user agent |
| **PRNG** | pseudorandom number generator | **UDP** | User Datagram Protocol |
| **QNR** | quadratic nonresidue | **URL** | uniform resource locator |
| **QR** | quadratic residue | **WWW** | World Wide Web |